WORLD DIRECTORY OF HYDROBIOLOGICAL AND FISHERIES INSTITUTIONS

Edited by
Robert W. Hiatt

Supported by the
BIOLOGY BRANCH, OFFICE OF NAVAL RESEARCH,
UNITED STATES NAVY

Prepared under the auspices of the
INTERNATIONAL COMMITTEE FOR THE COMPILATION
OF A DIRECTORY OF MARINE AND
FRESH-WATER BIOLOGICAL LABORATORIES

the
UNITED NATIONS EDUCATIONAL, SCIENTIFIC
AND CULTURAL ORGANIZATION

and the
HYDROBIOLOGY COMMITTEE, AIBS

with the collaboration of the
FOOD AND AGRICULTURE ORGANIZATION OF THE
UNITED NATIONS, FISHERIES BIOLOGY BRANCH

AMERICAN INSTITUTE OF BIOLOGICAL SCIENCES
WASHINGTON, D.C. *1963*

WORLD DIRECTORY OF HYDROBIOLOGICAL
AND FISHERIES INSTITUTIONS

Library of Congress Catalog Card Number is 63-18290.

This book was printed by the Garamond Press
in Baltimore, Maryland.

PREFACE

THIS DIRECTORY stems from a recommendation made by the Hydrobiology Committee of the American Institute of Biological Sciences in 1951, which resulted in the publication of the Directory of Hydrobiological Laboratories and Personnel in North America. Although aware of the need for a world directory, the Hydrobiology Committee was not prepared at that time to tackle a project of this magnitude. Substantial further impetus was given the idea of a world directory at the International Conference on Marine Biological Laboratories sponsored by the International Union of Biological Sciences held in Rome, Italy, in 1955. Participants in this meeting were impressed by accounts of the apparently large number of laboratories throughout the world devoted to research and instruction in marine biology, yet none of the assembled leaders had a comprehensive view of the extent and location of these centers. Accordingly, a small international committee was formed to expedite the compilation of a world-wide directory of marine biological stations. Professor Louis Fage (France) was appointed chairman, and the committee consisted of Professor A. Buzzatti-Traverso (Italy), Professor Robert W. Hiatt (United States), Dr. F. S. Russell (United Kingdom), and Professor Gunnar Thorson (Denmark).

Although both the AIBS Hydrobiology Committee and the Biology Branch of the U. S. Office of Naval Research had placed a world directory high on their lists of important projects since 1951, the magnitude of the task and the considerable costs involved in the preparation of such a directory resulted in its delay until 1959. At this time, the Biology Branch of the U. S. Office of Naval Research, long a forceful advocate of improved exchange of information among aquatic scientists, found it possible to finance the preparation of this world directory under the aegis of the AIBS Hydrobiology Committee, with the writer undertaking the responsibility for the compilation. The committee formed at Rome was mobilized and proceeded with the task.

In view of the similarity in facilities and general objectives of both marine and fresh-water biological laboratories, and because of the great need for a world-wide inventory of all such centers, the committee agreed that the Directory should encompass both marine and fresh-water institutions. Accordingly, Professor Arthur D. Hasler (United States) was invited to join the committee to advise on the fresh-water facilities.

In the course of initial correspondence between Professor Fage and selected country representatives, it was discovered that UNESCO had also embarked on a compilation of marine scientific stations. Further correspondence between Professor Fage, Dr. A. Perez-Vitoria (responsible for compiling the UNESCO directory) and the writer resulted in a collaborative project between UNESCO, FAO, and the international committee, whereby UNESCO made all their data available for inclusion in the present Directory.

The purpose of the Directory is to describe, on a world-wide basis, existing facilities, together with the scope of activities in research and instruction in the marine and fresh-water biological sciences. Early in our compilation, it became apparent that some restrictions would have to be placed on the kinds of institutions to be included, so as to maintain a reasonable degree of homogeneity among the centers listed.

Accordingly, only laboratories are included which are devoted exclusively, or to a great extent of their total program, to marine or fresh-water biology. Within this context we have excluded marine and fresh-water scientific institutions devoted exclusively to physical and chemical sciences, laboratories involved exclusively with fishery technology, and college or university departments or institutes not concerned exclusively with marine or fresh-water biology. The committee is well aware that a great amount of the significant research and instruction in marine and fresh-water biology is accomplished in regular departments of biology, zoology or botany of many colleges and universities. However, to include all such departments would require the listing of virtually all colleges and universities in the world. We considered this task to be beyond the scope of our objectives.

The committee feels strongly that a primary objective of the Directory should be to facilitate communication between scientists in different geographical locations who are engaged in similar or related research projects. For this reason, the major research programs and their scientific leaders have been included. No attempt has been made to list all the professional staff of any station, because of the frequent change in personnel and the inevitable shifting of scientists from one station to another.

Because many stations are small or in isolated areas, library facilities are often inadequate. The committee has included, therefore, a list of the publications issued by each laboratory or its parent organization in the expectation that exchanges of such publications between research centers will be facilitated.

The need for such a Directory requires no justification. There is no up-to-date, world-wide account of marine and fresh-water biological stations. Following World War II, interest increased greatly in the development and expansion of marine and fresh-water biological research, particularly when these subjects were related to development and management of aquatic resources. Economic development in recently independent nations and older nations economically poorly developed has also influenced significantly the expansion of research and utilization of aquatic resources. National and international programs of oceanographic research are now placing obligations upon all maritime countries to establish centers for such investigations. It is appropriate at this time, therefore, to compile a comprehensive account of existing facilities to provide aquatic scientists with a framework upon which to plan future activities.

This compilation has necessarily been a co-operative enterprise. Primary sponsoring agencies were the American Institute of Biological Sciences, UNESCO, and the U. S. Office of Naval Research. Many sources of published information were used to provide the initial listings, including information collected by UNESCO in preparation for its directory of marine scientific institutions. The Department of Natural Sciences of UNESCO has been particularly helpful to the committee by making available all its information on marine scientific institutions and by serving as liaison between the committee and some country representatives. Most of the detailed information was contributed by the executive officers of the institutions listed. The writer wishes to express his gratitude to all those who contributed information.

The committee chairman, Professor Fage, enlisted the cooperation of special country representatives who served in a liaison capacity between the committee and executive officers of the institutions to be included in the Directory. In most instances the country representatives have checked the listings to make certain of their accuracy. The committee is especially appreciative of the cooperation given by these key individuals.

Special acknowledgement is due Dr. S. J. Holt, Chief, Fisheries Branch, FAO, for making both information and extensive checking services of his office available to the committee. Without his assistance, the Directory would be substantially less complete than it is.

As in all undertakings of this kind, there is one individual without whose assistance the project would not have proceeded so well. In this case, the committee owes its deepest gratitude to Mrs. Arthur H. Dole who assisted the editor in all aspects of the work. Special credit is also due Mr. Wayne Clark for his excellent assistance in checking the material and preparing it for the printer. Many persons gave freely of their time to assist with translations and to check the typescript where language other than English was used. To them, also, the committee is deeply grateful.

Robert W. Hiatt

University of Hawaii
December 23, 1962

INTRODUCTION

THE COMMITTEE responsible for compiling the material for this Directory placed prime importance on its usefulness to research scholars and students of aquatic biology. Accordingly, aside from listing the executive officer and address for each station, the matter of working space for guest scientists, costs for such space, and opportunities to live at or near the laboratory were investigated and reported. Likewise helpful to prospective guest workers is general information on facilities, including library holdings and vessels, and a knowledge of areas of specialization of the laboratory. These data are included along with a listing, where it was available, of the more easily collected organisms which would be available to persons wishing to engage in experimental work using living specimens.

Descriptions of institutions are arranged in alphabetical order by country, except in those instances where a parent organization sponsors several laboratories, for example, the United States Fish and Wildlife Service or the Institut Scientifique et Technique des Peches Maritimes, in which cases the laboratories are listed alphabetically under the parent institution which, in turn, is listed alphabetically under a country.

Laboratories with distinctive names are indexed separately, as well as cross-indexed with their sponsoring institution. Laboratories without distinctive names are indexed under their sponsoring agency only. All institutions are indexed in English, and usually also indexed in the language of the country involved.

Information on institutions of the USSR was secured from the USSR Academy of Sciences, UNESCO, and FAO. In no case was the information as complete as from those institutions which returned the committee's questionnaire directly, and in many instances only the name and address of the institution were given. However, for Soviet oceanographic institutes the name and address was supplemented by the date founded, types of scientific activity and titles of publications issued. Very scant information on institutions of the Peoples Republic of China was available through FAO and UNESCO.

A section on museums has been included at the back of the Directory. No attempt has been made to treat museums comprehensively, as this would be beyond the scope of this volume. However, many museums are devoted extensively to aquatic biology, mostly from a taxonomic standpoint, but not exclusively so. A few of these institutions for which we had information about aquatic activities are listed in the Directory.

The first directory for any extensive political area was on the marine laboratories of Europe, and was published in 1893 by Bashford Dean (*Am. Nat.,* 27:625-37, 697-707). Since that time, several accounts have been written covering stations in particular countries or on a world-wide basis. The more important of these accounts, which now serve as historical milestones, have been summarized by H. A. Jack in his "Biological Field Stations of the World" (*Chron. Botan.,* 9:1-73, 1945). Since Jack's directory was issued, the most comprehensive accounts of marine biological and fisheries centers have been issued by FAO. To date, the following have been published: "Fishery Research and Educational Institutions in North and South America," 1950; "Directory of Fisheries Institutions, Europe," 1955 (revised 1957) and "Directory of Fisheries Institutions, Asia and Far East," 1957.

In 1953, the writer compiled a Directory of Hydrobiological Laboratories and Personnel in North America (University of Hawaii Press) which listed 187 marine and fresh-water stations. The present Directory revises and brings up-to-date the stations of this geographic area.

Especially helpful for the present compilation have been the numerous reports of European marine and fresh-water biological laboratories issued by the United States Office of Naval Research, London Office, in their publications, "European Scientific Notes" and "Technical Reports, ONRL." Lastly, the writer has made extensive use of his personal knowledge of marine and fresh-water biological laboratories secured during visits to such institutions in many parts of the world.

TABLE OF CONTENTS

This book is dedicated to the memory of ANTON BRUUN, *1901-1961, Danish explorer of the ocean, pioneer of the deeps, organizer and leader of expeditions and global programs, scientific statesman, citizen of the world and friend and inspiration to a generation of oceanographers.*

ALBANIA

Laboratories for Which No Detailed Information Was Available:

Fisheries Management Research Station, Durres, Shquipnija (Albania).

ALGERIA

Station Experimentale d'Aquiculture et de Peche de Castiglione

CASTIGLIONE AQUICULTURE AND FISHERY EXPERIMENTAL STATION

POSTAL ADDRESS: Castiglione, Algerie (Algeria).
EXECUTIVE OFFICER: Professor Dr. R. Dieuzeide.
SPONSORING AGENCY: Delegation federal de Gouvernement, Direction de l'Aquiculture (Federal Government Delegation, Directorate of Aquiculture).
YEAR FOUNDED: 1921.
SCOPE OF ACTIVITIES: Unrestricted research on general marine biology.
SEASON OF OPERATION: All year.
PHYSICAL ENVIRONMENT ACCESSIBLE: Mediterranean Sea.
PROVISIONS FOR VISITING SCIENTISTS: Space for 2 visitors.
MAJOR RESEARCH FACILITIES: Small library; running sea and fresh-water, small aquarium tanks; research collection of fauna; small boats and outboard motors.
SIZE OF STAFF: Five technicians.
PUBLICATIONS ISSUED: *Bulletin de Travaux de la Station d'Aquiculture et de Peche de Castiglione* (regularly published journal).

STATION EXPERIMENTALE D'AQUICULTURE ET DE PECHE DE CASTIGLIONE

INSTITUT OCEANOGRAPHIQUE D'ALGER

Institut Oceanographique d'Alger

OCEANOGRAPHIC INSTITUTE OF ALGERIA

POSTAL ADDRESS: Jetee Nord, Alger, Algerie (Algiers, Algeria).
EXECUTIVE OFFICER: Professeur Francis Bernard, Directeur.
SPONSORING AGENCY: Mission Culturelle de France.
YEAR FOUNDED: 1883.
SCOPE OF ACTIVITIES: Unrestricted research on general marine biology, plankton, bottom ecology and general oceanography; graduate instruction.
SEASON OF OPERATION: All year.
PHYSICAL ENVIRONMENT ACCESSIBLE: Mediterranean Sea; rocky and gravelly shores.
PROVISIONS FOR VISITING SCIENTISTS: Space for 2 visitors; no fees charged; living quarters available nearby.
MAJOR RESEARCH AND TEACHING FACILITIES: No library; running sea and fresh-water, small aquarium tanks; small boats and outboard motors; vessels, 13 m and 20 m LOA.
SIZE OF STAFF: Fourteen at professional level; 6 technicians.
MAJOR CURRENT RESEARCH PROJECTS AND SCIENTIFIC LEADERS:
Plankton (F. Bernard)
Taxonomy, biology, vision and behaviour of copepods (R. Vaissiere)

ANGOLA

Junta de Investigacoes do Ultramar, Centro de Biologia Piscatoria Angola Ramo

COUNCIL FOR OVERSEAS INVESTIGATIONS, CENTER FOR FISHERIES BIOLOGY, ANGOLA BRANCH

POSTAL ADDRESS: Baia Farta, Angola.

No detailed description of this branch was available but see Lisbon, Portugal headquarters, page 157.

ARGENTINA

Argentina Ministerio de Agricultura y Ganaderia, Direccion General de Pesca y Conservacion de la Fauna

ARGENTINE MINISTRY FOR AGRICULTURE AND LIVESTOCK, BUREAU OF FISHERIES AND WILDLIFE CONSERVATION

POSTAL ADDRESS:
Headquarters: Paseo Colon 922, Buenos Aires, Argentina.
Branch laboratories:
1. Estacion de Biologia Marina y Tecnologia Pesquera, Puerto Mar del Plata
2. Estacion Hidrobiologica de Bella Vista
3. Estacion Hidrobiologica de Rosario
4. Estacion Hidrobiologica del Rio de la Plata

(Descriptions follow.)

EXECUTIVE OFFICER: Dr. Jaun Manuel Cordini, Director.
SCOPE OF ACTIVITIES: Economic biology and fishery technology, hydrobiology, fish culture, and biology of guano birds.
MAJOR RESEARCH FACILITIES: Four fish culture stations, 2 salt water fishing control stations, 5 hydrobiological centers for tests on salt and fresh-water; several motor boats for fish-culture and fresh-water fishing; one schooner for coastal fishing investigations.
SIZE OF STAFF: One hundred and fifty, including professional level personnel, specialists, clerks, and technicians.
PUBLICATIONS ISSUED: *Publicacion Miscelanea* (issued irregularly)

Estacion de Biologia Marina y Tecnologia Pesquera, Puerto Mar Del Plata

MAR DEL PLATA STATION OF MARINE BIOLOGY AND FISHERY TECHNOLOGY

POSTAL ADDRESS: Puerto Mar del Plata, Argentina.
LOCATION: Near Mar del Plata city (7 kilometers)
EXECUTIVE OFFICER: Raymundo Santiago Castagnola, Jefe.
YEAR FOUNDED: 1954.
SCOPE OF ACTIVITIES: Restricted research on general marine biology and biochemistry of fish and shellfish in Argentine Coastal waters.
SEASON OF OPERATION: All year.
PHYSICAL ENVIRONMENT ACCESSIBLE: Atlantic Ocean.
PROVISIONS FOR VISITING SCIENTISTS: None.
MAJOR RESEARCH FACILITIES: Small library; no sea water supply in station; one 20 m LOA power vessel.
SIZE OF STAFF: One at professional level.

ESTACION DE BIOLOGIA MARINA Y TECNOLOGIA PESQUERA, PUERTO MAR DEL PLATA

IMPORTANT SPECIES AVAILABLE FOR LABORATORY STUDIES:
Cephalopoda: *Ommastrephes* spp., *Rossia tenera*
Crustacea: *Hymenopenaeus mulleri, Artemesia longinaris*
Pisces: *Galeorhinus galeus, Pneumatophorus japonicus, Sparus pagrus, Engraulis anchovita, Merluccius hubbsi, Genypterus blacodes*
MAJOR RESEARCH PROJECTS AND SCIENTIFIC LEADERS: Chemical studies of shrimp, anchovy and mackerel (Oscar R. Chiodi)

Estacion Hidrobiologica de Bella Vista

BELLA VISTA HYDROBIOLOGICAL STATION

POSTAL ADDRESS: Jose Manuel Estrada S/No. Bella Vista, Corrientes, Argentina.
EXECUTIVE OFFICER: Ambrosio Leonardo Rosenzvaig.
YEAR FOUNDED: 1954.
SCOPE OF ACTIVITIES: Restricted research on the bio-ecology of the principle fish species of the Parana River, lakes and swamps.
SEASON OF OPERATION: All year.
PHYSICAL ENVIRONMENT ACCESSIBLE: Rios (Rivers) Parana, Corrientes and Santa Lucia, Laguna Ibera (Lake Ibera) and its swamps.
PROVISIONS FOR VISITING SCIENTISTS: Research and living space for 2-4 visitors; no fees charged for research space.
MAJOR RESEARCH FACILITIES: Small library; large outdoor ponds and tanks, small aquarium tanks; research collections of fishes, mollusks and crustaceans; one canoe.
SIZE OF STAFF: One at professional level.
IMPORTANT SPECIES AVAILABLE FOR LABORATORY STUDIES:
Pisces: *Rhinoderas* sp., *Pimelodus* sp., *Pseudopimelodus parahybae, Luciopimelodus pati, Prochilodus linneatus, Brycon orbignyanus, Salminus maxillosus, Potamotrygon* (elasmobranch)

ESTACION HIDROBIOLOGICA DE BELLA VISTA

MAJOR CURRENT RESEARCH PROJECTS AND SCIENTIFIC LEADERS:
- Biology of the sabalo (*Prochilodus linneatus*) (A. L. Rosenzvaig)
- Bio-ecology of the midget pejerray (*Odonothestes perugiae*) (A. L. Rosenzvaig)

Estacion Hidrobiologica de Rosario

ROSARIO HYDROBIOLOGICAL STATION

POSTAL ADDRESS: Parguo Alem, Rosario, Argentina.
EXECUTIVE OFFICER: Dr. Oscar Angel Canzio, Jefe.
YEAR FOUNDED: 1940.
SCOPE OF ACTIVITIES: Restricted research on the biology of the principle fish species of the Rio Parana; general fluvial biology.
SEASON OF OPERATION: All year.
PHYSICAL ENVIRONMENT ACCESSIBLE: Rio Parana systems; eutrophic lake.
PROVISIONS FOR VISITING SCIENTISTS: Space for 4 visitors; no fees charged; living space available nearby.
MAJOR RESEARCH FACILITIES: Large outdoor ponds and tanks; small aquarium tanks; research and identified reference collections of fishes; machine and wood shop, electrical and electronic shop, skilled shop workman available; small boats and outboard motors; 6.5 m LOA power vessel.
SIZE OF STAFF: Two at professional level.
IMPORTANT SPECIES AVAILABLE FOR LABORATORY STUDIES:
- Pelecypoda: *Diplodon* sp.
- Pisces: *Salminus maxillosus, Leporinus obtusidens, Prochilodus platensis, Pseudoplatystoma coruscans, Basilichthys bonariensis, Luciopimelodus pati, Colossoma mitrei, Pimelodus* sp., *Lysengraulis olidus*

MAJOR CURRENT RESEARCH PROJECTS AND SCIENTIFIC LEADERS:
- Taxonomic studies on Parana fishes (Oscar A. Canzio and Juan C. Vidal)
- Ecological studies on Parana fishes (Oscar A. Canzio and Juan C. Vidal)

Estacion Hidrobiologica del Rio de la Plata

RIO DE LA PLATA HYDROBIOLOGICAL STATION

POSTAL ADDRESS: Calle Avenida Alta. G. Brown, Columna 204 Punta Lara, Argentina. Casilla de Correo No. 11, Ensenada, Argentina.
EXECUTIVE OFFICER: Dr. Sarah Exilda Cabrera, Jefe.
SCOPE OF ACTIVITIES: Restricted research on general biology of the fauna of the Rio de La Plata.
SEASON OF OPERATION: All year.
PHYSICAL ENVIRONMENT ACCESSIBLE: Rio (River) de La Plata.
PROVISIONS FOR VISITING SCIENTISTS: Space for 2 visitors; no living facilities available at the station.
MAJOR RESEARCH FACILITIES: Small library; small research collection of fauna and flora.
SIZE OF STAFF: Two at professional level; 1 technician.
IMPORTANT SPECIES AVAILABLE FOR LABORATORY STUDIES:
- Pelecypoda: *Diplodon* sp., *Anodontites* sp.
- Pisces: *Basilichthys* sp., *Lysengraulis* sp., *Luciopimelodus* sp., *Mugil* sp., *Acestrorhamphus* sp., *Prochilodus* sp., *Loricaria* sp., *Plecostomus* sp., *Pimelodus* sp., *Astianax* sp., *Sorubi* sp.

MAJOR CURRENT RESEARCH PROJECTS AND SCIENTIFIC LEADERS:
- Catch records of principal domestic species of fish (Sarah Cabrera and Margarita Beruatto)
- Studies on the pejerray (*Basilichthys* sp.) of the Rio de La Plata (Sarah Cabrera and Antonio Fernandez)
- Reproduction of pejerray (Sarah Cabrera)
- Ecology of sabalo (*Prochilodus* sp.) (Sarah Cabrera)
- Food habits of fishes of the Rio de La Plata (Sarah Cabrera and Zulma A. de Castellanos)
- Biology of fresh-water clams (Zulma A. de Castellanos)

ESTACION HIDROBIOLOGICA DE ROSARIO

Direccion General de Recursos Naturales, Laboratorio de Hidrobiologia

GENERAL BUREAU OF NATURAL RESOURCES, HYDROBIOLOGICAL LABORATORY

POSTAL ADDRESS: Casilla Correo No. 58, Boulevard 3100, Santa Fe, Argentina.

EXECUTIVE OFFICER: Argentino Aurelio Bonetto, Director. Almafuerte 3157, Santa Fe, Argentina.

SPONSORING AGENCY: Consejo National de Investigaciones Cientificas y Tecnicas.

YEAR FOUNDED: 1958.

SCOPE OF ACTIVITIES: Unrestricted research on the biology, taxonomy and ecology of fishes, malacology, fish culture, water pollution and general limnology.

SEASON OF OPERATION: All year.

PHYSICAL ENVIRONMENT ACCESSIBLE: Rio (River) Parana; eutrophic lake.

PROVISIONS FOR VISITING SCIENTISTS: Space for 2 visitors; no fees charged; living quarters available nearby.

MAJOR RESEARCH FACILITIES: Small library; large outdoor ponds and tanks, small aquarium tanks; research collections of Pisces, Pelecypoda (Naiades), Gastropoda (fresh-water snails), Crustacea and Porifera; identified reference collections of naiades, fishes and sponges; machine and wood shop, skilled shop workman available; small boats and outboard motors; one 10 m LOA vessel.

SIZE OF STAFF: Eight at professional level; 6 technicians.

MAJOR CURRENT RESEARCH PROJECTS AND SCIENTIFIC LEADERS:

Fish population studies using tagging methods (Argentino A. Bonetto and Clarice Pignalberi)

Biology, taxonomy and geographical distribution of South American Naiades (A. A. Bonetto and Ines Ezcurra)

Water pollution in the Parana River (Ruben Manzi and Roberto Conte)

Taxonomy and geographical distribution of Porifera in the Parana and Paraguay Rivers (A. A. Bonetto and Ines Ezcurra)

General Limnology in the Saladillos basin, especially in the Guadalupe lagoon (Ignacio Maciel and Ruben Manzi)

Algae in the marginal ponds of the Parana River (Ruben Manzi and Ignacio Maciel)

Fish-culture studies; especially on *Leporinus obtusidens*, and *Salminus maxillosus* (A. A. Bonetto, Clarice Pignalberi and Elly Cordiviola)

DIRECCION GENERAL DE RECURSOS NATURALES, LABORATORIO DE HIDROBIOLOGICA

Estacion de Biologia Marina "Puerto Deseado"

PUERTO DESEADO MARINE BIOLOGICAL STATION

POSTAL ADDRESS: Puerto Deseado, Provincia de Santa Cruz, Argentina.

EXECUTIVE OFFICERS: Professor O. Kuhnemann, Director de la Estacion, Departamento de Botanica, Universidad de Buenos Aires, Buenos Aires, Argentina.

SPONSORING AGENCIES: Universidad de Buenos Aires; Instituto Nacional de Tecnologia Industrial (University of Buenos Aires, National Institute of Industrial Technology).

YEAR FOUNDED: 1960.

SCOPE OF ACTIVITIES: Restricted research on zoo- and phytoplankton, systematics and ecology of algae and Foraminifera; unrestricted research on general marine biology; graduate instruction.

SEASON OF OPERATION: All year, but Station utilized mainly from January to April.

PHYSICAL ENVIRONMENT ACCESSIBLE: Ria del Rio Deseado (Estuary of the Deseado River), Atlantic Ocean; sandy and silty beaches, rocky and gravelly shores and brackish, shallow bays.

PROVISIONS FOR VISITING SCIENTISTS: Research and living space for visitors; no fees charged for research space.

MAJOR RESEARCH AND TEACHING FACILITIES: Small library; large outdoor ponds and tanks, small aquarium tanks; research collections of sponges, coelenterates, nemerteans, sipunculids, priapulids, bryozoans, mollusks, brachiopods, annelids, arthropods, echinoderms, ascidians, fishes and all major groups of algae of the area; machine and wood shop, one 14 m LOA motor launch.

INSTRUCTIONAL PROGRAM: Systematics and ecology of benthonic marine algae, invertebrate zoology and plankton.

SIZE OF STAFF: Six at professional level; 2 technicians.

IMPORTANT SPECIES AVAILABLE FOR LABORATORY STUDY: All species found along Patagonian coast, plus many marine birds including nesting grounds of the Patagonian penquin, *Spheniscus magellanicus*.

MAJOR CURRENT RESEARCH PROJECTS AND SCIENTIFIC LEADERS:

Systematics and ecology of Foraminifera (Estaben Boltovskoy)

ESTACION DE BIOLOGIA MARINA "PUERTO DESEADO"

Ecology of vegetation of the littoral zone (Oscar Kuhnemann)
Copepoda (Rosa Pallares)
Systematics of Rhodophyta (Carmen Pujals)
Systematics of Cyanophyta (Delia Rabinovich)
Systematics of Phaeophyta (Aldo Asensi)
Ecology of fauna of the littoral zone (Raul Ringuelet)

Estacion Hidrobiologica de Chascomus

CHASCOMUS HYDROBIOLOGICAL STATION

POSTAL ADDRESS: Avenida Lastra esq. Juarez, Chascomus FCNGR, Buenos Aires, Argentina.

EXECUTIVE OFFICER: Fernando Ramirez, Jefe, Division Limnologia y Piscicultura, Direccion de Conservacion de la Fauna, calle 50 no 723, La Plata, Buenos Aires, Argentina.

SPONSORING AGENCY: Ministerio de Asuntos Agrarios de la Provincia de Buenos Aires, Direccion de Conservation de la Fauna (Ministry of Agriculture of the Province of Buenos Aires, Bureau of Wildlife Conservation).

YEAR FOUNDED: 1942-43.

SCOPE OF ACTIVITIES: Restricted research on limnology and conservation of aquatic resources; undergraduate instruction.

SEASON OF OPERATION: All year.

PHYSICAL ENVIRONMENT ACCESSIBLE: Laguna de Chascomus (Chascomus Lake, eutrophic); sistema de las Encadenadas de Chascomus y Rio Salado (Chascomus Lake system and tributaries including the Salado River).

PROVISIONS FOR VISITING SCIENTISTS: Research and living space for 4 visitors; no fees charged for research space.

MAJOR RESEARCH AND TEACHING FACILITIES: No library; large outdoor ponds and tanks; small aquarium tanks; research collection of plankton samples; identified reference collections of local flora and fauna available at the Museo de La Plata; machine and wood shop, electrical and electronic shop; small boats and outboard motors, one 6 m LOA vessel.

INSTRUCTIONAL PROGRAM: Occasional courses in practical fish-culture.

SIZE OF STAFF: Six at professional level; 5 technicians.

IMPORTANT SPECIES AVAILABLE FOR LABORATORY STUDIES:
Potamogetonaceae: *Potamogeton striatus*
Ceratophyllaceae: *Ceratophyllum demersum*
Ciperaceae: *Scirpus californicus*
Mollusca: *Littoridina parchappei*
Pisces: *Basilichthys bonariensis, Jenysia lineata*

MAJOR CURRENT RESEARCH PROJECTS AND SCIENTIFIC LEADERS:
Food and feeding habits of the fishes of Laguna Chascomus (Fernando C. Ramirez)
Relationship between neurosecretions and euryhaline habits in *Jenysia lineata* (Federico Garcia Romeu)
General limnology of Laguna Vitel (Santiago R. Olivier)
Ostracods of Lake Chascomus (Fernando C. Ramirez)
Transplantation of Rio Parana fishes (Raul A. Ringuelet)

ESTACION HIDROBIOLOGICA DE CHASCOMUS

Estacion Hidrobiologica de Puerto Quequen del Instituto Nacional de Investigacion de las Ciencias Naturales

PUERTO QUEQUEN HYDROBIOLOGICAL STATION OF THE NATIONAL INSTITUTE FOR NATURAL SCIENCE RESEARCH

POSTAL ADDRESS:
Instituto Nacional: Museo Argentino de Ciencias Naturales "Bernadino Rivadavia," Avenida Angel Gallardo 470, Casilla de Correo 10, Sucursal 5, Buenos Aires, Argentina.
Estacion Hildrobiologica: Puerto Quequen, Argentina.

EXECUTIVE OFFICERS: Dr. Max Biraben, Director del Instituto. Professor Enrique Balech, Jefe de Estacion.
SPONSORING AGENCY: Ministry of Education, Argentine Museum of Natural Sciences "B. Rivadavia."
YEAR FOUNDED: 1928.
SCOPE OF ACTIVITIES: Unrestricted research on general marine biology, plankton and fisheries.
SEASON OF OPERATION: All year.
PHYSICAL ENVIRONMENT ACCESSIBLE: Atlantic Ocean, Rio (River) Quequen; sandy beaches, estuarine conditions.
PROVISIONS FOR VISITING SCIENTISTS: Space for 3 visitors; no fees charged; living quarters for 2, other living quarters available nearby.
MAJOR RESEARCH FACILITIES: Small library, small aquarium tanks; research and identified reference collections available at the Museo Argentino de Ciencias Naturales "B. Rivadavia"; shop facilities available in Puerto Quequen and Necochea; boats and larger vessels available from fishermen. New building with improved facilities in planning stage.
SIZE OF STAFF: One at professional level.
IMPORTANT SPECIES AVAILABLE FOR LABORATORY STUDIES:
Ctenophora: *Bolinopsis* sp.
Coelenterata: *Bunodactis* sp.
Annelida: *Mercierella enigmatica*..
Echinodermata: *Astropecten* sp., *Luidia* sp., *Arbacia* sp., *Notechinus* sp.
Mollusca: *Mytilus* sp., *Amiantis* sp., *Chione* sp., *Tagelus* sp., *Olivancillaria* sp., *Zidona* sp., *Cymbiola* sp.
Pisces: *Galeorhinus* sp., *Carcharinus* sp., *Mustelus* sp., *Raja* sp., *Engraulis* sp., *Micropogon* sp., *Cynoscion* sp., *Acanthistius* sp., *Basilichthys* sp.
MAJOR CURRENT RESEARCH PROJECTS AND SCIENTIFIC LEADERS:
Plankton (taxonomy, morphology and annual variation) (E. Balech)
Foraminifera (taxonomy, ecology and distribution) (E. Boltovskoy)
Fish and fisheries (R. Lopez)
Parasites (L. Szidat)
Sea urchins and sea stars (taxonomy and distribution) (I. Bernasconi)
Mollusks (biometry, commensals and epizoa on *Mytilus*) (E. Martinez Fontes)
Marine algae (taxonomy and distribution) (C. Pujals).

Instituto Antartico Argentino

ARGENTINE ANTARCTIC INSTITUTE

POSTAL ADDRESS: Cerrito 1248, Buenos Aires, Argentina.
EXECUTIVE OFFICERS: Contraalmirante Rodolfo N. Panzarini, Director. Dr. Otto Schneider, Chief of the Scientific Department.

INSTITUTO ANTARTICO ARGENTINO

SPONSORING AGENCY: Secretaria de Marina (Secretary of the Navy). The Institute is a civilian organization but under the jurisdiction of the Argentine Navy Department.
YEAR FOUNDED: 1951; activated 1956.
SCOPE OF BIOLOGICAL ACTIVITIES: Restricted research on the general biology of the Antarctic region; administration and operation of Ellsworth Scientific Station in the Antarctic (latitude 77° 43′ S., longitude 41° 07′ W.); instruction.
SEASON OF OPERATION: All year.
PHYSICAL ENVIRONMENT ACCESSIBLE: Antarctic Ocean, Drake Passage, Weddell and Bellingshausen Seas, Mar de la Flota, Gerlache Strait; rocky and gravelly shores.
PROVISIONS FOR VISITING SCIENTISTS: Space for 2 visitors; no fees charged; living quarters available in Buenos Aires.
MAJOR RESEARCH FACILITIES: Moderately complete library; small research collection of Antarctic specimens; machine and wood shop, skilled shop workman available; small boats and outboard motors; the icebreaker *General San Martin* is available from the Navy, other vessels of the Navy to be used eventually.
INSTRUCTIONAL PROGRAM: Short courses for Antarctic observers.
SIZE OF BIOLOGICAL STAFF: Four at professional level; 1 technician. Total staff of 30 at Ellsworth Scientific Station (not all biologists).
MAJOR CURRENT RESEARCH PROJECTS AND SCIENTIFIC LEADERS:
Migration and behavior of Antarctic birds (R. Novatti)
Microbiology of Antarctic environment (A. Corte)
Antarctic phytoplankton (H. A. Orlando)
Antarctic invertebrates (Z. de Castellanos)

PUBLICATIONS ISSUED:
Publicaciones del Instituto Antartico Argentino (scientific reports or monographs)
Contribuciones del Instituto Antártico Argentino (short papers)
Recopilacion de las Contribuciones del Instituto Antartico Argentino (collected contributions)
Boletin del Instituto Antartico Argentino (regularly published journal for the general public)

Instituto de Biologia Marina de Mar del Plata

MAR DEL PLATA MARINE BIOLOGICAL INSTITUTE

POSTAL ADDRESS: Playa Grande, Mar del Plata, Argentina.
EXECUTIVE OFFICER: Director has not been appointed.
SPONSORING AGENCIES: Facultad de Ciencias Naturales y Museo de la Universidad Nacional de La Plata y Facultad de Ciencias Exactas y Naturales de la Universidad Nacional de Buenos Aires (Faculty of Natural Sciences and Museum of the National University of La Plata and the Faculty of Exact and Natural Sciences of the National University of Buenos Aires).
YEAR FOUNDED: 1960.
SCOPE OF ACTIVITIES: Unrestricted research on fisheries, general marine biology, plankton and coastal ecology; graduate and undergraduate instruction.
SEASON OF OPERATION: All year.
PHYSICAL ENVIRONMENT ACCESSIBLE: South Atlantic Ocean, Albufera Mar Chiquita, Lagunas de Los Padres and La Brava, (eutrophic lakes), Rio (River) Quequen Grande; sandy and silty beaches, brackish shallow bays and mountain creeks.
PROVISIONS FOR VISITING SCIENTISTS: Research and living space for 6 visitors; no fees charged for research space.
MAJOR RESEARCH AND TEACHING FACILITIES: Small library; running sea and fresh-water, small aquarium tanks, all under construction; research and identified reference collection of sponges, coelenterates, mollusks, echinoderms, annelids, fishes and marine algae available at the Museo de La Plata; skilled shop workman available; vessels available from the Navy and from fishermen.
INSTRUCTIONAL PROGRAM: General zoology, invertebrate zoology, vertebrate zoology, comparative anatomy of vertebrates, animal ecology, zoogeography, plant systematics (cryptogams), plant anatomy and morphology, physiological botany and ecological botany.
SIZE OF STAFF: Five at professional level; 2 technicians.
MAJOR CURRENT RESEARCH PROJECTS AND SCIENTIFIC LEADERS:
Fisheries investigations (Francisco Gneri, Victor Angelescu and Alberto Nani)

INSTITUTO DE BIOLOGIA MARINA DE MAR DEL PLATA

Zooplankton (Santiago R. Olivier)
Phytoplankton (Sebastian A. Guarrera)
Marine algae (Rhodophyceae) (Isabel Kreibhon)
Carcinological studies (Eduardo E. Boschi)
PUBLICATIONS ISSUED: *Revista de la Estacion de Biologia Marina de Mar del Plata* (journal to be regularly published)

Universidad Nacional de la Plata, Division Biologia Animal, Laboratorio de Limnologia

NATIONAL UNIVERSITY OF LA PLATA, DIVISION OF ANIMAL BIOLOGY, LIMNOLOGICAL LABORATORY

POSTAL ADDRESS: Museo de La Plata, Paseo del Bosque, La Plata, Argentina.
EXECUTIVE OFFICER: Santiago Raul Olivier, Jefe de la Division.
SPONSORING AGENCY: Facultad de Ciencias Naturales y Museo de la Universidad Nacional de La Plata (Faculty of Natural Sciences and Museum of the National University of La Plata).
YEAR FOUNDED: 1952.
SCOPE OF ACTIVITIES: Unrestricted research on the general limnology, plankton and ecology of the lakes of the Province of Buenos Aires; graduate and undergraduate instruction.
SEASON OF OPERATION: All year.
PHYSICAL ENVIRONMENT ACCESSIBLE: Rios (Rivers) de la Plata and Parana, Chascomus Lake System, Laguna (Lake) de Monte; estuarine conditions and eutrophic lakes.
PROVISIONS FOR VISITING SCIENTISTS: Space for 8 visitors; no fees charged; living quarters available nearby.
MAJOR RESEARCH AND TEACHING FACILITIES: Very extensive library with moderately complete limnological section; small aquarium tanks; research collection of microfauna (cladocerans, copepods and rotifers), Insecta, Crustacea, Pisces, Amphibia, Aves, aquatic

higher plants and phytoplankton; identified reference collection of local flora and fauna; machine and wood shop, electrical and electronic shop, skilled shop workman available; small boats and outboard motors.

INSTRUCTIONAL PROGRAM: General zoology, invertebrate zoology, vertebrate zoology, comparative anatomy of vertebrates, animal ecology, zoogeography, limnology, planktology, systematic botany, plant anatomy and morphology, plant physiology and plant ecology.

SIZE OF STAFF: Eight at professional level; 4 technicians.

IMPORTANT SPECIES AVAILABLE FOR LABORATORY STUDIES:

Algae: *Chlorella* sp.
Rotifera: *Keratella vulga, Brachionus caudatus*
Gastropoda: *Ampullaria canaliculata*
Crustacea: *Bosmina obtusirostris, Daphnia pulex, Simosa vetula*
Pisces: *Jenysia lineata, Cichlasoma facetum*

MAJOR CURRENT RESEARCH PROJECTS AND SCIENTIFIC LEADERS:

General limnology and zooplankton (Santiago R. Olivier)
Phytoplankton (Sebastian A. Guarrera)
Crustacea and general ecology (Raul A. Ringuelet)
Ichthyophysiology (Federico Garcia Romeu)
Periphyton and physiology of algae (Raquel Guitman)
Ostracoda (Fernando Ramirez)

MUSEO DE LA PLATA

Laboratories for Which No Detailed Information Is Available:

Departamento Caza Pesca y Proteccion de la Fauna

Julio A. Roca 143, Resistencia, Pica Chaco, Argentina. Dra. Corina E. Acervo.

AUSTRALIA

Commonwealth Scientific and Industrial Research Organization (CSIRO)

Division of Fisheries and Oceanography

POSTAL ADDRESS:

Headquarters: Marine Biological Laboratory, P. O. Box 21, Cronulla, New South Wales, Australia.

Branch laboratories:

1. Eden, New South Wales (Tuna)
2. c/o Fisheries and Wildlife, 4 Canterbury Road, Camberwell, Melbourne, Victoria (Barracouta, Salmon, Tuna)
3. "Stowell," Stowell Avenue, Hobart, Tasmania, (Crayfish)
4. University Grounds, Nedlands, Perth, Western Australia (Crayfish)

LOCATION: Headquarters located on shores of Port Hacking, Sydney.

EXECUTIVE OFFICER: George F. Humphrey, Chief of Division.

YEAR FOUNDED: 1938.

SCOPE OF ACTIVITIES: Research on fisheries and oceanography to assist Australian industries; graduate and undergraduate instruction.

SEASON OF OPERATION: All year.

PHYSICAL ENVIRONMENT ACCESSIBLE: Port Hacking, Tasman Sea; sandy and silty beaches, rocky and gravelly shores, estuarine conditions, and brackish, shallow bays. Field stations have access to coral reefs, eutrophic and oligotrophic lakes, rivers and streams.

PROVISIONS FOR VISITING SCIENTISTS: Space for about 6 visitors; no fees charged; living quarters available nearby.

MAJOR RESEARCH AND TEACHING FACILITIES: Very extensive library; running sea and fresh-water, large outdoor ponds and tanks, small aquarium tanks; limited research and identified reference collections of fishes, phytoplankton and zooplankton; machine and wood shop, electrical and electronic shop, skilled shop workman available; small boats and outboard motors: 3 vessels (35-300 ft LOA).

INSTRUCTIONAL PROGRAM: Short courses in marine biology and oceanography for advanced students from Australian universities.

SIZE OF STAFF: Thirty at professional level; 30 technicians.

IMPORTANT SPECIES AVAILABLE FOR LABORATORY STUDIES:

Marine plants: *Zostera capricorni, Posidonia* sp., *Gracilaria* spp.
Coelenterata: *Aurelia caerulea*. .
Echinodermata: *Heliocidaris erythrogramma, Tripneustes gratilla, Astropecten pectinatus*
Annelida: *Chaetopterus variopedatus, Hydroides norvegica*

CSIRO MARINE BIOLOGICAL LABORATORY, CRONULLA

Crustacea: *Balanus amphitrite cirratus, Halicarcinus australis, Mictyris longicarpus*
Polyzoa: *Bugula neritina, Watersipora cucullata*
Plankton (taken in samplers throughout the year) *Skeletonema costatum* (diatom), *Isochrysis galbana* (chrysomonad), *Dunaliella marina* (flagellate); *Temora turbinata, Acartia danae, A. clausii* (copepods); *Nyctiphanes australis* (euphausiid); *Evadne tergestina, Penilia schmackeri* (cladocerans); *Thalia democratica, Oikopleura longicauda* (tunicates)
Gastropoda: *Pyrazus ebeninus, Dolabella scapula, Aplysia angasi*
Pelecypoda: *Anadara trapezia, Tapes turgida, Crassostrea commercialis, Mytilus planulatus, Trichomya hirsuta*
Cephalopoda: *Octopus cyaneus*
Ascidia: *Pyura pachydermatina, P. stolonifera, Ciona intestinalis*
Pisces: *Mugil dobula, Myxus elongatus, Girella tricuspidata, Sillago ciliata, Urolophus testaceus*

MAJOR CURRENT RESEARCH PROJECTS AND SCIENTIFIC LEADERS:
Fisheries (G. L. Kesteven)
Physiology (W. J. R. Lanzing)
Crayfish (A. M. Olsen and R. G. Chittleborough)
Demersal fish (V. C. F. Han)
Fisheries oceanography (D. Vaux)
Population dynamics (G. L. Kesteven)
Taxonomy (I. S. R. Munro)
Tuna (T. R. Cowper, J. S. Hynd, A. G. Nicholls and J. P. Robins)
Salmon (W. B. Malcolm and J. M. Thomson)
Oceanography (G. F. Humphrey)
Benthos (R. J. MacIntyre)
Biochemistry (S. W. Jeffrey, J. C. Madgwick and G. F. Humphrey)
Fouling (H. B. Wisely)
Hydrology (B. S. Newell and D. J. Rochford)
Physics (B. V. Hamon and F. de Castillejo)
Phytoplankton (E. J. F. Wood)
Productivity(H. R. Jitts)
Zooplankton (D. J. Tranter)

PUBLICATIONS ISSUED:
Australian Journal of Marine and Freshwater Research (regularly published journal)
CSIRO Division of Fisheries and Oceanography Technical Papers (occasionally published journal)

Heron Island Research Station

POSTAL ADDRESS: Great Barrier Reef, Heron Island via Gladstone, Queensland, Australia.
LOCATION: Near Brisbane.
EXECUTIVE OFFICER: Dr. O. A. Jones, Chairman, c/o Department of Geology, University of Queensland, Brisbane, Queensland, Australia.
SPONSORING AGENCIES: Great Barrier Reef Committee; University of Queensland.
YEAR FOUNDED: 1953.
SCOPE OF ACTIVITIES: Unrestricted research on the flora and fauna of the Great Barrier Reef.
SEASON OF OPERATION: March 1-January 31.
PHYSICAL ENVIRONMENT ACCESSIBLE: Coral Sea; coral reefs.
PROVISIONS FOR VISITING SCIENTISTS: Research and living space for about 20 visitors; fees charged for research space.
MAJOR RESEARCH FACILITIES: Small library; running sea water, large outdoor ponds and tanks, small aquarium tanks; identified reference collections of local corals, echinoderms, crabs, mollusks and fishes; machine and wood shop; small boats and outboard motors; one 16 ft LOA launch.
SIZE OF STAFF: One technician.
IMPORTANT SPECIES AVAILABLE FOR LABORATORY STUDIES:
Madreporaria: *Acropora sarmentosa, Goniastrea pectinata*

HERON ISLAND RESEARCH STATION

Gastropoda: *Conomurex luhuanus, Darioconus textile*
Pelecypoda: *Tridacna fossor*
Asteroidea: *Linckia laevigata*
Echinoidea: *Echinometra mathaei*
Holothurioidea: *Holothuria leucospilota*
Crustacea: *Gonodactylus chiragra*
Reptilia: *Chelonia mydas*

MAJOR CURRENT RESEARCH PROJECTS AND SCIENTIFIC LEADERS:
Study of reef sediments (G. Maxwell)
Studies of cone shell venom (R. Endean)
Underwater sound studies (J. Moulton)
Ecological studies (W. Stephenson)
Biosynthesis of collagen in holothurians (R. Endean)
Taxonomic studies of crabs (W. Stephenson)
Taxonomic studies of echinoderms (R. Endean)

PUBLICATIONS ISSUED: *Reports of the Great Barrier Reef Committee* (regularly published journal)

New Guinea Department of Agriculture, Stock, and Fisheries

Division of Fisheries

POSTAL ADDRESS:
Headquarters: Port Moresby, New Guinea.
Fresh-water Biological Laboratory: Dobel, Mt. Hagen, Western Highlands, New Guinea.
Marine Biological Station: Kanudi, Tatana Road, Port Moresby, New Guinea.
(Descriptions follow.)

EXECUTIVE OFFICER: A. M. Rapson, Chief, Division of Fisheries

Fresh-Water Biological Laboratory

This laboratory is, at present, a field station which may well develop into a permanent laboratory in a few years. Because of the paucity of hydrobiological laboratories in this territory, it has been included in the *Directory*.

LOCATION: Near Madang, New Guinea.
YEAR FOUNDED: 1960.
SCOPE OF ACTIVITIES: Restricted research on development of fresh-water fisheries with particular emphasis on pond culture.
SEASON OF OPERATION: All year.
PHYSICAL ENVIRONMENT ACCESSIBLE: Wahgi River; ponds.
MAJOR RESEARCH FACILITIES: Large outdoor ponds and small aquarium tanks.
IMPORTANT SPECIES AVAILABLE FOR LABORATORY STUDIES:
Convolvulaceae: *Ipomaea batata*
Caricaceae: *Carica papaya*
Araceae: *Colocasia esculata*
Leguminoseae: *Arachis hypogea*
Euphorbiaceae: *Manihot esculenta*

MAJOR CURRENT RESEARCH PROJECTS AND SCIENTIFIC LEADERS:
Feeding experiments on pond culture species (R. Bucknell)

Marine Biological Station

EXECUTIVE OFFICER: A. W. Charles, Acting Director.
YEAR FOUNDED: 1960.
SCOPE OF ACTIVITIES: Research on marine, inshore and estuarine biology with particular emphasis on fishery development.
SEASON OF OPERATION: All year.
PHYSICAL ENVIRONMENT ACCESSIBLE: Idlers Bay, Port Moresby and Fairfax Harbours; rocky and gravelly shores, estuarine conditions, coral reefs, mangrove zone.
PROVISIONS FOR VISITING SCIENTISTS: Some facilities for visitors can be provided; living quarters available nearby.
MAJOR RESEARCH AND TEACHING FACILITIES: Very small library; research collections of fauna and flora to be developed; vessels, 60 ft LOA, R. V. *Tagula*, 30 ft LOA, M. V. *Diama*, and some 16 ft open motor boats.
INSTRUCTIONAL PROGRAM: Elementary courses in general fisheries development, biology, and gear technology.
SIZE OF STAFF: Two at professional level; 4 technicians; 20 field workers.
MAJOR CURRENT RESEARCH PROJECTS AND SCIENTIFIC LEADERS:
Barramundi research
Gear research (A. Quinlan)
Trawling survey (R. Price)
Inshore fishery development (L. Malcolmson)
Fresh-water fisheries

New South Wales Secretary's Department, Fisheries Branch

Inland Fisheries Research Station

POSTAL ADDRESS: P. O. Box No. 182, Narrandera, New South Wales, Australia.
LOCATION: Near Wagga Wagga.
EXECUTIVE OFFICER: John S. Lake, Officer-in-Charge.
YEAR FOUNDED: 1960.
SCOPE OF ACTIVITIES: Restricted research on general fresh-water biology, fishery management and improvement programs.
SEASON OF OPERATION: All year.
PHYSICAL ENVIRONMENT ACCESSIBLE: Murrumbidgee River; inland lakes.
MAJOR RESEARCH FACILITIES: Small library; large outdoor ponds and tanks; pumped Murrumbidgee River

water; research and identified reference collections of fresh-water fish.

SIZE OF STAFF: Three at professional level; 1 technician, 2 field assistants.

IMPORTANT SPECIES AVAILABLE FOR LABORATORY STUDIES:

Pisces: *Maccullochella macquariensis, Plectroplites ambiguus, Bidyanus bidyanus, Macquaria australasica, Tandanus tandanus*

MAJOR CURRENT RESEARCH PROJECTS AND SCIENTIFIC LEADERS:

Study of the biology of callop (*Plectroplites ambiguus*). Pond culture of Murray cod (*Maccullochella macquariensis,* callop (*Plectroplites ambiguus*) and catfish (*Tandanus tandanus*) (J. S. Lake)

Study of the biology of Murray cod (*Maccullochella macquariensis*). Ecology—Darling River system

Study of the biology of catfish (*Tandanus tandanus*). Ecology—Murray, Murrumbidgee River systems

The Marine Laboratory of the University of Adelaide Zoology Department

POSTAL ADDRESS: Zoology Department, University of Adelaide, Adelaide, South Australia, Australia.

LOCATION: Outer Harbour, about 14 miles from the University of Adelaide.

EXECUTIVE OFFICER: Professor W. P. Rogers.

YEAR FOUNDED: 1956.

SCOPE OF ACTIVITIES: Unrestricted research on general marine biology; graduate and undergraduate instruction.

SEASON OF OPERATION: All year.

PHYSICAL ENVIRONMENT ACCESSIBLE: Gulf of St. Vincent; sandy and silty beaches.

PROVISIONS FOR VISITING SCIENTISTS: Space for 1-2 visitors; fees charged; living quarters available nearby.

MAJOR RESEARCH AND TEACHING FACILITIES: Small library within University library; running sea water, small aquarium tanks; identified reference collections of local fauna and flora in the Zoology and Botany Departments of the University; small boats and outboard motors.

INSTRUCTIONAL PROGRAM: General vertebrate and invertebrate zoology at the University.

SIZE OF STAFF: One at professional level; 1 technician.

IMPORTANT SPECIES AVAILABLE FOR LABORATORY STUDIES:

Anthozoa: *Actinia terselrosa*

Crustacea: *Jasus lalandii, Helice haswelianus*

Tunicata: *Ciona intestinalis, Lyura irregularis*

MAJOR CURRENT RESEARCH PROJECTS AND SCIENTIFIC LEADERS:

Growth rate and behavior of *Jasus lalandii* (I. M. Thomas)

Iodine metabolism in invertebrates and lower chordates (I. M. Thomas)

University of New England Marine Laboratory

A small marine laboratory has been established on the north coast of New South Wales about 30 miles south of Grafton. Enquiries may be addressed to the Department of Zoology, University of New England, Armidale, New South Wales, Australia.

Victoria Department of Fisheries and Wildlife, Marine and Freshwater Laboratories

POSTAL ADDRESS: 605 Flinders Street Extension, Melbourne, C.3, Victoria, Australia.

EXECUTIVE OFFICER: Mr. A. Dunbavin Butcher, Director of Fisheries and Wildlife.

SPONSORING AGENCY: Government of Victoria.

YEAR FOUNDED: 1941.

SCOPE OF ACTIVITIES: Restricted research on the biology and management of marine and fresh-water fisheries; graduate and undergraduate instruction.

SEASON OF OPERATION: All year.

PHYSICAL ENVIRONMENT ACCESSIBLE: Port Phillip and Western Port Bays, Corner Inlet; sandy and silty beaches, rocky and gravelly shores, estuarine conditions, brackish, shallow bays, eutrophic and oligotrophic lakes, rivers and streams.

PROVISIONS FOR VISITING SCIENTISTS: Space for 2-3 visitors; no fees charged; living quarters available nearby.

MAJOR RESEARCH AND TEACHING FACILITIES: Small library; small aquarium tanks; research collections of indigenous fresh-water fish, bottom marine invertebrates and bottom marine substrates; machine and wood shop, skilled shop workman available; small boats and outboard motors; vessels, 45 ft and 33 ft LOA.

SIZE OF STAFF: Ten at professional level; 10 technicians.

VICTORIA DEPARTMENT OF FISHERIES AND WILDLIFE, MARINE AND FRESHWATER LABORATORIES

MAJOR CURRENT RESEARCH PROJECTS AND SCIENTIFIC LEADERS:

Native percoid biology and management (Ian Cannon Smith)

Ecology and fisheries of the Gippsland Lakes (large estuary) (Terence Gorman)

Management of marine fisheries (Daniel David Lynch)

Bottom ecology of Port Philip Bay (Daniel David Lynch)

Trout management (David Ian Felstead)

Snobs Creek Freshwater Fisheries Research Station and Hatchery

POSTAL ADDRESS: Private Bag, via Alexandria, Victoria, Australia.

EXECUTIVE OFFICER: Mr. J. C. F. Wharton, Scientific Superintendent.

SPONSORING AGENCY: Victoria Department of Fisheries and Wildlife.

YEAR FOUNDED: 1953.

SCOPE OF ACTIVITIES: Restricted research on economic production, distribution and pathology of Rainbow trout, Brown trout and important native percoids.

SEASON OF OPERATION: All year.

PHYSICAL ENVIRONMENT ACCESSIBLE: Eildon Reservoir, Goulburn River, Snobs Creek; oligotrophic lake, and fast mountain streams.

PROVISIONS FOR VISITING SCIENTISTS: Research and living space for visitors; no fees charged for research space.

MAJOR RESEARCH AND TEACHING FACILITIES: Small library; large outdoor ponds and tanks, small aquarium tanks; machine and wood shop, skilled shop workman available; small boats and outboard motors.

SIZE OF STAFF: Two at professional level; 2 technicians.

SNOBS CREEK FRESHWATER FISHERIES RESEARCH STATION AND HATCHERY

MAJOR CURRENT RESEARCH PROJECTS AND SCIENTIFIC LEADERS:

Factors necessary in small ponds for gonad development and spawning of selected native percoids. (James C. F. Wharton)

Role of dietary carotenoids in development of trout larvae (James C. F. Wharton)

Development of cheap, dry diet for trout (James C. F. Wharton)

Identification of factors limiting stock density in rearing units (James C. F. Wharton)

Western Australia Fisheries Department

POSTAL ADDRESS: 108 Adelaide Terrace, Perth, Western Australia, Australia.

EXECUTIVE OFFICER: Mr. A. J. Fraser, Director of Fisheries.

SPONSORING AGENCY: Government of Western Australia.

YEAR FOUNDED: 1958.

SCOPE OF ACTIVITIES: Restricted research on fresh-water and marine fisheries biology.

SEASON OF OPERATION: All year.

PHYSICAL ENVIRONMENT ACCESSIBLE: Swan River; estuarine conditions.

PROVISIONS FOR VISITING SCIENTISTS: Space for 2 visitors; no fees charged; living quarters available nearby.

MAJOR RESEARCH AND TEACHING FACILITIES: Small library; vessels, 75 ft LOA *Peron* and 45 ft LOA *Lancelin*.

SIZE OF STAFF: One at professional level; 3 technicians.

IMPORTANT SPECIES AVAILABLE FOR LABORATORY STUDIES:

Crustacea: *Panulirus longipes, Cheraps tenuimanus*

MAJOR CURRENT RESEARCH PROJECTS AND SCIENTIFIC LEADERS:

Farm dam fish culture (B. K. Bowen)

PUBLICATIONS ISSUED: *Western Australia Fisheries Bulletin* (occasionally published journal)

AUSTRIA

Biologische Station, Lunz

LUNZ BIOLOGICAL STATION

POSTAL ADDRESS: Lunz am See, Oesterreich (Austria).

LOCATION: Near Wien (Vienna).

EXECUTIVE OFFICER: Professor Ingo Findenegg, Leiter.

SPONSORING AGENCY: Akademie der Wissenschaften (Academy of Sciences).

YEAR FOUNDED: 1906.

SCOPE OF ACTIVITIES: Unrestricted research on plankton and bottom ecology of lakes and streams; limnological instruction.

BIOLOGISCHE STATION, LUNZ

SEASON OF OPERATION: All year.

PHYSICAL ENVIRONMENT ACCESSIBLE: Lunzer Seen, River Ybbs; oligotrophic lake.

PROVISIONS FOR VISITING SCIENTISTS: Space for 15 visitors; fees charged.

MAJOR RESEARCH AND TEACHING FACILITIES: Moderately complete library; small aquarium tanks; machine and wood shop, skilled shop workman available; small boats and outboard motors.

INSTRUCTIONAL PROGRAM: Plankton, bottom fauna and flora of lakes.

SIZE OF STAFF: Three at professional level; 2 technicians.

MAJOR CURRENT RESEARCH PROJECTS AND SCIENTIFIC LEADERS:

Primary production of Austrian lakes (Ingo Findenegg)

Taxonomy of Rotatoria (Ruttner-Kolisko)

Bundesinstitut fuer Gewaesserforschung und Fischereiwirtschaft

FEDERAL INSTITUTE FOR HYDROLOGY AND FISHERIES INVESTIGATIONS

POSTAL ADDRESS: Scharfling am Mondsee, Oesterreich (Austria).

EXECUTIVE OFFICER: Dr. W. Einsele, Direktor.

YEAR FOUNDED: 1945.

SCOPE OF ACTIVITIES: Limnological and fishery research; production of fish stock for lakes and research in hatchery methods.

SEASON OF OPERATION: All year.

PHYSICAL ENVIRONMENT ACCESSIBLE: Many oligotrophic and dystrophic alpine and lowland lakes; mountain streams; Danube River.

PROVISIONS FOR VISITING SCIENTISTS: Research and living space for 5-20 investigators. Space upon application.

MAJOR RESEARCH AND TEACHING FACILITIES: Boats, trucks, motors, tanks, chemical laboratory, full supply of limnological gear.

INSTRUCTIONAL PROGRAM: Short courses in limnology and fisheries.

MAJOR CURRENT RESEARCH PROJECTS:

Chemical limnology

Production studies of plankton and fish.

PUBLICATIONS ISSUED: *Oesterreichische Fischerei.* W. Einsele, Editor.

Institut fuer Hydrobiologie und Fischereiwirtschaft

INSTITUTE FOR HYDROBIOLOGY AND FISHERY MANAGEMENT

POSTAL ADDRESS: Hochschule fuer Bodenkultur, Feistmantelstrasse 4, Wien, Oesterreich (Vienna, Austria).

EXECUTIVE OFFICER: Doz. Dr. Reinhard Liepolt, Direktor.

SPONSORING AGENCY: Bundesministerium fuer Unterricht (Federal Ministry for Education).

YEAR FOUNDED: 1897.

SCOPE OF ACTIVITIES: Unrestricted research on theoretical and applied limnology, fishery biology; instruction.

SEASON OF OPERATION: All year.

PROVISIONS FOR VISITING SCIENTISTS: Space for visitors; no fees charged.

INSTRUCTIONAL PROGRAM: Limnology and fishery biology.

MAJOR RESEARCH AND TEACHING FACILITIES: Small library; small aquarium tanks.

SIZE OF STAFF: One at professional level; 1 technician.

HOCHSCHULE FUER BODENKULTUR, WIEN

Universitaet Innsbruck, Limnologische Station Kuehtai

UNIVERSITY OF INNSBRUCK, KUEHTAI LIMNOLOGICAL STATION

POSTAL ADDRESS: Universitaetsstrasse 4, Innsbruck, Oesterreich (Austria).

LOCATION: Kuehtai.

EXECUTIVE OFFICER: Professor Dr. Otto Steinboeck, Direktor.

YEAR FOUNDED: 1959.

SCOPE OF ACTIVITIES: Unrestricted research on the limnology of high mountain lakes, pools and brooks.

SEASON OF OPERATION: All year.

PHYSICAL ENVIRONMENT ACCESSIBLE: High mountain lakes, pools and brooks in large numbers. Station located on shore of Vorderer Finstertalersee at 2,240 m.

PROVISIONS FOR VISITING SCIENTISTS: Space for 4 visitors; living quarters in Kuehtai (one hour walk from Station).

MAJOR RESEARCH FACILITIES: Small library in Innsbruck, none at Kuehtai; small aquarium tanks, several natural ponds for experimental work; skilled shop workman occasionally available; small boats.

SIZE OF STAFF: No permanent staff.

MAJOR CURRENT RESEARCH PROJECTS AND SCIENTIFIC LEADERS:

- Bottom fauna and sediment of Vorderer Finstertalersee (O. Steinboeck)
- Physical, chemical and biological studies on a high mountain brook (O. Steinboeck)
- Phytoplankton of high mountain lakes (Herbert Reisigl)
- Limnology of high mountain lakes (Roland Pechlaner)

LIMNOLOGISCHE STATION, KUEHTAI

BUNDESANSTALT FUER WASSERBIOLOGIE UND ABWASSERFORSCHUNG

Bundesanstalt fuer Wasserbiologie und Abwasserforschung

FEDERAL INSTITUTE FOR WATER BIOLOGY AND SEWAGE RESEARCH

POSTAL ADDRESS: Postfach 7, Kaisermuehlen 39/XXII, Wien, Oesterreich. (Vienna, Austria)

EXECUTIVE OFFICER: Doz. Dr. R. Liepolt, Direktor.

SPONSORING AGENCY: Bundesministerium fuer Land- und Forstwirtschaft (Federal Ministry of Agriculture and Forestry)

YEAR FOUNDED: 1945.

SCOPE OF ACTIVITIES: Unrestricted research on theoretical and applied limnology, sewage biology and radiology of water.

SEASON OF OPERATION: All year.

PHYSICAL ENVIRONMENT ACCESSIBLE: Eutrophic and oligotrophic lakes, rivers and streams.

PROVISIONS FOR VISITING SCIENTISTS: Space for visitors; no fees charged.

MAJOR RESEARCH AND TEACHING FACILITIES: Small library; large outdoor ponds and tanks, small aquarium tanks; machine and joiner's shop, electrical and electronic shop, skilled shop workman available; small boats and outboard motors.

INSTRUCTIONAL PROGRAM: Annual courses in sewage and pollution problems of streams and rivers.

SIZE OF STAFF: Twelve at professional level; 19 technicians.

PUBLICATIONS ISSUED: *Wasser und Abwasser* (regularly published journal).

BAHAMAS

American Museum of Natural History, Lerner Marine Laboratory

POSTAL ADDRESS: Bimini, Bahamas.

EXECUTIVE OFFICER: Dr. Robert Mathewson, Resident Director, 1211 duPont Building, Miami 32, Florida.

SPONSORING AGENCY: American Museum of Natural History, New York 24, New York.

YEAR FOUNDED: 1947.
SCOPE OF ACTIVITIES: Unrestricted marine biological research.
SEASON OF OPERATION: All year.
PHYSICAL ENVIRONMENT ACCESSIBLE: Florida Current, Great Bahama Bank; open ocean, rocky shore, coral reefs, shallow lagoon, and tropical shallow limestone sea.
PROVISIONS FOR VISITING SCIENTISTS: Research and living space for 14 visitors; fees charged for research space.
MAJOR RESEARCH FACILITIES: Small library; running sea water, small aquarium tanks, large outdoor pens in lagoon; machine and wood shop; small boats and outboard motors, two 28 ft LOA inboard launches, two 40 ft research vessels, diesel, long range, laboratory equipped; one 65 ft T boat, steel hull, diesel, all navigation aids, laboratory equipped.
SIZE OF STAFF: Two at professional level.
IMPORTANT SPECIES AVAILABLE FOR LABORATORY STUDIES:
Chlorophyceae: *Acetabularia crenulata*
Porifera: *Cryptotethya crypta*
Gorgonacea: *Xiphigorgia anceps*
Polychaeta: *Dasybranchus caducus*
Echinodermata: *Lytechinus variegatus, Actinopyga agassizi*
Cephalopoda: *Octopus briareus*
Crustacea: *Cardisoma guanhumi*
Teleosts: *Negaprion brevirostris, Bathygobius soporator*
Elasmobranchs: an abundance of rays, skates, saw fish, and sharks—Nurse, Bull, Hammerheads, Lemons, Tigers, Cuban, etc.
MAJOR CURRENT RESEARCH PROJECTS AND SCIENTIFIC LEADERS:
Olfactory and visual physiology in sharks (Perry W. Gilbert)
Neuro chemical and electrophysiological studies using teleosts and elasmobranchs

LERNER MARINE LABORATORY

BELGIUM

Institut d'Etudes Maritimes

INSTITUTE FOR MARINE RESEARCH

POSTAL ADDRESS: Zeewezengebouw, Quai des Nations, Ostende, Belgique (Belgium).
EXECUTIVE OFFICER: Dr. E. Leloup, Directeur.
SPONSORING AGENCY: Ministere de l'Agriculture (Ministry of Agriculture).
YEAR FOUNDED: 1927.
SCOPE OF ACTIVITIES: Unrestricted research in general marine biology and general oceanography, with the objective of developing and conserving the fisheries.
SEASON OF OPERATION: All year.
PHYSICAL ENVIRONMENT ACCESSIBLE: North Sea, sandy beach.
PROVISIONS FOR VISITING SCIENTISTS: Space for 1 or 2 visitors; no fees charged.
MAJOR RESEARCH FACILITIES: Small library; running fresh-water; one 28 m LOA vessel, R. V. Hinders.
SIZE OF STAFF: Two part time at professional level; 2 full time and 1 part time technician.
IMPORTANT SPECIES AVAILABLE FOR LABORATORY STUDIES:
Crustacea: *Cragon vulgaris, Mytilicola* sp.
Mollusca: *Ostrea* sp.
Pisces: *Solea vulgaris, Clupea harengus, Gadus merlangus*
MAJOR CURRENT RESEARCH PROJECTS AND SCIENTIFIC LEADERS:
Marine biology, plankton (E. Leloup)
Fisheries biology (Ch. Gilis)

Station de Recherches des Eaux et Forets, Section d'Hydrobiologie

RESEARCH STATION OF WATERS AND FORESTS, SECTION OF HYDROBIOLOGY

POSTAL ADDRESS: Groenendael-Hoeilaart, Belgique (Belgium).
LOCATION: Near Bruxelles (Brussels).
EXECUTIVE OFFICER: Mr. M. Huet, Directeur.
SPONSORING AGENCY: Ministere de l'Agriculture (Ministry of Agriculture).
YEAR FOUNDED: 1940.
SCOPE OF ACTIVITIES: Restricted research on the fresh-water fisheries and their management in Belgium.
SEASON OF OPERATION: All year.
PHYSICAL ENVIRONMENT ACCESSIBLE: Rivers, streams and artificial ponds for fish culture.
PROVISIONS FOR VISITING SCIENTISTS: None.
MAJOR RESEARCH FACILITIES: Moderately complete library.
SIZE OF STAFF: Two at professional level; 1 technician.

MAJOR CURRENT RESEARCH PROJECTS AND SCIENTIFIC LEADERS:
- Biology of running waters (M. Huet and J. A. Timmermans)
- Fish-culture of fresh-water fish (M. Huet and J. A. Timmermans)
- Populations of rivers and streams (J. A. Timmermans)

PUBLICATIONS ISSUED: *Travaux de la Station de Recherches des Eaux et Forets, Serie D., Hydrobiologie* (occasionally published journal).

Institut pour la Recherche Scientifique en Afrique Centrale

INSTITUTE FOR SCIENTIFIC RESEARCH IN CENTRAL AFRICA

POSTAL ADDRESS: Rue Defacqz, 1, Bruxelles, Belgique (Brussels, Belgium).
EXECUTIVE OFFICER: L. Soyer, Secretaire General.
YEAR FOUNDED: 1947.
SCOPE OF ACTIVITIES: To create centres of research in the Congo and in Central Africa.
CENTRE DE RECHERCHE DE TANGANYIKA: See description, page 39.

BERMUDA

Bermuda Biological Station for Research, Inc.

POSTAL ADDRESS: St. George's West, Bermuda.
EXECUTIVE OFFICER: Dr. William H. Sutcliffe, Jr., Director.
SPONSORING AGENCY: Privately financed laboratory with a Board of Trustees and an endowment for research.
YEAR FOUNDED: 1903.
SCOPE OF ACTIVITIES: Unrestricted research on the productivity and hydrography of the Sargasso Sea, and on general marine biology; graduate instruction.
SEASON OF OPERATION: All year.
PHYSICAL ENVIRONMENT ACCESSIBLE: Atlantic Ocean; sandy beaches, rocky shores and coral reefs.
PROVISIONS FOR VISITING SCIENTISTS: Research and living space for 25 visitors; fees charged for research space.
MAJOR RESEARCH AND TEACHING FACILITIES: Small library; running sea water, small aquarium tanks, 4 indoor concrete tanks; machine and wood shop, electrical and electronic shop, skilled shop workman available; small boats and outboard motors, one 65 ft LOA power vessel.
INSTRUCTIONAL PROGRAM: Experimental embryology, carbonate sedimentation, and oceanography.
SIZE OF STAFF: Three at professional level; 2 technicians.
IMPORTANT SPECIES AVAILABLE FOR LABORATORY STUDIES:
- Chlorphyceae: *Acetabularia crenulata*
- Amphineura: *Chiton tuberculatus*
- Crustacea: *Gecarcinus lateralis, Panulirus argus*
- Ascidiacea: *Ascidia nigra*
- Amphioxi: *Branchiostoma bermudae*
- Pisces: *Sparisoma squalidum*

MAJOR CURRENT RESEARCH PROJECTS AND SCIENTIFIC LEADERS:
- Productivity of the Sargasso Sea (John H. Ryther)
- Mucopolysaccharides in invertebrates (Saul Roseman)
- Cytochemical investigation of development and muscle cytology in some marine animals (Ronald R. Cowden)
- Mucopolysaccharides in invertebrates (Saul Roseman)

BERMUDA BIOLOGICAL STATION FOR RESEARCH, INCORPORATED

BRAZIL

Ministerio de Agricultura de Brasil, Departemente Nacional de Producao Animal, Divisao de Caca E Pesca

BRAZILIAN MINISTRY OF AGRICULTURE, NATIONAL DEPARTMENT OF ANIMAL PRODUCTION, DIVISION OF FISH AND GAME

Estacao Experimental de Biologia E Piscicultura

EXPERIMENTAL STATION OF BIOLOGY AND FISH CULTURE

POSTAL ADDRESS: Pirassununga, Sao Paulo, Brasil (Brazil).
EXECUTIVE OFFICER: Dr. Almir Peracio, Chefe.

ESTACAO EXPERIMENTAL DE BIOLOGIA E PISCICULTURA

SCOPE OF ACTIVITIES: Restricted research on the biology and culture of fresh-water fishes.

SEASON OF OPERATION: All year.

PHYSICAL ENVIRONMENT ACCESSIBLE: Mogi Guassu River (tributary of the Parana).

PROVISIONS FOR VISITING SCIENTISTS: Space for 5 visitors; living quarters available nearby.

MAJOR RESEARCH FACILITIES: Small library; large outdoor ponds and tanks, small aquarium tanks; identified reference collections of fishes and other fresh-water fauna; small boats and outboard motors.

SIZE OF STAFF: Four at professional level; 2 technicians.

MAJOR CURRENT RESEARCH PROJECTS AND SCIENTIFIC LEADERS:

Biology and systematics of fresh-water fishes (Otto Schubart)

Tagging of fresh-water fishes (Manuel Perira de Godoy)

Instituto Oswaldo Cruz, Estacao de Hidrobiologia

OSWALDO CRUZ INSTITUTE, HYDROBIOLOGICAL LABORATORY

POSTAL ADDRESS: Caixa Postal 926, Rio de Janeiro, Brasil (Brazil)

LOCATION: Pinheiro Island, Guanabara Bay.

EXECUTIVE OFFICER: Dr. Lejeune P. H. de Oliveira, Residente Oficial.

SPONSORING AGENCY: Ministerio de Saude (Ministry of Health).

YEAR FOUNDED: 1937; at present location since 1947.

SCOPE OF ACTIVITIES: Unrestricted research on general marine biology and plankton in relation to mortality of fishes and other marine life in polluted sections of the Rio de Janeiro harbor; limnology of brackish water lagoons.

SEASON OF OPERATION: All year.

PHYSICAL ENVIRONMENT ACCESSIBLE: Atlantic Ocean, Guanabara Bay; sandy and silty beaches, rocky and gravelly shores, estuarine conditions, brackish, shallow bays and lagoons, and mangroves.

PROVISIONS FOR VISITING SCIENTISTS: Research and living space for 2 visitors; no fees charged for research space.

MAJOR RESEARCH FACILITIES: Very extensive library; small museum of marine animals; partially identified reference collections of local fauna and flora; machine and wood shop, electrical and electronic shop at main headquarters of the institute which is nearby; one small boat and outboard motor.

SIZE OF STAFF: Two at professional level; 7 technicians.

IMPORTANT SPECIES AVAILABLE FOR LABORATORY STUDIES:

Brachyura: *Uca olympioi* and other *Uca* spp., *Cardisoma guanhumi, Callinectes sapidus*

Mollusca: *Anomalocardia brasiliana*

Echinodermata: *Enoplopatiria emarginata*

Algae: *Anabaena spiroides, Microcystis aeruginosa, Glenodinium, Oscillatoria putrida.*

MAJOR CURRENT RESEARCH PROJECTS AND SCIENTIFIC LEADERS:

Ecology of Guanabara Bay (Lejeune de Oliveira)

Pollution ecology (Lejeune de Oliveira)

Mortality of fishes in the coastal lagoons of Brazil (Lejeune de Oliveira)

Echinodermata (Luiza Krau)

Plankton of brackish water lagoons (Luiza Krau)

PUBLICATIONS ISSUED: *Memorias do Instituto Oswaldo Cruz* (regularly published journal)

Laboratorio de Biologia Marinha de Sao Sebastiao

SAN SEBASTIAN MARINE BIOLOGICAL LABORATORY

POSTAL ADDRESS: Caixa, Postal 11.230, Sao Paulo, 9, Brasil (Brazil).

LOCATION: Near Sao Sebastiao.

EXECUTIVE OFFICER: Dr. Paulo Sawaya, Director.

SPONSORING AGENCY: Departamento de Fisiologia Geral e Animal, Universidade de Sao Paulo (University of Sao Paulo, Department of General and Animal Physiology).

YEAR FOUNDED: 1951.

SCOPE OF ACTIVITIES: Unrestricted research on general marine biology; graduate and undergraduate instruction.

SEASON OF OPERATION: All year.

PHYSICAL ENVIRONMENT ACCESSIBLE: Atlantic Ocean; sandy beaches, rocky shores, estuarine conditions and brackish, shallow bays.

PROVISIONS FOR VISITING SCIENTISTS: Research and living space for 20 visitors; fees charged for living space.

MAJOR RESEARCH AND TEACHING FACILITIES: Small library at the laboratory, very extensive library at the university; running fresh-water, large outdoor ponds and tanks planned, small aquarium tanks; very small machine and woodshop, skilled shop workman available; small boats and outboard motors.

INSTRUCTIONAL PROGRAM: General invertebrate zoology, phytoplankton, comparative physiology, comparative biochemistry, comparative pharmacology, and ecology.

SIZE OF STAFF: Two permanent assistants; 1 technician.

IMPORTANT SPECIES AVAILABLE FOR LABORATORY STUDIES: List being prepared. Will be available from the director in the near future.

MAJOR CURRENT RESEARCH PROJECTS AND SCIENTIFIC LEADERS:

Biology of Enteropneusta (Paulo Sawaya)
Pharmacology of holothurian muscles (Paulo Sawaya)
Biochemistry of smooth muscles (Erasmo Garcia Mendes)
Electron microscopy of crustacean muscles (Roger Jean Lavallard)
Marine ecology (Roger Jean Lavallard)
Neurosecretion (Domingos Valente)
Holothurian taxonomy (Anna Amelia Ancona Lopez)
Biology of ascidians (Sergio A. Rodrigues)
Biology of mollusks—*Mytilus* (Jorge A. Petersen)

PUBLICATIONS ISSUED: *Boletin de Zoologia* (regularly published journal edited by the Departamento de Fisiologia Geral e Animal)

Secretaria da Agricultura de Sao Paulo, Departamento da Producao Animal

SAO PAULO MINISTRY OF AGRICULTURE, DEPARTMENT OF ANIMAL PRODUCTS

Divisao de Caca E Pesca, Seccao de Hidrobiologia

DIVISION OF FISH AND GAME, HYDROBIOLOGY SECTION

POSTAL ADDRESS: Av. Francisco Matarazzo 455, Sao Paulo, Brasil (Brazil).

EXECUTIVE OFFICER: Emilio Varoli, Director. Dr. Francisco Bergamin, Officer-in-charge of Hydrobiology Section.

YEAR FOUNDED: 1928.

SCOPE OF ACTIVITIES: Restricted research on pollution. Research expected to extend to hydrobiology in general.

SEASON OF OPERATION: All year.

PHYSICAL ENVIRONMENT ACCESSIBLE: Tiete River.

PROVISIONS FOR VISITING SCIENTISTS: None.

MAJOR RESEARCH FACILITIES: Small library; large outdoor ponds and tanks; small boats and outboard motors, one 23 ft LOA vessel.

SIZE OF STAFF: Four at professional level; 1 technician.

MAJOR CURRENT RESEARCH PROJECTS AND SCIENTIFIC LEADERS:

Chemical analysis for trace quantities of metals in river water (Francisco Bergamin)
Effects of insecticides in running waters (Francisco Bergamin)

Universidade do Recife, Instituto Oceanografico

UNIVERSITY OF RECIFE, INSTITUTE OF OCEANOGRAPHY

POSTAL ADDRESS: Caixa postal 1076, Recife, Pernambuco, Brasil (Brazil).

EXECUTIVE OFFICER: Dr. Ramon Nobrega, Director.

SPONSORING AGENCY: Ministerio da Educacao e Cultura do Brasil (Brazilian Ministry of Education and Culture).

UNIVERSIDADE DO RECIFE, INSTITUTO OCEANOGRAFICO

YEAR FOUNDED: 1958.

SCOPE OF ACTIVITIES: Unrestricted research on general marine biology, oceanography, geology, and fisheries.

SEASON OF OPERATION: All year, but September to March is the best season.

PHYSICAL ENVIRONMENT ACCESSIBLE: Atlantic Ocean, Rios Capibaribe and others nearby; sandy and silty beaches, estuarine conditions, mangroves and banks of calcareous sandstone.

MAJOR RESEARCH FACILITIES: Small library; research collection of fauna and flora being built up; machine and wood shop and electrical and electronic shop available at the university; small boats and outboard motors, one 20 m LOA vessel, *Rio Formoso*.

SIZE OF STAFF: Ten or 12 at professional level; 2 technicians.

MAJOR CURRENT RESEARCH PROJECTS AND SCIENTIFIC LEADERS:

Oceanography (Ramon Nobrega, Lourinaldo Barreto Cavalcanti, and Julio Vicente Alves de Araujo)
Marine biology (Jacques Louis Laborel, Olimpio Carneiro da Silva, and Petronio Alves Coelho)
Algology (Maria Leda Labanca)
Geology (Paulo da Nobrega Coutinho)
Planktonology (Shigekatsu Sato and Maryse Nogueiro Paranagua)
Fish and fisheries will be organized in 1963.

PUBLICATIONS ISSUED: *Trabalhos do Instituto de Biologia Maritima e Oceanografia da Universidade do Recife* (regularly published journal)

Universidade de Sao Paulo, Instituto Oceanografico

UNIVERSITY OF SAO PAULO, OCEANOGRAPHIC INSTITUTE

POSTAL ADDRESS:
Main laboratory and headquarters: Caixa Postal 9075, Alameda Eduardo Prado, 698, Sao Paulo, Brasil (Brazil).
Marine stations:
1. Northern Station in Ubatuba.
2. Southern Station in Cananeia.

EXECUTIVE OFFICER: Dr. Ingvar Emilsson, Director.

SPONSORING AGENCY: Universidade de Sao Paulo (University of Sao Paulo).

YEAR FOUNDED: 1946; reorganized in 1960.

SCOPE OF ACTIVITIES: Unrestricted research in oceanography, marine biology, fisheries biology and marine products technology; graduate instruction.

SEASON OF OPERATION: All year.

PHYSICAL ENVIRONMENT ACCESSIBLE: South Atlantic Ocean with special emphasis on subtropical convergence, Brazil Current; sandy and silty beaches, rocky and gravelly shores, estuarine conditions, brackish, shallow bays and shallow lagoons with mangrove vegetation.

PROVISIONS FOR VISITING SCIENTISTS: Research and living space for 6 at Cananeia, 4 at Ubatuba, and 2-3 at Sao Paulo.

MAJOR RESEARCH AND TEACHING FACILITIES: Moderately complete library; large outdoor pond at Cananeia, small aquarium tanks; research collections of Brazilian marine fishes, crustaceans, mollusks, foraminiferans, diatoms and other elements of the local marine fauna and flora; identified reference collections of crustaceans, mollusks, foraminiferans, and diatoms; machine and wood shop; small boats and outboard motors; vessels, 15 m LOA, *Emilia,* 7 m LOA, *Juva,* and a new 49 m LOA oceanographic and fishery research vessel under construction.

INSTRUCTIONAL PROGRAM: Special 4 year courses in oceanography planned to start in 1961.

SIZE OF STAFF: Twenty-one at professional level; 17 technicians.

IMPORTANT SPECIES AVAILABLE FOR LABORATORY STUDIES:
Pisces: *Mugil cephalus, Sardinella allecia*
Subtropical Atlantic invertebrates

MAJOR CURRENT RESEARCH PROJECTS AND SCIENTIFIC LEADERS:
Taxonomic and biological studies of fishes (Luiz Roberto Tommasi)
Plankton (Marta Vannucci)
Benthos (J. Paiva Carvalho and Liliana Forneris)
Nekton (Tagea K. S. Bjornberg)
Fisheries biology (Plinio Soares Moreira)

PUBLICATIONS ISSUED:
Boletim do Instituto Oceanografico (regularly published journal)
Catalogue of Marine Larvae
Contribuicoes Avulsas: Tecnologia

UNIVERSIDADE DE SAO PAULO, STATION CANANEIA

UNIVERSIDADE DE SAO PAULO, STATION UBATUBA

BULGARIA

Institut po Ribarstvo

INSTITUTE OF FISHERY RESEARCH

POSTAL ADDRESS:
Marine laboratory: Vaena, Bulgaria (Varna, Bulgaria).
Fresh-water laboratory: Plovdiv, Bulgaria.

EXECUTIVE OFFICERS: Professor Al. Valkanov, Direktor, Marine laboratory. Mr. N. Gheorghiev, Direktor, Fresh-water laboratory.

SPONSORING AGENCY: Bulgarische Akademie der Wissenschaften (Bulgarian Academy of Science).

YEAR FOUNDED: 1932.

SCOPE OF ACTIVITIES: The marine laboratory engages in research on oceanography, plankton, benthos, ichthyology and faunistics of the Black Sea. The fresh-water laboratory engages in research on the biology of lakes and rivers, and pisciculture. Instruction at both laboratories.

INSTITUT PO RIBARSTVO, MARINE LABORATORY, VARNA

SEASON OF OPERATION: All year.

PHYSICAL ENVIRONMENT ACCESSIBLE: Black Sea; seashore lakes, inland lakes, rivers and ponds; sandy and silty beaches, rocky and gravelly shores, estuarine conditions, brackish, shallow bays, eutrophic and oligotrophic lakes.

PROVISIONS FOR VISITING SCIENTISTS: Space for two visitors in Varna; no fees charged; living quarters available nearby.

MAJOR RESEARCH AND TEACHING FACILITIES: Very extensive library; running sea and fresh-water, large outdoor ponds and tanks in Plovdiv, small aquarium tanks; identified reference collections of Polychaeta, Malacostraca, Mollusca, Pisces, phyto- and zooplankton; machine and wood shop; small boats and outboard motors; one 22 m LOA power vessel.

INSTRUCTIONAL PROGRAM: Courses in hydrology, hydrobiology and ichthyology given for university students.

SIZE OF STAFF: Twenty-three scientific workers; 39 technicians.

IMPORTANT SPECIES AVAILABLE FOR LABORATORY STUDIES:
Algae: *Enteromorpha intestinalis, Cystoseira barbata*
Turbellaria: *Leptoplana tremellaris*
Polychaeta: *Nereis succinea*
Mollusca: *Cardium edule, Mytilus galoprovincialis*
Crustacea: *Leander squilla, Carcinus maenas*
Pisces: Gobiidae, *Pleuronectes* sp.

MAJOR CURRENT RESEARCH PROJECTS AND SCIENTIFIC LEADERS:
Hydrobiology and faunistics of the Black Sea (A. Valkanov
Ichthyology of the Black Sea (S. Stojanov)
Hydrochemistry of the Black Sea (A. Rojdestvensky)
Pisciculture (N. Georgiev)

PUBLICATIONS ISSUED: *Trudove na Institut po ribarstvo* (regularly published journal).

Laboratories for Which No Detailed Information Was Available:

Bulgarische Akademie der Wissenschaften, Zoologisches Institut mit Museum, Boulev. Ruski 1, Sofia, Bulgariya. Professor Dr. G. Paspalev. The laboratory for studying aquatic fauna was still in the process of organization by the Institute at the time of preparation of the *Directory*.

BURMA

Laboratories About Which No Detailed Information Was Available:

While there were no hydrobiological stations in Burma at the time of preparation of the Directory, a small section on oceanography was planned by the Union of Burma Applied Research Institute. Further information about this section may be had by writing to Dr. F. Ba Hli, Director-General of the Research Institute, Kanbe, Rangoon, Myanma (Burma).

CAMBODIA

Direction Nationale Des Peches

NATIONAL DIRECTORATE OF FISHERIES

Institut National Des Recherches Pisciocoles

NATIONAL INSTITUTE OF PISCICULTURAL RESEARCH

POSTAL ADDRESS: B. P. 243, Coulevard Norodom, Phnom-Penh, Cambodge (Cambodia).
EXECUTIVE OFFICER: You Kim Chhon, Officier en charge.
SPONSORING AGENCY: Direction Nationale des Peches.
YEAR FOUNDED: 1950.
SCOPE OF ACTIVITIES: Officially restricted program of research and technology on fresh-water fisheries and plankton.
SEASON OF OPERATION: All year.
PHYSICAL ENVIRONMENT ACCESSIBLE: Rivers and streams.
PROVISIONS FOR VISITING SCIENTISTS: Research space for 3 visitors; no fees charged; living quarters nearby and at the Institute.
MAJOR RESEARCH FACILITIES: Research collections of fresh-water fish, but no named reference collections accessible; some workshop facilities and about 10 skilled workmen available; a small outboard motorboat; vessel, one 15 m LOA M/V.
SIZE OF STAFF: No permanent staff; technicians come from the Ecole d'Agriculture, d'Elevage et de Sylviculture, Phnom-Penh.
IMPORTANT SPECIES AVAILABLE FOR LABORATORY STUDIES:
Pisces: Pangasidae, Cyprinidae, Bagridae, Ophiocephalidae.
MAJOR CURRENT RESEARCH PROJECTS AND SCIENTIFIC LEADERS:
Studies on the reproduction and migration of pangasids and the cyprinid, *Cyprinus auratus* (You Kim Chhon)

CANADA

Bellairs Research Institute, McGill University

POSTAL ADDRESS:
McGill University: Montreal, Canada.
Bellairs Research Institute: St. James, Barbados, British West Indies. See description, page 270.

Bowdoin Scientific Station

POSTAL ADDRESS: Kent Island, Grand Manan, New Brunswick, Canada.

BOWDOIN SCIENTIFIC STATION

LOCATION: Near St. John, New Brunswick.
EXECUTIVE OFFICER: Dr. Charles E. Huntington, Director of Station, Department of Biology, Bowdoin College, Brunswick, Maine, U. S. A.
SPONSORING AGENCY: Bowdoin College.
YEAR FOUNDED: 1935.
SCOPE OF ACTIVITIES: Unrestricted research on the ecology and behavior of sea birds.
SEASON OF OPERATION: June 5 to September 15. Arrangements may be made for work at other times of the year.
PHYSICAL ENVIRONMENT ACCESSIBLE: Bay of Fundy; open ocean, rocky and gravelly shores.
PROVISIONS FOR VISITING SCIENTISTS: Research and living space for 3 or more visitors; no fees charged for research space.
MAJOR RESEARCH FACILITIES: Small library; one 40 ft LOA gasoline-powered fishing boat available for charter from caretaker.
SIZE OF STAFF: One at professional level; 1 caretaker-commercial fisherman.
IMPORTANT SPECIES AVAILABLE FOR LABORATORY STUDIES:
Echinoidea: *Strongylocentrotus droehbachiensis*
Aves: *Larus argentatus, Oceanodroma leucorhoa*
MAJOR CURRENT RESEARCH PROJECTS AND SCIENTIFIC LEADERS:
Reproductive and mortality rates in Leach's petrel (Charles E. Huntington)

British Columbia Fish and Game Branch, Research Division

POSTAL ADDRESS:
Headquarters: British Columbia Fish and Game Branch, Department of Recreation and Conservation, Parliament Buildings, Victoria, B. C., Canada.
Laboratory: c/o Institute of Fisheries, University of British Columbia, Vancouver 8, British Columbia, Canada.

LOCATION: On campus of University of British Columbia.
EXECUTIVE OFFICER: Mr. R. G. McMynn, Chief Fisheries Biologist.
SPONSORING AGENCIES: Province of British Columbia and University of British Columbia.
YEAR FOUNDED: 1952.
SCOPE OF ACTIVITIES: Restricted research on general fresh-water biology with special emphasis on problems relating to sport fish.
SEASON OF OPERATION: All year.
PHYSICAL ENVIRONMENT ACCESSIBLE: Most lake types, rivers and streams.
PROVISIONS FOR VISITING SCIENTISTS: Space for 1 visitor.
MAJOR RESEARCH FACILITIES: Small library in Division, but very extensive University library available; large outdoor ponds and tanks, small aquarium tanks; small boats and outboard motors.
SIZE OF STAFF: Two at professional level; 1 technician.
MAJOR CURRENT RESEARCH PROJECTS AND SCIENTIFIC LEADERS:
Spawning migrations of catostomid and cyprinid fishes to inlet and outlet streams of lakes (T. G. Northcote)
Spawning migration of kokanee to inlet streams of lakes (T. G. Northcote)
Vertical distribution of fishes in lakes (T. G. Northcote)
Competitive relations between salmonids in streams (G. F. Hartman)

Canadian Wildlife Service, Department of Northern Affairs and National Resources

POSTAL ADDRESS: Ottawa, Ontario, Canada.
EXECUTIVE OFFICER: Jean-Paul Cuerrier, Chief Limnologist.
SCOPE OF ACTIVITIES: Unrestricted research on limnology, fishery biology and fisheries management.
SEASON OF OPERATION: All year.
PHYSICAL ENVIRONMENT ACCESSIBLE: Lakes Waskesiu, Minnewanka, Clear, Waterton, and Maligne. Both eutrophic and oligotrophic lakes available for study.
PROVISIONS FOR VISITING SCIENTISTS: No special provisions for visiting scientists, but space can be arranged.
MAJOR RESEARCH FACILITIES: Small library; large outdoor ponds and tanks at fish hatcheries; very limited research collections of fauna and flora; shop facilities are available from local National Park Superintendent; small boats and outboard motors.
SIZE OF STAFF: Three at professional level; 2 technicians.
MAJOR CURRENT RESEARCH PROJECTS AND SCIENTIFIC LEADERS:
Limnology of Alpine lakes (J. C. Ward)
Reclamation of lakes (J. C. Ward and D. R. Foskett)
Hybridization among trout (J. C. Ward and D. R. Foskett)
Ecology of lake trout (J. C. Ward and D. R. Foskett)
PUBLICATIONS ISSUED: Wildlife Management Bulletin.

Fisheries Research Board of Canada

POSTAL ADDRESS:
Headquarters: Room A-306, Sir Charles Tupper Building, Confederation Heights, Ottawa, Ontario, Canada.
Branch laboratories:
1. Arctic Unit
2. Atlantic Oceanographic Group
3. Biological Station, London, Ontario
4. Biological Station, St. Andrews, New Brunswick
5. Biological Sub-station, Ellerslie
6. Biological Station, St. John's Newfoundland
7. Biological Station, Nanaimo, British Columbia
8. Pacific Oceanographic Group

(Descriptions follow.)
EXECUTIVE OFFICER: Dr. J. L. Kask, Chairman.
SPONSORING AGENCY: Canadian Department of Fisheries.
YEAR FOUNDED: 1898.
SCOPE OF ACTIVITIES: Fisheries biology, limnology, and oceanography as related to the development and conservation of commercial fisheries of Canada.
MAJOR CURRENT RESEARCH PROJECTS AND SCIENTIFIC LEADERS: Research programs are centered in a series of regional fisheries and oceanographic laboratories, detailed accounts of which appear below.

Arctic Unit

POSTAL ADDRESS: *Headquarters,* 505 Pine Avenue West, Montreal 18, Quebec, Canada.
LOCATION: Seasonal base camps established at various locations throughout Northwest Territories.
EXECUTIVE OFFICER: Dr. H. D. Fisher, Scientist-in-charge.
YEAR FOUNDED: 1948.
SCOPE OF ACTIVITIES: Restricted research on distribution, abundance, life-histories, and population dynamics of marine and fresh-water biological resources (including marine mammals) in the Canadian Arctic, plus marine mammals on Atlantic coast of Canada; biological oceanography of Canadian Arctic.
SEASON OF OPERATION: All year at headquarters; most field work done May 30-October 15.
PHYSICAL ENVIRONMENT ACCESSIBLE: James and Hudson Bays; estuarine conditions, brackish, shallow bays.
PROVISIONS FOR VISITING SCIENTISTS: No special policy

for accommodating visiting scientists, although space for 1 could be made by special arrangement.

MAJOR RESEARCH FACILITIES: Small library, although larger libraries of McGill University and Arctic Institute of North America are available; preserved research and identified reference collections of marine invertebrate fauna and fishes from northern Canada, especially eastern Arctic and sub-Arctic regions; very small machine and wood shop; small boats and outboard motors; vessels, 49.5 ft LOA diesel wooden ketch, M/V *Calanus* (eastern Arctic), and 38 ft LOA diesel shallow draft fishing vessel, M/V *Salvelinus* (western Arctic).

SIZE OF STAFF: Seven at professional level; 5 technicians.

IMPORTANT SPECIES AVAILABLE FOR LABORATORY STUDIES:

Chaetognatha: *Sagitta*

Crustacea: *Calanus* and other copepods, *Themisto libellula*

Mollusca: *Mytilus edulis*

Pisces: *Salvelinus alpinus,* coregonids

Mammalia: *Odobaenus rosmarus, Delphinapterus leucas, Globicephala melaena,* arctic phocids.

MAJOR CURRENT RESEARCH PROJECTS AND SCIENTIFIC LEADERS:

Arctic fisheries investigations (John Gerald Hunter)

Marine mammal investigations:

Walrus (Arthur Walter Mansfield)

Beluga, pilot whale, harp seal (David Ernest Sergeant)

Bearded seal and ringed seal dynamics (Ian Alexander McLaren)

ARCTIC UNIT, MONTREAL

Primary productivity, plankton populations, and seastar taxonomy (Edward Henry Grainger)

PUBLICATIONS ISSUED:

Circulars of the Arctic Unit, Fisheries Research Board of Canada.

Manuscript Report Series.

Translation Series.

Atlantic Oceanographic Group

POSTAL ADDRESS: Bedford Institute of Oceanography, P.O. Box 1006, Dartmouth, Nova Scotia, Canada.

EXECUTIVE OFFICER: Dr. N. J. Campbell, Oceanographer-in-Charge.

YEAR FOUNDED: 1946.

SCOPE OF ACTIVITIES: Restricted research on physical and chemical oceanography, dynamics, and the ocean environment relating to application for understanding fisheries problems.

SEASON OF OPERATION: All year.

PHYSICAL ENVIRONMENT ACCESSIBLE: Atlantic Ocean, Gulf of St. Lawrence, Bay of Fundy; estuarine conditions.

PROVISIONS FOR VISITING SCIENTISTS: Excellent research space for visitors; living quarters nearby.

MAJOR RESEARCH FACILITIES: Small library; large machine, wood, electrical and electronic shops; one 270 ft LOA motor-powered oceanographic vessel.

SIZE OF STAFF: Eight at professional level; 8 technicians.

MAJOR CURRENT RESEARCH PROJECTS AND SCIENTIFIC LEADERS:

Oceanographic investigations, Gulf of St. Lawrence (L. M. Lauzier, R. W. Trites and D. L. Peer)

Physical oceanography of the Northwest Atlantic (N. J. Campbell)

Continental shelf studies of the mud-water interface (D. H. Loring and R. F. Platford)

Biological Station, London, Ontario

POSTAL ADDRESS: 539 Richmond Street, London, Ontario, Canada.

EXECUTIVE OFFICER: Dr. William A. Kennedy, Director.

YEAR FOUNDEDS 1944.

SCOPE OF ACTIVITIES: Restricted research on inland fisheries of Canada.

SEASON OF OPERATION: All year.

PHYSICAL ENVIRONMENT ACCESSIBLE: Great Lakes.

PROVISIONS FOR VISITING SCIENTISTS: Space for 1 visitor depending on circumstances; no fees charged.

MAJOR RESEARCH FACILITIES: Small library; small aquarium tanks; machine and wood shop, electrical and electronic shop, skilled shop workman available; small boats and outboard motors; two power vessels, 45 ft LOA, *Cottus,* on Lake Superior and 45 ft LOA, *Stenodus,* on Great Slave Lake.

BIOLOGICAL STATION, LONDON, ONTARIO

SIZE OF STAFF: Nineteen at professional level; 31 technicians.

IMPORTANT SPECIES AVAILABLE FOR LABORATORY STUDIES:

Cyclostomata: *Petromyzon marinus*

MAJOR CURRENT RESEARCH PROJECTS AND SCIENTIFIC LEADERS:

Triaenophorus crassus (G. H. Lawler)
Fish population dynamics (G. F. M. Smith)
Fish populations—Great Slave Lake (J. J. Keleher)
Fish populations—Lake Superior (A. H. Lawrie)
Fish tagging with radio-isotopes (D. P. Scott)
Fish and lamprey physiology (R. M. McCauley)
Ammocoete biology (M. L. H. Thomas)
Experiment in sea lamprey control (J. J. Tibbles)

Biological Station, St. Andrews, New Brunswick

POSTAL ADDRESS: St. Andrews, New Brunswick, Canada.

Field Stations: Chatham, New Brunswick and Ellerslie Brook, Prince Edward Island.

EXECUTIVE OFFICERS: Dr. John L. Hart, Director. Dr. C. J. Kerswill, Assistant Director.

YEAR FOUNDED: 1898.

SCOPE OF ACTIVITIES: Research on biology applicable to sound use of fisheries resources. Field stations devoted to biological work on salmonid fishes.

SEASON OF OPERATION: All year.

PHYSICAL ENVIRONMENT ACCESSIBLE: Northwest Atlantic Ocean, Bay of Fundy, Passamaquoddy Bay; estuarine conditions; dystrophic lakes, rivers and streams available from field stations.

PROVISIONS FOR VISITING SCIENTISTS: Space for 3-6 visitors; no fees charged; living quarters available nearby.

MAJOR RESEARCH FACILITIES: Running sea and fresh-water, large outdoor tanks, small aquarium tanks; systematic plankton collections; identified reference collections of fishes and mollusks (partial); machine and wood shop, skilled shop workman available; small boats and outboard motors; power vessels, 85 ft, 54 ft, and 50 ft LOA.

BIOLOGICAL STATION, ST. ANDREWS

SIZE OF STAFF: Twenty-seven at professional level; 40 technicians.

IMPORTANT SPECIES AVAILABLE FOR LABORATORY STUDIES:

Crustacea: *Homarus*
Pelecypoda: *Placopecten*
Pisces: *Gadus, Melanogrammus, Salmo*
Agnatha: *Myxine*

MAJOR CURRENT RESEARCH PROJECTS AND SCIENTIFIC LEADERS:

Groundfish (W. R. Martin)
Lobster (D. G. Wilder)
Anadromous fishes (M. W. Smith)
Pelagic fishes (S. N. Tibbo)
Molluscan shellfish (J. C. Medcof)
Oceanography (L. M. Lauzier)

Biological Sub-Station, Ellerslie (Administered by Biological Station, St. Andrews)

POSTAL ADDRESS: Ellerslie, Prince Edward Island, Canada.

LOCATION: Near Summerside.

BIOLOGICAL SUB-STATION, ELLERSLIE

EXECUTIVE OFFICER: Mr. R. E. Drinnan, In Charge.
YEAR FOUNDED: 1929.
SCOPE OF ACTIVITIES: Research on oyster culture.
SEASON OF OPERATION: All year.
PHYSICAL ENVIRONMENT ACCESSIBLE: Malpeque Bay, Gulf of St. Lawrence; estuarine conditions.
PROVISIONS FOR VISITING SCIENTISTS: Space for 1-2 visitors; living quarters can be obtained nearby, but with difficulty.
MAJOR RESEARCH FACILITIES: Small library; large outdoor ponds and tanks, small aquarium tanks; small boats and outboard motors; one 30 ft LOA power vessel.
SIZE OF STAFF: One at professional level; 2 technicians.

Biological Station, St. John's, Newfoundland

POSTAL ADDRESS: Water Street East, St. John's, Newfoundland, Canada.
EXECUTIVE OFFICER: Dr. Wilfred Templeman, Director.
YEAR FOUNDED: 1931.
SCOPE OF ACTIVITIES: Restricted research on practical and economic problems connected with marine and fresh-water fisheries and the flora and fauna of Newfoundland.
SEASON OF OPERATION: All year.
PHYSICAL ENVIRONMENT ACCESSIBLE: Atlantic Ocean; rocky and gravelly shores, estuarine conditions, rivers and streams.
PROVISIONS FOR VISITING SCIENTISTS: No space available for visitors except for short visits and occasional trips on the large research vessel; no fees charged.
MAJOR RESEARCH FACILITIES: Small library; identified reference collection of decapod Crustacea; small boats and outboard motors; otter-trawlers of 170 ft, 80 ft, and 60 ft LOA.
SIZE OF STAFF: Eleven at professional level; 36 technicians.
IMPORTANT SPECIES AVAILABLE FOR LABORATORY STUDIES:
Marine fishes and invertebrates of the area.

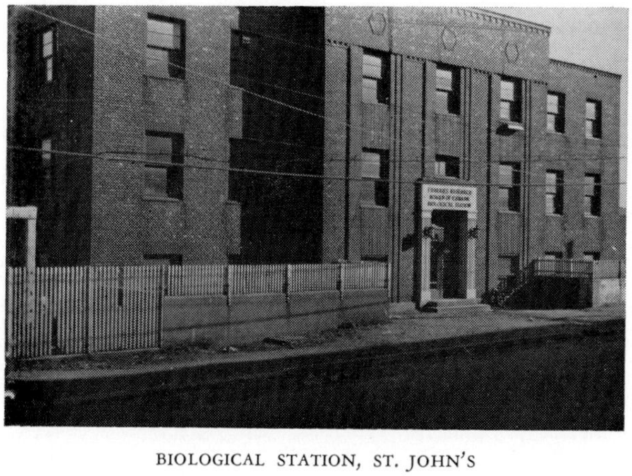

BIOLOGICAL STATION, ST. JOHN'S

MAJOR CURRENT RESEARCH PROJECTS AND SCIENTIFIC LEADERS:
Groundfish biology and distribution (Wilfred Templeman)
Redfish: general biology (E. J. Sandeman)
Redfish: food and feeding (E. I. S. Rees)
Haddock: age, growth, mortality (V. M. Hodder)
Cod: age, growth, mortality (Labrador area) (A.W. May)
Cod: age, growth, mortality (Newfoundland, inshore) (A. M. Fleming)
American plaice: age, growth, mortality, maturity, fecundity, feeding, migration (T. K. Pitt)
Pacific salmon: transplant to Newfoundland (A. A. Blair)
Atlantic salmon: basic capacity of a river to produce salmon (A. R. Murray)
Plankton; species of Newfoundland and Labrador area (H. J. Squires)
Squid: distribution (H. T. Squires)

Biological Station, Nanaimo, British Columbia

POSTAL ADDRESS: P. O. Drawer 100, Nanaimo, British Columbia, Canada.
EXECUTIVE OFFICER: Dr. A. W. H. Needler, Director.
YEAR FOUNDED: 1908.
SCOPE OF ACTIVITIES: Restricted research on general fisheries biology and oceanography relating to the development, conservation and management of commercial stocks of fish, invertebrates and marine mammals on Canada's Pacific Coast.
SEASON OF OPERATION: All year.
PHYSICAL ENVIRONMENT ACCESSIBLE: Strait of Georgia, northeastern Pacific Ocean; rocky and gravelly shores, eutrophic and oligotrophic lakes, rivers and streams.
PROVISIONS FOR VISITING SCIENTISTS: Space for 3-6 visitors; living quarters nearby.
MAJOR RESEARCH FACILITIES: Moderately complete library; running sea and fresh-water, small aquarium tanks; machine and wood shop, electrical and electronic shop, skilled shop workman available; small boats and outboard motors; power vessels 177 ft, 78 ft, 54 ft, and 30 ft LOA; extensive development for model studies.
SIZE OF STAFF: Fifty-five at professional level; 60 technicians, 65 others and 65 seasonals.
IMPORTANT SPECIES AVAILABLE FOR LABORATORY STUDIES: Abundance of marine and fresh-water forms found in the waters of this area.
MAJOR CURRENT RESEARCH PROJECTS AND SCIENTIFIC LEADERS:
Oceanography (J. P. Tully)
Studies of salmon in the ocean (F. Neave)
Studies of salmon parasites to distinguish stocks (L. Margolis)

BIOLOGICAL STATION, NANAIMO

Salmon management (M. P. Shepard)
Salmon propagation (F. C. Withler)
Studies of physiology and behavior of salmon (J. R. Brett)
Pollution (M. Waldichuk)
Herring (F. H. C. Taylor)
Groundfish (K. S. Ketchen)
Crabs and shrimps (T. H. Butler)
Marine mammals (G. C. Pike)
Marine invertebrates (D. B. Quayle)

Pacific Oceanographic Group

POSTAL ADDRESS: P. O. Drawer 100, Nanaimo, British Columbia, Canada.
EXECUTIVE OFFICER: Dr. J. P. Tully, Oceanographer-in-charge.
YEAR FOUNDED: 1947.
SCOPE OF ACTIVITIES: Restricted research on general oceanography with emphasis on environment of fisheries in northeast Pacific Ocean.
SEASON OF OPERATION: All year.
PHYSICAL ENVIRONMENT ACCESSIBLE: Strait of Georgia, Pacific Ocean.
PROVISIONS FOR VISITING SCIENTISTS: Space for 2-3 visitors; no fees charged; living quarters available nearby.
MAJOR RESEARCH FACILITIES: Moderately complete library; hydraulic model base; machine and wood shop, electrical and electronic shop, skilled shop workman available; small boats and outboard motors, 200 ft LOA, CNAV *Oshawa,* 165 ft LOA, CNAV *Whitethroat,* and 300 ft LOA, CCS *Ste. Catharines.*
SIZE OF STAFF: Fourteen at professional level; 13 technicians.
MAJOR CURRENT RESEARCH PROJECTS AND SCIENTIFIC LEADERS:
North Pacific oceanography (A. J. Dodimead and L. F. Giovando)
Time series, Ocean Station "P" (S. Tabata)
Coastal oceanography (R. K. Lane)
Inland sea ways (R. H. Herlinveaux)
Marine physics (N. P. Fofonoff)
Productivity (J. D. H. Strickland)
Daily sea water observations (H. J. Hollister)

International Pacific Salmon Fisheries Commission

POSTAL ADDRESS: Box 30, New Westminster, British Columbia, Canada.
EXECUTIVE OFFICER: Mr. Loyd A. Royal, Director of Investigations.
SPONSORING AGENCIES: Governments of Canada and USA.
YEAR FOUNDED: 1937.
SCOPE OF ACTIVITIES: Restricted research on problems relating to the conservation of sockeye and pink salmon of the Fraser River system.
SEASON OF OPERATION: All year.
PHYSICAL ENVIRONMENT ACCESSIBLE: Fraser River.
PROVISIONS FOR VISITING SCIENTISTS: None.
MAJOR RESEARCH FACILITIES: Small library; small boats and outboard motors.
SIZE OF STAFF: Twenty-three at professional level; 25 technicians.

Manitoba Department of Mines and Natural Resources, Fisheries Laboratory

POSTAL ADDRESS: 401 York Avenue at Kennedy, Winnipeg, Manitoba, Canada.
EXECUTIVE OFFICER: Mr. B. Kooyman, Director of Fisheries Branch.
SPONSORING AGENCY: Province of Manitoba.
YEAR FOUNDED: 1952.
SCOPE OF ACTIVITIES: Restricted research on management problems of sport and commercial fishes; pollution problems.
SEASON OF OPERATION: All year.
PHYSICAL ENVIRONMENT ACCESSIBLE: Red River, Lake Winnipeg (eutrophic lake).
PROVISIONS FOR VISITING SCIENTISTS: None.
MAJOR RESEARCH FACILITIES: Small library; limited small aquaria; limited reference collection of fish fauna; small boats and outboard motors.
SIZE OF STAFF: Six at professional level; 6 technicians.
MAJOR CURRENT RESEARCH PROJECTS AND SCIENTIFIC LEADERS:
Whitefish population dynamics, Lake Winnipeg (K. H. Doan)
Pollution of lakes and streams (A. B. Sparling)
Fish population dynamics, northern lakes (L. A. Sunde)

National Research Council of Canada, Atlantic Regional Laboratory

POSTAL ADDRESS: Oxford Street, Halifax, Nova Scotia, Canada.
EXECUTIVE OFFICER: Dr. G. Young, Director.
SPONSORING AGENCY: National Research Council of Canada.
YEAR FOUNDED: 1952.
SCOPE OF ACTIVITIES: Unrestricted research, related to possible development of the natural resources of the Atlantic provinces (including marine resources) and to assist in solving technical problems of industry. Marine research has been devoted mostly to biological and experimental studies of marine algae and to physiology of marine bacteria.
SEASON OF OPERATION: All year.
PHYSICAL ENVIRONMENT ACCESSIBLE: Atlantic Ocean; estuarine conditions.
PROVISIONS FOR VISITING SCIENTISTS: Space for 2-3 visitors; no fees charged; living quarters available nearby.
MAJOR RESEARCH FACILITIES: Extensive library; isophoto thermostated room; machine and wood shop, skilled shop workman available.
SIZE OF STAFF: Nineteen at professional level; 17 technicians.
IMPORTANT SPECIES AVAILABLE FOR LABORATORY STUDIES:
Rhodophyceae: *Rhodymenia palmata, Chondrus crispus, Furcellaria fastigiata*
Phaeophyceae: *Fucus vesiculosus, Ascophyllum nodosum, Laminaria longicruris*
MAJOR CURRENT RESEARCH PROJECTS AND SCIENTIFIC LEADERS:
The nitrogenous constituents of seaweeds (E. G. Young)
The chemical constitution of alginic acid (D. L. Vincent)
Polysaccharides of *Furcellaria* (T. J. Painter)
Hydrolysis of algal polysaccharides by marine bacteria (W. Yaphe)
Optimum conditions of drying large seaweeds (J. H. J. Merritt)
Photosynthesis in the Phaeophyceae (R. G. S. Bidwell)
Biological values of algal proteins (W. W. Hawkins)

ATLANTIC REGIONAL LABORATORY OF THE NATIONAL RESEARCH COUNCIL OF CANADA

Nova Scotia Research Foundation

POSTAL ADDRESS: P. O. Box 1027, Halifax, Nova Scotia, Canada.
EXECUTIVE OFFICERS: Dr. H. D. Smith, President of Foundation. Constance MacFarlane, Director of Seaweeds Research Program.
SPONSORING AGENCY: Province of Nova Scotia.
YEAR FOUNDED: 1947.
SCOPE OF ACTIVITIES Restricted research in seaweeds, particularly seaweeds of commercial importance; surveys, ecological studies and mapping.
SEASON OF OPERATION: All year, but field work curtailed in colder months.
PHYSICAL ENVIRONMENT ACCESSIBLE: Atlantic Ocean, Bay of Fundy, Gulf of St. Lawrence, Northumberland Strait; sandy and silty beaches, rocky and gravelly shores, estuarine conditions and brackish, shallow bays.
PROVISIONS FOR VISITING SCIENTISTS: None at the Foundation headquarters, but arrangements can be made for visiting scientists at the Department of Botany, Dalhousie University. Other possibilities of working space may be had at Atlantic Regional Laboratory of the National Research Council of Canada, with the Fisheries Technological Station of the Department of Fisheries, etc.
MAJOR RESEARCH FACILITIES: Small library (plus interlibrary loans) ; aquarium tanks; research and identified reference collections of local and other marine algae; shop facilities available at nearby institutions; small boats and outboard motors; one 13 ft LOA vessel, larger 38-40 ft LOA vessels hired from fisherman. New building with laboratory facilities is being planned by Foundation.
SIZE OF STAFF: Two at professional level; student assistants.
IMPORTANT SPECIES AVAILABLE FOR LABORATORY STUDIES:
Rhodophyta: *Chondrus crispus,* etc.
Bangioideae: *Porphyra* spp.
Phaeophyta: *Laminaria longicruris, L. agardhii, L. intermedia, L. digitata,* etc.
Chlorophyta: *Enteromorpha* spp., *Ulva lactuca, Cladophora* spp.
MAJOR CURRENT RESEARCH PROJECTS AND SCIENTIFIC LEADERS:
Systematic and ecological studies on marine algae (Constance I. MacFarlane)

Ontario Department of Lands and Forests, Research Branch

POSTAL ADDRESS:

1. Southern Research Station, Maple, Ontario. Mr. K. H. Loftus, Supervisor of Fisheries Research.
2. South Bay Fisheries Research Station, South Bay Mouth, Manitoulin Island, Ontario. Mr. J. C. Budd, Officer-in-charge.
3. Glenora Fisheries Research Station, R. R. #5, Picton, Ontario. Mr. W. J. Christie, Officer-in-charge.
4. Opeongo Fisheries Research Laboratory, Whitney, Ontario. Mr. N. V. Martin, Officer-in-charge.
5. Lake Erie Research Station, P.O. Box 550, Wheatley, Ontario.

YEAR FOUNDED:

Southern Research Station, 1947.
South Bay Fisheries Research Station, 1947.
Glenora Fisheries Research Station, 1954.
Opeongo Fisheries Research Laboratory, 1936.

SCOPE OF ACTIVITIES: Restricted research on life histories and population dynamics of fishes of Ontario. Special studies on population dynamics and fish genetics undertaken at Southern Research Station.

SEASON OF OPERATION: All year except at Opeongo Fisheries Research Laboratory which is open for 8 months of the year.

PHYSICAL ENVIRONMENT ACCESSIBLE: Georgian Bay, North Channel; Lakes Ontario, Huron, Erie, and Opeongo.

PROVISIONS FOR VISITING SCIENTISTS: Space for visitors; no fees charged; living quarters available at Opeongo Fisheries Research Laboartory and near the other laboratories.

MAJOR RESEARCH FACILITIES: Library very extensive at Southern Research Station, moderately complete at South Bay Research Station, and small at Glenora Fisheries Research Station and Opeongo Fisheries Research Laboratory; small aquarium tanks; holding troughs at Southern Research Station; small boats and outboard motors at South Bay Fisheries Research Station, Glenora Fisheries Research Station, and Opeongo Fisheries Research Laboratory; one 42 ft LOA vessel at South Bay Fisheries Research Station and three vessels at St. Lukes Station.

SIZE OF STAFF: Twelve at professional level; 15 technicians.

MAJOR CURRENT RESEARCH PROJECTS AND SCIENTIFIC LEADERS:

Hybridization of trout species with lake trout (J. S. Tait)
Population and life history studies of blue pike-perch (R. G. Ferguson)
Population and life history of smelt (H. Resier)
Whitefish, lake trout, hybrids, rainbow trout, sea lampreys, and smallmouth bass (J. C. Budd)
Lake trout, whitefish, sea lampreys, yellow pike-perch (W. J. Christie)
Trout, smallmouth bass, and lake productivity (N. V. Martin)

Quebec Departement des Pecheries, Centre Biologique

QUEBEC DEPARTMENT OF FISHERIES, BIOLOGICAL CENTER

POSTAL ADDRESS: Hotel du Gouvernement, Quebec, Canada.

EXECUTIVE OFFICER: Paul Montreuil, Conservateur.

YEAR FOUNDED: 1943.

SCOPE OF ACTIVITIES: Unrestricted research on population dynamics, ecology, ethology, fish physiology and pathology.

SEASON OF OPERATION: All year.

PHYSICAL ENVIRONMENT ACCESSIBLE: St. Lawrence River.

PROVISIONS FOR VISITING SCIENTISTS: Space for two visitors; living quarters available nearby.

MAJOR RESEARCH FACILITIES: Moderately complete library; small aquarium tanks, closed circuit aquarium sea water supply; research collection of fish; machine and wood shop; skilled shop workmen available.

SIZE OF STAFF: Four at professional level; 10 technicians.

IMPORTANT SPECIES AVAILABLE FOR LABORATORY STUDIES:

Pisces: *Acipenser oxyrhynchus, A. fulvescens, Anguilla rostrata, Roccus saxatilis*

MAJOR CURRENT RESEARCH PROJECTS AND SCIENTIFIC LEADERS:

Physiology and pathology (Paul Montreuil)
Biometry and migration studies (Gerard Beaulieu)
Feeding habits of fishes (J. M. Roy)

PUBLICATIONS ISSUED: See Quebec Department des Pecheries, Station de Biologie Marine, below.

CENTRE BIOLOGIQUE AQUARIUM, LABORATORY AND OTHER SERVICES, QUEBEC

Quebec Departement des Pecheries, Station de Biologie Marine

QUEBEC DEPARTMENT OF FISHERIES, MARINE BIOLOGICAL STATION

POSTAL ADDRESS:
Headquarters: Grande-Riviere, Gaspe, Quebec, Canada.
Branch laboratories:
1. Laboratoire de Biologie Marine.
2. La Tabatiere Station de Peche Experimentale.
(Descriptions follow.)

EXECUTIVE OFFICER: Alexandre Marcotte, Directeur.

YEAR FOUNDED: 1929.

SCOPE OF ACTIVITIES: Unrestricted basic research on general marine biology with particular emphasis on management of commercial fisheries; graduate and undergraduate instruction for teachers.

SEASON OF OPERATION: All year.

PHYSICAL ENVIRONMENT ACCESSIBLE: Baie des Chaleurs, Gulf of St. Lawrence; open ocean, sandy and silty beaches, rocky shores, estuarine conditions, brackish shallow bays and salmon streams.

PROVISIONS FOR VISITING SCIENTISTS: Research and living space for 4 visitors; no fees charged for research space.

MAJOR RESEARCH AND TEACHING FACILITIES: Small library; running sea and fresh-water, large indoor tanks, small aquarium tanks; machine and wood shop, electrical and electronic shop; power vessels, 25 ft LOA and 60 ft LOA.

INSTRUCTIONAL PROGRAM: General physiology of marine invertebrates (for biology students); marine biology (for teachers).

SIZE OF STAFF: Four at professional level; 3 technicians.

MAJOR CURRENT RESEARCH PROJECTS AND SCIENTIFIC LEADERS:
Plankton studies (Guy Lacroix)
Benthonic fauna survey and ecology (Pierre Brunel)
Salmon (Atlantic) and pelagic fishes (Julien Bergeron)
Groundfish (codfish, plaice, etc.) (A. Marcotte)

PUBLICATIONS ISSUED BY THE DEPARTMENT OF FISHERIES:
Actualites Marines (regularly published journal).
Contributions du Department des Pecheries, Quebec (occasionally published).

Laboratoire De Biologie Marine

LABORATORY OF MARINE BIOLOGY

POSTAL ADDRESS: Cap-aux-Meules, Iles-de-la-Madeleine, Quebec, Canada.

YEAR FOUNDED: 1950.

QUEBEC DEPARTMENT DES PECHERIES, STATION DE BIOLOGIE MARINE

SCOPE OF ACTIVITIES: Management of lobster fishery, herring and mackerel.

SEASON OF OPERATION: April to November.

PHYSICAL ENVIRONMENT ACCESSIBLE: Gulf of St. Lawrence; open ocean, sandy and silty beaches.

PROVISIONS FOR VISITING SCIENTISTS: Space for 2 visitors; no fees charged.

MAJOR RESEARCH FACILITIES: Small library; running sea and fresh-water, small aquarium tanks; skilled shop workman available; small boats and outboard motors; one 25 ft LOA vessel.

La Tabatiere Station De Peche Experimentale

LA TABATIERE EXPERIMENTAL FISHING STATION

POSTAL ADDRESS:
December to June: Department of Fisheries, Parliament Buildings, Quebec, Canada.
June to December: Duplessis Co., Province de Quebec, Canada.

EXECUTIVE OFFICER: Director of Marine Biological Station of Grande Riviere, Gaspe Sud, Quebec.

YEAR FOUNDED: 1950.

SCOPE OF ACTIVITIES: Intermittent and restricted research on exploratory and experimental fishing gear and some work in biometrics, bottom ecology and oceanography.

SEASON OF OPERATION: June to December.

PHYSICAL ENVIRONMENT ACCESSIBLE: Gulf of Saint Lawrence, North Shore, Strait of Belle Isle to Anticosti, Newfoundland to Quebec; sandy and silty beaches, rocky and gravelly shores, brackish, shallow bays, very numerous lakes of undetermined types, rivers and streams.

PROVISIONS FOR VISITING SCIENTISTS: Research and living space for 1-2 visitors.

MAJOR RESEARCH FACILITIES: No library at La Tabatiere, although main library of Quebec Department of Fisheries is accessible and is moderately complete; running sea and fresh-water; machine and wood shop, electrical and electronic shop, skilled shop workman available; one 55 ft LOA power vessel.

SIZE OF STAFF: One at professional level; 2-3 technicians.

MAJOR CURRENT RESEARCH PROJECTS AND SCIENTIFIC LEADERS:

Exploratory fishing for cod and ocean perch (J. M. Boulanger)
Experimental fishing with various types of bottom and pelagic trawls (J. M. Boulanger)
Gear research on trawls (resistance to towing, behaviour, etc.) (J. M. Boulanger)
Gear selectivity: Cod traps, ocean perch trawl and gill nets for codfish (J. M. Boulanger)

Quebec Dept. des Pecheries et de la Chasse, Station D'Amenagement du Parc des Laurentides

QUEBEC DEPARTMENT OF FISHERIES AND GAME, LAURENTIDES PARK MANAGEMENT STATION

POSTAL ADDRESS: Parliament Buildings, Quebec City, Canada.

EXECUTIVE OFFICER: Dr. Gustave Prevost, Directeur.

YEAR FOUNDED: 1951.

SCOPE OF ACTIVITIES: Restricted research on and management of fresh-water lakes and streams; general biological research on native trout and other species of fresh-water fishes.

SEASON OF OPERATION: All year.

PHYSICAL ENVIRONMENT ACCESSIBLE: Lac Jacques-Cartier; eutrophic and oligotrophic lakes, rivers and streams.

PROVISIONS FOR VISITING SCIENTISTS: Research and living space for 3-4 visitors (to be extended); no fees charged for research space.

MAJOR RESEARCH FACILITIES: No library at the field laboratory but library facilities available at head office in Quebec City; large outdoor ponds and tanks, hatching facilities; identified reference collection of local flora; small boats and outboard motors.

SIZE OF STAFF: Two at professional level; 3 technicians.

IMPORTANT SPECIES AVAILABLE FOR LABORATORY STUDIES:

Pisces: *Salvelinus fontinalis, Salmo salar*

MAJOR CURRENT RESEARCH PROJECTS AND SCIENTIFIC LEADERS:

Breeding of landlocked salmon (Pierre Paulhus)
Experimental management of lakes (Pierre Paulhus)

Quebec Ministere des Pecheries et de la Chasse, Nabisipi Station

QUEBEC MINISTRY OF FISHERIES AND GAME, NABISIPI STATION

POSTAL ADDRESS: Parliament Buildings, Quebec City, Canada.

EXECUTIVE OFFICER: Robert W. Bourassa, Directeur.

SPONSORING AGENCY: Province de Quebec.

YEAR FOUNDED: 1960.

SEASON OF OPERATION: May 15-November 15.

PHYSICAL ENVIRONMENT ACCESSIBLE: Nabisipi River, Gulf of St. Lawrence; open ocean, sandy and silty beaches, rocky and gravelly shores, estuarine conditions, brackish, shallow bays and oligotrophic lakes.

PROVISIONS FOR VISITING SCIENTISTS: Research and living space for visitors; no fees charged for research space.

MAJOR RESEARCH AND TEACHING FACILITIES: No library at Station but library facilities available at head office in Quebec City; small boats and outboard motors.

INSTRUCTIONAL PROGRAM: Arrangements have been made with the University of Montreal to have lectures given.

SIZE OF STAFF: Two at professional level; 2 technicians.

IMPORTANT SPECIES AVAILABLE FOR LABORATORY STUDIES:

Pisces: *Salmo salar, Salvelinus fontinalis, S. alpinus, Anguilla rostrata;* various species available along the sub-arctic marine coasts.

MAJOR CURRENT RESEARCH PROJECTS:

Tagging of Atlantic salmon
River biology of Atlantic salmon
Ecology of the estuary of Nabisipi River

Quebec Office de Biologie

QUEBEC BIOLOGICAL BUREAU

POSTAL ADDRESS:

Headquarters: G3, University of Montreal, P. O. Box 6128, Montreal 26, Quebec, Canada.
Sub-station: Mont Tremblant Biological Station, Via Lac Superieur, Cte Terrebonne, Quebec, Canada.

EXECUTIVE OFFICER: Dr. Gustave Prevost, Directeur.

SPONSORING AGENCY: Quebec Departements des Pecheries et de la Chasse (Quebec Departments of Fisheries and Game).

YEAR FOUNDED: 1942.

SCOPE OF ACTIVITIES: Both restricted and unrestricted research programs relating to management of lakes and streams; ecology and limnology of lakes and streams; biological studies on fresh-water fishes; co-operative institutional program with University of Montreal Institute of Biology.

SEASON OF OPERATION: All year at headquarters; May to September at Mont Tremblant Biological Station.

PHYSICAL ENVIRONMENT ACCESSIBLE: St. Lawrence River, Lac Monroe; open ocean, sandy and silty beaches, rocky and gravelly shores, estuarine conditions, brackish, shallow bays, eutrophic and oligotrophic lakes, and streams.

PROVISIONS FOR VISITING SCIENTISTS: Research and living space for 15 visitors at Mont Tremblant, research space for 15 at Montreal with living quarters nearby; no fees charged for research space.

MAJOR RESEARCH AND TEACHING FACILITIES: In cooperation with the University of Montreal there is a very extensive library; large outdoor ponds and tanks, small aquarium tanks; research collections of fish and plants; identified reference collection of fish from Province of Quebec, and flora from Mont Tremblant district; machine and wood shop, electrical and electronic shop, skilled shop workman available at Montreal; small boats and outboard motors; 25 ft LOA lobster boat.

INSTRUCTIONAL PROGRAM: In cooperation with the University of Montreal Institute of Biology: Limnology, ecology, biochemistry, microbiology, parasitology, general invertebrate zoology, ichthyology, general physiology, fishery biology, fisheries management, algology, biogeography and botany.

SIZE OF STAFF: Ten at professional level; 5 technicians.

IMPORTANT SPECIES AVAILABLE FOR LABORATORY STUDIES:

Algae: Many species of Chlorophyceae, Desmidiaceae, Chysophyceae, and Rhodophyceae.

Aquatic Insects: *Diptera, Odonata, Tricoptera.*

Pisces: *Catostomus commersoni, Esox lucius, Salvelinus fontinalis, Semotilus corporalis.*

MAJOR CURRENT RESEARCH PROJECTS AND SCIENTIFIC LEADERS:

Relations of herbicides and insecticides to fish and aquatic vegetation (Bernard Vincent, Gustave Prevost, and Florian Grenier)

Effects of fish poisons and their residual toxicity on fish population (Gustave Prevost, Florian Grenier, and Bernard Vincent)

MONT TREMBLANT BIOLOGICAL STATION

Sturgeons of the Province of Quebec: trial raising of sturgeons in La Verendrye Park (G. Roussow)

Study of the role of sulphur-reducing bacteria in the transformation of sulphur contained in polluted and natural waters. (Raymond Desrochers)

Biological inventory of the lakes in Mont Tremblant Park; reconditioning lakes with fish poisoning techniques and introductions of new species. (Albert Courtemanche)

Behaviour of speckled trout raised in a hatchery and released at an adult stage in rivers. (Albert Courtemanche)

Inventory of aquatic insects in Mont Tremblant Park. (Adrien Robert)

Feeding habits of speckled trout in Mont Tremblant Park. (Adrien Robert)

Biology and feeding habits of northern pike in Mont Tremblant Park (Jean-Rene Mongeau)

Parasites of fish in Mont Tremblant Park. (Georges Roussow)

The cycles of the principle mineral elements in the metabolism of a lake in Mont Tremblant Park. (Florian Grenier)

Queen's University Biological Station

POSTAL ADDRESS: Kingston, Ontario, Canada.

EXECUTIVE OFFICER: Seward R. Brown, Director.

YEAR FOUNDED: 1944.

SCOPE OF ACTIVITIES: Unrestricted research in primary productivity of lakes, geochemistry of lake sediments, lichenology, palynology and plant and animal ecology.

SEASON OF OPERATION: May 15 to September 15.

PHYSICAL ENVIRONMENT ACCESSIBLE: Lake Ontario and other lakes connected by the Rideau Canal System.

PROVISIONS FOR VISITING SCIENTIST: Research and living space for about 5 visitors; no fees charged for research space.

MAJOR RESEARCH FACILITIES: Small library; small aquarium tanks, aquatic cages; wood shop; small boats and outboard motors.

MAJOR CURRENT RESEARCH PROJECTS AND SCIENTIFIC LEADERS:

Primary productivity and geochemistry of lake sediments (Seward R. Brown)

Palynological studies (J. G. Ogden)

Lichenology (Roland E. Beschel)

Mosquito and Black-fly serology (A. S. West)

Saskatchewan Department of Natural Resources, Fisheries Laboratory

POSTAL ADDRESS: 122 Saskatchewan Research Council Building, University of Saskatchewan, Saskatoon, Saskatchewan, Canada.

EXECUTIVE OFFICER: F. M. Atton, Biologist-in-Charge.

SCOPE OF ACTIVITIES: Restricted research on aquatic resources through lake and stream surveys, ecological

SASKATCHEWAN RESEARCH COUNCIL BUILDING

studies, statistical studies and pollution investigations.

SEASON OF OPERATION: All year.

PHYSICAL ENVIRONMENT ACCESSIBLE: Lac la Ronge and other lakes and fresh-water habitats in Saskatchewan.

PROVISIONS FOR VISITING SCIENTISTS: None.

MAJOR RESEARCH FACILITIES: Small library; small aquarium tanks; research collections of bottom fauna, plankton, and fish collections; small boats and outboard motors; one 30 ft LOA power fishing boat.

SIZE OF STAFF: Four at professional level; 1 technician.

MAJOR CURRENT RESEARCH PROJECTS AND SCIENTIFIC LEADERS:

Pollution survey of Qu'Appelle River (J. P. Doyle)
Biological survey of Madge Lake (E. D. Kirch)
Biological survey of Buffalo Pound Lake (R. P. Johnson)
Ecology of carp (R. P. Johnson)

University of Alberta, Alberta Biological Station

POSTAL ADDRESS: Department of Zoology, University of Alberta, Edmonton, Alberta, Canada.

EXECUTIVE OFFICER: Head, Department of Zoology.

SPONSORING AGENCIES: Province of Alberta and University of Alberta.

YEAR FOUNDED: 1950.

SCOPE OF ACTIVITIES: Unrestricted research.

SEASON OF OPERATION: April through October and irregularly during winter.

PHYSICAL ENVIRONMENT ACCESSIBLE: Sheep River (South Saskatchewan drainage).

PROVISIONS FOR VISITING SCIENTISTS: Research and living space for two visitors for short period; no fees charged for research space.

MAJOR RESEARCH AND TEACHING FACILITIES: Small library at field station.

INSTRUCTIONAL PROGRAM: No formal instructional program, but field practice in limnology, fisheries management and ecology.

ALBERTA BIOLOGICAL STATION

IMPORTANT SPECIES AVAILABLE FOR LABORATORY STUDIES:

Salmonidae: *Salmo gairdneri, Salmo clarki*
Coregonidae: *Prosopium williamsoni*

University of British Columbia, Institute of Fisheries

POSTAL ADDRESS: Vancouver 8, British Columbia, Canada.

EXECUTIVE OFFICER: Dr. P. A. Larkin, Director.

YEAR FOUNDED: 1953.

SCOPE OF ACTIVITIES: Unrestricted research on fish physiology, systematics, population dynamics and limnology; graduate instruction.

SEASON OF OPERATION: All year.

PHYSICAL ENVIRONMENT ACCESSIBLE: Straits of Georgia, Fraser River, many small oligotrophic and eutrophic lakes, streams, open ocean, sandy and silty beaches, rocky and gravelly shores, estuarine conditions and brackish, shallow bays.

PROVISIONS FOR VISITING SCIENTISTS: Space available for visitors; no fees charged; living quarters nearby.

MAJOR RESEARCH AND TEACHING FACILITIES: Moderately complete library; running sea water, outdoor ponds and tanks, small aquarium tanks; large research collection of fresh-water fish from Pacific northwest, eastern tropical marine fishes and British Columbia marine fishes; identified reference collection of all fresh-water and marine fishes from British Columbia waters; shop facilities available at the University; small boats and outboard motors.

INSTRUCTIONAL PROGRAM: Fisheries (fisheries law, hydraulics, anthropology, economics), limnology, fisheries biology and management, systematic ichthyology, fisheries technology, seminar in fisheries biology, problems in ichthyology, marine zoogeography.

SIZE OF STAFF: Seven at professional level; 1 technician.

IMPORTANT SPECIES AVAILABLE FOR LABORATORY STUDIES:

Crustacea: *Hemigrapsus*

Pisces: *Salmo gairdneri, Oncorhynchus* (all species), *Isopsetta*

Virtually any species of indigenous fresh-water or marine fishes.

MAJOR CURRENT RESEARCH PROJECTS AND SCIENTIFIC LEADERS:

Systematics and distribution of fresh-water fishes of Arctic and Pacific North America (C. C. Lindsey)

Factors influencing meristic variation in fishes (C. C. Lindsey)

Zoogeography and systematics of Pacific marine fishes (N. J. Wilimowsky)

Endocrine physiology of fishes (W. N. Holmes)

Physiology and behavior of migrating anadromous fish (W. S. Hoar)

Interspecific competition in fish populations (P. A. Larkin)

Growth in fishes (P. A. Larkin)

Fatigue in fishes (E. C. Black)

University of British Columbia, Institute of Oceanography

POSTAL ADDRESS: Vancouver 8, British Columbia, Canada.

EXECUTIVE OFFICER: Dr. G. L. Pickard, Director.

SPONSORING AGENCIES: University of British Columbia and National Research Council.

YEAR FOUNDED: 1949.

SCOPE OF ACTIVITIES: Unrestricted research in oceanography of fjord type estuaries and of coastal seas; graduate instruction.

SEASON OF OPERATION: All year.

PHYSICAL ENVIRONMENT ACCESSIBLE: Strait of Georgia, Pacific Ocean; rocky and gravelly shores, estuarine conditions.

PROVISIONS FOR VISITING SCIENTISTS: Space for 2-4 visitors by arrangement; no fees charged; living quarters available nearby.

MAJOR RESEARCH AND TEACHING FACILITIES: Very extensive library; phycological research collections of benthonic marine algae, particularly representative of northeast Pacific (5,000 specimens); wood shop; vessels, small vessel available from another agency, occasional access to larger vessels.

INSTRUCTIONAL PROGRAM: Biological, chemical and physical oceanography.

SIZE OF STAFF: Eight at professional level; 4 technicians.

MAJOR CURRENT RESEARCH PROJECTS AND SCIENTIFIC LEADERS:

Estuarine circulation (fjord type) (George L. Pickard)

Phytoplankton distribution v. water properties (Robert F. Scagel)

Marine benthonic algae and water properties (Robert F. Scagel)

Zooplankton distribution in relation to water properties and movement (Brian McK. Bary)

Distribution of Foraminifera (Anthony E. Cockbain)

Waves and currents (Robert W. Stewart)

University of Saskatchewan, Limnological Laboratories

POSTAL ADDRESS:

Headquarters: Limnological Laboratory, Department of Biology, University of Saskatchewan, Saskatoon, Saskatchewan, Canada.

Field Station: Lac la Ronge, Saskatchewan, Canada.

EXECUTIVE OFFICER: Dr. D. S. Rawson, Head, Biology Department.

SPONSORING AGENCIES: Province of Saskatchewan; University of Saskatchewan.

YEAR FOUNDED: Headquarters 1929; Lac la Ronge Station, 1948.

SCOPE OF ACTIVITIES: Research on limnology and its application to fisheries management.

SEASON OF OPERATION: May 1 to September 15 at Lac la Ronge; remainder of year at University headquarters.

PHYSICAL ENVIRONMENT ACCESSIBLE: Lac la Ronge; eutrophic and oligotrophic lakes, artificial reservoirs in prairie area.

PROVISIONS FOR VISITING SCIENTISTS: Space for 3 at University, 6 at Lac la Ronge; no fees charged; living quarters available nearby.

MAJOR RESEARCH AND TEACHING FACILITIES: Small library; small aquarium tanks; extensive research collections at University of plankton, bottom fauna, and a smaller research collection of fish; limited identified reference collection of Entomostraca, bottom organisms and fish; machine and wood shop, electrical and electronic shop, skilled shop workman available; small boats and outboard motors; one 28 ft LOA heavy work boat.

INSTRUCTIONAL PROGRAM: Limnology, animal and plant ecology, general invertebrate zoology, fishery biology, fisheries management.

SIZE OF STAFF: Six at professional level; 2 technicians.

MAJOR CURRENT RESEARCH PROJECTS AND SCIENTIFIC LEADERS:

Lake typology as related to fish productivity (D. S. Rawson)

Population and life history studies of Saskatchewan fish (F. M. Atton)

PUBLICATIONS ISSUED: *Fisheries Reports, Saskatchewan Department of Natural Resources* (occasionally published contribution).

University of Toronto, Ontario Fisheries Research Group

POSTAL ADDRESS:

Headquarters: Department of Zoology, University of Toronto, Toronto, Ontario, Canada.

Branch laboratory: Laboratory for Experimental Limnology, Southern Research Station, Maple, Ontario.
Field station: Opeongo Limnological Laboratory, Algonquin Park, Ontario.

EXECUTIVE OFFICER: Dr. F. E. J. Fry, Professor of Limnology.

SPONSORING AGENCIES: University of Toronto and Ontario Department of Lakes and Forests.

YEAR FOUNDED: 1920.

SCOPE OF ACTIVITIES: Unrestricted research in general limnology, fish populations, physiology, plankton studies, productivity, bottom organisms and stream ecology; graduate instruction.

SEASON OF OPERATION: All year at University and Maple Laboratories; May 1 to November 30 at Opeongo field station.

PHYSICAL ENVIRONMENT ACCESSIBLE: Lake Ontario and others of the Great Lakes; numerous other oligotrophic lakes in Canadian Shield and in Algonquin Park; rivers.

PROVISIONS FOR VISITING SCIENTISTS: Space for about 10 visitors at various stations; living quarters available at field station.

MAJOR RESEARCH AND TEACHING FACILITIES: Very extensive limnological library at the Department of Zoology; large outdoor ponds, aquarium tanks; extensive research and identified reference collections of fish available at the Royal Ontario Museum; machine and wood shop, electrical and electronic shop, skilled shop workmen available, all at the Department of Zoology; small boats and outboard motors.

INSTRUCTIONAL PROGRAM: Limnology, autecology, aquatic entomology at graduate level; usual variety of zoological courses at undergraduate level.

SIZE OF STAFF: Eight at professional level; 8 technicians.

IMPORTANT SPECIES AVAILABLE FOR LABORATORY STUDIES:

Pisces: *Salvelinus namaycush, S. fontinalis, Coregonus clupeaformis, Leucichthys artedi,* hybrids of *Salvelinus* (*namaycush* x *fontinalis*)
Aquatic insects (lake and stream)

MAJOR CURRENT RESEARCH PROJECTS AND SCIENTIFIC LEADERS:

Activity patterns of fish with respect to light (R. R. Langford and K. C. Fisher)
Analysis of locomotion of fish in gradients (C. Sullivan)
Distribution of zooplankton in relation to water movements (R. R. Langford)
Dynamics of bottom fauna of lakes (F. P. Ide)
Ecology of stream insects with particular reference to Ephemeroptera (F. P. Ide)
Effect of temperature and oxygen content on the development of fish eggs (F. E. J. Fry)
Effect of temperature and salinity on life processes in fish (O. Kinne)
Effect of the ionic content of water on morphological and physiological features of fish (F. E. J. Fry)
Effect of yolk content on myomere count in fish embryos (F. E. J. Fry)
Effects of end products of metabolism on respiration of fish (F. E. J. Fry)
Electron microscope studies of the capsular membrane of fish eggs and its hardening (K. C. Fisher)
Factors influencing reproductive cycle in fish (F. E. J. Fry)
Feeding behavior of zooplankton (F. Rigler)
Genetic studies of hybrids of *Salvelinus* (F. E. J. Fry and L. Butler)
Irrigation of fish gills (F. E. J. Fry)
Nutrient dynamics of lakes (F. Rigler)
Population changes in zooplankton (R. R. Langford)
Population dynamics of aquatic insects in salmon streams following spraying with D.D.T. (F. P. Ide)
Swim bladder studies on salmonoids (F. E. J. Fry)
Transfer of nutrients, phytoplankton to zooplankton (R. R. Langford)

Vancouver Public Aquarium Association Laboratory

POSTAL ADDRESS: Box 8, Stanley Park, Vancouver 8, British Columbia, Canada.

EXECUTIVE OFFICER: M. A. Newman, Curator.

SPONSORING AGENCY: Vancouver Public Aquarium Association. Close cooperation maintained with the University of British Columbia.

YEAR FOUNDED: 1956.

SCOPE OF ACTIVITIES: Unrestricted aquatic research.

SEASON OF OPERATION: All year.

PHYSICAL ENVIRONMENT ACCESSIBLE: Sandy and silty beaches, rocky and gravelly shores, brackish, shallow

VANCOUVER PUBLIC AQUARIUM ASSOCIATION LABORATORY

bays in the vicinity of Vancouver Harbor and Strait of Georgia.

PROVISIONS FOR VISITING SCIENTISTS: Space for 5-6 visitors; no fees charged; living quarters available nearby.

MAJOR RESEARCH FACILITIES: Small library; running sea and fresh-water, small aquarium tanks, large experimental tank, wooden holding tanks; research and identified reference collections of local flora and fauna available at the University; machine and wood shop; one 10 ft LOA boat with outboard motor and one 30 ft LOA power vessel with live well available.

SIZE OF STAFF: Two at professional level; 3 technicians.

IMPORTANT SPECIES AVAILABLE FOR LABORATORY STUDIES:

Coelenterata: *Leioptilus* sp., *Metridium* sp.
Annelida: *Eudistylia vancouveri*
Mollusca: *Octopus apollyon*
Echinodermata: *Pisaster ochraceus*
Crustacea: *Cancer magister*
Pisces: *Oncorhynchus gorbuscha, O. kisutch, Salmo gairdneri Platichthys stellatus*

MAJOR CURRENT RESEARCH PROJECTS AND SCIENTIFIC LEADERS:

Studies on glycolytic enzymes in fish tissues (R. A. MacLeod)
Odor perception in Pacific salmon (D. Idler and R. A. MacLeod)
Growth and behavior of the Medaka fish (John Magnuson)
Osmoregulation in flatfishes (C. P. Hickman, Jr.)
Bioassay experiments with young salmon (Kenneth Jackson)

Other Laboratories About Which No Details Were Available:

Alberta Department of Lands and Mines, Fish and Game Branch, *Edmonton, Alberta, Canada.*
Supervisor: Mr. M. J. Paetz.

Bedford Institute of Oceanography, *Dartmouth, Nova Scotia, Canada*
Director: Dr. William N. English.

Dalhousie University Institute of Oceanography, *Halifax, Nova Scotia, Canada.*
Director: Professor F. Ronald Hayes.

CEYLON

Ceylon Department of Fisheries, Fisheries Research Station

POSTAL ADDRESS: P. O. Box 531, Galle Face, Colombo 3, Ceylon.

FISHERIES RESEARCH STATION, CEYLON

EXECUTIVE OFFICER: Mr. D. T. E. A. de Fonseca, Director of Fisheries.

SPONSORING AGENCY: Ceylon Ministry of Industries and Fisheries.

YEAR FOUNDED: 1946.

SCOPE OF ACTIVITIES: Restricted research on the biology and technology of Ceylon's fisheries.

SEASON OF OPERATION: All year.

PHYSICAL ENVIRONMENT ACCESSIBLE: Indian Ocean; sandy and silty beaches, estuarine conditions, brackish, shallow bays, coral reefs, eutrophic and oligotrophic lakes, rivers and streams.

PROVISIONS FOR VISITING SCIENTISTS: None.

MAJOR RESEARCH FACILITIES: Small library; small aquarium tanks; small research collection of Ceylon fish fauna; identified reference collection of fresh-water fauna and some marine fauna; machine and wood shop; small boats and outboard motors; one 40 ft LOA vessel in part-time use.

SIZE OF STAFF: Nine at professional level; 6 technicians.

MAJOR CURRENT RESEARCH PROJECTS AND SCIENTIFIC LEADERS:

Chemistry of fisheries products (C. E. St. C. Gunasekera)
Mackerel and tuna fisheries (T. P. Goonewardene)
Spiny lobster, prawn and crab fisheries; biology, behavior, physiology and gear technology (G. H. P. de Bruin)
Limnology and fresh-water fishery biology (A. S. Mendis)
Demersal fisheries and pearl oyster fishery (S. Sivalingam)
Oceanography, planktology and algology (M. Durairatnam)
Beach seine fishery and bait fishes (P. Canagaratnam)
Inshore hydrology and planktology (zooplankton) (N. Mahadeva)
Bacteriology of fish (N. N. de Silva)

CHILE

Estacion de Biologia Pesquera, San Antonio, Chile

SAN ANTONIO FISHERY BIOLOGY STATION

POSTAL ADDRESS: Casilla 492, Correo 2, San Antonio, Chile.

EXECUTIVE OFFICER: Oscar Miranda Brandt, Jefe.

SPONSORING AGENCY: Departamento de Pesca y Caza, Direccion de Agricultura y Pesca, Ministerio de Agriculture; Centro de Investigaciones Zoologicas, Universidad de Chile (Department of Fish and Game, Division of Agriculture and Fish, Ministry of Agriculture; Zoology Investigations Center, University of Chile).

YEAR FOUNDED: 1960.

SCOPE OF ACTIVITIES: Restricted research on fishery biology.

SEASON OF OPERATION: All year.

PHYSICAL ENVIRONMENT ACCESSIBLE: Bahia de San Antonio, Playa Barrancas, Llolleo (sandy and silty beaches) and Río Maipo.

PROVISIONS FOR VISITING SCIENTISTS: Research and living space for 2 visitors; no fees charged for research space.

MAJOR RESEARCH FACILITIES: No library; small aquarium tanks.

SIZE OF STAFF: Two at professional level; 1 technician.

IMPORTANT SPECIES AVAILABLE FOR LABORATORY STUDIES:

Pelecypoda: *Mesodesma donacium, Choromytilus chorus*

Cephalopoda: *Dosodicus tunicata*

Crustacea: *Cancer porteri, Homalapsis plana*

Pisces: *Merluccius gayi, Hippoglossina macrops, Odonthesthes regia, Genypterus blacodes*

ESTACION DE BIOLOGIA PESQUERA. SAN ANTONIO

MAJOR CURRENT RESEARCH PROJECTS AND SCIENTIFIC LEADERS:

Population dynamics of *Merluccius gayi* and associated species (Oscar Miranda B.)

Relationships between interstitial fauna and size of sand grains (Tarsicio Antezana)

Instituto de Zoologia, Universidad Austral de Chile

ZOOLOGICAL INSTITUTE, SOUTHERN UNIVERSITY OF CHILE

POSTAL ADDRESS: Casilla 956, Jola Teja, Valdivia, Chile.

EXECUTIVE OFFICER: Dr. Ernest Kilian, Professor.

YEAR FOUNDED: 1955.

SCOPE OF ACTIVITIES: Unrestricted research on shore ecology and fresh-water biology; undergraduate and graduate instruction.

SEASON OF OPERATION: All year.

PHYSICAL ENVIRONMENT ACCESSIBLE: Humboldt Current, sandy and silty beaches, rocky shores, estuarine conditions and rivers.

PROVISIONS FOR VISITING SCIENTISTS: Space for 2 at the marine laboratory at Mehuin; space for 2 at the fresh-water laboratory in Valdivia.

MAJOR RESEARCH AND TEACHING FACILITIES: Small library; running sea water, small aquarium tanks; identified reference collections of sponges and fishes; small wood and machine shop; small boats and outboard motors; 1 vessel 8.2 m LOA.

INSTRUCTIONAL PROGRAM: General invertebrate zoology, limnology and fish culture.

IMPORTANT SPECIES AVAILABLE FOR LABORATORY STUDIES:

Annelida: *Lumbricus terrestris, Rhabditis* sp.

Onycophora: *Peripatus* sp.

Crustacea: *Daphnia pulex, Parastacus nicoleti*

Pisces: *Galaxia maculatus*

PUBLICATIONS ISSUED: *Publ. Scientificas de la Universidad Austral* (occasionally published journal)

Ministerio de Agricultura, Departmento de Pesca y Caza, Laboratorio de Biologia Pesquera

MINISTRY OF AGRICULTURE, DEPARTMENT OF FISH AND GAME, FISHERIES LABORATORY

POSTAL ADDRESS: Casilla 183-V, Valparaiso, Chile.

EXECUTIVE OFFICER: Dr. Wilhelm Brandhorst, Experto en Oceangrafia y Biologia Marina de la Asistencia Tecnica de la Republica Federal de Alemania (Expert in oceanography and marine biology of the Foreign Technical Assistance Program of the Federal Republic of Germany).

YEAR FOUNDED: 1960.

SCOPE OF ACTIVITIES: Unrestricted research on commercially important fishes, and the relationship between physical conditions in the ocean and the fishery for various species; no experimental studies.

SEASON OF OPERATION: All year.

PHYSICAL ENVIRONMENT ACCESSIBLE: Open ocean, upwelling water of the Humboldt Current, water of subsurface Gunther Current, sandy and silty beaches, rocky and gravelly shores, estuarine conditions, brackish, shallow bays, eutrophic and oligotrophic lakes, rivers and streams.

MAJOR RESEARCH FACILITIES: No library; hatcheries; research collection of fish available at the Museo Nacional de Historia Natural; vessel in planning stage.

SIZE OF STAFF: Three at professional level; 7 technicians.

MAJOR CURRENT RESEARCH PROJECTS AND SCIENTIFIC LEADERS:

Descriptive oceanographic expedition "Marchile I" (W. Brandhorst)

Anchoveta investigation in the Northern and Central zone of Chile (W. Brandhorst)

Universidad de Chile, Centro de Investigaciones Zoologicas, Departamento de Hidrobiologia

UNIVERSITY OF CHILE, CENTER FOR ZOOLOGICAL INVESTIGATIONS, DEPARTMENT OF HYDROBIOLOGY

POSTAL ADDRESS: Casilla 10135, Santiago, Chile.

EXECUTIVE OFFICER: Guillermo Mann, Director del Centro. Maria Teresa Lopez, Jefe del Departamento.

YEAR FOUNDED: 1955.

SCOPE OF ACTIVITIES: Unrestricted research on the biology of local marine and fresh-water fauna; instruction.

SEASON OF OPERATION: All year.

PHYSICAL ENVIRONMENT ACCESSIBLE: Sandy and silty beaches, estuarine conditions, oligotrophic lake, rivers and streams.

PROVISIONS FOR VISTING SCIENTISTS: Space for a few visitors.

MAJOR RESEARCH AND TEACHING FACILITIES: Small library; small aquarium tanks; small boats and outboard motors.

INSTRUCTIONAL PROGRAM: General and marine zoology.

IMPORTANT SPECIES AVAILABLE FOR LABORATORY STUDIES:

Crustacea: *Aegla laevis, Cervimunida johni, Jasus lalandi, Heterocarpus reedi, Parastacus pugnax*

MAJOR CURRENT RESEARCH PROJECTS AND SCIENTIFIC LEADERS:

Ecological aspects of Aculeo pond (N. Bahamonde and others)

Taxonomy of Crustacea (N. Bahamonde and Maria T. Lopez)

Studies on populations of *Aegla laevis* from Mapocho River (N. Bahamonde and Maria T. Lopez)

Biology of some commercial shrimps (N. Bahamonde and Maria T. Lopez)

Systematics of Chilean fishes (Fernando De Buen)

Universidad de Chile, Estacion de Biologia Marina

UNIVERSITY OF CHILE, MARINE BIOLOGICAL STATION

POSTAL ADDRESS: Casilla 13-D, Vina del Mar, Chile.

LOCATION: Near Valparaiso.

EXECUTIVE OFFICER: Parmenio Yanez Andrade, Director.

YEAR FOUNDED: 1945.

SCOPE OF ACTIVITIES: Unrestricted research on general marine biology.

SEASON OF OPERATION: All year.

PHYSICAL ENVIRONMENT ACCESSIBLE: Valparaiso Bay; open ocean, sandy and silty beaches, rocky and gravelly shores.

PROVISIONS FOR VISITING SCIENTISTS: Research and living space for 4 visitors; no fees charged for research space.

MAJOR RESEARCH FACILITIES: Very extensive library; running sea and fresh-water, large outdoor ponds and tanks; research collections of fishes, bottom fauna and plankton; identified reference herbarium of local algae; small museum of comparative marine zoology with Chilean specimens; machine and wood shop, skilled shop workman available; small boats and outboard motors, one 22 m LOA vessel under construction.

SIZE OF STAFF: Eight at professional level; 7 technicians.

PUBLICATIONS ISSUED: *Revista de Biologia Marina* (regularly published journal)

UNIVERSIDAD DE CHILE, ESTACION DE BIOLOGIA MARINA

Universidad de Chile en la Zona Norte, Departamento de Investigaciones Cientificas Antofagasta, Seccion de Biologia Marina

UNIVERSITY OF CHILE OF THE NORTH ZONE, DEPARTMENT OF SCIENTIFIC INVESTIGATIONS OF ANTOFAGASTA, MARINE BIOLOGICAL SECTION

POSTAL ADDRESS: Casilla 1240, Antofagasta, Chile.
EXECUTIVE OFFICER: Celestino Castro A., Jefe de Seccion.
YEAR FOUNDED: 1958.
SCOPE OF ACTIVITIES: Unrestricted research on general marine biology.
SEASON OF OPERATION: All year.
PHYSICAL ENVIRONMENT ACCESSIBLE: Pacific Ocean; sandy and silty beaches, rocky and gravelly shores.
PROVISIONS FOR VISITING SCIENTISTS: None.
MAJOR RESEARCH AND TEACHING FACILITIES: Small library; small aquarium tanks; identified reference collections of birds, fishes and plankton; machine and wood shop, electrical and electronic shop, skilled shop workman available; small boats and outboard motors, one 10 m LOA vessel.

UNIVERSIDAD DE CHILE, EN LA ZONA NORTE, DEPARTAMENTO DE INVESTIGACIONES CIENTIFICAS

INSTRUCTIONAL PROGRAM: Course in marine biology.
SIZE OF STAFF: Three at professional level; 1 technician.
IMPORTANT SPECIES AVAILABLE FOR LABORATORY STUDIES:
Rhodophyceae: *Ahnfeltia durvillaei*
Pisces: *Sardinops sagaz, Engraulis ringens*
MAJOR CURRENT RESEARCH PROJECTS AND SCIENTIFIC LEADERS:
Cataloging of marine species of the North Zone of Chile (Celestino Castro)
PUBLICATIONS ISSUED: *Zonarida* (regularly published journal)

Universidad de Concepcion, Instituto Central de Biologia

UNIVERSITY OF CONCEPCION, CENTRAL INSTITUTE OF BIOLOGY

POSTAL ADDRESS: Casilla 301, Concepcion, Chile.
EXECUTIVE OFFICER: Dr. H. L. Barrales, Director.
SCOPE OF ACTIVITIES: Unrestricted research on plankton, bottom ecology and systematic zoology; undergraduate instruction.
SEASON OF OPERATION: All year.
PHYSICAL ENVIRONMENT ACCESSIBLE: Pacific Ocean, Bahia de Concepcion, San Vicente, Golfo de Arauco, Bio-Bio River; eutrophic and oligotrophic lakes.
PROVISIONS FOR VISITING SCIENTISTS: Space for 1-3 visitors; no fees charged; living quarters available nearby.
MAJOR RESEARCH AND TEACHING FACILITIES: Small library; small aquarium tanks; research collections of insects and fishes, herbarium and other collections in preparation; identified reference herbarium and entomological collection; skilled shop workman available; boats and larger power vessels may be rented.
INSTRUCTIONAL PROGRAM: Courses at the University in general and systematic zoology and botany leading to a B. Sc. in Biology.
SIZE OF STAFF: Six at professional level; 12 technicians.
MAJOR CURRENT RESEARCH PROJECTS AND SCIENTIFIC LEADERS:
Larval development of fishes; systematics (Walter Fischer)
Plankton investigations (Elda Fagetti)
Systematics and ecology of mollusks (Jose Stuardo)
Systematics and ecology of polychaetes (Fidel Geldes)
Sublittoral communities (A. Gallardo)

CHINESE PEOPLE'S REPUBLIC

The following laboratories are known to be in existence although no detailed information is available concerning their research facilities, physical environment accessible, species available for laboratory studies, current research projects, etc.:

Ministry of Fisheries, Peking.

1. ***Yellow Sea Fisheries Institute,*** Peking.
2. ***Huang Hai Fisheries Research Institute,*** *19 Lai-Yang Road, Tsing Tao.*

***Chinese Society of Oceanography and Limnology**, Head Office, Tsing Tao.*

***Chinese Society of Surveying and Cartography**, Peking*

***Shantung University, Marine Biological Laboratory**, Shantung.*

COLOMBIA

Asociacion Nacional de Piscicultura y Pesca Bogota

BOGOTA NATIONAL ASSOCIATION OF FISH-CULTURE AND FISHERIES

POSTAL ADDRESS: Apartado aereo No. 10329 (Apartado Nacional 4443), Bogota, Colombia.
EXECUTIVE OFFICER: Sr. Alfonso Archila A., Presidente. Arenida Jimenes No. 4-49 Of. 706/8, Bogota, Colombia.
SPONSORING AGENCY: Privately sponsored by sport fishermen.
YEAR FOUNDED: 1940.
SCOPE OF ACTIVITIES: Sport fishery research, particularly on trout and alevin production in lakes and rivers.
SEASON OF OPERATION: All year.
PHYSICAL ENVIRONMENT ACCESSIBLE: Rivers and streams of Colombia.
MAJOR RESEARCH FACILITIES: Aluminum boats with outboard motors.
PUBLICATIONS ISSUED: *Pispesca* (magazine)

CONGO

Former Belgium and French Territories

Institut pour la Recherches Scientifique en Afrique Centrale, Centre de Recherche de Tanganyika

THE TANGANYIKA RESEARCH CENTER OF THE INSTITUTE FOR SCIENTIFIC RESEARCH IN CENTRAL AFRICA

POSTAL ADDRESS:
Headquarters: 1, rue Defacqz, Bruxelles, Belgique (Brussels, Belgium).
Laboratory: P.O. Box 69, Uvira, Republic of the Congo.
LOCATION: Near Bukavu.
EXECUTIVE OFFICER: G. Marlier, Chief de Centre, Uvira.
SPONSORING AGENCY: Institut pour la Recherche Scientifique en Afrique Centrale (Institute for Scientific Research in Central Africa).
YEAR FOUNDED: 1949.
SCOPE OF ACTIVITIES: Unrestricted research on general limnology, plankton, ichthyology, and ecology of fish migration.
SEASON OF OPERATION: All year.
PHYSICAL ENVIRONMENT ACCESSIBLE: Lake Tanganyika (oligotrophic lake) and the Ruzizi River.
PROVISIONS FOR VISITING SCIENTISTS: Research space for 4 visitors; fees charged.
MAJOR RESEARCH FACILITIES: Small library; small aquarium tanks; research collection of cichlid fishes and fresh-water jelly fish; machine and wood shop, skilled workman available, but not on premises; small boats and outboard motors.
SIZE OF STAFF: Three at professional level; 1 technician.
IMPORTANT SPECIES AVAILABLE FOR LABORATORY STUDIES:
Pisces: *Protopterus aethiopicus* (Dipnoi), *Malapterurus electricus* (Siluridae), and many other species of fish and pelecypods.
MAJOR CURRENT RESEARCH PROJECTS AND SCIENTIFIC LEADERS:
Taxonomy of African fishes (H. Matthes)
Plankton of great African lakes (D. Kiss)
Humus fauna (N. Leleup)
Littoral fauna of Tanganyika (G. Marlier)
Taxonomy of aquatic insects (G. Marlier)
Ecology of fish migration (M. Magis)
Chemistry of humic waters (J. Dubois)
Hydrology of lakes (J. Dubois)
PUBLICATIONS ISSUED: *Folia Scientifica Africae Centralis* (regularly published journal)

Centre d'Oceanographie et des Peches

OCEANOGRAPHIC AND FISHERIES CENTER

POSTAL ADDRESS: B.P. 1086, Pointe-Noire, Congo.
LOCATION: Near Brazzaville.
EXECUTIVE OFFICER: G. R. Berrit, Chef de Centre.
SPONSORING AGENCY: Office de la Recherche Scientifique et Technique Outre Mer (O.R.S.T.O.M.), (Office of Overseas Scientific Research and Technology), 20 rue Monsieur, Paris VIIe, France.
YEAR FOUNDED: 1950.
SCOPE OF ACTIVITIES: Unrestricted research on general marine biology and ecology, systematics of marine organisms, and marine hydrology.
SEASON OF OPERATION: All year.
PHYSICAL ENVIRONMENT ACCESSIBLE: Tropical eastern Atlantic Ocean (from South of Angola to Nigeria) L 5° N to 12° S; sandy beaches, and brackish, shallow bays.
PROVISIONS FOR VISITING SCIENTISTS: Research and

CENTRE D'OCEANOGRAPHIE ET DES PECHES, CONGO

living space for 3 visitors; no fees charged for research space.

MAJOR RESEARCH FACILITIES: Small library; small aquarium tanks; research and identified reference collections of benthonic, pelagic and bathypelagic fishes and Crustacea, Cephalopoda, Mollusca, zoo- and phytoplankton; machine and wood shop, electrical shop; 25 m LOA vessel, *Ombango.*

SIZE OF STAFF: Four at professional level; 2 technicians assigned to ship.

IMPORTANT SPECIES AVAILABLE FOR LABORATORY STUDIES:

Pisces: *Sardinella eba, S. aurita*

Many kinds of marine invertebrates.

MAJOR CURRENT RESEARCH PROJECTS AND SCIENTIFIC LEADERS:

Biomass study (0-1,000m) of tropical waters between L 5° N to L 12° S (M. Blache)

Systematics of fishes, Crustacea, and Cephalopoda (M. Rossignol and M. Repelin)

Biology and ecology of tuna (*Neothunnus albacora*), *Sardinella eba* and *S. aurita* (M. Rossignol and M. Repelin)

Fisheries survey (M. Rossignol and M. Repelin)

Seasonal movements of water masses in the Gulf of Guinea (G. R. Berrit)

COSTA RICA

Comision Interamericana del Atun Tropical

INTER-AMERICAN TROPICAL TUNA COMMISSION, COSTA RICA BRANCH

POSTAL ADDRESS: Puntarenas, Costa Rica.

No detailed description of this branch was available, but see La Jolla California, USA headquarters, page 209.

CUBA

Centro de Investigaciones Pesqueras

FISHERIES RESEARCH CENTER

POSTAL ADDRESS: Playa Habana, Bauta, Habana (Havana), Cuba.

EXECUTIVE OFFICER: Rene J. Buesa Mas, Director.

SPONSORING AGENCY: Departamento de Pesca del Instituto Nacional de Reforma Agrarian (Fisheries Department of the National Institute of Agrarian Reform).

YEAR FOUNDED: 1952.

SCOPE OF ACTIVITIES: Restricted research on general marine biology, oceanography, and statistics as applied to the development and conservation of fisheries and other marine resources; fisheries biology.

SEASON OF OPERATION: All year.

PHYSICAL ENVIRONMENT ACCESSIBLE: Straits of Florida and Gulf of Mexico; rocky and gravelly shores, estuarine conditions, coral reefs.

PROVISIONS FOR VISITING SCIENTISTS: Space for 12 visitors; living quarters available nearby.

MAJOR RESEARCH FACILITIES: Small library; running sea and fresh-water, large outdoor ponds, small aquarium tanks; research and identified collections of local fauna and plankton; shop facilities of government available; small boats and outboard motors; motor vessels, 64 ft and 35 ft LOA also 50 ft, 60 ft and 92 ft.

SIZE OF STAFF: Ten at professional level; 5 technicians.

IMPORTANT SPECIES AVAILABLE FOR LABORATORY STUDIES:

Crustacea: *Panulirus guttatus, P. argus; Penaeus duoarum, P. brasiliensis, P. aztecus, Trachipenaeus constrictus, Periclemenes* sp.

Pisces: *Xiphias gladius, Lutianus* sp.

MAJOR CURRENT RESEARCH PROJECTS AND SCIENTIFIC LEADERS:

Shrimp (Lidia Pas Martinez)

Lobster (Rene J. Buesa Mas)

CENTRO DE INVESTIGACIONES PESQUERAS, HABANA

Ichthyology (Roselia Romero Hidalgo)
Oysters (Audres Mena Millar)
Biochemistry (Jose A. Perez Sori)
Sardines, tuna, albacore, and sharks (Staff and visiting Cuban scientists)

PUBLICATIONS ISSUED: *Contribuciones del Centro de Investigaciones Pesqueras* (occasionally published journal)

Instituto Cubano de Investigaciones Tecnologicas (ICIT)

CUBAN INSTITUTE OF TECHNOLOGICAL INVESTIGATIONS

POSTAL ADDRESS: Apartado 4026, Via Blanca y Carretera Central, Habana (Havana), Cuba.

EXECUTIVE OFFICER: Ing. Jorge Duerra Deben, Director.

SPONSORING AGENCY: Ministerio de Industrias.

YEAR FOUNDED: 1955.

SCOPE OF AQUATIC ACTIVITIES: Research on marine resources, plankton, fisheries and economic algology.

SEASON OF OPERATION: All year.

PHYSICAL ENVIRONMENT ACCESSIBLE: Caribbean Sea, Gulf of Mexico; open ocean, sandy and silty beaches, estuarine conditions, brackish, shallow bays, and coral reefs.

PROVISIONS FOR VISITING SCIENTISTS: None at present.

MAJOR RESEARCH FACILITIES: Small library; running sea and fresh-water, large outdoor ponds and tanks, small aquarium tanks; research and identified reference collections of fishes, plankton and algae; machine and wood shop, electrical and electronic shop, skilled shop workman available; small boats and outboard motors; research vessel in planning stage.

SIZE OF STAFF: Four at professional level; 9 technicians.

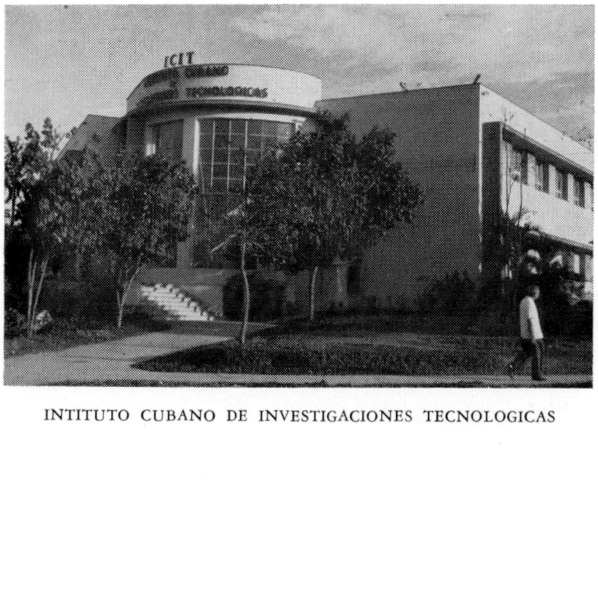

INTITUTO CUBANO DE INVESTIGACIONES TECNOLOGICAS

MAJOR CURRENT RESEARCH PROJECTS AND SCIENTIFIC LEADERS:

Marine algae as supplementary diet for broilers, laying hens and cattle (Manuel Díaz-Piferrer and Juan M. Navia)
Agar and alginic acid extracted from several species of Cuban seaweeds (Joaquin Losada and Manuel Díaz-Piferrer)
Medical products from Cuban seaweeds (Joaquin Losada and Manuel Diaz-Piferrer)
Fishery biology of the Cuban "bonito" (*K. pelamis*) and "albacore" (*T. atlanticus*) (Jose Suarez Caabro, Pedro Duarte Bello and Georgina Morales)
Fishery biology and technology of Cuban sardines (Jose Suarez Caabro, Pedro Duarte Bello and Julia Alvarez)
Fishery biology and technology of Cuban species of shrimps (Isabel Pérez Farfante and Milagros Alemany)

PUBLICATIONS ISSUED: *"ICIT" Boletin Informativo* (regularly published journal)

Universidad de Oriente, Laboratorio Marino

UNIVERSITY OF ORIENTE, LABORATORY OF MARINE BIOLOGY

POSTAL ADDRESS: Santiago de Cuba, Cuba.

EXECUTIVE OFFICER: Dr. Manuel Diaz-Piferrer, Director.

SPONSORING AGENCIES: Instituto Cubana de Investigaciones Tecnologicas and Universidad de Oriente (Cuban Institute of Technological Investigations and University of Oriente).

YEAR FOUNDED: 1956.

SCOPE OF ACTIVITIES: Unrestricted biological research on Cuban marine flora; undergraduate instruction.

SEASON OF OPERATION: All year.

PHYSICAL ENVIRONMENT ACCESSIBLE: Caribbean Sea, Gulf of Mexico; sandy and silty beaches, rocky and gravelly shores, estuarine conditions, brackish, shallow bays, coral reefs.

PROVISIONS FOR VISITING SCIENTISTS: None.

MAJOR RESEARCH AND TEACHING FACILITIES: Small library; small aquarium tanks; research and identified reference collections of Cuban and Caribbean marine algae; vessels of the Cuban Navy are available.

INSTRUCTIONAL PROGRAM: General invertebrate zoology, general zoology, plankton, general marine biology, marine botany, marine ecology.

SIZE OF STAFF: Three at professional level; 2 technicians.

IMPORTANT SPECIES AVAILABLE FOR LABORATORY STUDIES:

Algae: *Ulva fasciata u. lactuca, Enteromorpha lingulata, Caulerpa racemosa*

MAJOR CURRENT RESEARCH PROJECTS AND SCIENTIFIC LEADERS:

Taxonomy, ecology and utilization of Cuban marine flora (M. Diaz-Piferrer)

Nutritional value of marine algae for poultry and livestock; vitaminic values of Cuban algae (projects being investigated in conjunction with the Cuban Institute for Technological Investigations)

Universidad de Villaneueva, Departamento de Investigaciones Marinas

UNIVERSITY OF VILLANUEVA, DEPARTMENT OF MARINE RESEARCH

POSTAL ADDRESS: Apartado 6, 5ta. Avenida No. 16, 607, Marianao, Habana (Havana), Cuba.

EXECUTIVE OFFICER: Dr. Jose A. Suarez Caabro, Director.

YEAR FOUNDED: 1957.

SCOPE OF ACTIVITIES: Unrestricted research on general oceanography with emphasis on plankton studies and fisheries biology.

SEASON OF OPERATION: All year.

PHYSICAL ENVIRONMENT ACCESSIBLE: Caribbean Sea, Straits of Florida and Yucatan, Gulf of Mexico; sandy and silty beaches, rocky and gravelly shores, estuarine conditions, brackish, shallow bays, coral reefs.

PROVISIONS FOR VISITING SCIENTISTS: Space for visitors; living quarters available nearby.

MAJOR RESEARCH FACILITIES: Small library; small research collection of Cuban fishes; identified reference collection of plankton samples of western Cuba; machine and wood shop, electrical and electronic shop, skilled shop workman available; vessels for research use are rented.

SIZE OF STAFF: Three at professional level; 1 technician.

UNIVERSIDAD DE VILLANUEVA, DEPARTAMENTO DE INVESTIGACIONES MARINAS

MAJOR CURRENT RESEARCH PROJECTS AND SCIENTIFIC LEADERS:

Oceanography of the Gulf of Batabano (Suarez-Caabro and Duarte-Bello).

Biology and fishery of the Cuban tuna (Suarez-Caabro and Duarte-Bello).

Biology and technology of the Cuban sardine-like fishes (Suarez-Caabro and Duarte-Bello).

PUBLICATIONS ISSUED: *Monografias* (regularly published journal).

CZECHOSLOVAKIA

Hydrobiologicka Laborator CSAV

HYDROBIOLOGICAL LABORATORY CSAV (CZECHOSLOVAK ACADEMY OF SCIENCE)

POSTAL ADDRESS:

Headquarters: 17 Vltavska, Praha 5, Ceskoslovensko (Prague, Czechoslovakia).

Field laboratory: On Slapy Reservoir.

EXECUTIVE OFFICER: Dr. Jaroslav Hrbacek, Vedouci (Head).

SPONSORING AGENCY: Czechoslovak Academy of Science.

YEAR FOUNDED: 1951.

SCOPE OF ACTIVITIES: Unrestricted research on productivity and self-purification of reservoirs, plankton, bottom ecology, water chemistry and bacteriology.

SEASON OF OPERATION: All year.

PHYSICAL ENVIRONMENT ACCESSIBLE: Slapy Reservoir on the Vltava River.

PROVISIONS FOR VISITING SCIENTISTS: Space for 4 visitors; no fees charged; living quarters available nearby.

MAJOR RESEARCH FACILITIES: Small library; small aquarium tanks; research and identified reference collections of plankton and benthos; machine and wood shop; small boats and outboard motors; one 9 m LOA power vessel.

SIZE OF STAFF: Eleven at professional level; 4 technicians.

IMPORTANT SPECIES AVAILABLE FOR LABORATORY STUDIES:

Algae: *Scenedesmus* spp., *Microcystis* sp.

Crustacea: *Daphnia* (all central European species)

MAJOR CURRENT RESEARCH PROJECTS:

Zooplankton, phytoplankton and benthos of the reservoirs

Physiology of metabolism of invertebrates and fishes

Water chemistry (especially nitrogen and phosphorus)

Water bacteriology (BOD studies and self-purification)

Biology of ground water

OBORA FIELD STATION

Karlova Universita, Prirodovedecka Fakulta, Hydrobiologicke Oddeleni

CARL'S UNIVERSITY, FACULTY OF NATURAL HISTORY, HYDROBIOLOGICAL DEPARTMENT

POSTAL ADDRESS:
Headquarters: Vinicna 7, Praha 2, Bohemia, Ceskoslovensko (Prague, Czechoslovakia).
Field station: Obora (near Blatna), South Bohemia.
EXECUTIVE OFFICER: Dr. Jan Lellak.
YEAR FOUNDED: About 1920.
SCOPE OF ACTIVITIES: Research on the biology of Czechoslovakian fresh-water communities and fish ponds, especially biocoenology, taxonomy and ecology; instruction.
SEASON OF OPERATION: All year.
PHYSICAL ENVIRONMENT ACCESSIBLE: Lakes, fish ponds, and water reservoirs on the rivers.
PROVISIONS FOR VISITING SCIENTISTS: Research and living space for about 15 visitors; no fees charged for research space.
MAJOR RESEARCH AND TEACHING FACILITIES: Very extensive library in Prague, small library in Blatna; large outdoor ponds and tanks, small aquarium tanks; research collections of the bottom and plankton fauna and flora of Bohemian fish ponds; machine and wood shop; small boats and outboard motors.
INSTRUCTIONAL PROGRAM: Hydrobiology, saprobiology, biocoenology and taxonomy of fresh-water fauna at Carl's University.
SIZE OF STAFF: Four at professional level; 2 technicians.
IMPORTANT SPECIES AVAILABLE FOR LABORATORY STUDIES:
Ciliata: *Paramecium caudatum*
Crustacea: *Daphnia magna*
Pisces: Many species of central European fresh-water fishes
MAJOR CURRENT RESEARCH PROJECTS AND SCIENTIFIC LEADERS:
Productivity of benthos in ponds (Jan Lellak)
Crustacean communities in Czechoslovak waters (V. Korinek)

Pobocka Ceskoslovenskej Akademie Polnohospodarskych Vied, Laboratorium Rybarstva

CZECHOSLOVAKIAN ACADEMY OF AGRICULTURAL SCIENCES, LABORATORY OF FISHERY BIOLOGY

POSTAL ADDRESS: Cesta mladeze, Zelezna Studienka, 806, Bratislava, Ceskoslovensko (Czechoslovakia).
EXECUTIVE OFFICER: Ing. Frantisek K. Havlena, Direktor.
YEAR FOUNDED: 1953.
SCOPE OF ACTIVITIES: Restricted research on ichthyology, fisheries biology and hydrobiology—specifically taxonomy, life histories, growth, nutrition, hybridization, acclimatization, morphology and ecology of fishes; instruction.
SEASON OF OPERATION: All year.
PHYSICAL ENVIRONMENT ACCESSIBLE: Eutrophic and oligotrophic lakes, rivers and riverine lakes of Slovakia.
MAJOR RESEARCH AND TEACHING FACILITIES: Very extensive library; no water supply and tanks at present; ichthyological research collection; one 7 m LOA power vessel.
INSTRUCTIONAL PROGRAM: Fresh-water invertebrates, phytoplankton and ichthyology.
SIZE OF STAFF: Nine at professional level; 6 technicians.
MAJOR CURRENT RESEARCH PROJECTS AND SCIENTIFIC LEADERS:
Life history, growth and fish populations (E. K. Balon)
Dynamics of bottom organisms (N. D. Borodic)
Biometry, morphology and fecundity of fishes (I. Bastl)
Taxonomy and ecology of algae (F. Hindak)
Food of fishes, experimental ecology of water organisms (F. K. Havlena)
Faunistics, taxonomy, growth and hybridization of fishes (J. M. Holcik)
Morphology and growth of fishes (A. Kirka)
Biometry and faunistics of fishes (V. Misik)
Fish pathology (S. Pacak)

Vysoke Skoly Zemedelske V Brne, Biologicka Stanice

AGRICULTURAL COLLEGE, BRNO, BIOLOGICAL STATION

POSTAL ADDRESS: Hydrobiological and Ornithological Departments: Zamek, 1, Lednice na Morave, Ceskoslovensko (Czechoslovakia).
LOCATION: Southern Moravia, near town of Breclav.
EXECUTIVE OFFICER: RNDr. Bohumil Losos, Direktor, Vodova 96 v Brne, Ceskoslovensko.

YEAR FOUNDED: 1922.
SCOPE OF ACTIVITIES: Unrestricted research on the biology of ponds and rivers, especially plankton and bottom fauna.
SEASON OF OPERATION: All year.
PHYSICAL ENVIRONMENT ACCESSIBLE: Fish ponds, Dyje and Svratka Rivers, periodic and permanent pools in the inundation area of the River Dyje.
PROVISIONS FOR VISITING SCIENTISTS: Research and living space available for 4-6 visitors; no fees charged for research space.
MAJOR RESEARCH AND TEACHING FACILITIES: Moderately complete library; small aquarium tanks; research collection of plankton; identified reference collections of Rotatoria, Cladocera, Copepoda, algae (freshwater); skilled shop workman available; one 5 m LOA vessel.
INSTRUCTIONAL PROGRAM: Zooplankton and phytoplankton of ponds.

BIOLOGICKA STANICE, LEDNICE

SIZE OF STAFF: Three at professional level; 1 technician.
IMPORTANT SPECIES AVAILABLE FOR LABORATORY STUDIES:
Polygonaceae: *Salicornia herbacea*
Chlorophyta: *Enteromorpha intestinalis*
Cladocera: *Daphnia magna, D. pulex*
MAJOR CURRENT RESEARCH PROJECTS AND SCIENTIFIC LEADERS:
Productivity investigations of fish ponds (B. Losos and Jiri Hetesa)
Limnological investigations of periodic and permanent pools in southern Moravia (B. Losos and Jiri Hetesa)
Limnological research of rivers in Moravia (B. Losos and Jiri Hetesa)
Biology of aquatic birds (Ing. Zdenek Bauer)

Vysoke Skoly Zemedelske V Brne, Oddeleni pro Hydrobiologii A Ichthyologii

AGRICULTURAL COLLEGE, BRNO, HYDROBIOLOGY AND ICHTHYOLOGY DEPARTMENT

POSTAL ADDRESS: Zemedelska 1 v Brne, Ceskoslovensko (Brno, Czechoslovakia).
EXECUTIVE OFFICER: Professor Dr. Boris Kostomarov, Direktor.
YEAR FOUNDED: 1928.
SCOPE OF ACTIVITIES: Unrestricted research on ichthyology, fishery biology and hydrobiology.
SEASON OF OPERATION: All year.
PHYSICAL ENVIRONMENT ACCESSIBLE: Reservoir Kninicky, Svratka River at Svitava, fish ponds at Pohorelice.
PROVISIONS FOR VISITING SCIENTISTS: Research and living space for 4 visitors.
MAJOR RESEARCH AND TEACHING FACILITIES: Moderately complete library; small aquarium tanks; research and identified reference collections of fishes; skilled shop workman available; small boats.
INSTRUCTIONAL PROGRAM: Ichthyology and fishery biology.
SIZE OF STAFF: Three at professional level; 1 technician.
IMPORTANT SPECIES AVAILABLE FOR LABORATORY STUDIES:
Pisces: *Cyprinus carpio, Silurus glanis, Coregonus lavaretus*
MAJOR CURRENT RESEARCH PROJECTS AND SCIENTIFIC LEADERS:
Ichthyological and hydrobiological investigation of rivers in Moravia (B. Kostomarov, L. Hochman and J. Jirasek)
Pond culture studies of *Cyprinus carpio, Trutta trutta, Silurus glanis,* and *Coregonus lavaretus* (L. Hochman and J. Jirasek)
PUBLICATIONS ISSUED: *Sbornik Vysoke skoly zemedelske a lesnicke v Brne* (occasionally published writings).

Other Laboratories for Which No Detailed Information Was Available:

Vyzkumny ustav rybarsky (Fishery Research Institute), *Vodnany, South Bohemia, Ceskoslovensko (Czechoslovakia).*
Director: Ing. F. Chytra.

Zoologicky ustav, Masarykova Universita, *Kotlarska 2, Brno, Ceskoslovensko. Hydrobiological substation in the Bitov (castle) near Vranov water-reservoir on the river Dyje, South Moravia. No permanent staff.*
Director: Professor Dr. Sergej Hrabe.

DAHOMEY

Centre d'Etudes Scientifiques et Techniques Appliquees a la Peche

CENTER FOR SCIENTIFIC STUDY AND APPLIED FISHERY TECHNOLOGY

POSTAL ADDRESS: B. P. 383, 1 rue Bel-Air, Cotonou, Dahomey.
EXECUTIVE OFFICER: Dr. L. Vincent-Cuaz, Directeur.
SPONSORING AGENCY: Service de l'Elevage et des Industries Animales du Ministere de l'Agriculture (Animal Husbandry Department of the Ministry of Agriculture).
YEAR FOUNDED: 1958.
SCOPE OF ACTIVITIES: Unrestricted research on oceanography and fishery biology; technological studies of marine and lagoon fishes.
SEASON OF OPERATION: All year.
PHYSICAL ENVIRONMENT ACCESSIBLE: Bight of Benin, Gulf of Guinea, Atlantic Ocean, Lacs Nokoue, Aheme, and Toho (lagoons), Niger River; sandy and silty beaches, estuarine conditions, and brackish, shallow bays.
PROVISIONS FOR VISITING SCIENTISTS: None at present, but research space for 5 visitors and living space for 3 in new laboratory under construction; living quarters available nearby.
MAJOR RESEARCH FACILITIES: Small library; running sea and fresh-water, small aquarium tanks and culture tanks available in new building; research collection of coastal fauna from the Bight of Benin; small boats and outboard motors; one 24 m LOA vessel.
SIZE OF STAFF: Seven.
IMPORTANT SPECIES AVAILABLE FOR LABORATORY STUDIES:
Crustacea: *Panulirus regins*

CENTRE D'ETUDES SCIENTIFIQUES TECHNIQUES APPLIQUEES A LA PECHE, DAHOMEY

Pisces: *Sardinella eba, S. aurita, Pellona africana, Otolithus sp., Macrognathus sp., Cybium tritor, Euthynnus alleteratus, Neothunnus albacora, Caranx* sp.
MAJOR CURRENT RESEARCH PROJECTS AND SCIENTIFIC LEADERS:
Inventory of the fauna of the Bight of Benin and lagoons (L. Vincent-Cuaz)
Smoking and drying of fish (L. Vincent-Cuaz)
Hydrobiological studies of coastal regimes (L. Vincent-Cuaz)

DENMARK

Carlsbergfondet, Skalling-Laboratoriet

CARLSBERG FOUNDATION, MARINE LABORATORY

POSTAL ADDRESS: Gl. Havn, Esbjerg, Danmark (Denmark).
EXECUTIVE OFFICERS: Professor Niels Nielsen, Gl. Havn, Esbjerg, Danmark. Dr. Erik Ursin, Kejsergade 2, Koebenhavn K., Danmark.
SPONSORING AGENCIES: Carlsbergfondet and Danmarks Fiskeri-og Havundersogelser (Carlsberg Foundation and the Danish Institute for Fishery and Marine Research).
YEAR FOUNDED: 1930.
SCOPE OF ACTIVITIES: Unrestricted research on physical geography and marine biology in tidal and coastal areas.
SEASON OF OPERATION: Primarily seasonal.
PHYSICAL ENVIRONMENT ACCESSIBLE: North and Wadden Seas; sandy and silty beaches, dune areas, salt marshes and tidal flats.
PROVISIONS FOR VISITING SCIENTISTS: Space for a few visitors; no fees charged; living quarters available nearby.
MAJOR RESEARCH FACILITIES: Small library in Copenhagen; one two-ton vessel, M/B *Skallingen.*
SIZE OF STAFF: Six at professional level.
MAJOR CURRENT PROJECTS: The Skalling Laboratory works very closely with the Danish Institute for Fishery and Marine Research and with the Geographical Institute of the University of Copenhagen.

Danmarks Akvarium, Fysiologisk Laboratorium

DENMARKS AQUARIUM, PHYSIOLOGICAL LABORATORY

POSTAL ADDRESS: Danmarks Akvarium, Charlottenlund, Danmark (Denmark).
LOCATION: Near Koebenhavn (Copenhagen).
EXECUTIVE OFFICER: Dr. J. Boetius, Director.

FYSIOLOGISK LABORATORIUM, CHARLOTTENLUND

SPONSORING AGENCIES: Danmarks Fiskeri-og Havundersoegelser and Danmarks Akvarium (Danish Institute for Fishery and Marine Research and Denmark Aquarium).
YEAR FOUNDED: 1952.
SCOPE OF ACTIVITIES: Unrestricted research on the physiology of fishes.
SEASON OF OPERATION: All year.
PHYSICAL ENVIRONMENT ACCESSIBLE: Baltic Sea, Oeresund, Kattegat.
PROVISIONS FOR VISITING SCIENTISTS: Space for 1-2 visitors; no fees charged.
MAJOR RESEARCH FACILITIES: Library of Danmarks Fiskeri-og Havundersoegelser available nearby; closed, circulating fresh- and sea water systems, small aquarium tanks; machine and wood shop, skilled shop workman available; vessels of D.F.H. used.
SIZE OF STAFF: One at professional level; 2 technicians.
IMPORTANT SPECIES AVAILABLE FOR LABORATORY STUDIES: All species of fish and invertebrates from the Kattegat and North Sea.
MAJOR CURRENT RESEARCH PROJECTS AND SCIENTIFIC LEADERS:
Studies in sexual maturation in the European eel (I. and J. Boetius)
Toxicological studies on fishes (J. Boetius)
Osmoregulation (*Salmo* sp.) (I. Boetius)

Danmarks Fiskeri-og Havundersoegelser

DANISH INSTITUTE FOR FISHERY AND MARINE RESEARCH

POSTAL ADDRESS: Charlottenlund Slot, Charlottenlund, Danmark (Denmark).
LOCATION: Near Koebenhavn (Copenhagen).
EXECUTIVE OFFICER: Dr. E. Bertelsen, Director, Jaegersborg Alle 1.E., Charlottenlund.
SPONSORING AGENCY: Ministry of Fisheries.
YEAR FOUNDED: 1902.
SCOPE OF ACTIVITIES: Restricted research on general marine biology, bottom ecology, oceanography, estuarine and plankton studies, general fisheries investigations, and pollution studies.
SEASON OF OPERATION: All year.
PHYSICAL ENVIRONMENT ACCESSIBLE: North Sea, Skagerak, Baltic, Belt and Norwegian Seas, North Atlantic Ocean, Davis Strait; sandy beaches, brackish, shallow bays, eutrophic lakes, rivers and streams.
PROVISIONS FOR VISITING SCIENTISTS: Space for 1-2 visitors; no fees charged; living quarters available nearby.
MAJOR RESEARCH FACILITIES: Very extensive library; large tanks and aquaria at Danmarks Akvarium; research and identified reference collections; machine and wood shop; vessels, 55 m LOA M/S *Dana,* 33 m LOA S/S *Biologen* and 9 m LOA *Havkatten.*
SIZE OF STAFF: Twenty-one at professional level; 22 technicians.
PUBLICATIONS ISSUED: *Meddelelser fra Danmarks Fiskeri-og Havundersoegelser* (regularly published journal).

Fiskirannsoknarstovan, Faeroerne

FISHERIES RESEARCH LABORATORY, FAEROES

POSTAL ADDRESS: Torshavn, Faeroerne, Danmark (Faeroe Islands, Denmark).
EXECUTIVE OFFICER: J. S. Joensen, Director.
SPONSORING AGENCIES: Danmarks Fiskeri-og Havundersoegelser (Danish Institute for Fishery and Marine Research) and Faeroese Government.
YEAR FOUNDED: 1951.
SCOPE OF ACTIVITIES: Restricted research on fisheries of the Faeroe Islands.
SEASON OF OPERATION: All year.

DANMARKS FISKERI-OG HAVUNDERSOGELSER, CHARLOTTENLUND SLOT

PHYSICAL ENVIRONMENT ACCESSIBLE: Atlantic Ocean.
PROVISIONS FOR VISITING SCIENTISTS: Research and living space for 2 visitors.
MAJOR RESEARCH FACILITIES: Small library.
SIZE OF STAFF: One at professional level; 3 technicians.
PUBLICATIONS ISSUED: *Frooeskaparrit* (*Annal. societ. scient. Faeroensis*) (regularly published journal).

I/S DANSK FORSOEGSDAMKULTUR

I/S Dansk Forsoegsdamkultur

DANISH TROUT POND FARM EXPERIMENTAL STATION

POSTAL ADDRESS: Broens, Danmark (Denmark).
LOCATION: Near Ribe.
EXECUTIVE OFFICER: C. J. Rasmussen, Director.
SPONSORING AGENCY: Ministry of Fisheries.
YEAR FOUNDED: 1955.
SCOPE OF ACTIVITIES: Restricted research on pond culture, diseases and nutrition of trout.
SEASON OF OPERATION: All year.
PHYSICAL ENVIRONMENT ACCESSIBLE: Broens ae (River Broens).
PROVISIONS FOR VISITING SCIENTISTS: None.
MAJOR RESEARCH FACILITIES: Seventy-nine earth ponds, 26 concrete tanks, large concrete aquarium and small aquarium tanks; machine and wood shop, electrical shop, skilled shop workman available.
SIZE OF STAFF: Two at professional level; 5 technicians.

Isefjordlaboratoriet

THE ISEFJORD-LABORATORY

POSTAL ADDRESS: Vellerup Vig, prr. Skibby, Danmark (Denmark).
LOCATION: Near Koebenhavn (Copenhagen)
EXECUTIVE OFFICER: Dr. Erik Rasmussen, Leader and owner.
SPONSORING AGENCY: Privately financed laboratory.
YEAR FOUNDED: 1942.
SCOPE OF ACTIVITIES: Unrestricted research on general marine ecology, mainly invertebrate.
SEASON OF OPERATION: All year.
PHYSICAL ENVIRONMENT ACCESSIBLE: Isefjord, Roskildefjord (connecting with the Kattegat); sandy and silty beaches, rocky and gravelly shores, estuarine conditions, brackish, shallow bays.
PROVISIONS FOR VISITING SCIENTISTS: Space for 4 visitors; fees charged; living quarters nearby.
MAJOR RESEARCH FACILITIES: Small library; small aquarium tanks; research collection of local invertebrates; identified reference collections of Coelenterata, Annelida, Arthropoda and Mollusca; small boats and outboard motors.
SIZE OF STAFF: One at professional level.
IMPORTANT SPECIES AVAILABLE FOR LABORATORY STUDIES:
Coelenterata: *Aurelia aurita, Metridium senile* var. *dianthus*
Annelida: *Nereis diversicolor, Arenicola marina*
Crustacea: *Sacculina carcini, Gammarus locusta, G. zaddachi, G. duebeni, Carcinus maenas*
Mollusca: *Mytilus edulis*
Echinodermata: *Asterias rubens*
Tunicata: *Ciona intestinalis*
Algae: *Ulva lactuca, Fucus vesiculosus*
MAJOR CURRENT RESEARCH PROJECTS AND SCIENTIFIC LEADERS:
Taxonomy of invertebrates (Erik Rasmussen)
Reproduction and larval development of Polychaeta and Mollusca (Erik Rasmussen)

ISEFJORDLABORATORIET, NR. COPENHAGEN

Koebenhavns Universitets, Ferskvands-Biologiske Laboratorium

COPENHAGEN UNIVERSITY, FRESH-WATER BIOLOGICAL LABORATORY

POSTAL ADDRESS:
Headquarters: Hilleroed, Danmark (Denmark).

Field laboratories: Suserup laboratory, Sora, Silkeborg laboratory, Virklund, Silkeborg.

LOCATION: Near Koebenhavn (Copenhagen).

EXECUTIVE OFFICER: Dr. Kaj Berg, Director and Professor of Fresh-water Biology.

YEAR FOUNDED: 1900.

SCOPE OF ACTIVITIES: Limnological research; graduate and undergraduate instruction.

SEASON OF OPERATION: All year.

PHYSICAL ENVIRONMENT ACCESSIBLE: Frederiksborg Castle Lake; eutrophic and oligotrophic lakes, rivers and streams.

PROVISIONS FOR VISITING SCIENTISTS: Research and living space for 5 visitors; no fees charged for research space.

MAJOR RESEARCH AND TEACHING FACILITIES: Very extensive library; large outdoor ponds and tanks, small aquarium tanks; limited identified reference collections of local fauna and flora, especially plankton; wood shop; small boats and outboard motors; all types of limnological equipment.

INSTRUCTIONAL PROGRAM: Limnology, fresh-water zoology, and fresh-water botany for students of Copenhagen University.

SIZE OF STAFF: Eleven at professional level; 3 technicians.

MAJOR CURRENT RESEARCH PROJECTS AND SCIENTIFIC LEADERS:

Respiration of invertebrates (Kaj Berg)
Productivity of bottom fauna (Petuer M. Jonasson)
Primary productivity of phytoplankton (Hans Mathiesen)
Primary productivity and milieu of oligotrophic lake (Guennar Nygaard)
Arctic plankton (Ulrik Roen)
Flagellates (Jorgen Kristiansen)
Spring fauna (Jens Thoruep)
Higher vegetation of lakes, and phosphates in lakes (Siguerd Olsen)
Respiration of invertebrates of brackish-water (Jorgen Luembye)
Bottom sediment (Kaj Hansen)
Temperature and fauna of running water (Bent Lauege Madsen)
Hydrography (Aage Rebsdorf)

PUBLICATIONS ISSUED: *Hydrobiologia* (regularly published journal).

FERSKVANDS-BIOLOGISKE LABORATORIUM, COPENHAGEN UNIVERSITY

Koebenhavns Universitets, Marinbiologisk Laboratorium

COPENHAGEN UNIVERSITY, MARINE BIOLOGICAL LABORATORY

POSTAL ADDRESS: Helsingoer, Danmark (Elsinore, Denmark).

EXECUTIVE OFFICER: Gunnar Thorson, Professor of Marine Biology.

YEAR FOUNDED: 1958.

SCOPE OF ACTIVITIES: Unrestricted research on ecology of marine invertebrates, general marine biology, plankton studies, bottom ecology; graduate and undergraduate instruction.

SEASON OF OPERATION: All year.

PHYSICAL ENVIRONMENT ACCESSIBLE: Oeresuend (the Sound), connecting the Baltic with the Kattegat and the North Sea; sandy and silty beaches, estuarine conditions, brackish, shallow bays, two-layered system in Oeresuend (brackish 1-15 m; normal oceanic salinity below to 45 m).

PROVISIONS FOR VISITING SCIENTISTS: Research and living space for 4-6 visitors in all months except June through August; fees charged for research space.

MAJOR RESEARCH AND TEACHING FACILITIES: Small, growing library; small aquarium tanks, a few large indoor tanks; research collections from the Oeresuend available at Universitets Zoologiske Museum, knowledgeable taxonomists available; small machine and wood shop, but better facilities available nearby; small boats, one 45 ft power vessel, *Ophelia;* specially built trawling, dredging and bottom sampling equipment.

INSTRUCTIONAL PROGRAM: Undergraduate summer courses in marine biology for students from Lund University (Sweden); graduate course in marine ecology each summer for students from Copenhagen University; special short courses in marine ecology for graduate students from all of Scandinavia.

SIZE OF STAFF: Four at professional level; 6 technicians.

IMPORTANT SPECIES AVAILABLE FOR LABORATORY STUDIES:

Mollusca: *Mytilis edulis, Cardium edule, Buccinum undatum*
Echinodermata: *Asterias rubens, Ophiocoma nigra, Psammechinus miliaris, Astropecten irregularis*
Polychaeta: *Terebellides stroemi*

Crustacea: *Eupagurus bernhardus, Nephrops norwegicus*

MAJOR CURRENT RESEARCH PROJECTS AND SCIENTIFIC LEADERS:

Balance between predators and prey animals on the sea bottom (G. Thorson)

Feeding ecology of sea stars (Aage Moeller Christensen)

Reproductive biology of lamellibranches (K. W. Ockelmann)

ECUADOR

Laboratories About Which No Detailed Information Was Available:

Ecuador Ministerio de Fomento, Departamento de Pesca, Escuela Politecnica Nacional, Quito, Ecuador.

Executive Officer: Professor Gustavo Orces Villagomez. A laboratory is planned, through funds from the FAO and the Ecuadorian government. Research collections of fauna and flora are accessible at the Escuela Politecnica Nacional. Identified reference collection of fishes is accessible in Quito.

EL SALVADOR

El Salvador Ministerio de Agricultura y Ganaderia, Centro Experimental Piscicola

EL SALVADOR MINISTRY OF AGRICULTURE AND LIVESTOCK, FISH CULTURE EXPERIMENT STATION

POSTAL ADDRESS: Santa Cruz Porrillo, El Salvador.

LOCATION: Near Zacatecoluca.

EXECUTIVE OFFICER: Carlos Alberto Fuentes, Director.

YEAR FOUNDED: 1958.

SCOPE OF ACTIVITIES: Unrestricted research on fish culture, limnology, and fresh-water biology.

SEASON OF OPERATION: All year.

PHYSICAL ENVIRONMENT ACCESSIBLE: Estuary Jiquilisco, Lagos (Lakes) de Ilopango, Olomega and Coatepeque; estuarine conditions, eutrophic and oligotrophic lakes, rivers, streams, and fish ponds.

PROVISIONS FOR VISITING SCIENTISTS: Research and living space for 1-2 visitors; no fees charged for research space.

MAJOR RESEARCH FACILITIES: No library at present; large outdoor ponds, small aquarium tanks; skilled shop workman available; small boats and outboard motors.

CENTRO EXPERIMENTAL PISCICOLA, SANTA CRUZ PORRILLO

SIZE OF STAFF: Three at professional level.

IMPORTANT SPECIES AVAILABLE FOR LABORATORY STUDIES:

Crustacea: *Potamocarcinus guatemalensis*

Pisces (fresh-water): *Cichlasoma managuense, C. dovii, C. guttulatum, Tilapia mossambica, Cyprinus carpio, Micropterus salmoides*

MAJOR CURRENT RESEARCH PROJECTS AND SCIENTIFIC LEADERS:

Carp reproduction in tropical waters (C. A. Fuentes)

Natural productivity of ponds in Porrillo (C. A. Fuentes)

Efficiency of chemical fertilizers in ponds (C. A. Fuentes)

Food efficiency in fish feeding (C. A. Fuentes)

Production experiments on various pond fishes (C. A. Fuentes)

Value of *Tilapia* to largemouth bass (C. A. Fuentes)

Experiments on association of species (C. A. Fuentes)

Production experiments on *Cichlosoma managuense* and *Tilapia* (C. A. Fuentes)

Monosexual culture experiment on *Cichlasoma* and *Tilapia* (C. A. Fuentes)

Life history of lake crab (Hector Hinds)

ETHIOPIA

University College of Addis Ababa

The University College of Addis Ababa is planning to open a field station located at Lake Awassa in October 1963. The site for the station was chosen because of its accessibility and its central location among the lakes of the Ethiopian Rift Valley. Inquiries may be addressed to Prof. J. T. Macfarlane, Dean, Faculty of Science, University College of Addis Ababa, P. O. Box 399, Addis Ababa, Ethiopia.

FEDERAL REPUBLIC OF GERMANY

Anstalt fuer Bodenseeforschung

LAKE CONSTANCE RESEARCH INSTITUTE

POSTAL ADDRESS: 56 Schiffstrasse, 775 Konstanz, Bundesrepublik Deutschland (West Germany).

EXECUTIVE OFFICER: Professor Dr. M. Auerbach, Direktor.

SPONSORING AGENCIES: City of Konstanz with aid of state.

YEAR FOUNDED: 1919.

SCOPE OF ACTIVITIES: Unrestricted limnological research of Lake Constance.

SEASON OF OPERATION: All year.

PHYSICAL ENVIRONMENT ACCESSIBLE: Bodensee (Lake Constance), Obersee (oligotrophic lake), and Untersee (eutrophic lake).

PROVISIONS FOR VISITING SCIENTISTS: Space for 1 visitor; no fees charged.

MAJOR RESEARCH FACILITIES: Library; small boats and outboard motors; vessels, 5 m and 17 m LOA power vessels, and a 6.5 m floating blind for ornithological observations.

SIZE OF STAFF: Five at professional level; 3 technicians.

MAJOR CURRENT RESEARCH PROJECTS AND SCIENTIFIC LEADERS:

- Permanent currents of the Rhine in Lake Constance (M. Auerbach)
- Distribution of water in the different parts of the Untersee (M. Auerbach)
- Ecological studies on the genus *Daphnia* (Crust. Cladoc.) (R. Muckle and G. Rottengatter)
- Internal seiches and temperature in the Uberlinger See (H. Lehn)

Universitaet Muenchen, Demoll-Hofer-Institut, Bayerische Biologische Versuchsanstalt

UNIVERSITY OF MUNICH, DEMOLL-HOFER INSTITUTE, BAVARIAN BIOLOGICAL TESTING STATION

POSTAL ADDRESS:

Headquarters: Kaulbachstrasse 37, Muenchen 22, Bundesrepublik Deutschland (Munich, West Germany).

Branches: Teichwirtschaftliche Abteilung, Wielenbach, Oberbayern. Abwasserversuchsfeld Grosslappen b. Muenchen.

EXECUTIVE OFFICER: Professor Dr. Hans Liebmann, Vorstand.

YEAR FOUNDED: 1900.

SCOPE OF ACTIVITIES: Officially restricted research on water pollution control; general fresh-water and waste water biology, ichthyology, bacteriology, fish diseases, fish pond culture.

SEASON OF OPERATION: All year.

PHYSICAL ENVIRONMENT ACCESSIBLE: Rivers Donau (Danube) and Main and tributaries, Lake Starnberg and other Upper Bavarian lakes (eutrophic and oligotrophic), streams, springs and fish ponds.

PROVISIONS FOR VISITING SCIENTISTS: Space for 2 visitors; living quarters available in Munich and at laboratory in Wielenbach.

MAJOR RESEARCH AND TEACHING FACILITIES: Moderately complete library; large outdoor ponds and tanks, small aquarium tanks; research collection of fish parasites; identified reference collections of local fish fauna and water organisms; skilled shop workman available; small boats and outboard motors.

INSTRUCTIONAL PROGRAM: General zoology, parasitology, hydrobiology, fish biology and fish diseases, chemistry of water and sewage treatment, and waste water biology.

SIZE OF STAFF: Seventeen at professional level; 32 technicians.

IMPORTANT SPECIES AVAILABLE FOR LABORATORY STUDIES:

Pisces: *Cyprinus carpio, Salmo irideus, S. trutta, S. fario, Tinca tinca, Salvelinus alpinus, Anguilla anguilla, Abramis brama, Lebistes reticulatus*

MAJOR CURRENT RESEARCH PROJECTS AND SCIENTIFIC LEADERS:

- Biological and chemical research on water quality in Bavarian lakes and rivers for a Bavarian Water Quality-Atlas
- Chemical research on industrial wastes, especially B.O.D. and population equivalent
- Self-purification of fresh-waters; chemical research on sludges and industrial wastes
- Bacteriological research on fish diseases; bacteriological research on polluted rivers

UNIVERSITAET MUENCHEN, BAYERISCHE BIOLOGISCHE VERSUCHSANSTALT

Electrophoretic research on blood-proteins in carp and trout
Research on the relations between the most important fish diseases; research on the special and quantitative composition of fish populations in Bavarian rivers and lakes
Research on fat and lipids in carp; histological research on the liver of carp and trout
Research on vitamin A and carotinoids in fish
Documentation of literature on waste waters
Control of radioactive substances in sewage and surface water of Bavaria
Biological radioactive contamination studies in the environments of an atomic reactor
Radiochemical analysis of dangerous radionuclides in sewage and surface water
Carp, tench and trout culture, fish feeding, nutrition, artificial breeding; diseases of pond fish; pond mansuring; relation of stocking to feeding

Biologische Anstalt Helgoland

HELGOLAND BIOLOGICAL STATION

POSTAL ADDRESS:
Headquarters (Zentrale und Verwaltung): Palmaille 9, Hamburg-Altona 1, Bundesrepublik (West Germany).
Branch laboratories:
1. Forschungsstation, Helgoland.
2. Wattenmeerstation, List auf Sylt.
(Descriptions follow.)

EXECUTIVE OFFICER: Prof. Dr. O. Kinne.
SPONSORING AGENCY: Bundesministerium fuer Ernaehrung, Landswirtschaft, und Forsten (Federal Ministry of Food, Agriculture and Forestry).
YEAR FOUNDED: 1892.
SIZE OF STAFF: Fourteen at professional level; 48 technicians.
PUBLICATIONS ISSUED: *Helgolaender Wissenschaftliche Meeresuntersuchungen*

Central Laboratory

SCOPE OF ACTIVITIES: Unrestricted research on fundamental and applied marine biology.
PROVISIONS FOR VISITING SCIENTISTS: Research space for 3 visitors.
MAJOR RESEARCH FACILITIES: Library; small aquarium tanks; machine and wood shop, skilled workmen available.

Helgoland

YEAR FOUNDED: 1892.
SCOPE OF ACTIVITIES: Research on general marine biology; graduate and undergraduate instruction.
SEASON OF OPERATION: All year.

BIOLOGISCHE ANSTALT HELGOLAND

PHYSICAL ENVIRONMENT ACCESSIBLE: North Sea; sandy and silty beaches, rocky and gravelly shores.
PROVISIONS FOR VISITING SCIENTISTS: Research and living space for 15 visitors; fees charged for research and living space.
MAJOR RESEARCH AND TEACHING FACILITIES: Moderately complete library; running sea water, outdoor ponds and tanks; identified reference collections of bivalves of the North Sea, algae herbarium, other groups in preparation; machine and wood shop, skilled shop workmen available; vessels, 24.5 m LOA, *Uthorn,* 10 m LOA, *Ellenbogen,* and 8 m LOA, *Gelk.*
INSTRUCTIONAL PROGRAM: General marine biology; ecology and physiology of marine organisms; comparative physiology and botany (algae).
IMPORTANT SPECIES AVAILABLE FOR STUDIES:
Algae: *Ectocarpus siliculosus, Chaetomorpha* spp.
Anthozoa: *Metridium senile*
Lamellibranchiata: *Spisula solida, Nucula nitida*
Gastropoda: *Buccinum undatum, Littorina nitida*
Crustacea: *Eupagurus bernhardus*
Asteroidea: *Asterias rubens*
Acrania: *Branchiostoma lanceolatum,* and many others.
MAJOR CURRENT RESEARCH PROJECTS AND SCIENTIFIC LEADERS:
Physiology and ecology of crustaceans and fishes (O. Kinne)
Development of hydroids (B. Werner)
Feeding habits of invertebrates (B. Werner)
Ecology of macrobenthos (E. Ziegelmeier)
Physiology of development of marine invertebrates (D. Uhlig)
Metabolism of marine invertebrates (F. Krueger)
Neurophysiology of the crustacean eye (H. Stieve)
Developmental cycles and ecology of marine algae (P. Kornmann)
Cell physiology in marine algae (H. Kesseler)
Ecology and metabolism of marine bacteria (W. Gunkel)
Zooplankton ecology (H. Aurich)

Phytoplankton, nutrients, dissolved organic substances (M. Gillbricht)
Fishery biology, redfish, plaice, herring (A. Kotthaus)
Fishery biology and ecology (F. W. Tesch)
Radiation biology (K. J. Gotting)

Wattenmeerstation

LOCATION: On the North Sea about 50 miles west of Flensburg.
YEAR FOUNDED: 1911.
SCOPE OF ACTIVITIES: Unrestricted research on ecology and general marine biology.
SEASON OF OPERATION: All year. Up to 1960 this laboratory was the main field research station; with the opening of the new main research laboratory on Helgoland, the Wattenmeerstation will be used mainly for studies on littoral forms.
PHYSICAL ENVIRONMENT ACCESSIBLE: North Sea, German shallows; sandy and silty beaches, polyhaline, brackish, shallow bays.

BIOLOGISCHE ANSTALT HELGOLAND, WATTENMEERSTATION

PROVISIONS FOR VISITING SCIENTISTS: Space for 6 visitors; living available nearby.
MAJOR RESEARCH FACILITIES: Running seawater; small boats and outboard motors. All other facilities available at the headquarters in Hamburg.
IMPORTANT SPECIES AVAILABLE FOR LABCRATORY STUDIES:
Scyphozoa: *Cyanea lamarckii*
Lamellibranchiata: *Mya arenaria, Mytilus edulis*
Gastropoda: *Crepidula fornicata*
Polychaeta: *Lanice conchilega, Arenicola marina*
Crustacea: *Carcinus maenas*
Echinoidea: *Psammechinus miliaris*
Pisces: *Pleuronectes platessa, Ammodytes* spp., and many others.

Bundesanstalt fuer Gewaesserkunde

FEDERAL INSTITUTE FOR HYDROLOGY

POSTAL ADDRESS: Kaiserin-Augusta-Anlagen 15, Koblenz, Bundesrepublik Deutschland (West Germany).
LOCATION: On Rhine River.
EXECUTIVE OFFICER: Dr. Herbert Knoepp, Dipl.-Biol., Referent fuer Hydrobiologie und Fischereibiologie.
SPONSORING AGENCY: Bundesministerium fuer Verkehr (Ministry of Traffic, German Federal Republic).
YEAR BIOLOGICAL LABORATORY FOUNDED: 1952.
SCOPE OF ACTIVITIES: Unrestricted research on ecology, water pollution and fisheries of West German waterways; restricted research on the physical, chemical and biological hydrology of West German waterways.
SEASON OF OPERATION: All year.
PHYSICAL ENVIRONMENT ACCESSIBLE: Rhein (Rhine River) and impounded streams.
PROVISIONS FOR VISITING SCIENTISTS: Space for 1-2 visitors; no fees charged; living quarters available nearby.
MAJOR RESEARCH AND TEACHING FACILITIES: Very extensive library; small aquarium tanks; small identified reference collections from saprobic system of Kolkwitz and Marsson; vessels of the West German Administration available.
INSTRUCTIONAL PROGRAM: Courses for engineers of the West German Administration for waterways on water pollution control and fisheries.
SIZE OF STAFF IN THE BIOLOGICAL LABORATORY: Two at professional level; 2 technicians.
MAJOR CURRENT RESEARCH PROJECTS AND SCIENTIFIC LEADERS:
Investigations on oxygen balance of free and impounded streams (Herbert Knoepp)
Factors affecting the oxygen balance of polluted streams (Herbert Knoepp)
Toxicology of industrial wastes (Herbert Knoepp)
PUBLICATIONS ISSUED:
Deutsche Gewaesserkundliche Mitteilungen (regularly published journal)
Besondere Mitteilungen zum Deutschen Gewaesserkundlichen Jahrbuch (occasionally published journal)

Bundesforschungsanstalt fuer Fischerei

FEDERAL INSTITUTION FOR FISHERY RESEARCH

The Bundesforschungsanstalt fuer Fischerei has four subordinate institutes in its organization, and each institute performs research in a particular field of the total fishery program. The four institutes are:

1. Institut fuer Fischverarbeitung (not described in the *Directory*)
2. Institut fuer Kuesten- und Binnenfischerei
3. Institut fuer Netz- und Materialforschung

BUNDESFORSCHUNGSANSTALT FUER FISCHEREI, HAMBURG

4. Institut fuer Seefischerei
(Descriptions follow.)

The Bundesforschungsanstalt fuer Fischerei is sponsored by the Bundesministerium fuer Ernaehrung, Landwirtschaft und Forsten (Ministry for Food, Agriculture and Forests).

Institut fuer Kuesten- und Binnenfischerei

INSTITUTE FOR COASTAL AND INLAND FISHERIES

POSTAL ADDRESS:
Headquarters: Palmaille 9, Hamburg-Altona, Bundesrepublik Deutschland (West Germany).
Field Station: An der Alten Liebe 1, Cuxhaven.

EXECUTIVE OFFICE: Professor Dr. Paul-Friedrich Meyer-Waarden, Direktor.

YEAR FOUNDED: Headquarters in 1890; Cuxhaven in 1932.

SCOPE OF ACTIVITIES: Officially restricted research on the biology and fishery economics of coastal and inland fisheries, fouling, and marine borers.

SEASON OF OPERATION: All year.

PHYSICAL ENVIRONMENT ACCESSIBLE: North and Baltic Seas, the Elbe River and estuary brackish, shallow bays, rivers and streams.

PROVISIONS FOR VISITING SCIENTISTS: Research space for 6 visitors at headquarters; 2 visitors at Cuxhaven; no fees charged.

MAJOR RESEARCH FACILITIES: Small library; running sea and fresh-water, small aquarium tanks; machine and wood shop; vessels of the Fishery Protection available.

SIZE OF STAFF:
Headquarters: Five at professional level; 6 technicians.
Cuxhaven: Two at professional level; 3 technicians.

IMPORTANT SPECIES AVAILABLE FOR LABORATORY STUDIES:
Crustacea: *Crangon vulgaris, Eriocheir sinensis,* cladocerans
Mollusca: *Mytilus edulis*
Annelida: Tubificidae
Salmonidae: *Trutta iridea*

MAJOR CURRENT RESEARCH PROJECTS AND SCIENTIFIC LEADERS:
Expansion of the German mussel fishery (Paul-Friedrich Meyer-Waarden)
Expansion of the German bluefin tuna fishery, herring fishery for high sea cutters and coastal cutters (Paul-Friedrich Meyer-Waarden and K. Tiews)
Assessment of by-catches of undersized protected fish in the German oilherring, and sand eel fishery (H. Kuehl); as well as in the shrimp fishery (K. Tiews)
Research into the biotic and abiotic factors responsible for the fluctuation of the German shrimp fishery (Paul-Friedrich Meyer-Waarden, H. Kuehl, and K. Tiews)
Research into the biological and hydrographic properties of the estuaries of the Rivers; Elbe, Weser, and Ems (H. Mann and H. Kuehl)
Stock assessment of fish populations in the Elbe River with special reference to eels (H. Mann)
Investigation of water pollution by oil and detergents (H. Mann)

INSTITUT FUER KUESTEN- UND BINNENFISCHEREI, CUXHAVEN STATION

Fundamental research on the behavior of fish in electrical fields and development of electrical fishing gear (E. Halsband)
Ecology of barnacles; fouling of ships (H. Kuehl)
Migrations of shrimps (H. Kuehl)
Estuarine biology (H. Kuehl and H. Mann)
Fat metabolism of fishes and crustaceans (Herr Luhmann)

Institut fuer Netz- und Materialforschung

INSTITUTE FOR NETS AND GEAR INVESTIGATION

POSTAL ADDRESS: Palmaille 9, Hamburg-Altona, Bundesrepublik Deutschland (West Germany).

EXECUTIVE OFFICER: Professor Dr. A. v. Brandt, Direktor.

YEAR FOUNDED: 1936.

SCOPE OF ACTIVITIES: Fishing gear, fishing methods, detection and behavior of fish, and underwater acoustics.

SEASON OF OPERATION: All year.

PHYSICAL ENVIRONMENT ACCESSIBLE: North and Baltic Seas; estuarine conditions, brackish, shallow bays, eutrophic and oligotrophic lakes, rivers and streams.

PROVISIONS FOR VISITING SCIENTISTS: Research space for 1-2 visitors; no fees charged; living quarters available nearby.

MAJOR RESEARCH FACILITIES: Small library; small aquarium tanks; skilled shop workman available; small boats and outboard motors.

SIZE OF STAFF: Six at professional level; 5-7 technicians.

MAJOR CURRENT RESEARCH PROJECTS AND SCIENTIFIC LEADERS:

- Net materials:
  - Qualities (Dr. Klust)
  - Test methods (Prof. v. Brandt)
- Knotless nets (Prof. v. Brandt)
- Net preparation (Prof. v. Brandt)
- Fishing gear and methods in general (Prof. v. Brandt)
  - Midwater trawls (Dr. Schaerfe)
  - Midwater trawls in small boats (Dr. Steinberg)
  - Gillnets (Dr. Mohr)
  - Mesh measurement (Dr. Bohl)
  - Gear selection (Dr. Bohl)
  - Stow nets (Dr. Klust)
- Behavior of fish to fishing gear (Dr. Mohr)
- Fish detection:
  - Echosounding and echoranging (Dr. Schaerfe)
  - Underwater acoustics (Dr. Freytag)

PUBLICATIONS ISSUED: *Protokolle zur Fischereitechnik* (occasionally published journal)

Institut fuer Seefischerei

INSTITUTE FOR SEA FISHERIES

POSTAL ADDRESS:

Headquarters: Palmaille 9, Hamburg-Altona, Bundesrepublik (West Germany).

Branch Laboratory: F.A. -Pust Platz, Aussenstelle Bremerhaven, Bremerhaven 4.

EXECUTIVE OFFICER: Professor Dr. Johanes Lundbeck, Direktor.

YEAR FOUNDED: 1910.

SCOPE OF ACTIVITIES: Officially restricted research and advisory assistance concerning deep sea fisheries.

SEASON OF OPERATION: All year.

PHYSICAL ENVIRONMENT ACCESSIBLE: North Sea and North Atlantic Ocean.

PROVISIONS FOR VISITING SCIENTISTS: None.

MAJOR RESEARCH FACILITIES: Very extensive library; one 63 m LOA vessel (under administration of the Ministerium).

SIZE OF STAFF: Nine at professional level; 14 technicians.

MAJOR CURRENT RESEARCH PROJECTS AND SCIENTIFIC LEADERS:

- Biology of North Sea herring (Kurt Schubert)
- Ichthyology (Gerhard Krefft)
- Cod fishery of North Atlantic (Arno Meyer)
- Biology of the coalfish (Ulrich Schmidt)
- Population dynamics of commercial fish stocks (Dietrich Sahrhage)

PUBLICATIONS ISSUED: *Mitteilungen aus dem Institut fuer Seefischerei* (occasionally published journal)

Senckenbergische Naturforschende Gesellschaft, Forschungsanstalt fuer Meeresgeologie und -Biologie "Senckenberg"

SENCKENBERG ASSOCIATION FOR SCIENTIFIC RESEARCH, "SENCKENBERG" INSTITUTE FOR MARINE GEOLOGY AND BIOLOGY

POSTAL ADDRESS: Schleuseninsel 10, Wilhelmshaven, Bundesrepublik Deutschland (West Germany).

EXECUTIVE OFFICER: Dr. H. E. Reinem.

YEAR FOUNDED: 1928.

SCOPE OF ACTIVITIES: Restricted research on general marine biology and geology, bottom ecology, functional morphology and marine sediments; instruction.

SEASON OF OPERATION: All year.

PHYSICAL ENVIRONMENT ACCESSIBLE: Deutsche Bucht; sandy and silty beaches, rocky and gravelly shores, estuarine conditions, brackish, shallow bays, tidal flats.

PROVISIONS FOR VISITING SCIENTISTS: Space for 4 visitors; living quarters available for 2 at the Institute, other quarters available nearby.

SENCKENBERGISCHE NATURFORSCHENDE GESELLSCHAFT, FORSCHUNGSANSTALT FUER MEERESGEOLOGIE UND -BIOLOGIE "SENCKENBERG"

MAJOR RESEARCH AND TEACHING FACILITIES: Small library; small aquarium tanks; research collections of local fauna and flora available at the Forschungsinstitut und Museum Senckenberg in Frankfurt am Main; machine and wood shop, skilled shop workman available; one 24 m LOA vessel.

INSTRUCTIONAL PROGRAM: Structure of marine sediments, ecology of bottom fauna, comparative functional morphology.

MAJOR CURRENT RESEARCH PROJECTS AND SCIENTIFIC LEADERS:

Structure of marine sediments (Hans-Erich Reineck)
Functional morphology (Wolfgang Gutmann)
Ecology of foraminiferans (Gotthard Richter)
Marine ecology (invertebrates) (Wilhelm Schafer)

PUBLICATIONS ISSUED:

Senckenbergiana lethaea (regularly published journal)
Natur und Museum, Bericht Senc. Naturf. Ges. (occasionally published journal)

Forschungstelle Norderney

NORDERNEY RESEARCH STATION

POSTAL ADDRESS: An der Muhle 5, Norderney, Bundesrepublik Deutschland (West Germany).

LOCATION: Friesian Islands (near Wilhelmshaven).

EXECUTIVE OFFICERS: J. Kramer, Leiter und Regierungsbaurat. Dr. C. D. Miller, Abteilungsleiter fuer Biologie und Bodenkulture (in charge, biology and soil science).

SPONSORING AGENCY: Landesregierung Niedersaechsen (State of Lower Saxony).

YEAR FOUNDED: 1937.

SCOPE OF AQUATIC ACTIVITIES: Restricted research on hydrology, geology and biology of shallow coastal waters.

SEASON OF OPERATION: All year.

PHYSICAL ENVIRONMENT ACCESSIBLE: North Sea; sandy and silty beaches, estuarine conditions, brackish, shallow bays.

PROVISIONS FOR VISITING SCIENTISTS: Space for 2 visitors; no fees charged; living quarters available nearby.

MAJOR RESEARCH FACILITIES: Small library; running fresh-water, small aquarium tanks; machine and wood shop, electrical and electronic shop, skilled shop workman available; small boats and outboard motors; three 20 m LOA power vessels.

SIZE OF STAFF: Three at professional level; 6 technicians.

IMPORTANT SPECIES AVAILABLE FOR LABORATORY STUDIES:

Polychaeta: *Arenicola marina, Lanice conchilega*
Lamellibranchiata: *Mytilus edulis, Mya arenaria, Teredo navalis*
Crustacea: *Carcinus maenas, Cancer pagurus*
Echinodermata: *Psammechinus miliaris, Asterias rubens*

FORSCHUNGSTELLE NORDERNEY

Pisces: *Pleuronectes,* sp.

MAJOR CURRENT RESEARCH PROJECTS AND SCIENTIFIC LEADERS:

Relationship of shoal fauna to sediments (C. Muller)
Significance of biological processes in coastal protection (C. Muller)
Preservation and habilitation of fauna of the eastern islands (J. Kramer)

PUBLICATIONS ISSUED: *Jahresbericht der Forschungsstelle Norderney* (regularly published journal)

Hydrobiologische Station des Bundes fuer Naturschutz

HYDROBIOLOGICAL STATION OF THE COUNCIL FOR NATURE CONSERVATION

POSTAL ADDRESS: Seeon, Chiemgau, Oberbayern, Bundesrepublik Deutschland (West Germany).

EXECUTIVE OFFICER: Professor Dr. F. Gessner, Leiter.

SPONSORING AGENCY: Privately owned station.

SCOPE OF ACTIVITIES: Unrestricted research on general limnology.

SEASON OF OPERATION: All year.

PHYSICAL ENVIRONMENT ACCESSIBLE: Chiemsee; eutrophic and oligotrophic lakes, rivers and streams.

PROVISIONS FOR VISITING SCIENTISTS: None.

MAJOR RESEARCH FACILITIES: Small library; small boats and outboard motors.

Institut fuer Seenforschung und Seenbewirtschaftung

INSTITUTE FOR INVESTIGATION AND MANAGEMENT OF LAKES

POSTAL ADDRESS: Untere Seestrasse 81, Langenargen/Bodensee, Bundesrepublik Deutschland (West Germany).

EXECUTIVE OFFICER: Dr. Wilhelm Nuemann, Director.

SPONSORING AGENCY: Verein der Freunde des Institut fuer Seenforschung und Seenbewirtschaftung (Society of Friends of the Institute for Investigation and Management of Lakes).

YEAR FOUNDED: 1920.

SCOPE OF ACTIVITIES: Unrestricted research on limnology, fishery biology, fish pathology, and purity of running water.

SEASON OF OPERATION: All year.

PHYSICAL ENVIRONMENT ACCESSIBLE: Bodensee (Lake Constance), eutrophic and oligotrophic lakes, rivers and streams, and fish ponds.

PROVISIONS FOR VISITING SCIENTISTS: Space for 4-5 visitors; fees charged; living quarters available nearby.

INSTITUT FUER SEENFORSCHUNG UND SEENBEWIRTSCHAFTUNG

MAJOR RESEARCH FACILITIES: Small library; 4 large outdoor ponds, small aquarium tanks; small boat with outboard motor; vessels, 9 m and 14 m LOA.

SIZE OF STAFF: Five at professional level; 6 technicians.

IMPORTANT SPECIES AVAILABLE FOR LABORATORY STUDIES:

Pisces: *Coregonus* spp., *Esox, Perca, Lucioperca, Salmo* spp.

MAJOR CURRENT RESEARCH PROJECTS AND SCIENTIFIC LEADERS:

Fishery biology, especially coregonids (Wilhelm Numann)

Hydrobiology (bottom fauna, ecology) (Rudolf Zahner)

Water bacteriology and fish pathology (Josef Deufel)

Hydrochemistry: metabolism of nutrient salts, polution-water (Werner Voss and Gustav Wagner)

Limnologisches Institut der Universitaet Freiburg i. Br. (Walter-Schlienz-Institut)

LIMNOLOGICAL INSTITUTE OF THE UNIVERSITY OF FREIBURG (WALTER-SCHLIENZ-INSTITUT)

POSTAL ADDRESS: (17b) Falkau/Schwarzwald, Bundesrepublik Deutschland (West Germany).

LOCATION: Near Freiburg/Baden.

EXECUTIVE OFFICER: Professor Dr. Hans-Joachim Elster, Leiter.

SPONSORING AGENCIES: Universitaet Freiburg.

YEAR FOUNDED: 1947.

SCOPE OF ACTIVITIES: Unrestricted research on general limnology and hydrobiology, metabolism of fresh- and brackish-waters, fisheries biology; graduate and undergraduate instruction.

SEASON OF OPERATION: All year.

PHYSICAL ENVIRONMENT ACCESSIBLE: Lakes Schluchsee, Titisee, Windgefaellweiher, Feldsee, Ursee, Haslach (brook), Rivers Wutach and Donau (Danube); eutrophic, oligotrophic lakes and dystrophic lakes.

PROVISIONS FOR VISITING SCIENTISTS: Space for 2 (later, more) visitors; no fees charged; living quarters available nearby.

MAJOR RESEARCH AND TEACHING FACILITIES: Small library; small aquarium tanks; research collection of plankton and bottom fauna; identified reference collections of Hydracarina, some groups of chironomids, Plecoptera, etc.; small boats and outboard motors.

INSTRUCTIONAL PROGRAM: Limnology, systematics and biology of fresh-water organisms, and fisheries biology.

SIZE OF STAFF: Five at professional level; 6 technicians.

IMPORTANT SPECIES AVAILABLE FOR LABORATORY STUDIES:

Crustacea: *Holopedium gibberum, Mixodiaptomus laciniatus, Acanthodiaptomus denticornis, Heterocope saliens*

Insecta: *Sergentia* spp.

HYDROBIOLOGISCHE STATION, FALKAU/SCHWARZWALD

MAJOR CURRENT RESEARCH PROJECTS AND SCIENTIFIC LEADERS:
Metabolism of organic substances (H. Krause)
Limnology of dam-reservoirs (Hans Elster)
Biology of underground water (J. Schwoerbel)
Population dynamics of zooplankton (Hans Elster)
Physiology of zooplankton (R. Schroeder)
Fisheries biology of the Black Forest's waters (Hans Elster)
Systematics and biology of chironomids (W. Wuelker)
PUBLICATIONS ISSUED: *Falkau-Schriften* (supplement of *Archiv fuer Hydrobiologie*)

Max Planck Gesellschaft zur Foerderung der Wissenschaften, Hydrobiologische Anstalt

MAX PLANCK SOCIETY FOR THE PROMOTION OF THE SCIENCES, HYDROBIOLOGICAL INSTITUTE

POSTAL ADDRESS:
Headquarters: Hydrobiologische Anstalt (Hydrobiological Institute) August Thienemannstrasse Ploen/Holstein, Bundesrepublik Deutschland (West Germany)
Branch laboratories:
1. Limnologische Station Niederrhein
2. Limnologische Flusstation Schlitz
(Descriptions follow.)
EXECUTIVE OFFICER: Professor Dr. Harold Sioli, Geschaeftsfuehrender Direktor.

Hydrobiologische Anstalt

HYDROBIOLOGICAL INSTITUTE

LOCATION: Southeast of Kiel.
YEAR FOUNDED: 1892.
SCOPE OF ACTIVITIES: Unrestricted research on general limnology.
SEASON OF OPERATION: All year.
PHYSICAL ENVIRONMENT ACCESSIBLE: Grosser Ploener See, Schoehsee, and many other eutrophic lakes in the Holsteinian lowlands.
PROVISIONS FOR VISITING SCIENTISTS: Space for 6 visitors; no fees charged; living quarters for 2 at the institute, other quarters available nearby.
MAJOR RESEARCH FACILITIES: Very extensive library; large outdoor ponds and tanks, small aquarium tanks; research collections of Plecoptera and Chironomidae; machine and wood shop, electrical and electronic shop, skilled shop workman available; small boats and outboard motors.
SIZE OF STAFF: Eleven at professional level; 10 technicians.
MAJOR CURRENT RESEARCH PROJECTS AND SCIENTIFIC LEADERS:
Relations between soils and waters; soil research (Hans Klinge)
Biology of running waters; taxonomy, ecology and biogeography of Plecoptera (Joachim Illies)

HYDROBIOLOGISCHE ANSTALT DER MAX PLANCK GESELLSCHAFT ZUR FOERDERUNG DER WISSENSCHAFTEN

Bog research; rhizopod analysis of peat (Theodor Grospietsch)
Taxonomy and ecology of Chironomidae (Ernst-Josef Fittkau)
Limnological landscape ecology; limnology of the Brazilian Amazon region (Harald Sioli)
Climatology in lake research (Albrecht Vaupel)
Production biology and chemistry of lakes; regional limnology; metabolism of sediments and bioactivity of water bodies (Waldemar Ohle)
Microbiology of lakes and ponds; physiology and taxonomy of bacteria (Jurgen Overbeck)
Algae research in lakes, springs and soils; importance of trace elements (Gerhard-Helmut Schwabe)
Pure cultures of phytoplankton; nutrition problems (Eva-Maria Bursche)

Limnologische Station Niederrhein

LIMNOLOGICAL STATION OF THE LOWER RHINE

POSTAL ADDRESS: Am Waldwinkel 70, 415 Krefeld-Huelserberg Bundesrepublik Deutschland (West Germany).
EXECUTIVE OFFICER: N.N., z. Zt. Dr. H. V. Herbst.
YEAR FOUNDED: 1928.
SCOPE OF ACTIVITIES: Restricted research on theoretical and general limnology.
SEASON OF OPERATION: All year.
PHYSICAL ENVIRONMENT ACCESSIBLE: Rhine River and tributaries, eutrophic lakes, artificial waters.
PROVISIONS FOR VISITING SCIENTISTS: None.
MAJOR RESEARCH FACILITIES: Small library; small boats and outboard motors.
SIZE OF STAFF: One at professional level; 4 assistants.
MAJOR CURRENT RESEARCH PROJECTS AND SCIENTIFIC LEADERS:
General theoretical limnology, Zooplankton investigations; systematics, ecology and geographical distri-

LIMNOLOGISCHE STATION NIEDERRHEIN IN DER MAX PLANCK GESELLSCHAFT

bution of Crustacea (Entomostraca) (Hans Herbst)
Systematics, ecology, and geographical distribution of Ephemeroptera, Plecoptera and Trichoptera (Ingrid Mueller-Liebenau)
Theoretical and applied ecology of limnic macrophyta (Kathe Seidel)

PUBLICATIONS ISSUED: *Gewasser und Abwasser* (regularly published journal)

Limnologische Flusstation Schlitz

SCHLITZ INSTITUTE OF RIVER LIMNOLOGY

POSTAL ADDRESS: Steinweg 21, Schlitz/Hessen Bundesrepublik Deutschland (West Germany)

LOCATION: Near Frankfurt am Main.

EXECUTIVE OFFICER: Dr. Karl Mueller, Leiter.

YEAR FOUNDED: 1950.

SCOPE OF ACTIVITIES: Research on river biology, especially migration of organisms.

SEASON OF OPERATION: All year.

PHYSICAL ENVIRONMENT ACCESSIBLE: Weser River and tributary streams.

PROVISIONS FOR VISITING SCIENTISTS: Space available for 2 visitors; no fees charged; living quarters available nearby.

MAJOR RESEARCH AND TEACHING FACILITIES: Small library; large outdoor ponds and tanks, small aquarium tanks; machine and wood shop, electrical shop, skilled shop workman available; small boats and outboard motors.

INSTRUCTIONAL PROGRAM: Occasional courses in freshwater invertebrates and fishes.

SIZE OF STAFF: Four at professional level; 7 technicians.

IMPORTANT SPECIES AVAILABLE FOR LABORATORY STUDIES:
Crustacea: *Niphargus puteanus, Gammarus tigrinus*
Insecta: Polycentropidae, Hydropsychidae (Trichoptera), Baetidae (Ephemeroptara)
Polychaeta: *Troglochaetus beranecki*
Acanthocephala: Echinorhynchidae
Mollusca: *Neritina fluviatilis, Potamopyrgus jenkinsi*

MAJOR CURRENT RESEARCH PROJECTS AND SCIENTIFIC LEADERS:
Systematics and ecology of groundwater fauna (S. Husmann)
Ecological and physiological studies on aquatic insect larvae (W. Sattler)
The biology of regulated running water (K. Mueller)
Experimental ecology (K. Mueller)
Causes of aggregations of unicellular algae (A. Mueller-Haeckel)

Max Planck Gesellschaft zur Foerderung der Wissenschaften, Max Planck Institut fuer Meeresbiologie

MAX PLANCK SOCIETY FOR THE PROMOTION OF THE SCIENCES, MAX PLANCK INSTITUTE FOR MARINE BIOLOGY

POSTAL ADDRESS: Anton Dohrn Weg, Wilhelmshaven, Deutsche Bundesrepublik (West Germany).

EXECUTIVE OFFICER: Professor Dr. Joachim Haemmerling, Direktor.

YEAR FOUNDED: 1947.

SCOPE OF ACTIVITIES: Unrestricted research on general biology, particularly cellular and nuclear physiology, cytogenetics.

SEASON OF OPERATION: All year.

PHYSICAL ENVIRONMENT ACCESSIBLE: Jadebusen (Jade Bay) and North Sea; sandy and silty beaches, estuarine conditions.

PROVISIONS FOR VISITING SCIENTISTS: Research and living space for 4-6 visitors; no fees charged for research space.

MAJOR RESEARCH FACILITIES: Medium library; sea water in carboys; machine and wood shop, skilled shop workmen available.

LIMNOLOGISCHE FLUSSTATION SCHLITZ DER MAX PLANCK GESELLSCHAFT

MAX PLANCK INSTITUT FUER MEERESBIOLOGIE

SIZE OF STAFF: Sixteen at professional level; 17 technicians.

MAJOR CURRENT RESEARCH PROJECTS AND SCIENTIFIC LEADERS:

Nucleo-cytoplasmic relationships, especially on *Acetabularia* and other cells (Joachim Haemmerling)

Morphology and physiology of chromosomes, especially giant chromosomes; physiology of mitosis and meiosis; cytological mechanism of sex determination (Hans Bauer)

Niedersaechsisches Institut fuer Binnenfischerei

FRESH-WATER FISHERIES STATION OF LOWER SAXONY

POSTAL ADDRESS: Lavesstrasse 79, Hannover, Bundesrepublik Deutschland (Hanover, West Germany).

EXECUTIVE OFFICER: Professor Dr. Friedrich Schiemenz, Direktor.

SPONSORING AGENCY: Niedersaechsisches Ministerium fuer Ernaehrung, Landwirtschaft und Forsten (Lower Saxony Ministry of Food, Agriculture and Forestry).

YEAR FOUNDED: 1951.

SCOPE OF ACTIVITIES: Unrestricted research on fishery biology and technology.

SEASON OF OPERATION: All year.

PHYSICAL ENVIRONMENT ACCESSIBLE: Large rivers, brooks, lakes and canals of Lower Saxony.

PROVISIONS FOR VISITING SCIENTISTS: Space for 1-2 visitors; no fees charged.

MAJOR RESEARCH FACILITIES: Small library; small aquarium tanks.

SIZE OF STAFF: One at professional level; 2 technicians.

MAJOR CURRENT RESEARCH PROJECTS AND SCIENTIFIC LEADERS:

Planting of submerged plants (Friedrich Schiemenz)

Providing shelters for submerged fauna in regulated rivers and in sewage oxidation fish ponds (Friedrich Schiemenz)

Improvement of fish-passes (Friedrich Schiemenz)

Senator fuer das Bildungswesen des Landes Bremen, Institut fuer Meeresforschung

COUNCIL FOR THE DEVELOPMENT OF BREMEN LANDS, THE INSTITUTE FOR MARINE RESEARCH

POSTAL ADDRESS: Handelshafen 12, Bremerhaven G, Bundesrepublik Deutschland (West Germany).

EXECUTIVE OFFICER: Dr. W. Hoehnk, Direktor.

YEAR FOUNDED: 1919.

SCOPE OF ACTIVITIES: Unrestricted research on general marine biology, marine mycology, hydrography of estuaries, ichthyology, chemistry and bacteriology of fish and fish products.

SEASON OF OPERATION: All year.

PHYSICAL ENVIRONMENT ACCESSIBLE: Weser River and estuary, North Sea; sandy and silty beaches, estuarine conditions.

PROVISIONS FOR VISITING SCIENTISTS: Research space for 2 visitors; no fees charged.

MAJOR RESEARCH FACILITIES: Small library; small machine and wood shop; 50 ft diesel powered trawler.

SIZE OF STAFF: Six at professional level; 14 technicians.

IMPORTANT SPECIES AVAILABLE FOR LABORATORY STUDIES:

Crustacea: *Crangon, Mysis, Portunus, Carcinus, Eriocheir*

Pelycopoda: *Mya, Macoma, Cardium, Mytilus*

Polychaeta: Many species

MAJOR CURRENT RESEARCH PROJECTS AND SCIENTIFIC LEADERS:

Distribution, ecology and taxonomy of marine fungi (W. Hoehnk)

Morphology and ecology of fish (G. v. Wahlert)

Morphology and systematics of nemertines (H. Friedrich)

Sedimentation and erosion in the estuary (H. Lueneburg)

Chemistry of fresh fish and fish products (R. Dietrich)

Bacteriology of canned fish (V. Meyer)

PUBLICATIONS ISSUED: *Veroeffentlichungen des Instituts fur Meeresforschung in Bremerhaven* (regularly published journal)

Universitaet Erlangen, Zoologischen Institut, Teichwirtschaftliche Untersuchhungsstelle

UNIVERSITY OF ERLANGEN, ZOOLOGICAL INSTITUTE, DEPARTMENT OF FISHFARMS

POSTAL ADDRESS: Universitaetstrasse 19, Erlangen, Bundesrepublik Deutschland (West Germany).

EXECUTIVE OFFICER: Professor Dr. Wilhelm Wunder, Leiter.

YEAR FOUNDED: 1949.

SCOPE OF ACTIVITIES: Research on fresh-water fish and the hydrobiology of fish farms (primarily carp production).

SEASON OF OPERATION: All year.
PHYSICAL ENVIRONMENT ACCESSIBLE: Fish ponds and fish farms.
MAJOR RESEARCH FACILITIES: Small library; large fish ponds, small aquarium tanks; research collections of the fauna and flora of the fish farms in Germany.
SIZE OF STAFF: One at professional level; 1 technician.
IMPORTANT SPECIES AVAILABLE FOR LABORATORY STUDIES:
Pisces: *Cyprinus carpio, Tinga vulgaris, Esox lucius*
Insecta: Chironomidae
MAJOR CURRENT RESEARCH PROJECTS AND SCIENTIFIC LEADERS:
Shore fauna in fish ponds (Wilhelm Wunder)
Bottom fauna in fish ponds (Wilhelm Wunder)
Histological investigations of the carp (Wilhelm Wunder)

Universitaet Hamburg, Institut fuer Hydrobiologie und Fischerei-Wissenschaft

UNIVERSITY OF HAMBURG, INSTITUTE FOR HYDROBIOLOGY AND FISHERIES SCIENCE

POSTAL ADDRESS: Olbersweg, Hamburg-Altona, Bundesrepublik Deutschland (West Germany).
EXECUTIVE OFFICER: Professor Dr. Adolf Bueckmann, Direktor.
YEAR FOUNDED: 1947.
SCOPE OF ACTIVITIES: Unrestricted research on fishery biology and marine hydrobiology; graduate and undergraduate instruction.
SEASON OF OPERATION: All year.
PHYSICAL ENVIRONMENT ACCESSIBLE: River Elbe, estuarine conditions, and eutrophic lake.
PROVISIONS FOR VISITING SCIENTISTS: Space for 1 visitor; no fees charged; living quarters available nearby.
MAJOR RESEARCH AND TEACHING FACILITIES: Moderately complete library; running well water, running artificial sea water if required, small aquarium tanks; research collections of food fish for teaching purposes only; machine and wood shop; small rubber boat, 7 m LOA motor boat available from Direktor of Fisheries, Hamburg.
INSTRUCTIONAL PROGRAM: General fishery biology, advanced marine and fresh-water fishery biology, pond culture, fish diseases, physiology and behavior of fishes, waste water problems, fishing gear, fishery economics, biometry; marine hydrobiology.
SIZE OF STAFF: Four at professional level; 2 technicians.
IMPORTANT SPECIES AVAILABLE FOR LABORATORY STUDIES:
Crustacea: *Eriocheir sinensis, Eurytemora affinis*
Pisces: *Anguilla vulgaris, Osmerus eperlanus, Salmo gairdneri, Alosa fallax, Lota lota, Leuciscus rutilus, Abramis brama*
MAJOR CURRENT RESEARCH PROJECTS AND SCIENTIFIC LEADERS:
Methodology of fishery biology (Dr. Bueckmann)
Elbe fisheries and damming (Dr. Lillelund)
Maternal effects and survival in herring larvae (Dr. Hempel)
Behavior in herring larvae (Dr. Bueckmann)
PUBLICATIONS ISSUED: *Kurze Mitteilungen aus dem Institut fuer Fischereibiologie der Universitaet Hamburg* (occasionally published journal)

Universitaet Hamburg, Zoologischen Staatsinstitut und Museum, Hydrobiologische Abteilung

UNIVERSITY OF HAMBURG, ZOOLOGICAL INSTITUTE AND MUSEUM, DIVISION OF HYDROBIOLOGY

POSTAL ADDRESS: Von Melle-Park, Hamburg 13, Bundesrepublik Deutschland (West Germany).
EXECUTIVE OFFICER: Professor Dr. Hubert Caspers, Leiter.
YEAR FOUNDED: 1919.
SCOPE OF ACTIVITIES: Unrestricted research on fresh- and brackish water and marine ecology; graduate and undergraduate instruction.
SEASON OF OPERATION: All year.
PHYSICAL ENVIRONMENT ACCESSIBLE: Elbe River; estuarine conditions, eutrophic lake.
PROVISIONS FOR VISITING SCIENTISTS: Research and living space for 2 visitors; no fees charged for research space.
MAJOR RESEARCH AND TEACHING FACILITIES: Small library; small aquarium tanks; research collections of fauna and flora available at the Museum.
INSTRUCTIONAL PROGRAM: Limnology, marine biology and aquatic invertebrates.
SIZE OF STAFF: Two at professional level; 1 technician.
IMPORTANT SPECIES AVAILABLE FOR LABORATORY STUDIES:
Oligochaeta: Tubificidae
Insecta: *Clunio* (Chironomidae)
MAJOR CURRENT RESEARCH PROJECTS AND SCIENTIFIC LEADERS:
Ecology of the Elbe estuary (Hubert Caspers)
Systematics and ecology of Tubificidae (Michael Dzwillo)
Comparative ecology of harbors (Hubert Caspers)
Biology of marine chironomids (Hubert Caspers)

Universitaet Kiel, Institut fuer Meereskunde

UNIVERSITY OF KIEL, INSTITUTE FOR MARINE SCIENCE

POSTAL ADDRESS: Hohenbergstrasse 2, Kiel, Bundesrepublik Deutschland (West Germany).
EXECUTIVE OFFICER: Prof. Dr. G. Dietrich, Director.
YEAR FOUNDED: 1937.

SCOPE OF ACTIVITIES: Unrestricted research on physical and chemical oceanography, marine meteorology and general marine biology.
SEASON OF OPERATION: All year.
PHYSICAL ENVIRONMENT ACCESSIBLE: Baltic and North Seas; sandy and silty beach, brackish, shallow bays.
PROVISIONS FOR VISITING SCIENTISTS: Research space for 1 visitor; no fees charged; living quarters available nearby.
MAJOR RESEARCH AND TEACHING FACILITIES: Very extensive library; small aquarium tanks; machine and wood shop, electrical and electronic shop; 24.5 m LOA vessel, R. V. *Hermann Wattenberg.* New oceanographic ship under construction.
INSTRUCTIONAL PROGRAM: General oceanography, general marine biology, fisheries biology, planktology, meteorology.
SIZE OF STAFF: Seven at professional level; 9 technicians.
IMPORTANT SPECIES AVAILABLE FOR LABORATORY STUDIES:
Phaeophycea: *Laminaria* sp., *Fucus vesiculosus*
Rhodophycea: *Delesseria sanguinea*
Lamellibranchiata: *Mytilus edulis*
Crustacea: *Carcinus maenas*
Copepoda: *Pseudocalanus minutus, Acartia bifilosa*
Echinodermata: *Asterias rubens*
Pisces: *Pleuronectes platessa, Gadus callarias, Zoarces viviparus*
Polychaeta: *Polydora ciliata*
MAJOR CURRENT RESEARCH PROJECTS AND SCIENTIFIC LEADERS:
Polarfront program IGY 1958 (G. Dietrich)
Internal waves (W. Krawfs)
Osmotic behavior of marine invertebrates (C. Schlieper)
Biology of fishes in the Baltic (R. Kaendler)
Fluctuations in the stock of fishes (R. Kaendler)
Osmotic and temperature resistance of algae (H. Schwenke)
Marine productivity (J. Krey)
Marine botany (F. Gessner)
PUBLICATIONS ISSUED: *Kieler Meeresforshungen* (regularly published journal)

Laboratories for Which No Details Were Available:

Bodensee-Laboratorium, *Suessenmuhle bei Ueberlingen, Bundesrepublik Deutschland (West Germany).*
Leiter: Dr. J. Grim.

Landesanstalt fuer Fischerei Nordrhein-Westfalen, *Albaum/Sauerland, Bundesrepublik Deutschland.*
Direktor: Dr. W. Denzer.

Staatliche Lehr-und Versuchsanstalt fuer Fischerei, *Starnberg/See (Oberbayern), Bundesrepublik Deutschland.*
Leiter: Dr. E. Rehbronn.

FEDERATION OF MALAYA AND SINGAPORE

Fisheries Research Laboratories, Malaya

POSTAL ADDRESS: Calthrop Road, Penang, Federation of Malaya.
EXECUTIVE OFFICER: Mr. Soong Min Kong, Director of Fisheries, Headquarters, Fisheries Department, Kuala Lumpur, Federation of Malaya and Singapore.
SPONSORING AGENCY: Government of Federation of Malaya and Singapore.
YEAR FOUNDED: 1956.
SCOPE OF ACTIVITIES: Restricted research on general oceanography, marine and fresh-water fisheries biology, general marine biology and plankton; undergraduate instruction occasionally.
SEASON OF OPERATION: All year.
PHYSICAL ENVIRONMENT ACCESSIBLE: Indian Ocean, Straits of Malacca, South China Sea; sandy and silty beaches, estuarine conditions, brackish, shallow bays, eutrophic lake, rivers and streams, mining pools and fish ponds.
PROVISIONS FOR VISITING SCIENTISTS: Space for 2 visitors; living quarters available nearby.
MAJOR RESEARCH AND TEACHING FACILITIES: Small

FISHERIES RESEARCH LABORATORIES, MALAYA

library; large outdoor ponds and tanks, small aquarium tanks; research collections of fauna and flora recently initiated; identified reference collections of local fauna and flora accessible at Raffles Museum, University of Malaya; small boats and outboard motors; vessels, 72 ft and 55 ft LOA.

INSTRUCTIONAL PROGRAM: Courses in fish culture to local inhabitants and junior department staff.

SIZE OF STAFF: Seven at professional level; 4 technicians.

IMPORTANT SPECIES AVAILABLE FOR LABORATORY STUDIES:

Crustacea: *Macrobrachium carcinus*
Pelecypoda: *Anadara granosa*

MAJOR CURRENT RESEARCH PROJECTS AND SCIENTIFIC LEADERS:

Biology and life history of *Rastrelliger* sp. (D. Pathansali)
Biology and life history of *Anadara granosa* (D. Pathansali)
Reproductive and feeding habits of *Probarbus jullieni* and *Macrobrachium carcinus* (A. B. O. Merican)
Experiments on improvements of methods of processing salt fish (V. Selvarajah)

Tropical Fish Culture Research Institute

POSTAL ADDRESS: Batu Berendam, Malacca, Federation of Malaya.

EXECUTIVE OFFICER: Dr. G. A. Prowse, Director.

SPONSORING AGENCIES: British and Federation of Malaya Governments.

YEAR FOUNDED: 1957.

SCOPE OF ACTIVITIES: Restricted research on fish culture; occasional graduate and undergraduate instruction.

SEASON OF OPERATION: All year.

PHYSICAL ENVIRONMENT ACCESSIBLE: Sandy and silty beaches, estuarine conditions, oligotrophic lake, rivers and streams, and fish ponds.

PROVISIONS FOR VISITING SCIENTISTS: Research and living space for two visitors; living quarters available nearby.

MAJOR RESEARCH AND TEACHING FACILITIES: Small library; large outdoor ponds, small aquarium tanks; research collections of algae, collections of Insecta and Crustacea being built up; identified reference collections of Raffles Museum and University of Malaya (Singapore) accessible; small shop facilities.

INSTRUCTIONAL PROGRAM: Occasional courses on fish pond biology, phytoplankton, etc.

SIZE OF STAFF: Three at professional level; 5 technicians.

IMPORTANT SPECIES AVAILABLE FOR LABORATORY STUDIES:

Pisces: *Ctenopharyngodon idellus* (Cyprinidae), *Betta splendens, Trichogaster* sp. (Anabantidae), *Tilapia* sp. (Cichlidae)

MAJOR CURRENT RESEARCH PROJECTS AND SCIENTIFIC LEADERS:

Phytoplankton and algal studies (G. A. Prowse)
Genetics of *Tilapia mossambica* (F. Y. Chen)
Breeding of grass carp (D. E. Kurth)
Study of bottom fauna and aquatic insects.

FEDERATION OF RHODESIA AND NYASALAND

Rhodesia and Nyasaland Ministry of Agriculture, Henderson Fishery Research Station

POSTAL ADDRESS: P. B. 4, Mazoe, Federation of Rhodesia and Nyasaland.

LOCATION: Near Salisbury, Southern Rhodesia.

EXECUTIVE OFFICER: A. Maar, Chief Fisheries Officer.

YEAR FOUNDED: 1950.

SCOPE OF ACTIVITIES: Restricted research on fish culture in ponds, reservoirs and natural inland waters.

SEASON OF OPERATION: All year.

PHYSICAL ENVIRONMENT ACCESSIBLE: Zambezi River and Kariba Lake (eutrophic lake).

PROVISIONS FOR VISITING SCIENTISTS: Space for 2 visitors; no fees charged; living quarters available nearby.

MAJOR RESEARCH FACILITIES: Small library; large outdoor ponds, small aquarium tanks, 33 acre reservoir; limited research collection of fish; machine and wood shop; small boats and outboard motors.

SIZE OF STAFF: Two at professional level; 1 technician.

IMPORTANT SPECIES AVAILABLE FOR LABORATORY STUDIES:

Pisces: *Tilapia* spp., *Clarias* spp.

HENDERSON FISHERY RESEARCH STATION, RHODESIA

JOINT FISHERIES RESEARCH ORGANISATION, NORTHERN RHODESIA SECTION

Joint Fisheries Research Organisation, Northern Rhodesia Section

POSTAL ADDRESS: P. O. Box 48, Samfya, Northern Rhodesia. Small laboratories operated at Lake Tanganyika and Lake Mweru.

LOCATION: Near Fort Rosebery, on shores of Lake Bangweulu.

EXECUTIVE OFFICER: P. B. N. Jackson, Chief Fisheries Research Officer.

SPONSORING AGENCY: Northern Rhodesia Government.

YEAR FOUNDED: 1954.

SCOPE OF ACTIVITIES: Restricted hydrobiological and fisheries research on the fresh-waters of Rhodesia and Nyasaland.

SEASON OF OPERATION: All year.

PHYSICAL ENVIRONMENT ACCESSIBLE: Lakes Bangweulu, Mweru, Kariba, Tanganyika, Nyasa (all oligotrophic lakes); rivers and streams, Kariba and other large dams.

PROVISIONS FOR VISITING SCIENTISTS: Research and living space for 2-3 visitors; no fees charged for research space.

MAJOR RESEARCH FACILITIES: Moderately complete library; large outdoor ponds and tanks, small aquarium tanks; research and identified reference collections of fresh-water fish and fresh-water insects; machine and wood shop, skilled shop workman available; three vessels, 48 ft, 40 ft and 32 ft LOA.

SIZE OF STAFF: Six at professional level; 2 technicians.

IMPORTANT SPECIES AVAILABLE FOR LABORATORY STUDIES:

Pisces: *Tilapia macrochir, T. melanopleura; Tylochromis bangwelensis*

Reptilia: *Crocodilus niloticus*

MAJOR CURRENT RESEARCH PROJECTS AND SCIENTIFIC LEADERS:

Illustrated book on fresh-water fish of Southern Africa (P. B. N. Jackson)

Hydrobiological studies on Kariba Dam (D. Harding)

Hydrobiological studies on Lake Tanganyika (G. W. Coulter)

Joint Fisheries Research Organisation, Nyasaland Section

POSTAL ADDRESS:

Present: P.O. Box Nkata Bay, Nyasaland.

Future: On Lake Nyasa. (Further information about the new laboratory may be obtained from the Director, Game, Fish and Tsetse Control, P. O. Box 585, Limbe, Nyasaland).

EXECUTIVE OFFICER: T. D. Iles, Research Officer in Charge.

SPONSORING AGENCY: Nyasaland Game, Fish and Tsetse Control Department.

YEAR FOUNDED: 1953.

SCOPE OF ACTIVITIES: Restricted investigations into the fish and fisheries of Nyasaland and of the related ecological and biological factors.

PHYSICAL ENVIRONMENT ACCESSIBLE: Lake Nyasa (oligotrophic lake); sandy and silty beaches, rocky and gravelly shores.

SEASON OF OPERATION: All year.

PROVISIONS FOR VISITING SCIENTISTS: Space for 1 visitor; no fees charged; living quarters available nearby.

MAJOR RESEARCH FACILITIES: Small library; research and identified reference collections of cichlid fishes of Lake Nyasa; small boats and outboard motors; 47 ft LOA launch.

SIZE OF STAFF: Two at professional level; 1 technician.

IMPORTANT SPECIES AVAILABLE FOR LABORATORY STUDIES:

Mollusca: *Bullinus* sp.

Diptera: *Anopheles, Culex*

Amphibia: *Xenopus* sp.

Teleostei: Cichlidae (more than 120 species)

MAJOR CURRENT RESEARCH PROJECTS AND SCIENTIFIC LEADERS:

Hydrology of northern Lake Nyasa (T. D. Iles)

Systematics of cichilid fishes (T. D. Iles)

Biology of *Engraulis cypris* (T. D. Iles)

Gear selectivity; gill nets (D. Eccles)

Age determination of *Tilapia* sp. (D. Eccles)

FINLAND

Helsingin Yliopisto, Limnologian Laitos

UNIVERSITY OF HELSINKI, LIMNOLOGICAL INSTITUTE

POSTAL ADDRESS: Unioninkatu 40, Helsingin, Suomi (Helsinki, Finland).

EXECUTIVE OFFICER: Professor Heikki Jaernefelt.

YEAR FOUNDED: 1939.

SCOPE OF ACTIVITIES: Unrestricted research on plankton and regional limnology; graduate and undergraduate instruction.

SEASON OF OPERATION: All year.

PHYSICAL ENVIRONMENT ACCESSIBLE: Lohjanjarvi (brown water lake).

PROVISIONS FOR VISITING SCIENTISTS: Research space for 1 visitor; no fees charged.

MAJOR RESEARCH AND TEACHING FACILITIES: The Institute has use of the Fisheries Foundation research station in Lohja. Very extensive library at the university; large outdoor ponds and tanks, small aquarium tanks, and running spring water at the F. F. research station; identified reference collections of local fauna and flora available for studies of plankton communities; small boats and outboard motors.

INSTRUCTIONAL PROGRAM: Applied limnology, biology, hydrobiology, fish culture, technology, and fisheries economics.

SIZE OF STAFF: Four at professional level; 2 technicians.

MAJOR CURRENT RESEARCH PROJECTS AND SCIENTIFIC LEADERS:

Sedimentation of the plankton organisms (H. Jaernefelt)

Studies of the plankton in brackish water (H. Jaernefelt)

Suomen Maatalousministerioe, Kalataloudellinen Tutkimustoimisto

FINNISH MINISTRY OF AGRICULTURE AND FISHERIES, BUREAU FOR FISHERIES RESEARCH

POSTAL ADDRESS: Fabianinkatu 32, Helsinki, Suomi (Finland).

EXECUTIVE OFFICER: Professor Erkki Halme, Director.

YEAR FOUNDED: 1923.

SCOPE OF ACTIVITIES: Officially restricted research on fish, fisheries, and fisheries statistics along the coastal area of the Baltic Sea (brackish water) and in the lakes of Finland.

SEASON OF OPERATION: All year.

PHYSICAL ENVIRONMENT ACCESSIBLE: Baltic Sea, Gulf of Finland; brackish shallow bays, eutrophic and oligotrophic lakes, rivers and streams.

PROVISIONS FOR VISITING SCIENTISTS: None.

MAJOR RESEARCH FACILITIES: Moderately complete library; small boats and outboard motors.

SIZE OF STAFF: Five at professional level; 4 technicians.

MAJOR CURRENT RESEARCH PROJECTS AND SCIENTIFIC LEADERS:

Limnological studies on lakes (Erkki Halme)

Population dynamics of coastal fisheries (Erkki Halme)

Pollution problems (Erkki Halme)

PUBLICATIONS ISSUED: *Suomen Kalatalous* (occasionally published journal)

Kalataloussaeaetioe

FISHERIES FOUNDATION

POSTAL ADDRESS:

Headquarters: Unioninkatu 40, Helsinki, Suomi (Finland).

Field Station: Porla, Lohja, Suomi.

EXECUTIVE OFFICERS: Tapani Sormunen, Director of Investigations. Professor Heikki Jaernefelt, Administrative Chairman.

YEAR FOUNDED: 1948.

SCOPE OF ACTIVITIES: Unrestricted research on fisheries biology, pond fish cultivation, and water pollution problems. Major activities at the field station.

SEASON OF OPERATION: All year.

PHYSICAL ENVIRONMENT ACCESSIBLE: Lohjanjaervi; eutrophic lakes, and brown water lakes.

PROVISIONS FOR VISITING SCIENTISTS: Space for visitors will be available in the future after reorganization.

MAJOR RESEARCH FACILITIES: Fifteen large outdoor ponds, small aquarium tanks, running spring water; skilled shop workman available, small boats and outboard motors.

SIZE OF STAFF: Four at professional level.

IMPORTANT SPECIES AVAILABLE FOR LABORATORY STUDIES:

Pisces: *Salmo trutta lacustris*

MAJOR CURRENT RESEARCH PROJECTS:

Biological changes caused by the installation of power stations in two large watercourses.

Pollution problems caused by pulp mills, beet-sugar factory and a plant oil factory

Studies on the biology and cultivation of *Salmo* sp.

Merentutkimuslaitoksen Biologinen Laboratorio

BIOLOGICAL LABORATORY OF THE INSTITUTE OF MARINE RESEARCH

POSTAL ADDRESS: Zoological Institute of the University of Helsinki, P. Rautatiekatu 13, Helsinki, Suomi (Finland).

EXECUTIVE OFFICERS: Professor Ilmo Hela, Director of Institute of Marine Research. Professor Sven Segerstraele, Director of Biological Laboratory.

SPONSORING AGENCY: Kauppa-ja Teollisuus-Ministerioe, (Dept. for Commerce and Industry).

SEASON OF OPERATION: All year.

PHYSICAL ENVIRONMENT ACCESSIBLE: Open and coastal parts of brackish Baltic Sea.

PROVISIONS FOR VISITING SCIENTISTS: None.

MAJOR RESEARCH FACILITIES: Moderately complete library. New building for the Institute of Marine Research will have running salt and brackish water, aquaria, etc. Present field work of the Biological Laboratory is carried out at the Tvaerminne Zoological Station during the summer where all the Station facilities are available. The 151 ft LOA research vessel, *Aranda,* of the Institute is also used by the Laboratory.

SIZE OF STAFF: Three part-time at professional level.

MAJOR CURRENT RESEARCH PROJECTS AND SCIENTIFIC LEADERS:

Population dynamics of bivalve *Macoma baltica* (Sven Segerstraele)

Hydrographical and biological changes in a recently closed bay Gennarbyviken on south coast of Finland (Kalle Purasjoki)

PUBLICATIONS ISSUED: *Merentutkimuslaitoksen julkaisuja* (official journal of the Institute of Marine Science)

Turun Yliopisto, Saaristomeren Biologinen Asema

UNIVERSITY OF TURKU, MARINE BIOLOGICAL STATION

POSTAL ADDRESS:

Summer; Lohm, Suomi (Lohm, Finland).

Winter; Turun, Suomi (Turku, Finland).

EXECUTIVE OFFICER: Professor Paavo Voipio, Director of the Station, University of Turku, Turun, Suomi.

YEAR FOUNDED: 1958.

SCOPE OF ACTIVITIES: Unrestricted research in general marine zoology and botany of brackish water; undergraduate instruction.

SEASON OF OPERATION: June 1 to August 31 at the Lohm Station.

PHYSICAL ENVIRONMENT ACCESSIBLE: Northern Baltic Sea; sandy and silty beaches, rock and gravelly shores, and brackish water.

PROVISIONS FOR VISITING SCIENTISTS: Research and living space for 1-2 visitors; no fees charged for research space.

MAJOR RESEARCH AND TEACHING FACILITIES: University library; running sea and fresh-water, small aquarium tanks; small boats and outboard motors.

INSTRUCTIONAL PROGRAM: General marine zoology and botany.

SIZE OF STAFF: One or two at professional level; 1 technician.

IMPORTANT SPECIES AVAILABLE FOR LABORATORY STUDIES:

Mollusca: *Mytilus edulis*

Polychaeta: *Nereis diversicolor*

Crustacea: *Asellus aquaticus, Mesidothea entomon* and other amphipods and isopods.

MAJOR CURRENT RESEARCH PROJECTS AND SCIENTIFIC LEADERS:

Survey of brackish water fauna (Paavo Tulkki)

Behavioral salinity reactions (Kari Lagerspetz)

Acclimatization to salinity and temperature in *Mytilus* (Kari Lagerspetz)

Helsingin Yliopisto, Tvaerminnen Elaeintieteellinen Asema

UNIVERSITY OF HELSINKI, TVAERMINNE ZOOLOGICAL STATION

POSTAL ADDRESS: From September 15 to May 14: P. Rautatiekatu 13, Helsinki, Finland. From May 15 to September 14: Tvaerminne.

EXECUTIVE OFFICERS: Professor Pontus Palmgren, Director. Dr. K. Purasjoki, Manager.

YEAR FOUNDED: 1902.

SCOPE OF ACTIVITIES: Unrestricted research in zoology and botany, especially in brackish water; graduate and undergraduate instruction.

SEASON OF OPERATION: May 15 to September 15 at Tvaerminne.

PHYSICAL ENVIRONMENT ACCESSIBLE: Baltic Sea, outermost part of the Gulf of Finland; sandy and silty beaches, rocky and gravelly shores, and brackish sea.

PROVISIONS FOR VISITING SCIENTISTS: Research and living space for 5 visitors; fees charged for research space.

MAJOR RESEARCH AND TEACHING FACILITIES: Moderately complete library; running sea and fresh-water, small aquarium tanks; small boats and outboard motors, power vessels, 29 ft LOA, *Esox,* and 24 ft LOA, *Perca.*

INSTRUCTIONAL PROGRAM: Hydrobiology (especially brackish water) and aquatic fauna and flora.

SIZE OF STAFF: Two at professional level; 2 technicians.

IMPORTANT SPECIES AVAILABLE FOR LABORATORY STUDIES:

Amphipoda: *Gammarus* sp.

Pisces: *Gasterosteus aculeatus, Phoxinus aphya, Pleuronectes flesus,* etc.

TVAERMINNEN ELAEINTIETEELLINEN ASEMA, HELSINGIN

MAJOR CURRENT RESEARCH PROJECTS AND SCIENTIFIC LEADERS:

Fish populations (tagging experiments, etc.) (Staff members)
Studies on the bivalve *Macoma baltica* (S. Segerstraele)
Studies on chironomids (E. Palmen)
Hydrographical and biological changes in an artificially closed bay on the south coast of Finland (K. Purasjoki)

Laboratories about Which No Detailed Information Was Available:

***Biologinen Asema,** (Biological Station) Lammi, Suomi (Finland).*

Dr. Jorma Soveri, Prefect.

Sponsoring agency: Helsingin Yliopisto (University of Helsinki).

FRANCE

Centre d'Ecologie Terrestre et Limnique

CENTER FOR TERRESTRIAL AND LIMNETIC ECOLOGY

POSTAL ADDRESS: Faculte des Sciences, 1, Place Victor Hugo, Marseille (Bouches du Rhoene) France.
EXECUTIVE OFFICERS: Professeur M. M. Abeloos, Directeur. Mme D. Schachter, Maitre de Recherche au Centre national de la Recherche scientifique.
SPONSORING AGENCY: Universite d'aix-Marseille (University of Marseille).
YEAR FOUNDED: 1957.
SCOPE OF ACTIVITIES: Restricted research on terrestrial and limnetic ecology.
SEASON OF OPERATION: All year.
PHYSICAL ENVIRONMENT ACCESSIBLE: Etangs de Berre, l'Olivier, Lavalduc, Gloria, Vaccares, Fournelet, Imperial, l'Or, etc.; estuarine conditions, brackish, shallow bays, eutrophic and oligotrophic lakes, rivers and streams.
PROVISIONS FOR VISITING SCIENTISTS: Space for visitors.
MAJOR RESEARCH AND TEACHING FACILITIES: Very extensive library at the University; identified reference collections of fauna of the Camargue and ponds of the Mediterranean region; electrical and electronic shop; small boats and outboard motors; one 18 m LOA vessel.
INSTRUCTIONAL PROGRAM: Community fauna, populations, geobotany, crops of the Iles, ecological factors, conservation, regional ecology, and physiochemistry of water and soil.
SIZE OF STAFF: Five at professional level; 2 technicians.
IMPORTANT SPECIES AVAILABLE FOR LABORATORY STUDIES:

Gastropoda: *Helix, Helicella, Limax*
Crustacea: *Gammarus locusta, Sphaeroma hookerii, Leander adsperas*
Pisces: *Sardina pilchardus, Mugil auratus, M. capito, M. cephalus, M. labrosus*

MAJOR CURRENT RESEARCH PROJECTS AND SCIENTIFIC LEADERS:

Ecology of the Camargue and ponds of the Mediterranean region (D. Schachter)
Ecology and physiology of the Mugilidae of the shallow bays (Y. Thouveny)
Ecology of the estuary of the Rhoene (G. Brun)
Biology of gastropods (M. and Mme. Bonavita)
Ecology of *Sphaeroma hookerii* of Vaccares (Mme. Girard)
Ecology and physiology of terrestrial gastropods and earthworms (M. Abeloos)

Centre d'Etudes et de Recherches Scientifiques de Biarritz

CENTER OF SCIENTIFIC STUDIES AND RESEARCH OF BIARRITZ

POSTAL ADDRESS: B. P. 28, Plateau de l'Atalaye, Biarritz (B-P), France.
LOCATION: Near Bordeaux.
EXECUTIVE OFFICER: L. Barriety, Directeur.
SPONSORING AGENCY: Autonomous public institution.
YEAR FOUNDED: 1955.
SCOPE OF ACTIVITIES: Unrestricted research on general marine biology.
SEASON OF OPERATION: All year.
PHYSICAL ENVIRONMENT ACCESSIBLE: Atlantic Ocean, Adour River; sandy and silty beaches, rocky and gravelly shores, and estuarine conditions.
PROVISIONS FOR VISITING SCIENTISTS: Space for 5 visitors; no fees charged; living quarters available nearby.
MAJOR RESEARCH FACILITIES: Moderately complete library; running sea and fresh-water, large outdoor ponds and tanks, small aquarium tanks; identified reference collections of local echinoderm fossils and

CENTER OF SCIENTIFIC STUDIES AND RESEARCH OF BIARRITZ

birds; machine and wood shop, skilled shop workman available; small boats and outboard motors.

SIZE OF STAFF: Seven at professional level; 4 technicians.

MAJOR CURRENT RESEARCH PROJECTS AND SCIENTIFIC LEADERS:

Study of rivers and lakes (Dr. Vibert)
Ecology (Dr. Jovet)
Oceanography (M. Percier)
Study of marine corrosion of metals (M. Hache)

PUBLICATIONS ISSUED: *Bulletin du Centre d'Etudes et de Recherches Scientifiques* (regularly published journal)

Centre National de la Recherche Scientifique

NATIONAL CENTER FOR SCIENTIFIC RESEARCH

POSTAL ADDRESS:
Headquarters: 15, Quai Anatole France, Paris VII, France.
Branch laboratories:
1. Centre de Recherches Hydrobiologiques
2. Laboratoire de Chimie Bacterienne et Corrosion Biologique

(Descriptions follow.)

EXECUTIVE OFFICERS: Gaston Dupouy, Directeur-General. P. Delaroche, Chef du Service des Activites Scientifiques.

SPONSORING AGENCY: Ministere de l'Education nationale (Ministry of Public Education).

PUBLICATIONS ISSUED:
Annales de la Nutrition et de l'Alimentation, Archives des Sciences Physiologiques, Archives de Zoologie Experimentale (all published regularly)
Biospeleologiques (published annually)

Centre de Recherches Hydrobiologiques

HYDROBIOLOGICAL RESEARCH CENTER

POSTAL ADDRESS: Gif sur Yvette (Seine et Oise), France.

LOCATION: Near Paris.

EXECUTIVE OFFICER: M. Lefevre, Directeur.

YEAR FOUNDED: 1946.

SCOPE OF ACTIVITIES: Unrestricted research on plankton and bottom ecology.

SEASON OF OPERATION: All year.

PHYSICAL ENVIRONMENT ACCESSIBLE: Eutrophic and oligotrophic lakes, rivers and streams.

PROVISIONS FOR VISITING SCIENTISTS: Space for 2 visitors.

MAJOR RESEARCH AND TEACHING FACILITIES: Small library; large outdoor ponds and tanks, small aquarium tanks; research collections of living algae in clonic culture, soil fungi and ciliates, machine and wood shop, electrical and electronic shop, skilled shop workman available; small boats and outboard motors; one 6 m LOA vessel.

CENTRE DE RECHERCHES HYDROBIOLOGIQUES, SEINE ET OISE

INSTRUCTIONAL PROGRAM: General invertebrate zoology, phytoplankton, and comparative physiology.

SIZE OF STAFF: Six at professional level; 7 technicians.

IMPORTANT SPECIES AVAILABLE FOR LABORATORY STUDIES:

Many species of fresh-water algae and invertebrates.

MAJOR CURRENT RESEARCH PROJECTS AND SCIENTIFIC LEADERS:

Nutrition of Rotatoria (R. Pourriot)
Morphogenesis of ciliates (M. Tuffrau)
Soil bacteria (Rhizospheres) (J. Duche)
Biochemistry (G. Farrugia)
Morphogenesis and nutrition of ciliates (E. Faure-Fremiet)
Systematics and ecology of fresh-water algae (M. Lefevre)
Biologically active substances secreted from fresh-water and thermal water algae (M. Lefevre)

PUBLICATIONS ISSUED: *Hydrobiologia* (occasionally published)

Laboratoire de Chimie Bacterienne et Corrosion Biologique

LABORATORY OF BACTERIAL CHEMISTRY AND BIOLOGICAL CORROSION

POSTAL ADDRESS: 31, chemin Joseph Aiquier, (Bouches du Rhoene), France.

EXECUTIVE OFFICER: Dr. Jacques C. Senez, Directeur de Recherche au CNRS, Chef de Laboratoire.

YEAR FOUNDED: 1951.

SCOPE OF ACTIVITIES: Unrestricted research on marine bacteriology and general microbiology.

SEASON OF OPERATION: All year.

PHYSICAL ENVIRONMENT ACCESSIBLE: Mediterranean Sea.

PROVISIONS FOR VISITING SCIENTISTS: Space for 5-6 visitors; no fees charged; living quarters available nearby.

MAJOR RESEARCH FACILITIES: Small library; research collections of marine bacterial strains; machine and wood shop. New laboratory completed in 1962.

SIZE OF STAFF: Ten at professional level; 7 technicians.

MAJOR CURRENT RESEARCH PROJECTS AND SCIENTIFIC LEADERS:

Biochemistry of sulfate reducing bacteria (J. C. Senez)

Biochemistry of nitrate reduction and N_2 fixation (F. Pichinoty and J. LeGall)

Biochemistry of hydrocarbon oxidizing bacteria (E. Azoulay)

Centre de Recherches et d'Etudes Oceanographiques

OCEANOGRAPHIC RESEARCH CENTER

POSTAL ADDRESS: 1, Quai Branly, Paris VIIe, France. Branch laboratories at La Rochelle and Antibes.

EXECUTIVE OFFICER: V. Romanovsky, Directeur.

SPONSORING AGENCY: French Government.

YEAR FOUNDED: 1948.

SCOPE OF ACTIVITIES: Restricted research on general oceanography.

SEASON OF OPERATION: All year.

PHYSICAL ENVIRONMENT ACCESSIBLE: Open ocean, sandy and silty beaches, rocky and gravelly shores, and estuarine conditions (Mediterranean and nearby Atlantic).

PROVISIONS FOR VISITING SCIENTISTS: Space for 5 visitors at La Rochelle and 2 at Antibes.

MAJOR RESEARCH FACILITIES: Small library; running sea water; machine and wood shop, skilled shop workman available; small boats and outboard motors, one 45 ft LOA vessel and one 77 ft vessel.

STATION OCEANOGRAPHIQUE D'ANTIBES

STATION OCEANOGRAPHIQUE DE LA ROCHELLE

SIZE OF STAFF: Ten at professional level; 15 technicians.

MAJOR CURRENT RESEARCH PROJECTS AND SCIENTIFIC LEADERS:

Estuarine environments (J. Le Floch)

Physical and geological deep sea research (V. Romanovsky and L. S. Roobaert)

Coastal currents (V. Romanovsky)

Corrosion and fouling in the sea (B. Callame and V. Romanovsky)

PUBLICATIONS ISSUED: *Travaux du Centre de Recherches et d'Etudes Oceanographiques* (regularly published journal)

Ministere de l'Agriculture, Direction Generale des Eaux et des Forets, Station Centrale d'Hydrobiologie Appliquee

MINISTRY OF AGRICULTURE, GENERAL DEPARTMENT OF WATER AND FORESTRY, CENTRAL STATION FOR APPLIED HYDROBIOLOGY

POSTAL ADDRESS:

Headquarters: 14 avenue de Saint-Mande, Paris, France.

Branch laboratories:

1. Station d'Hydrobiologie Appliquee de Biarritz
2. Station d'Hydrobiologie Appliquee du Paraclet
3. Station de Recherches Lacustres de Thonon

(Descriptions follow.)

EXECUTIVE OFFICER: Dr. P. Vivier, Directeur.

YEAR FOUNDED: 1943.

SCOPE OF ACTIVITIES: Restricted research on the improvement and development of fish production and protection against water pollution.

SEASON OF OPERATION: All year.

PHYSICAL ENVIRONMENT ACCESSIBLE: Seine River; lakes and ponds.

PROVISIONS FOR VISITING SCIENTISTS: Research and living space for 1 visitor; no fees charged.

STATION CENTRALE D'HYDROBIOLOGIE APPLIQUEE, PARIS

MAJOR RESEARCH FACILITIES: Very extensive library; small aquarium tanks, several small cement basins.

SIZE OF STAFF: Eleven at professional level; 21 technicians.

MAJOR CURRENT RESEARCH PROJECTS AND SCIENTIFIC LEADERS:

Studies on dammed lakes; water chemistry (Mlle. Nisbet)

Pernicious anemia of trout (Dr. Besse)

Dynamics of fish populations (Dr. Vibert)

PUBLICATIONS ISSUED: *Bulletin Francais de Pisciculture* (issued every 3 months for popular consumption)

Station d'Hydrobiologie Appliquee de Biarritz

BIARRITZ STATION OF APPLIED HYDROBIOLOGY

POSTAL ADDRESS: B. P. 28, Biarritz, France.

EXECUTIVE OFFICER: Dr. Richard Vibert, Ingenieur en Chef des Eaux et Forets.

YEAR FOUNDED: 1954.

SCOPE OF ACTIVITIES: Unrestricted research on salmon and trout biology; restricted research on continental fisheries, biology and management; graduate and undergraduate instruction.

SEASON OF OPERATION: All year.

PHYSICAL ENVIRONMENT ACCESSIBLE: Adour River, Adour watershed, Bay of Biscay; sandy and silty beaches, rocky and gravelly shores, and estuarine conditions.

PROVISIONS FOR VISITING SCIENTISTS: Space for 1-2 visitors during the year and for 10 during summer training courses; no fees charged for research space; living quarters available nearby.

MAJOR RESEARCH AND TEACHING FACILITIES: Small library; running sea and fresh-water, large outdoor ponds and tanks available at the Lees-Athas hatchery (140 kms), small aquarium tanks; machine and wood shop, skilled shop workman available; small boats and outboard motors.

INSTRUCTIONAL PROGRAM: Continental fisheries, biology and management.

SIZE OF STAFF: Three at professional level; 6 technicians.

IMPORTANT SPECIES AVAILABLE FOR LABORATORY STUDIES:

Pisces: *Salmo salar, S. trutta fario, S. gairdneri*

MAJOR CURRENT RESEARCH PROJECTS AND SCIENTIFIC LEADERS:

Continental fisheries biology—hatching and restocking devices (Richard Vibert)

Electric fishing devices (Pierre Lamarque)

Fish populations studies (Robin Cuinat)

Station d'Hydrobiologie Appliquee du Paraclet

PARACLET STATION OF APPLIED HYDROBIOLOGY

POSTAL ADDRESS: Boves (Somme), France.

LOCATION: Near Amiens.

EXECUTIVE OFFICER: A. Wurtz, Directeur.

YEAR FOUNDED: 1943.

SCOPE OF ACTIVITIES: Restricted research on general hydrobiology with special emphasis on algae and animal ecology; graduate instruction.

SEASON OF OPERATION: All year.

PHYSICAL ENVIRONMENT ACCESSIBLE: "La Noye" (tributary of Somme River); ponds.

PROVISIONS FOR VISITING SCIENTISTS: Research and living space for 3 visitors; no fees charged for research space.

MAJOR RESEARCH AND TEACHING FACILITIES: Large outdoor ponds and tanks, small aquarium tanks; extensive identified reference collections of aquatic plants and insect larvae; small boats and outboard motors.

INSTRUCTIONAL PROGRAM: Phyto- and zooplankton.

SIZE OF STAFF: Two at professional level; 6 technicians.

IMPORTANT SPECIES AVAILABLE FOR LABORATORY STUDIES:

Crustacea: *Atyaephyra desmaresti*

Pisces: *Salmo fario, S. gairdnerii, Micropterus salmoides, Gardonus rutilus, Scardinius erythrophthalmus, Petromyzon planeri, Anguilla anguilla, Abramis brama*

STATION D'HYDROBIOLOGIE APPLIQUEE DU PARACLET

MAJOR CURRENT RESEARCH PROJECTS AND SCIENTIFIC LEADERS:

Interaction of algae and bacteria (A. Wurtz)

Station de Recherches Lacustres de Thonon

THONON STATION FOR LACUSTRINE RESEARCH

POSTAL ADDRESS: B. P. 41, 13 Quai de Rives, Thonon les Bains, France.

LOCATION: Near Lausanne and Geneve, Suisse (Geneva, Switzerland).

EXECUTIVE OFFICER: P. J. Laurent, Directeur.

YEAR FOUNDED: 1929.

SCOPE OF ACTIVITIES: Restricted applied hydrobiological research on lakes and alpine streams; graduate instruction.

SEASON OF OPERATION: All year.

PHYSICAL ENVIRONMENT ACCESSIBLE: Lake Leman; eutrophic and oligotrophic lakes, rivers and streams; and underground water.

PROVISIONS FOR VISITING SCIENTISTS: Research and living space for 4 visitors; no fees charged for research space.

MAJOR RESEARCH AND TEACHING FACILITIES: Moderately complete library; lake, spring and fresh tap water; large outdoor ponds and tanks, small aquarium tanks; fish farm near laboratory; research collections of fresh-water plankton and Astacidae from all parts of France; identified reference collections of local fishes; machine and wood shop, electrical and electronic shop, skilled shop workman available; small boats; one 9 m LOA power vessel.

INSTRUCTIONAL PROGRAM: Courses on fresh-water biology.

SIZE OF STAFF: One at professional level; 5 technicians.

IMPORTANT SPECIES AVAILABLE FOR LABORATORY STUDIES:

Pisces: *Salmo trutta, Salvelinus alpinus, Coregonus* spp.

Crustacea: *Astacus pallipes*

STATION DE RECHERCHES LACUSTRES DE THONON

Lake plankton

Many spp. invertebrates of alpine streams.

MAJOR CURRENT RESEARCH PROJECTS AND SCIENTIFIC LEADERS:

Chemistry, bacteriology and ichthyology of regional lakes (P. J. Laurent)

Lake trout studies (P. J. Laurent)

Studies on benthos of streams (Richard Vibert)

Studies on the fats of fishes (Morawa)

Institut Oceanographique

OCEANOGRAPHICAL INSTITUTE

POSTAL ADDRESS:

Headquarters: 195 rue St. Jacques, Paris V^{e}, France.

Laboratories:

Physiologie des Etres Marins (Physiology of Marine Organisms)

Oceanographie Physique (Physical Oceanography)

Oceanographie Biologique (Biological Oceanography)

Musee Oceanographique de Monaco (Oceanographic Museum of Monaco) (See description page 135)

EXECUTIVE OFFICER: Professor Maurice Fontaine, Directeur.

SPONSORING AGENCY: Private institute.

YEAR FOUNDED: 1906.

SCOPE OF ACTIVITIES: Unrestricted research on general oceanography and marine biology; graduate instruction.

SEASON OF OPERATION: All year.

PHYSICAL ENVIRONMENT ACCESSIBLE: Mediterranean Sea, Atlantic Ocean; estuaries of French rivers.

PROVISIONS FOR VISITING SCIENTISTS: Space for 3 visitors; no fees charged; living quarters available in Paris.

MAJOR RESEARCH AND TEACHING FACILITIES: Very extensive library; large outdoor ponds and tanks, small aquarium tanks; research collections of the Museum national d'Histoire naturelle accessible; machine and wood shop, electronic shop, skilled shop workman available; small boats; one oceanographic vessel, 20 m LOA, *Vinaretta Singer*.

INSTRUCTIONAL PROGRAM: Comparative physiology and courses in biological and physical oceanography.

SIZE OF STAFF: Fourteen at professional level; 4 technicians.

MAJOR CURRENT RESEARCH PROJECTS AND SCIENTIFIC LEADERS:

Littoral biology and biological oceanography (Prof. Pierre Drach)

Physiology of migrants (Prof. Maurice Fontaine)

Radioecology (Prof. Maurice Fontaine)

Oceanographic optics (Prof. LeGrand)

PUBLICATIONS ISSUED: *Bulletin de l'Institut Oceanographique; Annales de l'Institut Oceanographique* (both regularly published journals).

Institut Scientifique et Technique des Peches Maritimes

SCIENTIFIC AND TECHNICAL INSTITUTE OF MARINE FISHERIES

POSTAL ADDRESS:
Headquarters: 59, Avenue Raymond-Poincare, Paris 16e, France.
Branch laboratories:
1. Laboratoire d'Arcachon
2. Laboratoire d'Auray
3. Laboratoire de Biarritz
4. Laboratoire de Boulogne-sur-Mur
5. Laboratoire de La Rochelle
6. Laboratoire de La Temblade
7. Laboratoire de Roscoff
8. Laboratoire de Sete
9. Laboratoire de Sete

(Descriptions follow.)

EXECUTIVE OFFICERS: Dr. Jean Furnestin, Directeur. Yves Pruja, Adjoint au Directeur.
SPONSORING AGENCY: Ministere de la Marine Marchande.
YEAR FOUNDED: 1918.
SCOPE OF ACTIVITIES: Biological and physical oceanography; instruction.
PROVISIONS FOR VISITING SCIENTISTS: None at branch laboratories.
VESSELS: *Thalassa,* 15 m LOA; *Roselys,* 65 m LOA oceanographic vessel under construction.
SIZE OF STAFF: Twenty-five at professional level; 35 technicians.
PUBLICATIONS ISSUED: *Revue des Travaux de l'Institut Scientifique et Technique des Peches Maritimes* (issued trimestrially)

Laboratoire d'Arcachon

POSTAL ADDRESS: 63, boulevard Deganne, Arcachon (Gironde), France.
EXECUTIVE OFFICER: M. Le Dantec, Chef.
SCOPE OF ACTIVITIES: Restricted research on the ecology, growth, reproduction and genetics of oysters; predator control.
PHYSICAL ENVIRONMENT ACCESSIBLE: Arcachon Basin and Bay of Biscay.

Laboratoire d'Auray

POSTAL ADDRESS: 4, place du Champ de Foire, Auray (Morbihan), France.
EXECUTIVE OFFICER: L. Marteil, Chef.
SCOPE OF ACTIVITIES: Restricted research on oyster culture and management.
PHYSICAL ENVIRONMENT ACCESSIBLE: Bay of Biscay.

Laboratoire de Biarritz

POSTAL ADDRESS: Centre scientifique, plateau de l'Atalaye, B. P. 28, Biarritz (Basses-Pyrenees), France.
SCOPE OF ACTIVITIES: Biological and physical oceanography, ichthyology and fishing methods.
PHYSICAL ENVIRONMENT ACCESSIBLE: Bay of Biscay.

Laboratoire De Boulogne-Sur-Mer

Note: The laboratory was destroyed during World War II and is not yet rebuilt. This description is, therefore, provisional.
POSTAL ADDRESS: Quai de la Poste, Boulogne-sur-Mer, France.
EXECUTIVE OFFICER: Dr. J. Ancellin, Chef.
SCOPE OF ACTIVITIES: Restricted research on methods of handling fish; biology and ecology of commercial marine species; fish population studies; special studies on sardines of the North Sea and English Channel.
PHYSICAL ENVIRONMENT ACCESSIBLE: English Channel and North Sea.

Laboratoire de La Rochelle

POSTAL ADDRESS: 74, allees du Mail, La Rochelle (Charente-Maritime), France.
EXECUTIVE OFFICER: H. Brienne, Chef.
SCOPE OF ACTIVITIES: Restricted research on the development of commercial fisheries of the continental slope and pelagic area of the Atlantic Coast; oyster culture; crustacean biology; fishery management.
PHYSICAL ENVIRONMENT ACCESSIBLE: Bay of Biscay.

Laboratoire de La Tremblade

POSTAL ADDRESS: 41, rue du General Leclerc, La Tremblade (Charente-Maritime), France.
EXECUTIVE OFFICER: P. Trochon, Chef.
SCOPE OF ACTIVITIES: Restricted research on the ecology, reproduction and genetics of oysters and other mollusks, predator control and general hygiene of oyster culture.
PHYSICAL ENVIRONMENT ACCESSIBLE: Bay of Biscay.

Laboratoire de Roscoff

POSTAL ADDRESS: Under reconstruction at Lorient. Temporary address: Laboratoire Lacaze-Duthiers, Roscoff (Finistere), France.
EXECUTIVE OFFICER: Louis Faure, Directeur.
SCOPE OF ACTIVITIES: Biological and oceanographic studies on fish and shellfish of the French coast.
PHYSICAL ENVIRONMENT ACCESSIBLE: Bay of Biscay; sandy and silty beaches, rocky and gravelly shores.
FACILITIES FOR VISITORS AND RESEARCH: Because laboratory is under construction, its final plans for equipment, etc., are not known at this time.

Laboratoire de Sete

POSTAL ADDRESS: 6 rue Voltaire, Sete (Herault) France.

EXECUTIVE OFFICER: Claude Maurin, Chef.

YEAR FOUNDED: 1957.

SCOPE OF ACTIVITIES: Unrestricted research on marine and fisheries biology.

SEASON OF OPERATION: All year.

PHYSICAL ENVIRONMENT ACCESSIBLE: Gulf of Lyons, Rhoene River; open ocean, sandy and silty beaches, rocky and gravelly shores.

PROVISIONS FOR VISITING SCIENTISTS: Space for visitors; living quarters available nearby.

MAJOR RESEARCH FACILITIES: Small library; small aquarium tanks; identified reference collections of local fauna and flora, particularly deep water species; one small boat and outboard motor; one 8 m LOA vessel.

SIZE OF STAFF: Five at professional level; 5 technicians.

IMPORTANT SPECIES AVAILABLE FOR LABORATORY STUDIES:

Cephalopoda: *Loligo, Ommatostrephes.*

Pisces: All sea fishes of the Mediterranean, particularly *Gadus, Clupea, Sardina, Trigla,* and *Scorpaena.*

MAJOR CURRENT RESEARCH PROJECTS AND SCIENTIFIC LEADERS:

Biology of the hake (Claude Maurin)
Biology of the sardine (J. Y. Lee)
Shrimp studies (Claude Maurin)
Studies on oyster culture (R. Raimbault)
Bacteriological studies (Y. Fauvel)

Laboratoire de Sete

POSTAL ADDRESS: Quai du Bosc, Sete (Herault), France.

EXECUTIVE OFFICER: J. Audouin, Directeur.

SCOPE OF ACTIVITIES: Restricted research on ichthyology and malacology.

PHYSICAL ENVIRONMENT ACCESSIBLE: Gulf of Lions and Mediterranean Sea.

Laboratoire Arago

ARAGO LABORATORY

POSTAL ADDRESS: Banyuls-sur-Mer (Pyrenees-Orientales), France.

LOCATION: Near Perpignan.

EXECUTIVE OFFICER: Professor G. Petit, Directeur.

SPONSORING AGENCY: Universite de Paris.

YEAR FOUNDED: 1881.

SCOPE OF ACTIVITIES: Unrestricted research on marine biology; undergraduate instruction.

LABORATOIRE ARAGO

SEASON OF OPERATION: All year.

PHYSICAL ENVIRONMENT ACCESSIBLE: Open sea, sandy and silty beaches, rocky and gravelly shores, estuarine conditions, and brackish, shallow bays.

PROVISIONS FOR VISITING SCIENTISTS: Research and living space for 50 visitors; no fees charged for research space.

MAJOR RESEARCH AND TEACHING FACILITIES: Very extensive library; running sea and fresh-water, large outdoor tanks, small aquarium tanks; collection room with specimens from all groups of marine fauna and marine algae; machine and wood shop, electrical shop, skilled shop workman available; vessels, 17 m LOA, *Prof. Lacaze Duthiers,* 11 m LOA under construction, 7 m LOA, *Amphioxus,* and 3 m LOA, *Sagitta.*

INSTRUCTIONAL PROGRAM: Organized courses for French students and visitors comprising laboratory work, marine excursions, conferences, etc. The laboratory exercises are concerned with marine invertebrates and fish.

SIZE OF RESIDENT STAFF: Five at professional level; 6 technicians.

IMPORTANT SPECIES AVAILABLE FOR LABORATORY STUDIES:

Echinodermata: *Arbacia, Paracentrotus, Astropecten*
Octocoralliaria: *Veretillum, Pennatula, Alcyonium*
Cephalopoda: *Octopus, Eledone, Sepia*
Crustacea: *Pachygrapsus, Pagurus, Penaeus*
Procordata: *Amphioxus*
Pisces: many Teleostei, *Scyliorhinus*

MAJOR CURRENT RESEARCH PROJECTS AND SCIENTIFIC LEADERS:

General ecology—ecology of brackish waters (G. Petit)
Marine parasitology (copepods); microfauna of sediments (M. Delamare-Deboutteville)
Biology of sponges (J. Paris)
Ecology of coral knolls (L. Laubier)
Systematics and biology of gobiid fish (H. Boutiere)
Biology and ecology of cephalopods (Mangold)

Systematics and biology of hermit crabs (Dechance)
Physiology of echinoderms (E. V. Buddenbrock)
Cytology of chaetognaths (Pasquet)
Plankton found in the stomachs of fish (R. Mizoule)

PUBLICATIONS ISSUED:
Vie et Milieu, Bulletin du Laboratoire Arago (issued 4 times a year plus supplements)
Faune Marine dese Pyrenees-Orientales (3 issues have been published)

College de France, Laboratoire de Biologie Marine, Concarneau

COLLEGE OF FRANCE, MARINE BIOLOGICAL LABORATORY, CONCARNEAU

POSTAL ADDRESS: Concarneau (Finistere), France.
EXECUTIVE OFFICER: Professor Dr. Jean Roche, Directeur de la Laboratoire, College de France, Paris V^e^, France.
YEAR FOUNDED: 1858.
SCOPE OF ACTIVITIES: Unrestricted research on the biochemistry of marine organisms.
SEASON OF OPERATION: April to November.
PHYSICAL ENVIRONMENT ACCESSIBLE: Atlantic Ocean; sandy and silty beaches, rocky and gravelly shores, estuarine conditions, oligotrophic lake, rivers and streams.
PROVISIONS FOR VISITING SCIENTISTS: Space for 10-15 visitors; no fees charged; living quarters available nearby.
MAJOR RESEARCH AND TEACHING FACILITIES: Moderately complete library; running sea and fresh-water, large outdoor tanks, small aquarium tanks; small research collection of algae of Britanny; herbarium of algae; machine and wood shop, electrical and electronic shop available in town, skilled shop workman available; small boats and outboard motors.
INSTRUCTIONAL PROGRAM: Comparative biochemistry.
SIZE OF STAFF: One at professional level; 2 technicians.
IMPORTANT SPECIES AVAILABLE FOR LABORATORY STUDIES:
Polychaeta: *Arenicola marina, Nereis diversicolor, Sipunculus nudus*
Mollusca: *Mytilus edulis, Cardium edulis*
Algae: *Laminaria digitata*

LABORATOIRE DE BIOLOGIE MARINE, CONCARNEAU

MAJOR CURRENT RESEARCH PROJECTS AND SCIENTIFIC LEADERS:
Biology of marine infusoria and microfauna of sands (E. Faure-Fremiet)
Biochemistry of phosphagens (Nguyen-van Thoai)
Biochemistry of guanidines (Y. Robin)
Biochemistry of iodine (J. Roche)

Station Aquicole Grimaldi de Saint-Jean-de-Losne

GRIMALDI HYDROBIOLOGICAL STATION OF SAINT-JEAN-DE-LOSNE

POSTAL ADDRESS: Saint Usage, par Saint-Jean-de-Losne (Cote d'Or), France.
EXECUTIVE OFFICER: Professeur J. R. Denis, Laboratoire de Zoologie, Faculte des Sciences, Dijon, France.
SPONSORING AGENCY: Universite de Dijon.
YEAR FOUNDED: 1911.
SCOPE OF ACTIVITIES: Unrestricted research on general biology and hydrobiology.
SEASON OF OPERATION: July and August.
PHYSICAL ENVIRONMENT ACCESSIBLE: Rivers, Saoene and Doubs, Canal de Bourgogne, Rhoene-Rhine Canal, Vouge, Ouche, Tille; marshes and ponds.
PROVISIONS FOR VISITING SCIENTISTS: Research and living space for 1-2 visitors.
MAJOR RESEARCH AND TEACHING FACILITIES: Small library at Station but library at Universite de Dijon accessible; small aquarium tanks; collections of insects and local fauna; one small boat.
INSTRUCTIONAL PROGRAM: Irregular courses for undergraduate and graduate students.
MAJOR CURRENT RESEARCH PROJECTS AND SCIENTIFIC LEADERS:
Projects vary with graduate students and visiting scientists.

Station Biologique d'Arcachon

ARCACHON BIOLOGICAL STATION

POSTAL ADDRESS: 2 rue du Professeur Jolyet, Arcachon (Gironde), France.
EXECUTIVE OFFICERS: Professeur Robert Weill, Directeur. Dr. M. Amanieu, Directeur-adjoint.
SPONSORING AGENCIES: Universite de Bordeaux; Ecole pratique des Hautes-Etudes; Societe scientifique d'Arcachon.
YEAR FOUNDED: 1867.
SCOPE OF ACTIVITIES: Unrestricted research on general marine biology, with emphasis on electrophysiology and endocrinology.
SEASON OF OPERATION: All year but working conditions from October to Easter are less favorable.
PHYSICAL ENVIRONMENT ACCESSIBLE: Bay of Biscay, Arcachon Basin, sand flats, mud banks, estuarine conditions, and brackish, shallow bays; 8 m tidal range.

STATION BIOLOGIQUE D'ARCACHON

PROVISIONS FOR VISITING SCIENTISTS: Research and living space for 30 visitors; no fees charged for research space.

MAJOR RESEARCH AND TEACHING FACILITIES: Moderately complete library; running sea and fresh-water, small aquarium tanks; identified reference collections of local Vertebrata and Invertebrata; special exhibition on *Ostrea* and local oyster culture; machine and wood shop, skilled shop workman available; small boats and outboard motors.

INSTRUCTIONAL PROGRAM: General invertebrate zoology.

SIZE OF STAFF: Four at professional level; 5 technicians.

IMPORTANT SPECIES AVAILABLE FOR LABORATORY STUDIES:

Coelenterata: *Tubularia, Anemonia, Actinia, Pleurobrachia*
Mollusca: *Sepia, Aplysia, Ostrea, Mytilus*
Crustacea: *Pagurus, Maia*
Echinodermata: *Astropecten, Ophiothrix*
Pisces: *Torpedo, Hippocampus, Solea*

MAJOR CURRENT RESEARCH PROJECTS AND SCIENTIFIC LEADERS:

Neurophysiology of *Torpedo* (Prof. Fessard)
Morphogenesis and nematocysts of actinians and hydroids (Prof. Weill)
Hormonal correlations in *Hippocampus* (Dr. Boisseau)

Station Biologique du Lac d'Oredon

LAKE OREDON BIOLOGICAL STATION

POSTAL ADDRESS: Aragnouet, par Saint-Lary (Hautes Pyrenees), France.

EXECUTIVE OFFICER: Professeur Eugene Angelier, Laboratoire de Zoologie, Faculte des Sciences, Toulouse, France.

SPONSORING AGENCY: Universite de Toulouse.

YEAR FOUNDED: 1922.

SCOPE OF ACTIVITIES: Research on the ecology of the aquatic and terrestrial fauna of high altitude.

SEASON OF OPERATION: All year but dependent upon snow conditions.

PHYSICAL ENVIRONMENT ACCESSIBLE: Eutrophic and oligotrophic lakes, rivers and streams, and all biotopes of high altitudes.

PROVISIONS FOR VISITING SCIENTISTS: Space for 16 visitors.

MAJOR RESEARCH AND TEACHING FACILITIES: Small library; 7 lakes and ponds, small aquarium tanks; one 3.5 m LOA vessel.

INSTRUCTIONAL PROGRAM: Zoology.

SIZE OF STAFF: Four at professional level.

MAJOR CURRENT RESEARCH PROJECTS AND SCIENTIFIC LEADERS:

Ecology of high altitude lakes (E. Angelier)
Ecology of Collembola (P. Cassagnau)
Ecology of Diplopoda (J. P. Mauries)
Ecology of Trichoptera (H. Decamps)

Station Biologique de Roscoff (Laboratoire Lacaze-Duthiers; Laboratoire Yves Delage)

ROSCOFF BIOLOGICAL STATION (LACAZE-DUTHIERS LABORATORY: YVES DELAGE LABORATORY)

POSTAL ADDRESS: Place Lacaze-Duthiers, Roscoff (Finistere), France.

LOCATION: Near Morlaix.

EXECUTIVE OFFICER: Professeur Georges Teissier, Directeur de la Station, Faculte des Sciences, 1, rue Victor Cousin, Paris V^{e}, France.

SPONSORING AGENCIES: Universite de Paris (Lacaze-Duthiers); Centre National de la Recherche Scientifique (Yves Delage).

YEAR FOUNDED: 1871 (Lacaze-Duthiers); 1949 (Yves Delage).

SCOPE OF ACTIVITIES: Unrestricted research on general marine biology; graduate and undergraduate instruction.

SEASON OF OPERATION: All year but because of climate, greater activity from June 1-October 1.

PHYSICAL ENVIRONMENT ACCESSIBLE: English Channel; sandy and silty beaches, rocky shores, estuarine conditions, numerous islands and bays; tidal range of 8-10 m.

PROVISIONS FOR VISITING SCIENTISTS: Research and living space for 30 visitors; fees charged for research space.

MAJOR RESEARCH AND TEACHING FACILITIES: Very extensive library at Universite de Paris, moderately complete library at the Station; running sea and fresh-water; research collections of Amphipoda, Porifera, and Polychaeta; identified reference collections of Algae, Bryozoa, Mollusca, Pisces and Hydroida; machine and wood shop; vessels, 20 m LOA, *Pluteus,* 12 m LOA, *Mysis,* and 6 m LOA, *Cydippe.*

LABORATOIRE LACAZE-DUTHIERS, ROSCOFF

INSTRUCTIONAL PROGRAM: Algology and marine zoology.

SIZE OF STAFF: Six at professional level; 25 technicians.

IMPORTANT SPECIES AVAILABLE FOR LABORATORY STUDIES:

Echinodermata: *Paracentrotus lividus, Echinocardium cordatum, Marthasterias glacialis*

Crustacea: *Carcinus maenas, Maia squinado*

Sipunculoidea: *Sipunculus nudus*

Annelida: *Sabellaria alveolata*

Selachii: *Scyliorhinus caniculus*

Teleostei: *Labrus mixtus* and *L. borgyeta*

MAJOR CURRENT RESEARCH PROJECTS AND SCIENTIFIC LEADERS:

Study of benthonic fauna (A. Boillot, L. Cabioch)

Sand microfauna (B. Swedmark L'Hasdy)

Biometry of Crustacea (G. Teissier)

Population genetics (G. Teissier and Cha. Bocquet)

Ecology of sand beaches (M. Prenant)

PUBLICATIONS ISSUED: *Cahiers de Biologie Marine* (regularly published journal)

Station Marine d'Endoume

MARINE STATION OF ENDOUME

POSTAL ADDRESS: Rue de la Batterie des Lions, Marseille VII, (Bouches du Rhoene), France.

EXECUTIVE OFFICER: J. M. Peres, Directeur et Professeur d'Oceanographie.

SPONSORING AGENCY: Universite d'aix-Marseille.

YEAR FOUNDED: 1889.

SCOPE OF ACTIVITIES: Unrestricted research on general oceanography with particular emphasis on benthonic biocoenoses and plankton; graduate instruction.

SEASON OF OPERATION: All year.

PHYSICAL ENVIRONMENT ACCESSIBLE: Mediterranean Sea; sandy beach, rocky shore, and brackish lagoons.

PROVISIONS FOR VISITING SCIENTISTS: Research and living space for 5-6 visitors; fees not usually charged for research space.

MAJOR RESEARCH AND TEACHING FACILITIES: Very extensive library at the University, moderately complete library at the Station; running sea and freshwater, small aquarium tanks; rather complete identified reference collections of flora and fauna of Mediterranean and nearest Atlantic, except fishes; small shop facilities; 16.5 m LOA vessel, *Antedon,* with accommodations for 5 scientists.

INSTRUCTIONAL PROGRAM: From October 15 to June 15: courses in oceanography (benthos, plankton, marine geology, and applied physical oceanography).

SIZE OF STAFF: About 30 at professional level; 9 technicians.

MAJOR CURRENT RESEARCH PROJECTS AND SCIENTIFIC LEADERS:

Comparative distribution of benthos (J. M. Peres and J. Picard)

Biology of calcareous seaweeds (H. Huve)

Vertical migrations of zooplankton (A. Bourdillon)

Minimum oxygen layer and physical and biological factors (L. Deveze)

Shallow water waves and sediment-transport (J. Blanc)

Station Zoologique de Villefranche

ZOOLOGICAL STATION OF VILLEFRANCHE

POSTAL ADDRESS: Villefranche-sur-Mer (Alpes-Maritimes), France.

LOCATION: Near Nice.

EXECUTIVE OFFICERS: Professeur M. Petit, Directeur. Dr. Paul Bougis, Directeur en residence.

SPONSORING AGENCY: Universite de Paris.

YEAR FOUNDED: 1884.

SCOPE OF ACTIVITIES: Unrestricted research in marine biology, particularly plankton; graduate instruction.

SEASON OF OPERATION: All year except for July.

PHYSICAL ENVIRONMENT ACCESSIBLE: Mediterranean Sea; 800 m channel nearby.

STATION MARINE D'ENDOUME

STATION ZOOLOGIQUE DE VILLEFRANCHE

PROVISIONS FOR VISITING SCIENTISTS: Research and living space for 3-5 visitors; no fees charged for research space.

MAJOR RESEARCH AND TEACHING FACILITIES: Moderately complete library; small aquarium tanks; identified reference collections of local fauna and flora; machine and wood shop; small boats and outboard motors.

INSTRUCTIONAL PROGRAM: Marine plankton (August and October).

SIZE OF STAFF: Twelve at professional level; 3 technicians.

IMPORTANT SPECIES AVAILABLE FOR LABORATORY STUDIES:

Echinodermata: *Paracentrotus lividus, Arbacia lixula*
Deep water plankton available in surface tows (siphonophores, medusae, chaetognaths, pteropods, heteropods, bathypelagic cephalopods, and fishes)

MAJOR CURRENT RESEARCH PROJECTS AND SCIENTIFIC LEADERS:

Plankton of the depths (G. Tregouboff)
Ecology of the Appendicularia (R. Fenaux)
Ecological role of heavy metals (P. Bougis)
Experimental embryology (R. Lallier)
Metabolism of calcium in mollusks (G. Gostan)

Laboratoire Maritime de Luc-Sur-Mer

MARINE LABORATORY OF LUC-SUR-MER

POSTAL ADDRESS: Rue Charcot, Luc-sur-Mer (Calvados), France.

LOCATION: Near Caen.

EXECUTIVE OFFICERS: Professeur C. Bocquet, Directeur. F. Benard, Chef de Travaux.

SPONSORING AGENCY: Universite de Caen.

YEAR FOUNDED: 1883; new laboratory founded in 1962.

SCOPE OF ACTIVITIES: Unrestricted research on general marine biology, ecology, zoology, genetics, and biometry.

SEASON OF OPERATION: All year.

PHYSICAL ENVIRONMENT ACCESSIBLE: Bay of the Seine, Canal de Caen a la mer; sandy beach, rocky shore, estuarine conditions, brackish, shallow bays, and rivers.

PROVISIONS FOR VISITING SCIENTISTS: Space for 8-10 visitors at new laboratory.

MAJOR RESEARCH AND TEACHING FACILITIES: Small library; running sea and fresh-water in new laboratory, large outdoor tanks, small aquarium tanks; small boats and outboard motors; one 6 m LOA vessel.

INSTRUCTIONAL PROGRAM: Systematics, zoology, and plankton.

IMPORTANT SPECIES AVAILABLE FOR LABORATORY STUDIES:

Isopoda: *Sphaeroma, Jaera, Idothea, Ligia*

MAJOR CURRENT RESEARCH PROJECTS AND SCIENTIFIC LEADERS:

Genetics (C. Bocquet)
Marine acarology (F. Benard)
Physiological ecology (F. Benard)

Universite Catholique de Lille, Station Biologique, Laboratoire Charles Maurice

CATHOLIC UNIVERSITY OF LILLE, BIOLOGICAL STATION, CHARLES MAURICE LABORATORY

POSTAL ADDRESS: Ambleteuse (Pas-de-Calais), France.

LOCATION: Near Boulogne-sur-Mer.

EXECUTIVE OFFICER: Professeur Henry Boulange, Directeur.

YEAR FOUNDED: 1895.

SCOPE OF ACTIVITIES: Unrestricted research on general marine biology; graduate instruction.

SEASON OF OPERATION: April to September.

STATION BIOLOGIQUE, AMBLETEUSE

PHYSICAL ENVIRONMENT ACCESSIBLE: Straits of Dover; open ocean, sandy beach, rocky shore, and estuarine conditions.

PROVISIONS FOR VISITING SCIENTISTS: Space for 8 visitors; variable fees charged for research space; living quarters for 6 at the Station, other quarters available nearby.

MAJOR RESEARCH AND TEACHING FACILITIES: Small library; small aquarium tanks; identified reference collection of local intertidal marine fauna.

INSTRUCTIONAL PROGRAM: Marine zoology and marine botany (irregularly).

IMPORTANT SPECIES AVAILABLE FOR LABORATORY STUDIES:

Echinodermata: *Asterias rubens*
Annelida: *Nereis diversicolor*
Crustacea: *Ligia oceanica*

MAJOR CURRENT RESEARCH PROJECTS AND SCIENTIFIC LEADERS:

Marine isopods (H. Hoestlandt)
Ostracods (R. Rome)
Marine Crustacea (J. Berthet and P. Berthet)
Littoral terrestrial mollusks (J. Boulange)

Universite Catholique de Lyon, Laboratoire de Biologie Animale

CATHOLIC UNIVERSITY OF LYON, LABORATORY OF ANIMAL BIOLOGY

POSTAL ADDRESS: 25 rue du Plat, Lyon (Rhoene), France.

EXECUTIVE OFFICER: M. Delsol, Directeur.

YEAR FOUNDED: 1880.

SCOPE OF ACTIVITIES: Unrestricted research on metamorphosis and endocrinology of batrachians; evolution.

SEASON OF OPERATION: All year.

PHYSICAL ENVIRONMENT ACCESSIBLE: Oligotrophic lake, rivers and streams.

PROVISIONS FOR VISITING SCIENTISTS: Space for 1 visitor; no fees charged.

MAJOR RESEARCH AND TEACHING FACILITIES: Small library; small aquarium tanks.

INSTRUCTIONAL PROGRAM: General biology.

SIZE OF STAFF: Two at professional level; 2 technicians.

IMPORTANT SPECIES AVAILABLE FOR LABORATORY STUDIES:

Amphibia: *Rana esculenta, R. temporaria, Alytes obstetricans, Triturus alpestris*

MAJOR CURRENT RESEARCH PROJECTS AND SCIENTIFIC LEADERS:

Metamorphosis and neoteny of batrachians (Michel Delsol)
Comparison between active and hibernating batrachians (J. Flatin)
Gonadotrophic hormones of batrachians (C. Fayolle)

Station Biologique de Besse-En-Chandesse

BIOLOGICAL STATION OF BESSE-EN-CHANDESSE

POSTAL ADDRESS: Besse-en-Chandesse (Puy-de-Doeme), France.

LOCATION: Near Clermont-Ferrand.

EXECUTIVE OFFICER: Professeur Raymond Hovasse, Faculte des Sciences, Universite de Clermont-Ferrand, Clermont-Ferrand, France.

SPONSORING AGENCY: Universite de Clermont-Ferrand.

YEAR FOUNDED: 1900.

SCOPE OF ACTIVITIES: Unrestricted research on plankton and fish culture; graduate and undergraduate instruction.

SEASON OF OPERATION: All year for research; December to February for fish culture; and June to September for instruction.

PHYSICAL ENVIRONMENT ACCESSIBLE: Lakes Pavin, Chambon, Chauvet; 9 lakes (oligotrophic, eutrophic and dystrophic) available in area; rivers and streams.

PROVISIONS FOR VISITING SCIENTISTS: Research and living space for visitors; no fees charged for research space.

MAJOR RESEARCH AND TEACHING FACILITIES: Small library at the Station but library of the University accessible; research collections of fauna and flora available at the University; identified reference collections of local fauna and flora; machine and wood shop, electrical and electronic shop; small boats and outboard motors.

INSTRUCTIONAL PROGRAM: Phytoplankton, protozoology, and entomology.

SIZE OF STAFF: One at professional level; 1 technician.

IMPORTANT SPECIES AVAILABLE FOR LABORATORY STUDIES:

Protozoa: *Goniostomum semen, Hydrurus foetidus*
Crustacea: *Branchipus* sp.
Insecta: Many species of aquatic insects.

STATION BIOLOGIQUE, BESSE-EN-CHANDESSE

MAJOR CURRENT RESEARCH PROJECTS AND SCIENTIFIC LEADERS:
- Chrysomonadina, particularly *Hydrurus foetidus* (R. Hovasse and Joyon)
- Volvocales (*Stephanosphaera*) (Joyon)
- Apostomes (ciliate parasites of *Gammarus*) (de Puytorac)

Faculte des Sciences de Grenoble, Institut de Zoologie, Laboratoire d' Hydrobiologie et de Pisciculture

FACULTY OF SCIENCE OF GRENOBLE UNIVERSITY, INSTITUTE OF ZOOLOGY, HYDROBIOLOGICAL AND FISH CULTURE LABORATORY

POSTAL ADDRESS: 14 rue Hebert, Grenoble (Isere), France.
EXECUTIVE OFFICER: Professeur A. Dorier.
YEAR FOUNDED: 1900.
SCOPE OF ACTIVITIES: Unrestricted research on limnology and rheobiology; instruction.
SEASON OF OPERATION: All year.
PHYSICAL ENVIRONMENT ACCESSIBLE: Oligotrophic lake, rivers and streams.
PROVISIONS FOR VISITING SCIENTISTS: Space for 2 visitors.
MAJOR RESEARCH AND TEACHING FACILITIES: Small library.
INSTRUCTIONAL PROGRAM: Zoology.
MAJOR CURRENT RESEARCH PROJECTS AND SCIENTIFIC LEADERS:
- Ecology of Simuliidae (A. Dorier)
- Ecology of Ephemeroptera (C. Degrange)
- Ecology of Psychodidae (F. Vaillant)

PUBLICATIONS ISSUED: *Travaux du Laboratoire d' Hydrobiologie et Pisciculture de l'Universite de Grenoble* (regularly published journal)

LABORATOIRE D'HYDROBIOLOGIE DE L'UNIVERSITE DE GRENOBLE

INSTITUT DE BIOLOGIE MARITIME REGIONALE, UNIVERSITE DE LILLE

Universite de Lille, Institut de Biologie Maritime Regionale

UNIVERSITY OF LILLE, INSTITUTE OF REGIONAL MARINE BIOLOGY

POSTAL ADDRESS: Avenue Foch, Wimereux (Pas de Calais), France.
EXECUTIVE OFFICER: Professeur Rene Defretin, Directeur.
YEAR FOUNDED: 1960.
SCOPE OF ACTIVITIES: Unrestricted research on general marine biology; graduate instruction.
SEASON OF OPERATION: All year.
PHYSICAL ENVIRONMENT ACCESSIBLE: Boulonnais, Detroit du Pas de Calais; open ocean, sandy beach, rocky shore, and estuarine conditions.
PROVISIONS FOR VISITING SCIENTISTS: Research and living space for 5-10 visitors.
MAJOR RESEARCH AND TEACHING FACILITIES: Small library; running sea and fresh-water, small aquarium tanks; identified reference collections of local fauna and flora in preparation; machine and wood shop; one small boat with motor; 10-12 m LOA vessel planned.
INSTRUCTIONAL PROGRAM: General invertebrate zoology, zoology, zooplankton, endocrinology of invertebrates, and biochemistry.
SIZE OF STAFF: One at professional level; 1 technician.
IMPORTANT SPECIES AVAILABLE FOR LABORATORY STUDIES:
- Porifera: *Halichondria panicea*
- Crustacea: *Carcinus maenas*
- Many other shore species available.

MAJOR CURRENT RESEARCH PROJECTS AND SCIENTIFIC LEADERS:
- Invertebrate endocrinology (Prof. R. Defretin and Prof. Durchon)
- Biochemistry (Prof. Montreuil)

Universite de Lyon, Laboratoire de Zoologie Generale

UNIVERSITY OF LYON, LABORATORY OF GENERAL ZOOLOGY

POSTAL ADDRESS: 16, Quai Claude Bernard, Lyon, France.
EXECUTIVE OFFICER: Professeur J. Wautier, Directeur.
YEAR FOUNDED: 1946.
SCOPE OF ACTIVITIES: Unrestricted research on fresh-water biology and zoology; graduate instruction.
SEASON OF OPERATION: All year.
PHYSICAL ENVIRONMENT ACCESSIBLE: Rivers Rhoene and Saoene, Etangs des Dombes; hypogean fresh-waters.
PROVISIONS FOR VISITING SCIENTISTS: Space for 2 visitors; no fees charged; living quarters available nearby.
MAJOR RESEARCH AND TEACHING FACILITIES: Small library; small aquarium tanks; research collections of Ephemeroptera, fresh-water Amphipoda (*Gammarus, Niphargus*); small boats and outboard motors, motor car.
INSTRUCTIONAL PROGRAM: General invertebrates, comprehensive zoology, ecology, and biocenotics.
SIZE OF STAFF: Twelve at professional level; 4 technicians.
IMPORTANT SPECIES AVAILABLE FOR LABORATORY STUDIES:
Mollusca: *Gundlachia* sp.
Crustacea: *Niphargus orcinus virei, Gammarus pulex pulex, G. pulex fossarum*
Insecta: *Prosopistoma foliaceum, Micropterna testacea*
MAJOR CURRENT RESEARCH PROJECTS AND SCIENTIFIC LEADERS:
General biocoenology of fresh-water ecology; biological cycle of a new Ancylidae (*Gundlachia*); fauna of streams (J. Wautier)
Ecology and biology of aquatic cavern fauna (R. Ginet)
Ecology and grouping of stream invertebrates (S. Fiasson)
Stenothermy and eurythermy of aquatic invertebrates; thermal adaptation as measured by respiratory metabolism in planaria and insect larvae (E. Pattee)
Interstitial lacustrine microfauna of littoral sand and of benthonic areas; ecological speciation of lacustrine regions (J. Juget)
Ecology of epigeous fresh-water Amphipoda; intersterility of *Gammarus pulex* subspecies (A. Roux)
Ecology and biology of Ephemeroptera (J. Fontaine)
Rheotropism of Trichoptera larvae (M. Bournaud)
Biospeleology; microbiology and enzymology of subterranean, submerged argils; food of limnetic cavern fauna (A. M. Gounot)
Respiratory metabolism and ecological distribution of Trichoptera larvae (C. Collardeau)
Digestive system of Trichoptera larvae (H. Tachet)

Universite de Lyon, Station Maritime de Biologie

UNIVERSITY OF LYON, MARINE BIOLOGICAL STATION

POSTAL ADDRESS: Avenue Michel Pacha, Tamaris (Var) France.
LOCATION: Near Toulon.
EXECUTIVE OFFICER: Professeur Gabriel Peres, Directeur de la Station, Faculte des Sciences, Universite de Lyon, 30 rue Cavenne, Lyon, France.
YEAR FOUNDED: 1899.
SCOPE OF ACTIVITIES: Unrestricted research on general marine biology, with particular emphasis on comparative physiology.
SEASON OF OPERATION: All year.
PHYSICAL ENVIRONMENT ACCESSIBLE: Mediterranean Sea.
PROVISIONS FOR VISITING SCIENTISTS: Research and living space for 4 visitors; no fees charged for research space.
MAJOR RESEARCH FACILITIES: Small library; running sea and fresh-water, small aquarium tanks; identified reference collection of marine fauna of the Mediterranean; small boats and outboard motors; one 7 m LOA power vessel.
IMPORTANT SPECIES AVAILABLE FOR LABORATORY STUDIES:
Mediterranean fishes and crustaceans.

Universite de Paris (Sorbonne), Centre de Recherches Geodynamiques

UNIVERSITY OF PARIS (SORBONNE), GEODYNAMICAL RESEARCH CENTER

POSTAL ADDRESS: 45 avenue de Corzent, Thonon-les-Bains (Haute-Savoie), France.
LOCATION: Near Geneve, Suisse (Geneva, Switzerland).

CENTRE DE RECHERCHES GEODYNAMIQUES, SORBONNE

EXECUTIVE OFFICERS: Professeur L. Glangeaud, Directeur, 1, rue Victor-Cousin, Paris Ve, France. B. H. Dussart, Directeur-adjoint.
YEAR FOUNDED: 1957.
SCOPE OF ACTIVITIES: Unrestricted research on general limnology and hydrology, particularly in geological phenomena; graduate and undergraduate instruction.
SEASON OF OPERATION: All year.
PHYSICAL ENVIRONMENT ACCESSIBLE: Lake Geneva; sandy beach, rocky and gravelly shores, eutrophic and oligotrophic lakes, rivers and streams.
PROVISIONS FOR VISITING SCIENTISTS: Research and living quarters for 5 visitors; no fees charged for research space.
MAJOR RESEARCH AND TEACHING FACILITIES: Moderately complete library; small aquarium tanks; machine and wood shop, electrical and electronic shop, skilled shop workman available; one 8 m LOA vessel.
INSTRUCTIONAL PROGRAM: General limnology, glaciology, and water analysis.
SIZE OF STAFF: Three at professional level; 5 technicians.

Universite de Paris, Laboratoire de Biologie Vegetale Marine

UNIVERSITY OF PARIS, LABORATORY OF MARINE BOTANY

POSTAL ADDRESS: Nouvelle Faculte des Sciences, Batiment A, Quai Saint-Bernard, Paris Ve, France.
EXECUTIVE OFFICER: Professeur Jean Feldmann.
YEAR FOUNDED: 1956.
SCOPE OF ACTIVITIES: Unrestricted research on the biology, cytology, ecology and taxonomy of marine plants (algae and fungi); graduate instruction.
SEASON OF OPERATION: All year.
PROVISIONS FOR VISITING SCIENTISTS: Space for 1-2 visitors; no fees charged; living quarters available nearby.
MAJOR RESEARCH AND TEACHING FACILITIES: Very small library; small aquarium tanks, climatized room for culture of marine algae; herbarium of marine algae collected mainly from the coasts of France and Mediterranean Sea.
INSTRUCTIONAL PROGRAM: Ecology of marine algae, and reproduction and classification of marine algae.
SIZE OF STAFF: Eight at professional level; 2 technicians.
MAJOR CURRENT RESEARCH PROJECTS AND SCIENTIFIC LEADERS:
- Morphology and cytology of marine algae (J. Feldmann and staff)
- Ecological floristic research on marine algae from the Channel and Mediterranean Sea (J. Feldmann and J. Ernst)
- Marine fungi (G. Feldmann)

Laboratories for Which No Detailed Information Was Available:

Group d'Etudes et de Recherches Sous-marines, *Direction du Port, Toulon, France.*

Laboratoire de Biologie marine, *Ecole de Medecine et de Pharmacie de Nantes Le Croisic (Loire-atlantique), France.*
Sponsoring agency: Universite de Rennes.

Station d'Etudes hydrobiologiques du lac du Bourget, *Le Petit Port, Aix-les-Baines (Savoie), France. R. Joly, Directeur.*
Sponsoring agency: Ecole nationale des Eaux et Foerets.

GERMAN DEMOCRATIC REPUBLIC

Universitaet Greifswald, Biologische Forschungsanstalt Hiddensee

GREIFSWALD UNIVERSITY, HIDDENSEE BIOLOGICAL RESEARCH STATION

POSTAL ADDRESS: Kloster auf Hiddensee, Deutsche Demokratische Republik (East Germany).
LOCATION: Near Stralsund.
EXECUTIVE OFFICER: Professor Dr. Hans Schildmacher, Direktor.
YEAR FOUNDED: 1930.
SCOPE OF ACTIVITIES: Unrestricted research on plant ecology, biology of brackish water, bird migration and physiology, parasitology; graduate and undergraduate instruction.

BIOLOGISCHE FORSCHUNGSANSTALT HIDDENSEE

SEASON OF OPERATION: All year.

PHYSICAL ENVIRONMENT ACCESSIBLE: Baltic Sea; brackish, shallow bays.

PROVISIONS FOR VISITING SCIENTISTS: Research and living space for 5-6 visitors; no fees charged for research space.

MAJOR RESEARCH AND TEACHING FACILITIES: Small library; small aquarium tanks; research collections of skins and palaeontologic materials from Hiddensee area; small boats and outboard motors; one 10 m LOA vessel.

INSTRUCTIONAL PROGRAM: Plant ecology, biology of brackish water, and ornithology.

SIZE OF STAFF: Eight at professional level; 8 technicians.

Deutsche Akademie der Landwirtschaftswissenschaften (DAL) zu Berlin, Institut fuer Fischerei

GERMAN ACADEMY OF AGRICULTURE AND SCIENCE OF BERLIN, FISHERIES INSTITUTE

POSTAL ADDRESS:
Headquarters: Mueggelseedamm 310, Berlin-Friedrichshagen, Deutsche Demokratische Republik (East Germany).
Branch laboratories:
1. Zweigstelle fuer Ostseefischerei
2. Zweigstelle fuer Karpfenteichwirtschaft
3. Zweigstelle fuer Fangtechnik und Mechanisierueng (Not described in the *Directory*)

(Descriptions follow.)

EXECUTIVE OFFICER: Professor Dr. Wilhelm Schaeperclaus, Direktor.

YEAR FOUNDED: 1893.

SCOPE OF ACTIVITIES: Unrestricted research on fishery biology, fish pathology, and sewage chemistry.

SEASON OF OPERATION: All year.

PHYSICAL ENVIRONMENT ACCESSIBLE: Ponds, reservoirs, open ocean, estuarine conditions, brackish, shallow bays, eutrophic and oligotrophic lakes, rivers and streams.

PROVISIONS FOR VISITING SCIENTISTS: None.

MAJOR RESEARCH FACILITIES: Moderately complete library; large outdoor ponds and tanks, fish hatchery; identified reference collections of bottom fauna and fish; machine and wood shop; vessels, 18 m and 8 m LOA.

SIZE OF STAFF: Twenty-three at professional level; 67 technicians.

MAJOR CURRENT RESEARCH PROJECTS AND SCIENTIFIC LEADERS:
- Pond management, fish breeding and fish pathology (W. Schaeperclaus)
- Fishery biology, sea and fresh-water fishing (H. Mueller)
- Fish chemistry (D. Nehring)

INSTITUT FUER FISCHEREI, BERLIN

PUBLICATIONS ISSUED: *Zeitschrift fur Fischerei und deren Hilfswissenschaften, Deutsche Fischerei-Zeitung,* Zweijahresbericht der DAL (regularly published journal)

Zweigstelle fuer Ostseefischerei

BALTIC FISHERIES BRANCH

POSTAL ADDRESS: Hafenstrasse 17, Sassnitz/Ruegen, Deutsche Demokratische Republik (East Germany).

EXECUTIVE OFFICER: Dr. H. Roy, Leiter.

YEAR FOUNDED: 1950.

SCOPE OF ACTIVITIES: Restricted research on the biology and hydrography of the middle Baltic and shallow inlets; unrestricted research on fishery biology.

SEASON OF OPERATION: All year.

PHYSICAL ENVIRONMENT ACCESSIBLE: Baltic Sea; brackish, shallow bays.

PROVISIONS FOR VISITING SCIENTISTS: None.

MAJOR RESEARCH FACILITIES: Small library; identified reference collections of sea and brackish water fauna; 24 m LOA cutter, *Gadus.*

MAJOR CURRENT RESEARCH PROJECTS AND SCIENTIFIC LEADERS:
- Salmon; echosounding (H. Roy)
- Fish of the Baltic Sea (Dr. M. Berner)
- Productivity of the Baltic; plankton (Dr. Waldmann)
- Productivity of the coastal waters; benthos (Dr. Loewe)
- Clupeids (Dipl. Fw. Anwand)
- Hydrography and sewage chemistry (Dipl. Chem. Bauer)

Zweigstelle fuer Karpfenteichwirtschaft

BRANCH FOR CARP POND MANAGEMENT

POSTAL ADDRESS: Koenigswartha/Kreis Bautzen, Deutsche Demokratische Republik (East Germany).

EXECUTIVE OFFICER: Dr. W. Mueller, Leiter.

YEAR FOUNDED: 1950.

ZWEIGSTELLE FUER KARPFENTEICHWIRTSCHAFT

SCOPE OF ACTIVITIES: Restricted research on fish pond fertilizing, feeding and breeding of carp.

SEASON OF OPERATION: All year.

PHYSICAL ENVIRONMENT ACCESSIBLE: Fish ponds.

PROVISIONS FOR VISITING SCIENTISTS: Research and living space for 2 visitors; no fees charged for research space.

MAJOR RESEARCH FACILITIES: Small library; small aquarium tanks.

SIZE OF STAFF: Two at professional level; 5 technicians.

MAJOR CURRENT RESEARCH PROJECTS AND SCIENTIFIC LEADERS:
- Chemistry of pond bottoms and water analysis (W. Mueller and G. Merla)
- Carp feeding investigations (W. Mueller and G. Merla)
- Phosphate fertilizing experiments (W. Mueller and G. Merla)

Forschungsstelle fuer Limnologie

LABORATORY OF LIMNOLOGY

POSTAL ADDRESS: Alte Landstrasse 3, Jena-Lobeda, Deutsche Demokratische Republik (Jena-Lobeda, East Germany).

EXECUTIVE OFFICER: Dozent Dr. habil. Theodor Schraeder, Leiter.

SPONSORING AGENCY: Deutsche Akademie der Wissenschaften zu Berlin, Forschungsgemeinschaft (German Academy of Science of Berlin, Research Society).

YEAR FOUNDED: 1959.

SCOPE OF ACTIVITIES: Unrestricted research on general fresh-water biology; ecology of adjacent areas.

SEASON OF OPERATION: All year.

PHYSICAL ENVIRONMENT ACCESSIBLE: All East German bodies of water; eutrophic and oligotrophic lakes, rivers, streams, subsoil water, and coastal areas.

PROVISIONS FOR VISITING SCIENTISTS: Research and living space for visitors to be made available soon.

MAJOR RESEARCH FACILITIES UNDER CONSTRUCTION: Moderately complete library; small aquarium; research collections of fauna and flora; small boats and outboard motors.

SIZE OF STAFF: Eleven at professional level; 3 technicians.

MAJOR CURRENT RESEARCH PROJECTS AND SCIENTIFIC LEADERS:
- Investigations of Stechlin Lake and adjacent areas in connection with the establishment of a nuclear power plant (T. Schraeder and A. Rieth).

PUBLICATIONS ISSUED: *Limnologica* (3 times a year)

Humboldt Universitaet zu Berlin, Institut fuer Fischereiwesen

HUMBOLDT UNIVERSITY OF BERLIN, FISHERY INSTITUTE

POSTAL ADDRESS: Josef-Nawrocki Strasse 7, Berlin-Friedrichshagen, Deutsche Demokratische Republik (Berlin, East Germany).

EXECUTIVE OFFICER: Professor Dr. Diethelm Scheer, Instituts-direktor.

YEAR FOUNDED: 1945.

SCOPE OF ACTIVITIES: Officially restricted research and instruction on general ichthyology, fish diseases, pond culture, fish genetics, fish nutrition, coastal fisheries, zooplankton, and littoral algology.

SEASON OF OPERATION: All year.

PHYSICAL ENVIRONMENT ACCESSIBLE: Mueggelsee, Seen der Spree, Dahme, and Havel; brackish, shallow bays, eutrophic lake, and ponds.

PROVISIONS FOR VISITING SCIENTISTS: Research space for 2 visitors.

MAJOR RESEARCH AND TEACHING FACILITIES: Small library; small aquarium tanks; research collection of plankton from nearby lakes; identified reference collections of local fish and aquatic flora; skilled shop workman available; small boats and outboard motors.

INSTRUCTIONAL PROGRAM: Fish diseases, histology, systematics of fresh-water fishes, bottom fauna and flora, water chemistry, general marine biology, and fishery biology.

SIZE OF STAFF: Seven at professional level; 8 technicians.

MAJOR CURRENT RESEARCH PROJECTS:
- Fish genetics
- Nutrition of carp
- Chemical control of aquatic plants
- Fish species in coastal waters

Institut fuer Hochseefischerei und Fischverarbeitung

INSTITUTE FOR MARINE FISHERIES AND FISH PROCESSING

POSTAL ADDRESS: Rostock-Merienehe, Deutsche Demokratische Republik (Rostock-Marienehe, East Germany).

EXECUTIVE OFFICER: Herr Schneider, Direktor.

SPONSORING AGENCY: Deutsche Demokratische Republik.

YEAR FOUNDED: 1953.

SCOPE OF ACTIVITIES: Unrestricted research on fishery biology, general marine biology, plankton, and oceanography.

SEASON OF OPERATION: All year.

PHYSICAL ENVIRONMENT ACCESSIBLE: Baltic Sea.

PROVISIONS FOR VISITING SCIENTISTS: None.

MAJOR RESEARCH FACILITIES: Moderately complete library; machine and wood shop, skilled workman available; vessels, 56 m LOA trawler, 39 m LOA logger, and a 32 m LOA cutter.

SIZE OF STAFF: Eleven at professional level; 12 technicians.

MAJOR CURRENT RESEARCH PROJECTS AND SCIENTIFIC LEADERS:

Herring (Herr Schultz)
Codfish (Herr Biester)
Red perch (Herr Freund)

PUBLICATIONS ISSUED: *Fischereiforschung* (published regularly)

Karl Marx Universitaet Leipzig, Abteilung fuer Trink-, Brauch- und Abwasserbiologie, am Zoologischen Institut

UNIVERSITY OF LEIPZIG, DEPARTMENT OF SEWAGE AND WATERBIOLOGY OF THE ZOOLOGICAL INSTITUTE

POSTAL ADDRESS:

Headquarters: Talstrasse 33, Leipzig C-1, Deutsche Demokratische Republik (East Germany).

Branch: Laboratory for reservoir studies at Neunzehnhain.

EXECUTIVE OFFICER: Professor Dr. A. Wetzel, Leiter.

YEAR FOUNDED: 1952.

SCOPE OF ACTIVITIES: Restricted research on biological self purification, running water, limnology of polluted ponds and streams, plankton problems of reservoirs and ground water biology; graduate and undergraduate instruction.

SEASON OF OPERATION: All year.

PHYSICAL ENVIRONMENT ACCESSIBLE: Rivers and streams, hypertrophic ponds and the Lautenbach reservoirs.

INSTITUT FUER HOCHSEEFISCHEREI UND FISCHVERARBEITUNG, ROSTOCK-MARIENEHE

PROVISIONS FOR VISITING SCIENTISTS: None.

MAJOR RESEARCH AND TEACHING FACILITIES: Small library; small aquarium tanks; small boats and outboard motors.

INSTRUCTIONAL PROGRAM: For students: Limnological methods, protozoa and unicellular algae, invertebrate animals, fishes, and water plants. For water engineers: biological problems of sewage purification, drinking water supply and supply of water for domestic and industrial purposes.

SIZE OF STAFF: Six at professional level; 1 technician.

IMPORTANT SPECIES AVAILABLE FOR LABORATORY STUDIES:

Protozoa: *Actinosphaerium eichhorni, Paramecium caudatum*
Turbellaria: *Dendrocoelum lacteum*
Crustacea: *Daphnia magna*
Gastropoda: *Limnaea stagnalis*

MAJOR CURRENT RESEARCH PROJECTS AND SCIENTIFIC LEADERS:

Limnology of hypertrophic ponds (D. Uhlmann)
Limnology of polluted streams (W. Beer)
Biological oxidation demand (BOD_5) studies (K. Madler)
Nutrient problems of reservoirs (R. Hedlich)
Groundwater biology (R. Wegelin)

GREECE

The Marine Biochemistry Laboratory

POSTAL ADDRESS: St. George, Limni, Hellaes (Greece).

EXECUTIVE OFFICER: Dr. Anast. A. Christomanos, Professor of Biochemistry, University of Thessaloniki.

SPONSORING AGENCIES: National Hellenic Oceanographic Society with the collaboration of the Institute of Biochemistry of the University of Thessaloniki.

YEAR FOUNDED: 1954.

SCOPE OF ACTIVITIES: Research on the pigments and proteins of marine invertebrates.
SEASON OF OPERATION: 1 June to 1 October.
PHYSICAL ENVIRONMENT ACCESSIBLE: Euboean Sea; sandy and silty beaches, rocky and gravelly shores.
PROVISIONS FOR VISITING SCIENTISTS: Research and living space for 2 visitors; no fees charged for research space.
MAJOR RESEARCH FACILITIES: Small library; small aquarium tanks; museum with research collection of mollusks, sponges, corals, etc.
SIZE OF STAFF: Three at professional level.
MAJOR CURRENT RESEARCH PROJECTS AND SCIENTIFIC LEADERS:
Melanotic pigments of mollusks (A. Christomanos)
Amino acid sequence in haemoglobins of fishes (J. Georgatsos, V. Gardiki and A. Dimitzidou)
Influence of insulin on the glycogen content of fish liver (Georgia Gitsa)
PUBLICATIONS ISSUED: *Marine Scientific Pages* and *Bulletin of the Marine Laboratory* (regularly published journals in Greek).

GREENLAND

Ministeriet for Groenland, Groenlands Fiskeriundersoegelser, Fiskeribiologisk Laboratorium

THE MINISTRY FOR GREENLAND, GREENLAND FISHERIES ORGANIZATION, FISHERIES LABORATORY

POSTAL ADDRESS: Godthaeb, Groenland (Greenland). Communications are limited in winter.
EXECUTIVE OFFICERS: Mr. J. Kreutzmann, Director of Laboratory. Dr. Paul M. Hansen, Leader, Groenlands Fiskeriundersoegelser Charlottenlund Slot, Charlottenlund, Danmark (Denmark).
YEAR FOUNDED: 1953.
SCOPE OF ACTIVITIES: Unrestricted research on applied fishery biology, plankton studies, and general marine ecology; some graduate instruction in Denmark.
SEASON OF OPERATION: All year.
PHYSICAL ENVIRONMENT ACCESSIBLE: Davis and Danmark straits; open ocean and fjords.
PROVISIONS FOR VISITING SCIENTISTS: Research and living space for two visitors; no fees charged for research space.
MAJOR RESEARCH FACILITIES: Small library; running sea and fresh-water, small aquarium tanks; machine and wood shop, skilled shop workman available; small boats and outboard motors; power vessels, 15 m LOA, M/K *Adolf Jensen,* and 30 ft LOA, *Tornak.*

FISKERIBIOLOGISK LABORATORIUM, GOTHAEB

SIZE OF STAFF: One at the laboratory and 4 at Charlottenlund Slot at the professional level; 1 technician.
IMPORTANT SPECIES AVAILABLE FOR LABORATORY STUDIES:
Crustacea: *Pandalus borealis*
Pisces: *Gadus callarias, G. ogac, Reinhardtius hippoglossoides, Hippoglossus hippoglossus, Anarchichas minor, Sebastes marinus, Mellotus villosus, Salmo salar, Salvelinus alpinus*
MAJOR CURRENT RESEARCH PROJECTS AND SCIENTIFIC LEADERS: Research arrangements along the coast of Greenland are made each summer under the leadership of Dr. Paul M. Hansen. Interested persons should contact Dr. Hansen direct.

Koebenhavns Universitet, Universitets Arktiske Station

COPENHAGEN UNIVERSITY, ARCTIC STATION

POSTAL ADDRESS: c/o L. E. Bruunsvejlo, Charlottenlund, Danmark (Denmark).
LOCATION: Godhavn, Disko Island, Groenland (Greenland).
EXECUTIVE OFFICER: Professor R. Spaerck, President of the Board, Universitet, Frue Plads, Koebenhavn K, Danmark.
YEAR FOUNDED: 1906.
SCOPE OF ACTIVITIES: Unrestricted research on arctic flora and fauna.
SEASON OF OPERATION: All year, but surrounding sea covered with ice from December to May.
PHYSICAL ENVIRONMENT ACCESSIBLE: Disko Bay, Jakobshavn Ice-fjord; sandy beach, rocky shore, oligotrophic lake, and river.
PROVISIONS FOR VISITING SCIENTISTS: Research and living space for 8-10 visitors; no fees charged for research space.
MAJOR RESEARCH FACILITIES: Very extensive library; identified reference collections of Greenland flora and

UNIVERSITETS ARKTISKE STATION, DISKO ISLAND

fauna; small boats and outboard motors, one 36 ft LOA motor vessel.

SIZE OF STAFF: One at professional level; 1 technician.

MAJOR CURRENT RESEARCH PROJECTS AND SCIENTIFIC LEADERS:

Quantitative investigation of bottom fauna and rock fauna of the tidal zone (G. Petersen)

Determination of productivity in the sea by the C-14 method (G. Petersen)

GUATEMALA

Estacion Nacional de Biologia y Piscicultura Experimental de Barcena

NATIONAL EXPERIMENTAL BIOLOGY AND FISH CULTURE STATION OF BARCENA

POSTAL ADDRESS: Finca "Barcena," Villa Nueva, Guatemala.

LOCATION: Near Guatemala City.

EXECUTIVE OFFICER: Julio Armando Anleu, Jefe del Departamento de Caza y Pesca, Direccion General Forestal, Zoologico "La Aurora," Guatemala.

SPONSORING AGENCY: Departamento de Caza y Pesca (Department of Fish and Game).

YEAR FOUNDED: 1954.

SCOPE OF ACTIVITIES: Restricted research on fish culture and fresh-water biology.

SEASON OF OPERATION: All year.

PHYSICAL ENVIRONMENT ACCESSIBLE: Rio de "Barcena" (Barcena River), Lago de Amatitlan (Amatitlan Lake); 25 artificial ponds with fresh-water supply from nearby stream.

PROVISIONS FOR VISITING SCIENTISTS: Space for visitors.

MAJOR RESEARCH FACILITIES: Small library; small aquarium tanks; machine and wood shop; small boats and outboard motors.

SIZE OF STAFF: Two technicians.

IMPORTANT SPECIES AVAILABLE FOR LABORATORY STUDIES:

Pisces (fresh-water): *Cichlasoma metaguense, C. guttulatum, C. macracanthum, C. trimaculatum, C. managuense, Poecilistes pleurospilus, Profundulus guatemalensis, Astyanax fasciatus, Micropterus salmoides, Lepomis macrochirus, Tilapia mossambica*

MAJOR CURRENT RESEARCH PROJECTS AND SCIENTIFIC LEADERS:

Fish culture and fresh-water fisheries (Shu Yen Lin and Harold Loesch)

HONG KONG

Hong Kong Fisheries Research Station

POSTAL ADDRESS:

Administrative headquarters: Li Po Chun Chambers, 11th Floor, Connaught Road C., Hong Kong.

Laboratory address: The Fish Market, Aberdeen, Hong Kong.

EXECUTIVE OFFICER: J. D. Bromhall, Director.

SPONSORING AGENCY: Co-operative Development and Fisheries Department, Government of Hong Kong.

YEAR FOUNDED: 1952.

SCOPE OF ACTIVITIES: Restricted research on demersal and pelagic fisheries of the South China Sea, pond fish culture, edible and pearl oyster culture.

SEASON OF OPERATION: All year.

PHYSICAL ENVIRONMENT ACCESSIBLE: South China Sea; sandy and silty beaches, rocky and gravelly shores, estuarine conditions and brackish, shallow bays.

PROVISIONS FOR VISITING SCIENTISTS: Space for 2-3 visitors; no fees charged.

MAJOR RESEARCH FACILITIES: Small library; large outdoor ponds and tanks, small aquarium tanks, opened or closed circuit sea water supply to inside aquaria and outside to 200 ft^3 tank; limited research collections of fish and crustaceans; limited identified reference collection of marine fishes; shop facilities available through other government departments; small boats and outboard motors; vessels, 117 ft LOA research trawler, *Cape St. Mary,* and 66 ft LOA research trawler, *Alister Hardy.*

SIZE OF STAFF: Eleven at professional level; 8 technicians (including ship's officers).

MAJOR CURRENT RESEARCH PROJECTS AND SCIENTIFIC LEADERS:

Otter trawling survey of continental shelf (J. D. Bromhall, P. Scholes and S. Tung)

Culture of Chinese carps and grey mullet in brackish water ponds (E. Hamblyn)

Experimental cultivation of edible and pearl oysters (J. D. Bromhall)

HUNGARY

Magyar Tudomanyos Akademia Biologiai Kutato Intezete

BIOLOGICAL RESEARCH INSTITUTE OF THE HUNGARIAN ACADEMY OF SCIENCE

POSTAL ADDRESS: Tihany/Lake Balaton, Magyarorszag (Hungary).

LOCATION: Near Veszprem.

EXECUTIVE OFFICER: Dr. Elek Woynarovich, Director.

YEAR FOUNDED: 1927.

SCOPE OF ACTIVITIES: Unrestricted research on general aquatic biology.

SEASON OF OPERATION: All year.

PHYSICAL ENVIRONMENT ACCESSIBLE: Lake Balaton, River Zala; artificial fish ponds, eutrophic and oligotrophic lakes.

PROVISIONS FOR VISITING SCIENTISTS: Research and living space for 2-5 visitors; no fees charged for research space.

MAJOR RESEARCH FACILITIES: Very extensive library; large outdoor ponds and tanks, small aquarium tanks, running Balaton water; identified reference collections of flora and fauna accessible at the Budapest National Museum and University institutes; machine and wood shop, electrical shop, skilled shop workman available; two small boats and outboard motors; one 11 m LOA power vessel.

SIZE OF STAFF: Fifteen at professional level; 7 technicians.

IMPORTANT SPECIES AVAILABLE FOR LABORATORY STUDIES:

Algae: *Fontinalis antipiretica*

Crustacea: *Daphnia* sp., *Leptodora* sp., *Gammarus* sp., *Limnomysis* sp., *Ceratium hirundinella*

Pisces: *Lucioperca sandra, Cyprinus carpio, Abramis brama,* etc.

MAGYAR TUDOMANYOS AKADEMIA BIOLOGIAI KUTATO INTEZETE

MAJOR CURRENT RESEARCH PROJECTS AND SCIENTIFIC LEADERS:

Oxygen consumption of various water organisms; temperature and environmental factors (Elek Woynarovich)

Fish breeding, feeding and growth (Elek Woynarovich)

Circulation of matter in ecological, physiological, and biochemical levels, etc. (Lajos Felfoeldy)

Role of aquatic plants in primary production of fresh-water bodies (Lajos Felfoeldy)

Quantitative and qualitative estimation of natural populations in phytoplankton (Lajos Felfoldy)

Physiological investigations on unicellular algae (Lajos Felfoldy)

Fat metabolism of water organisms (Tibor Farkas and Sandor Herodek)

Effects of temperature, food, etc. on fatty acid composition of fresh-water organisms (Tibor Farkas and Sandor Herodek)

Orszagos Mezogazdasagi Minosegvizsgalo Intezet (Ommi), Hydrobiologiai Osztalya

NATIONAL INSTITUTE FOR AGRICULTURAL QUALITY TESTING, DEPARTMENT OF HYDROBIOLOGY

POSTAL ADDRESS: Fresh-water laboratory: 4, Herman Otto ut 15, Budapest II, Magyarorszag (Hungary).

EXECUTIVE OFFICER: Dr. Erno Donaszy, Director of Department.

SPONSORING AGENCY: Ministry of Agriculture.

YEAR FOUNDED: 1906.

SCOPE OF ACTIVITIES: Restricted limnological research on fish culture and reed culture; effects of water pollution on biology of fresh-water organisms; graduate and undergraduate instruction.

SEASON OF OPERATION: All year.

PHYSICAL ENVIRONMENT ACCESSIBLE: Danube River and its backwater "Soroksari Dunaag"; eutrophic lake and fish ponds.

PROVISIONS FOR VISITING SCIENTISTS: Research space for 2 visitors; no fees charged; living quarters available nearby.

MAJOR RESEARCH AND TEACHING FACILITIES: Small library; small aquarium tanks; research and identified plankton collections from Hungarian fish ponds, collection of local fresh-water flora.

INSTRUCTIONAL PROGRAM: Productivity of Hungarian fresh-waters, limnology of Hungarian fish ponds, and the reeds.

SIZE OF STAFF: Four at professional level; 6 technicians.

MAJOR CURRENT RESEARCH PROJECTS AND SCIENTIFIC LEADERS:

Biological productivity of Hungarian fish ponds (Erno Donaszy)

Phytoplankton as an indicator of the productivity of fish ponds (Bela Veszpremi)

Ecology of Hungarian reeds (Andras Ruttkay)

ICELAND

Atvinnudeild Haskolans-Fiskideild

FISHERIES RESEARCH INSTITUTE

POSTAL ADDRESS: Skulagata 4, Reykjavik, Island (Iceland).
EXECUTIVE OFFICER: Mr. Jon Jonsson, Sjornar.
SPONSORING AGENCY: The Icelandic Government.
YEAR FOUNDED: 1937.
SCOPE OF ACTIVITIES: Restricted research on marine fisheries and general oceanography (chemical, physical, plankton, bottom ecology, etc.).
SEASON OF OPERATION: All year.
PHYSICAL ENVIRONMENT ACCESSIBLE: The Icelandic coastal waters, the Irminger, Iceland and southwestern Norwegian Seas; brackish, shallow bays.
PROVISIONS FOR VISITING SCIENTISTS: Space for visitors; no fees charged; living quarters available nearby.
MAJOR RESEARCH FACILITIES: Research collections of plankton, bottom invertebrates and fish from Icelandic waters; vessels, 52 m and 28 m LOA.
SIZE OF STAFF: Eight at professional level; 12 technicians.
MAJOR CURRENT RESEARCH PROJECTS AND SCIENTIFIC LEADERS:
Investigations on demersal fishes in Icelandic waters (Jon Jonsson)
Environmental studies in connection with the Icelandic herring fisheries (H. Einarsson)
Plankton recorder studies in the Irminger Sea (I. Hallgrimsson)
Redfish research in near and distant waters (J. Magnusson)
The International Overflow program, Faroe-Iceland Ridge (U. Stefansson)
Studies on prawn and lobster in Icelandic waters (A. Sigurdsson)
PUBLICATIONS ISSUED: *Rit Fiskideildar* (occasionally published journal)

ATVINNUDEILD HASKOLANS-FISKIDEILD, REYKJAVIK

ANDHRA UNIVERSITY, FIELD MARINE LABORATORY

INDIA

Andhra University, Department of Zoology, Field Marine Laboratory

POSTAL ADDRESS: Waltair, Andhra Pradesh State, India.
LOCATION: Near Visakhapatnam.
EXECUTIVE OFFICER: Professor P. N. Ganapati, Head of the Department of Zoology.
YEAR FOUNDED: 1946.
SCOPE OF ACTIVITIES: Unrestricted research on general marine biology, hydrography, plankton, bottom fauna, fishes, protozoology and parasitology; graduate and undergraduate instruction.
SEASON OF OPERATION: All year.
PHYSICAL ENVIRONMENT ACCESSIBLE: Bay of Bengal; open ocean, sandy and silty beaches, rocky and gravelly shores, estuarine conditions and brackish, shallow bays.
PROVISIONS FOR VISITING SCIENTISTS: Research and living space for 2 visitors.
MAJOR RESEARCH AND TEACHING FACILITIES: Moderately complete library; running sea and fresh-water; research and identified reference collections of local fauna and flora available; machine and wood shop; small boats and outboard motors; oceanographic vessel planned for the future.
INSTRUCTIONAL PROGRAM: General ecology, embryology, palaeontology, cytology and genetics, marine ecology, general oceanography, fisheries biology, animal physiology and animal ecology.
SIZE OF STAFF: Fourteen at professional level; 1 taxidermist.
IMPORTANT SPECIES AVAILABLE FOR LABORATORY STUDIES:
Diatom: *Nitzschia closterium*
Protozoa: *Euplotes* spp.
Polychaeta: *Mercierella enigmatica*

Cirripedia: *Balanus amphitrite*
Amphipoda: *Corophium triaenonoyx*
Pelecypoda: *Martesia striata, Teredo furcillatus*
Gastropoda: *Cellana* spp.

MAJOR CURRENT RESEARCH PROJECTS AND SCIENTIFIC LEADERS:

Hydrography and plankton of the Waltair coast (P. N. Ganapati)
Studies on marine fouling and boring (P. N. Ganapati)
Hydrography and faunistic survey of the Godavari estuary (P. N. Ganapati, T. Satyanarayana Rao and S. Dutt)
Chaetognatha of the Waltair coast (T. Satyanarayana Rao)
Intertidal ecology of the Waltair coast (T. Satyanarayana Rao)
Fishery biology of the Waltair coast (S. Dutt)
Helminth parasites of marine fishes (K. Hanumantha Rao)

PUBLICATIONS ISSUED: *Memoirs in Oceanography* (occasionally published journal of Andhra University)

Annamalai University, Marine Biological Station

POSTAL ADDRESS: Porto Novo, Madras State, India.
LOCATION: Near Madras.
EXECUTIVE OFFICER: Professor R. V. Seshaiya, Director.
YEAR FOUNDED: 1957.
SCOPE OF ACTIVITIES: Unrestricted research on general marine biology, plankton, ecology, biochemistry, cytology, cytogenetics; graduate instruction.
SEASON OF OPERATION: All year.
PHYSICAL ENVIRONMENT ACCESSIBLE: Bay of Bengal, Vellar and Coleroon Estuaries; sandy and silty beaches, estuarine conditions, brackish, shallow bays and rivers.
PROVISIONS FOR VISITING SCIENTISTS: Space for 2 visitors; no fees charged; living quarters available at the University campus at Annamalainagar.
MAJOR RESEARCH AND TEACHING FACILITIES: Small library; large outdoor ponds and tanks, small aquarium tanks; research collections of fishes, polychaetes, crabs, mollusks and plankton; identified reference collections of local fishes and polychaetes; small boats and outboard motors; one 35 ft LOA power vessel, *Medusa.*
INSTRUCTIONAL PROGRAM: Marine biology.
SIZE OF STAFF: Three at professional level; 1 technician.

IMPORTANT SPECIES AVAILABLE FOR LABORATORY STUDIES:

Coelenterata: *Edwardsia* sp.
Nemertinea: *Cerebratulus* sp.
Mollusca: *Umbonium vestiarium, Meretrix meretrix, Ostrea madrasensis, Sanguinolaria diphos*
Brachyura: *Uca annulipes*
Isopoda: *Apseudes* spp.

ANNAMALAI UNIVERSITY, MARINE BIOLOGICAL LABORATORY, PORTO NOVO

Pisces: *Boleophthalmus boddaerti, Ophichthys boro*

MAJOR CURRENT RESEARCH PROJECTS AND SCIENTIFIC LEADERS:

Ecology of the Vellar Estuary (R. V. Seshaiya)
Biochemistry of the integument of fishes (R. V. Seshaiya)
Plankton (R. V. Seshaiya)
Hydrography of the Vellar Estuary (J. Jacob)
Marine and estuarine fishes of Porto Novo (J. Jacob)
Cytochemistry and cytology of some marine and estuarine animals (J. Jacob)
Polychaetes of Porto Novo (systematics) (K. Balasubrahmanyan)
Ecology of marine and estuarine bottoms (K. Balasubrahmanyan)
Copepods associated with mollusks (K. Reddiah)
Mackerel fisheries (P. Vijayaraghavan of the Central Marine Fisheries, Government of India)

Central Inland Fisheries Research Institute

POSTAL ADDRESS:

Headquarters: Barrackpore, Via Calcutta, India.
Branch laboratories: Little or no detailed information is available for the following stations, and therefore these stations are not described in the *Directory.*

1. 28 Cantonment Road, Cuttack, Orissa State.
2. Seetampeta, Rajahmundry, Andhra Pradesh State.
3. 30 Panna Lal Road, Allahabad, Uttar Pradesh State.
4. Estuarine Fisheries Research Centre, Kakdwip, West Bengal State.
5. Estuarine Fisheries Research Centre, 47/1 Strand Road, Calcutta, West Bengal State.
6. Lacustrine Research Unit, Thungabhadra Dam, Hospet, Mysore State.
7. Chilka Fisheries Investigation Unit, Balugaon, Puri District, Orissa State.

8. Godavari-Krishna River Survey Unit, Rajamundhry, Andhra Pradesh State.
9. Pond Culture Research Unit, Joyasagar, Assam State.
10. Narmada-Tapti River Survey Unit, Hoshangabad, Madhya Pradesh State.

EXECUTIVE OFFICER: Dr. S. S. Bhimachar, Director and Head.

SPONSORING ACENCY: India Ministry of Food and Agriculture.

YEAR FOUNDED: 1947.

SCOPE OF ACTIVITIES: Restricted research on fishery biology, population dynamics, ecology, and fish culture; training of candidates for inland fisheries work.

SEASON OF OPERATION: All year.

PHYSICAL ENVIRONMENT ACCESSIBLE: River Hooghly; estuarine conditions, brackish, shallow bays.

PROVISIONS FOR VISITING SCIENTISTS: Space for visitors; no fees charged; living quarters available nearby.

MAJOR RESEARCH AND TEACHING FACILITIES: Extensive library; small aquarium tanks; reference collection museum in planning stage; small boats and outboard motors; vessels, 55 ft LOA research and exploratory fishing vessel, and 40 ft LOA motor launch.

INSTRUCTIONAL PROGRAM: Training course on inland fisheries development.

SIZE OF STAFF: One hundred seventy-five at professional level; 44 technicians.

MAJOR CURRENT RESEARCH PROJECTS AND SCIENTIFIC LEADERS:

Investigations on fish culture in impounded waters (K. H. Alikunhi)
Investigations on the fisheries of brackish water lakes (V. G. Jhingran)
Investigations on the lake fisheries (Y. R. Tripathi)
Investigations on the riverine fisheries (M. P. Motwani)

CENTRAL INLAND FISHERIES RESEARCH INSTITUTE, MAIN LABORATORY IN BARRACKPORE

Investigations on estuarine fisheries (V. R. Pantulu)
Investigations on Hilsa fisheries (S. R. Pillay)

PUBLICATIONS ISSUED: *Indian Journal of Fisheries* (published jointly with other Central Fisheries Institutions)

Central Marine Fisheries Research Station

POSTAL ADDRESS:

Headquarters: Manadapam Camp P. O., Ramanathapuram District, Madras State, India

Branch laboratories:

1. Peramanoor Thevara Road, Ernakulam-5, Kerala State, India
2. Botawalla Chambers, Sir-Pherozshah Mehta Road, Bombay-1, India

(Descriptions follow.)

Substations exist at the following addresses, but no detailed information is available as to the facilities, and these are therefore not described in the *Directory.*

3. Kandla, Gujerat State.
4. Veraval, Gujarat State.
5. Cannanore, Kerala State.
6. Neendakara, Quilon, Kerala State.
7. Vizhingam (Via) Trivandrum, Kerala State.
8. West Hill, P. O., Calicut-5, Kerala State.
9. Minicoy, Laccadive Islands.
10. University Campus, Chepauk, Madras-5, Madras State.
11. Tuticorin, Madras State.
12. Karwar, Mysore State.
13. Bolar, Mangalore-1, Mysore State.
14. Waltair, Andhra Pradesh State.
15. 47/1 Strand Road, Calcutta-7, West Bengal State.

LOCATION: The headquarters is located on the Gulf of Mannar.

EXECUTIVE OFFICER: Dr. S. Jones, Chief Research Officer and Head of the Department.

SPONSORING AGENCY: India Ministry of Food and Agriculture.

YEAR FOUNDED: 1947.

SCOPE OF ACTIVITIES: Restricted research on marine fisheries and marine biology; survey of fisheries along all the Indian coastline; oceanography.

SEASON OF OPERATION: All year.

PHYSICAL ENVIRONMENT ACCESSIBLE: Bay of Bengal, Gulf of Mannar, Palk Bay; open ocean, sandy and silty beaches, rocky and gravelly shores, and coral reefs.

PROVISIONS FOR VISITING SCIENTISTS: Research and living (unfurnished) space for visitors.

MAJOR RESEARCH FACILITIES: Moderately complete library; running sea and fresh-water, large outdoor tanks, marine fish farm, small aquarium tanks; research and identified reference collections of marine fishes and algae; machine and wood shop; vessels, 23 ft LOA, *Sagitta,* and 25 ft LOA, *Mathi.*

SIZE OF STAFF: Over 50 gazetted officers; about 100 class III technicians.

MAJOR CURRENT RESEARCH PROJECTS AND SCIENTIFIC LEADERS:

Fishery survey (R. Nair)
Fishery statistics (S. Banerjee)
Marine biology (planktology and hydrology) (R. Prasad)
Marine fish culture (P. Tampi)
Marine algology (F. Thivy)

PUBLICATIONS ISSUED: *Indian Journal of Fisheries* (journal published jointly with other Central Fisheries Institutions)

Ernakulam, Kerala State Sub-Station

EXECUTIVE OFFICER: Mr. M. K. Menon, Research Officer and Officer-in-Charge.

YEAR FOUNDED: 1951.

SCOPE OF ACTIVITIES: Restricted research on fishery biology and environmental studies.

PHYSICAL ENVIRONMENT ACCESSIBLE: Arabian Sea; backwaters.

PROVISIONS FOR VISITING SCIENTISTS: None.

MAJOR RESEARCH FACILITIES: Small library; identified reference collections of commercially important prawns and other Crustacea, and fishes; small boats and outboard motors; 50 ft LOA vessel, *Kalava,* on loan from Indo-Norwegian Project.

SIZE OF STAFF: Ten at professional level; 4 technicians.

MAJOR CURRENT RESEARCH PROJECTS AND SCIENTIFIC LEADERS:

Biology and fisheries of prawns and lobsters (M. Menon)
Population dynamics of offshore fisheries (K. Mohamed)
Oceanography and inshore hydrology (R. Jayaraman)

Bombay Sub-Station

EXECUTIVE OFFICER: Mr. K. Mohamed, Officer-in-Charge.

YEAR FOUNDED: 1951.

SCOPE OF ACTIVITIES: Restricted research on offshore fisheries and oceanography.

PHYSICAL ENVIRONMENT ACCESSIBLE: Gulfs of Kutch and Cambay, and the Arabian Sea.

MAJOR RESEARCH FACILITIES: Small library; small aquarium tanks; research collections of fish and other marine life; identified reference collections of fish fauna; vessels, 52 ft and two 40 ft LOA.

SIZE OF STAFF: Fourteen at professional level; 6 technicians.

IMPORTANT SPECIES AVAILABLE FOR LABORATORY STUDIES:

Crustacea: *Metapenaeus affinis, Palaemon tenuipes, Parapaenopsis sculptilis*
Pisces: *Polydactylus indicus, Otolithoides brunneus, Pseudosciaena diacanthus, Pomadasys hasta, Harpodon nehereus, Ilisha filigera, Muraenesox talabonoides*

MAJOR CURRENT RESEARCH PROJECTS AND SCIENTIFIC LEADERS:

Offshore fisheries investigations (K. Mohamed)
Fishery biology (M. Kutty)
Fish embryology (S. Bapat)
Shrimps (M. Kunju)
Oceanography (Vacant)

Madras State Department of Fisheries

POSTAL ADDRESS:

Headquarters: 35/2 Mount Road, Madras 2, India.
Branch laboratories:

1. Freshwater Fisheries Biological Station, Bhavanisagar Post
2. Marine Biological Station, Krusadai
3. Marine Biological Station, Ennur
4. Marine Biological Station, Tuticorin, Tinnevelly (Not described in the *Directory.*)

(Descriptions follow.)

EXECUTIVE OFFICER: Mr. S. Vardarajan, Director of Fisheries.

PROVISIONS FOR VISITING SCIENTISTS: None, at any of the stations.

PUBLICATIONS ISSUED: *Bulletin of the Madras Fisheries Department* (regularly published journal)

Freshwater Fisheries Biological Station

POSTAL ADDRESS: Bhavanisagar Post, Madras State, India.

LOCATION: Near Coimbatore.

EXECUTIVE OFFICER: B. Krishnamurthi, Assistant Director of Fisheries (Fresh-water Biology).

YEAR FOUNDED: 1942.

SCOPE OF ACTIVITIES: Restricted research on freshwater fishes and fisheries of lakes, reservoirs and rivers with emphasis on fish culture and commercial exploitation of natural resources; instruction.

SEASON OF OPERATION: All year.

PHYSICAL ENVIRONMENT ACCESSIBLE: Bhavanisagar and Mettur Reservoirs, Bhavani, Moyar, and Cauvery Rivers; eutrophic and oligotrophic lakes, ponds and paddy fields.

MAJOR RESEARCH AND TEACHING FACILITIES: Small library; large outdoor tanks, small aquarium tanks, cement cisterns constructed for experimental work; research and identified reference collections of freshwater fishes; small boats and outboard motors.

INSTRUCTIONAL PROGRAM: Fishery biology, plankton and hydrology.

SIZE OF STAFF: Eight at professional level.

IMPORTANT SPECIES AVAILABLE FOR LABORATORY STUDIES:

Copepoda: *Cyclops, Diaptomus, Pseudodiaptomus*

Cladocera: *Daphnia, Diaphanosoma, Ceriodaphnia*
Rotifera: *Schizooerca*

MAJOR CURRENT RESEARCH PROJECTS AND SCIENTIFIC LEADERS:
Population dynamics and fishery survey of Cauvery River (B. Krishnamurthi)
Studies on *Tilapia mossambica* (B. Kirshnamurthi)
Carp fry segregation (B. Kirshnamurthi)
Lake fishery studies and gear efficiency (B. Krishnamurthi)
Limnology of Bhavanisagar Reservior (B. Krishnamurthi)
Nutritive value of fresh-water fishes
Fish poisons

PUBLICATIONS ISSUED: *Contributions of the Freshwater Biological Research Station* (occasionally published journal)

Marine Biological Station, Krusadai

POSTAL ADDRESS: Pamban Post, Ramnad District, Madras State, India.
LOCATION: Krusadai Island near Madura.
EXECUTIVE OFFICER: M. A. Rasheed, Acting Research Assistant.
YEAR FOUNDED: 1928.
SCOPE OF ACTIVITIES: Restricted research on general marine biology and plankton.
SEASON OF OPERATION: All year.
PHYSICAL ENVIRONMENT ACCESSIBLE: Gulf of Mannar; coral reefs.
MAJOR RESEARCH AND TEACHING FACILITIES: Small library; running sea water; small museum of local fauna for taxonomic studies; identified reference collections of local fauna and flora; small boats and outboard motors.
SIZE OF STAFF: Two at professional level; 3 technicians.

Marine Biological Station, Ennur

POSTAL ADDRESS: Ennur, Chinglepet District, South India.
LOCATION: Near Madras.
EXECUTIVE OFFICER: A. Rajagopal, Research Assistant.
YEAR FOUNDED: 1907.
SCOPE OF ACTIVITIES: Restricted research on fishery biology, plankton and hydrography.
SEASON OF OPERATION: All year.
PHYSICAL ENVIRONMENT ACCESSIBLE: Bay of Bengal; estuarine conditions, and brackish, shallow bays.
MAJOR RESEARCH FACILITIES: Small library; representative research collection of available fauna; small boats, one 20 ft LOA vessel. Attached to the Station is a Marine Biological Supply Station which supplies specimens to educational institutions throughout India.
SIZE OF STAFF: Two at professional level; 4 technicians.
IMPORTANT SPECIES AVAILABLE FOR LABORATORY STUDIES:
Mollusca: *Ostrea madrasensis*
Pisces: *Chatoessus chacunda, C. nasus, Sillago sihama*

Maharashtra State Department of Fisheries, Marine Biological Research Station

POSTAL ADDRESS: Ratnagiri, Maharashtra State, India.
LOCATION: Near Bombay.
EXECUTIVE OFFICERS: M. R. Ranade, Curator of Station. Dr. C. V. Kulkarni, Director of Fisheries, Maharashtra State.
YEAR FOUNDED: 1959.
SCOPE OF ACTIVITIES: Restricted research on general marine biology and fisheries biology.
SEASON OF OPERATION: All year.
PHYSICAL ENVIRONMENT ACCESSIBLE: Arabian Sea; sandy and silty beaches, rocky and gravelly shores, and estuarine conditions.
PROVISIONS FOR VISITING SCIENTISTS: Research and living space for 2 visitors; no fees charged for research space.
MAJOR RESEARCH FACILITIES: Small library; running sea and fresh-water, large outdoor ponds and tanks, small aquarium tanks; extensive research and identified reference collections of fauna and flora.
SIZE OF STAFF: Three at professional level; 2 technicians.
MAJOR CURRENT RESEARCH PROJECTS AND SCIENTIFIC LEADERS:
Study of fish fauna and fisheries (M. Ranade)
Sardine fisheries (K. Sankolli)
Hydrography (R. Joshi)

Institute of Science, Department of Zoology

POSTAL ADDRESS: Mayo Road, Fort, Bombay 1, India.
EXECUTIVE OFFICER: Dr. D. V. Bal, Director and Professor of Zoology.
SPONSORING AGENCY: Maharashtra State Government.
YEAR FOUNDED: 1920.
SCOPE OF ACTIVITIES: Unrestricted research in fishery science and marine biology; graduate and undergraduate instruction.
SEASON OF OPERATION: All year.
PHYSICAL ENVIRONMENT ACCESSIBLE: Bombay Harbor,

MARINE BIOLOGICAL STATION, ENNUR

Gulf of Cambay, Arabian Sea; sandy and silty beaches, rocky and gravelly shores, and brackish, shallow bays.

PROVISIONS FOR VISITING SCIENTISTS: Space for 1 visitor; fees charged.

MAJOR RESEARCH AND TEACHING FACILITIES: Small library; small aquarium tanks; research collections of Polychaeta, Amphipoda, Copepoda, Chaetognatha, Gastropoda, and Lamellibranchiata; identified reference collections of Anthozoa, Amphipoda, Isopoda, Copepoda, and penaeid prawns; machine and wood shop, skilled shop workman available; vessels of the Central Deep Sea Fishing Station and State Fisheries are available.

INSTRUCTIONAL PROGRAM: Various courses in zoology, marine zoology and fisheries. Examinations are given at the University of Bombay.

SIZE OF STAFF: Four-five at professional level.

IMPORTANT SPECIES AVAILABLE FOR LABORATORY STUDIES:

Crustacea: *Ligia exotica, Neptunus pelagicus, Metapenaeus monoceros*

Gastropoda: *Nerita polita, Natica maculosa*

MAJOR CURRENT RESEARCH PROJECTS AND SCIENTIFIC LEADERS:

Plankton from Bombay waters (D. Bal)
Oysters investigations (D. Bal)
Systematics of marine wood borers (D. Bal)
Biology of *Balanus amphitrite* (D. Bal)
Biology of *Otolithus ruber* (D. Bal)

The Marine Biological Station, West Hill

POSTAL ADDRESS:

Headquarters: Kozhikode-5 (Calicut), Kerala State, India.

Branch laboratories:

1. Marine Survey Station, Vizhinjam, Trivandrum District
2. Freshwater Survey Station, Thiruvalla, Alleppey District
3. Estuarine Research Station, Perumanoor, Ernakulam-5

(Descriptions follow.)

EXECUTIVE OFFICERS: Sri. M. J. Mathew, Asst. Director of Fisheries (Research) and Controlling Officer; Sri. A. I. George, Head of Department of Fisheries.

SPONSORING AGENCY: Department of Fisheries, Kerala State.

YEAR FOUNDED: 1921.

SCOPE OF ACTIVITIES: Restricted research on marine biology, hydrography, plankton and oceanography.

SEASON OF OPERATION: All year.

PHYSICAL ENVIRONMENT ACCESSIBLE: Arabian Sea; sandy and silty beaches.

PROVISIONS FOR VISITING SCIENTISTS: None at any of the stations.

MAJOR RESEARCH FACILITIES: Small library; 1 well; research and identified reference collections of marine and fresh-water fish fauna; small boats; one 26.5 ft LOA vessel.

SIZE OF STAFF: Two at professional level; 1 technician.

IMPORTANT SPECIES AVAILABLE FOR LABORATORY STUDIES:

Pisces: *Sardinella longiceps, Rastrelliger kanagurta, Trichiurus savala, Arius dussumieria, Scoliodon laticodus, Cynoglossus semifasciatus, Leiognathus bindus*

Crustacea: *Penaeus indicus, Metapenaeus dobsoni*

Marine Survey Station

POSTAL ADDRESS: Vizhinjam, Via. Nenom, Trivandrum District, Kerala State, India.

EXECUTIVE OFFICER: V. K. Bhaskaran, Marine Survey Officer.

YEAR FOUNDED: 1955.

SCOPE OF ACTIVITIES: Restricted research on fishery biology.

SEASON OF OPERATION: All year.

PHYSICAL ENVIRONMENT ACCESSIBLE: Arabian Sea.

MAJOR RESEARCH FACILITIES: Small library; running sea water; research collections of marine and fresh-water fishes; identified reference collections of local marine fishes.

SIZE OF STAFF: One at professional level.

IMPORTANT SPECIES AVAILABLE FOR LABORATORY STUDIES:

Pisces: *Decapterus russelli, D. macrosoma, Sardinella fimbriata, Euthynnus alletteratus, Kishionella tungol, Auxis thazard, Serranus sonnerati, Callyodon ghoblean*

Fresh Water Survey Station

POSTAL ADDRESS: Kozhenchery, Quilon District, Kerala State, India.

LOCATION: Near Kottayam.

EXECUTIVE OFFICER: V. Achuthan Nair, Fresh Water Biologist and Controlling Officer.

YEAR FOUNDED: 1956.

SCOPE OF ACTIVITIES: Restricted research on the development of inland fisheries.

SEASON OF OPERATION: All year.

PHYSICAL ENVIRONMENT ACCESSIBLE: Fresh-water ponds, dams, lakes, and rivers.

MAJOR RESEARCH FACILITIES: Small library; large outdoor ponds; research collections of fish fauna; identified reference collections of local inland fishes.

SIZE OF STAFF: Three at professional level; 1 technician.

IMPORTANT SPECIES AVAILABLE FOR LABORATORY STUDIES:

Diatoms: *Navicula, Synedra*

Algae: *Spirogyra, Zygnemia*

Crustacea: *Cyclops, Diaptomus*

Pisces: *Saccobranchus fossilis, Ophiocephalus striatus, Etroplus maculatus*

Estuarine Research Station

POSTAL ADDRESS: Perumanoor, Ernakulam-5, Kerala State, India.

LOCATION: Near Cochin.

EXECUTIVE OFFICER: Sri. P. Unnikrishnan Nair, Estuarine Research Officer and Controlling Officer.

YEAR FOUNDED: 1955.

SCOPE OF ACTIVITIES: Restricted research on the development of the estuarine fisheries of Kerala.

SEASON OF OPERATION: All year.

PHYSICAL ENVIRONMENT ACCESSIBLE: Vembanadu Lake; estuarine conditions and brackish, shallow bays.

MAJOR RESEARCH FACILITIES: Small library; large outdoor ponds; research and identified reference collections of marine and fresh-water fish fauna; small boats and outboard motors.

SIZE OF STAFF: Two at professional level; 1 technician.

IMPORTANT SPECIES AVAILABLE FOR LABORATORY STUDIES:

Diatoms: *Coscinodiscus, Chaetoceros*

Zooplankton: *Noctiluca*

Crustacea: *Nauplius*

Pisces: *Gerres filamentosus, Tenthis java, Mugil kalaarti, M. troscheli, M. cephalus, Chanos chanos*

Mysore State Fishery Station

POSTAL ADDRESS:

Headquarters: Fisheries Department, Malleswaram, Bangalore-3, South India.

Field laboratories:

1. Markonahalli
2. Marjkandeya
3. Krishna Raja Sagar
4. Hesserghatta
5. Shantisagar
6. Neerasagar
7. Tungabhadra

EXECUTIVE OFFICER: Mr. V. V. Kalyani, Director of Fisheries.

YEAR FOUNDED: 1945 and 1959.

SCOPE OF ACTIVITIES: Restricted research on fisheries biology (growth rates, foods and feeding habits, reproduction and artificially induced breeding).

SEASON OF OPERATION: All year.

PHYSICAL ENVIRONMENT ACCESSIBLE: Eutrophic and oligotrophic lakes, rivers, and streams.

PROVISIONS FOR VISITING SCIENTISTS: None.

MAJOR RESEARCH FACILITIES: Small library; large outdoor ponds and tanks, small aquarium tanks; small boats and outboard motors.

SIZE OF STAFF: Six at professional level; 8 technicians.

IMPORTANT SPECIES AVAILABLE FOR LABORATORY STUDIES:

Pisces: *Cyprinus carpio, Catla catla, Labeo rohita, L. fimbriatus, L. calbasu, L. nukta, Cirrhina mrigala, Barbus carnaticus, B. tor, B. dubius, Thynnichthys sandkhol, Puntius kolus, Ophicephalus striatus, Tilapia mossambica, Etroplus suratensis*

MYSORE STATE GOVERNMENT FISHERY STATION

MAJOR CURRENT RESEARCH PROJECTS AND SCIENTIFIC LEADERS:

Breeding and culture of the carp, *Cyprinus carpio,* in the Mysore State (V. Kalyani)

Acclimitization and induced breeding of the Gangetic carps, *Catla catla, Labeo rohita,* and *Cirrhina mrigala* in the Mysore State (V. Kalyani)

Fish production in sewage-fed water (V. Kalyani)

Culture of *Tilapia mossambica* in coastal areas (V. Kalyani)

Taraporevala Aquarium and Marine Biological Research Station

POSTAL ADDRESS: Netaji Subhash Road,, Bombay 2, India.

EXECUTIVE OFFICER: Dr. C. V. Kulkarni, Director of Fisheries.

SPONSORING AGENCY: Department of Fisheries, Maharashtra State.

YEAR FOUNDED: 1951.

SCOPE OF ACTIVITIES: Unrestricted research on marine and fresh-water biology with special reference to fisheries.

SEASON OF OPERATION: All year.

PHYSICAL ENVIRONMENT ACCESSIBLE: Arabian Sea; sandy and silty beaches, rocky and gravelly shores, estuarine conditions and eutrophic lake.

PROVISIONS FOR VISITING SCIENTISTS: Space for 2 visitors; no fees charged; living quarters not available nearby.

MAJOR RESEARCH AND TEACHING FACILITIES: Moderately complete library; running sea and fresh-water, small aquarium tanks; research collections of Hydromedusae, Chaetognatha, Copepoda, fish and decapod larvae; identified reference collections of Brachyura,

Anomura, Macrura, fish copepods, echinoderms and mollusks; skilled shop workman available; one 48 ft LOA research vessel, *Mysis.*

INSTRUCTIONAL PROGRAM: The institution is affiliated with the University of Bombay for post-graduate research in Zoology. Guidance is afforded on problems relating to marine and fresh-water biology, including comparative nutritional physiology.

SIZE OF STAFF: Seven at professional level; 21 technicians.

IMPORTANT SPECIES AVAILABLE FOR LABORATORY STUDIES:

Extensive fauna and flora present.

MAJOR CURRENT RESEARCH PROJECTS AND SCIENTIFIC LEADERS:

Biology of flat fishes of Bombay (C. Kulkarni)
Investigations on the biology and fishery of the common lobsters of Bombay (C. Kulkarni)
Studies on the biology and fishery of prawns of Bombay (C. Kulkarni)
Vertebral counts in the commercial fishes of Bombay (H. Kewalramani)
Biology of dominant species of marine planktonic copepods of Bombay (H. Kewalramani)
Studies on the thermal tolerance of marine invertebrates of Bombay (H. Kewalramani)
Studies on Hydromedusae of Bombay (H. Kewalramani)
Comparative study of the oral appendages and the alimentary canal in some Brachyura with special reference to feeding habits (H. Kewalramani)
Biology and fishery of *Mugil dussumieri* (H. Kewalramani)
Studies on the nutritional physiology of major carps and *Mugil dussumieri* (H. Kewalramani)
Studies on the transportation of live aquatic animals (H. Kewalramani)
Bio-ecology of mollusks of Bombay (B. Desai)

TARAPOREVALA AQUARIUM AND MARINE BIOLOGICAL RESEARCH STATION, BOMBAY

University of Kerala, Department of Marine Biology and Fisheries

POSTAL ADDRESS:

Headquarters: Trivandrum-7, Kerala State, India.
Branch laboratories:

1. Marine Biology Laboratory, Trivandrum-7, Kerala State
2. Oceanographic Research Laboratory, Cochin-4, Kerala State
3. Estuarine Research Station, Alumpeedika, Kerala State

(Descriptions follow.)

EXECUTIVE OFFICER: Dr. C. C. John, Head and Professor of Marine Biology and Fisheries.

PUBLICATIONS ISSUED: *Bulletin of the Central Research Institute,* Series C—Natural Sciences

Marine Biology Laboratory

POSTAL ADDRESS: Trivandrum-7, Kerala State, India.

SCOPE OF ACTIVITIES: Research on hydrography and biology of the continental shelf; hydrobiology; brackish-water fish culture.

SEASON OF OPERATION: All year.

PHYSICAL ENVIRONMENT ACCESSIBLE: Arabian Sea, Vembanad and Kayamkulam backwaters; estuarine conditions, and brackish, shallow bays.

PROVISIONS FOR VISITING SCIENTISTS: Research and living space for 6 visitors; no fees charged for research space.

MAJOR RESEARCH AND TEACHING FACILITIES: Moderately complete library; running sea and fresh-water, large outdoor ponds and tanks; research collections of major groups of marine organisms; identified reference collections of crustaceans, fishes, coelentrates, foraminiferans, helminth parasites of fishes, chaetognaths and tunicates; small boats and outboard motors; vessels, 15 ft LOA with outboard motor and 50 ft LOA, *Conch.*

INSTRUCTIONAL PROGRAM: Marine biology, oceanography.

SIZE OF STAFF: Ten at professional level; 7 technicians.

MAJOR CURRENT RESEARCH PROJECTS AND SCIENTIFIC LEADERS:

Age determination of tropical fishes (C. John and G. Nair)
Life history and bionomics of *Villorita cyprinoides* (C. John and G. Nair)
Hydrobiological studies of Kayamkulam Lake (C. John and G. Nair)

Oceanographic Research Laboratory

POSTAL ADDRESS: Cochin-4, Kerala State.

LOCATION: Naval base on Wellington Island. A new

building is under construction at Eranakulan, along the harbor and facing the naval base.

PHYSICAL ENVIRONMENT ACCESSIBLE: Arabian Sea and Indian Ocean.

PROVISIONS FOR VISITING SCIENTISTS: Space for visitors.

MAJOR CURRENT RESEARCH PROJECTS AND SCIENTIFIC LEADERS:

Fishes of the Kerala coast (C. John)
Bottom fauna of the Kerala coast (C. Kurien)
Physico-chemical studies off Cochin (N. Bha)
Fish eggs and larvae of the Kerala coast (K. Padmanabhan)

Estuarine Research Station

POSTAL ADDRESS: Alumpeedika P. O. via Oachira, Alleppey District, Kerala State, India.

LOCATION: Near Quilon.

EXECUTIVE OFFICER: G. Sivankutty Nair, Research Officer.

YEAR FOUNDED: 1948.

SCOPE OF ACTIVITIES: Research on hydrobiology and limnology; instruction.

SEASON OF OPERATION: All year.

PHYSICAL ENVIRONMENT ACCESSIBLE: Kayamkulam and Ashtamudi backwaters; estuarine conditions.

PROVISIONS FOR VISITING SCIENTISTS: Space for 2 visitors; living quarters available nearby.

MAJOR RESEARCH AND TEACHING FACILITIES: Moderately complete library; large outdoor ponds, small aquarium tanks, tube well; research and identified reference collections of estuarine fauna; small boats and outboard motors.

INSTRUCTIONAL PROGRAM: Estuarine fauna (invertebrates and fishes).

IMPORTANT SPECIES AVAILABLE FOR LABORATORY STUDIES:

Pisces: *Mugil* spp., *Clupea longiceps*
Pelecypoda: *Villorita cyprinoides*

University of Madras, Zoological Research Laboratory

POSTAL ADDRESS: Madras, India.

EXECUTIVE OFFICER: Dr. C. P. Gnanamuthu, Director.

YEAR FOUNDED: 1927.

SCOPE OF ACTIVITIES: Research on ecology and physiology of marine animals; graduate instruction in marine biology, animal physiology and ecology.

PHYSICAL ENVIRONMENT ACCESSIBLE: Bay of Bengal.

PROVISIONS FOR VISITING SCIENTISTS: Space for visitors.

MAJOR RESEARCH FACILITIES: Running sea and freshwater; vessels of the Fisheries Department are hired. Department moved into new quarters in 1961.

SIZE OF STAFF: Six at professional level.

PUBLICATIONS: *Journal of the Madras University, Section: B*

UTTAR PRADESH STATE GOVERNMENT FISHERIES RESEARCH LABORATORY, LUCKNOW

Uttar Pradesh State Fisheries Research Laboratory

POSTAL ADDRESS: Badshahbagh, Lucknow, Uttar Pradesh State, India.

EXECUTIVE OFFICER: D. S. Sarbahi, Deputy Director of Fisheries.

YEAR FOUNDED: 1947.

SCOPE OF ACTIVITIES: Restricted research on fisheries biology, particularly pond culture; hydrobiology, weed eradication, gear technology, induced breeding.

SEASON OF OPERATION: All year.

PHYSICAL ENVIRONMENT ACCESSIBLE: Rivers, streams, ponds and reservoirs.

PROVISIONS FOR VISITING SCIENTISTS: Research and living space for 1 visitor; no fees charged for research space.

MAJOR RESEARCH FACILITIES: Small library; ponds and tanks; research and identified reference collections of State fishes and aquatic vegetation; small boats and outboard motors.

SIZE OF STAFF: Three at professional level.

IMPORTANT SPECIES AVAILABLE FOR LABORATORY STUDIES:

Pisces: cyprinoids, siluroids

MAJOR CURRENT RESEARCH PROJECTS AND SCIENTIFIC LEADERS:

Hydrobiological study of the fishery waters of the State (D. Sarbahi)
Study of factors responsible for poor survival and growth in nurseries and ponds (D. Sarbahi)

INDONESIA

Lembaga Pusat Penjelidikan Perairan dan Perikanan

CENTRAL RESEARCH INSTITUTE FOR HYDROLOGY AND FISHERIES

At the time of preparation of the *Directory,* it was the intention of the Indonesia government to create this Institute. The Institutes of Hydrology, Inland

Fisheries, and Marine Fisheries were all to be combined in one central institute. The research branch of the Sea Fisheries Service was to be dissolved.

POSTAL ADDRESS:
Head office and central laboratories: P. O. Box 51, 1 Sempur, Bogor, Indonesia.
Branches:
Pasar Minggu (Java)
Danau Panggang (Borneo)
Makassar (Celebes) (projected)
Palembang (Sumatra)

EXECUTIVE OFFICER: Hasanuddin Saanin, Direktor.
SPONSORING AGENCY: Departemen Pertanian (Department of Agriculture).

Before reorganization, information about the Inland Fisheries and Marine Research Institutes was as follows:

Balai Penjelidikan Perikanan Darat

INLAND FISHERIES RESEARCH INSTITUTE

POSTAL ADDRESS: P. O. Box 51, 1 Sempur, Bogor, Indonesia.
EXECUTIVE OFFICER: Hasanuddin Saanin, Direktor.
SPONSORING AGENCY: Departemen Pertanian (Department of Agriculture).
YEAR FOUNDED: 1930.
SCOPE OF ACTIVITIES: Restricted research on general fisheries biology, limnology, and technology; temporary graduate and undergraduate instruction.
SEASON OF OPERATION: All year.
PHYSICAL ENVIRONMENT ACCESSIBLE: Estuarine conditions, brackish, shallow bays, eutrophic and oligotrophic lakes, rivers, streams, brackish and fresh-water ponds, swamps, and marshes.
PROVISIONS FOR VISITING SCIENTISTS: None.
MAJOR RESEARCH AND TEACHING FACILITIES: Small library; large outdoor ponds, small aquarium tanks; identified reference collections of diatoms, chloromonads, cyanophyceans, dinophyceans, protozoans, rotifers, and crustaceans; small boats and outboard motors.
INSTRUCTIONAL PROGRAM: Invertebrate zoology, limnology, population dynamics, planktology, production theory, fisheries statistics, and fisheries management.
SIZE OF STAFF: Twenty-eight at professional level; 83 technicians.
IMPORTANT SPECIES AVAILABLE FOR LABORATORY STUDIES:
Diatomaceae: *Navicula, Melasira*
Cyanophyceae: *Nostoc, Oscillatoria*
Crustacea: *Streptocephalus, Moina, Cyclops*
Pisces: *Cyprinus, Puntius, Osteochilus, Tilapia*

BALAI PENJELIDIKAN PERIKANAN DARAT, BOGOR

MAJOR CURRENT RESEARCH PROJECTS AND SCIENTIFIC LEADERS:
Ecology of the lakes and marshes of Sumatra and Borneo (H. Saanin)
Biology of Cerithidae (R. Roestami Djajadiredja)
Trematodes in fishes and general pathology (M. Sachlan)
Manuring of brackish water ponds (R. Roestami Djajadiredja)
Manuring and cultural practices in fresh-water ponds (R. Soehardi)
Toxicity of insecticides and herpicides (H. Saanin)
Anesthetics and trace elements (H. Saanin)

Lembaga Penjelidikan Laut

INSTITUTE OF MARINE RESEARCH

POSTAL ADDRESS: P. O. Box 580/DAK, Pasar Ikan, Djakarta Kota (Jakarta), Indonesia.
EXECUTIVE OFFICER: Dr. Gatot Rahardjo Joenoes, Pendjabat Kepala.
SPONSORING AGENCY: Pemerintah Indonesia (Government of Indonesia).
YEAR FOUNDED: 1904.
SCOPE OF ACTIVITIES: Restricted research on general marine biology, physical and chemical oceanography, and plankton.

LEMBAGA PENJELIDIKAN LAUT, JAKARTA

Samudera, RESEARCH VESSEL OF THE LEMBAGA PENJELIDIKAN LAUT

SEASON OF OPERATION: Usually from January to October.

PHYSICAL ENVIRONMENT ACCESSIBLE: Malacca and Makassar Straits; Java, South China, Celebes, Banda, Arafura, Moluccas and Flores Seas; Indian Ocean; sandy and silty beaches, rocky and gravelly shores, estuarine conditions, and coral reefs.

PROVISIONS FOR VISITING SCIENTISTS: Space for 2 visitors; no fees charged; living quarters available nearby.

MAJOR RESEARCH FACILITIES: Moderately complete library; running sea and fresh-water; research collections of fish, coral, crustaceans and mollusks; identified reference collections of local fishes and crustaceans; skilled shop workman available; small boats and outboard motors; 36 m LOA research vessel, *Samudera.*

SIZE OF STAFF: Seven at professional level.

IMPORTANT SPECIES AVAILABLE FOR LABORATORY STUDIES:

Dinoflagellata: *Noctiluca* sp.

Pelecypoda: *Pinctada maxima*

Crustacea: *Pennaeus* sp.

Pisces: *Rastrelliger* sp., *Amphiprion percula, Clupea fimbriata, Anguilla* sp., *Chanos chanos, Euthynnus* sp.

MAJOR CURRENT RESEARCH PROJECTS AND SCIENTIFIC LEADERS:

Surface water movement in correlation with the strength of the monsoons (Gatot Rahardjo and staff)

Deep sea circulation (Gatot Rahardjo and staff)

Surface and deep sea salinity, temperature, density, oxygen, PO_4 phosphorus (Gatot Rahardjo and staff)

Reference collection of the marine flora and fauna of the Indonesian and adjacent waters (Gatot Rahardjo and staff)

Monthly mean surface salinities in the Indonesian and adjacent waters (Gatot Rahardjo and staff)

IRAN

Laboratories about Which No Detailed Information Was Available:

There is a well equipped biological laboratory in Teheran, Iran whose activities include the analysis and study of bacteria and plankton. Information about the laboratory can be obtained from the Southern Fisheries Development Company, No. 3, Aoicho, Akasaka, Minato-Ko, Tokyo, Japan.

IRELAND

University College, Cork Biology Station

POSTAL ADDRESS: Lough Ine (Skibbereen, County Cork), Ireland.

LOCATION: Near Baltimore, Ireland.

EXECUTIVE OFFICER: Professor F. J. O'Rourke, Director, Department of Zoology, University College, Cork, Ireland.

SCOPE OF ACTIVITIES: Unrestricted research on the ecology of local species, serological and chromatographic studies on taxonomic problems; undergraduate instruction in marine biological research.

SEASON OF OPERATION: Easter vacation and summer.

PHYSICAL ENVIRONMENT ACCESSIBLE: Lough Ine (marine lake), Atlantic Ocean; sandy beach, rocky and gravelly shores, brackish, shallow bays.

PROVISIONS FOR VISITING SCIENTISTS: No space available.

MAJOR RESEARCH AND TEACHING FACILITIES: No library; no water supply nor tanks; no shop facilities; small boats and outboard motors; one fibre-glass dinghy.

INSTRUCTIONAL PROGRAM: Used as a field station for students during Easter vacation.

UNIVERSITY COLLEGE, CORK BIOLOGY STATION

IMPORTANT SPECIES AVAILABLE FOR LABORATORY STUDIES:
Pisces: *Gadus pollacius*
Echinodermata: *Paracentrotus lividus*
Many other marine animals and plants readily available.
MAJOR CURRENT RESEARCH PROJECTS AND SCIENTIFIC LEADERS:
Comparative serology of fishes (F. J. O'Rourke)
Comparative chromatography of fishes (F. J. O'Rourke)

An Roinn Tailte, Fo Roinn Iascaigh

DEPARTMENT OF LANDS, FISHERIES DIVISION

A new fisheries laboratory in Ireland is in the planning stages. Inquiries may be addressed to the: Secretary, Department of Lands, Fisheries Division, Dublin, Ireland.

ISRAEL

Baeit Hasefer Lirfua Sheleyad Hauniversita Haivrit Hadassah, Hamaabada Lemachalot Dagim

HEBREW UNIVERSITY-HADASSAH MEDICAL SCHOOL, LABORATORY FOR FISH DISEASES

POSTAL ADDRESS: Jerusalem, Israel.
EXECUTIVE OFFICER: M. Shilo, Minahel, hamachlaka lechimia mikrogiologit.
SCOPE OF ACTIVITIES: Research on fish diseases; instruction.
SEASON OF OPERATION: All year.
PHYSICAL ENVIRONMENT ACCESSIBLE: Mediterranean Sea, Lake of Tiberias; brackish water fish ponds.
PROVISIONS FOR VISITING SCIENTISTS: Space for 1-2 visitors.
MAJOR RESEARCH AND TEACHING FACILITIES: Very extensive library; large outdoor ponds, small aquarium tanks; machine and wood shop, electrical and electronic shop, skilled shop workman available.
INSTRUCTIONAL PROGRAM: Microbial ecology, microbiology.
SIZE OF STAFF: Four at professional level; 3 technicians.
MAJOR CURRENT RESEARCH PROJECTS AND SCIENTIFIC LEADERS:
Nature of toxins formed by the phytoflagellate *Prymnesium pareum* (M. Shilo and R. Rosenberger)
Control of *P. pareum* (M. Shilo and S. Sarig)
Mechanism of osmotic lysis of *P. pareum* by weak electrolytes (Moshe Shilo and Miriam Shilo)
Survey of diseases of carp (M. Shilo and S. Sarig)
PUBLICATIONS ISSUED: *Prymnesium* (regularly published journal for fish breeders in Hebrew and English by the Ministry of Agriculture of the State of Israel and the Israel Fish-breeders Association).

Hauniversita Haivrit, Hamachlaka Lebotanika, Maabadat Azot

HEBREW UNIVERSITY, DEPARTMENT OF BOTANY, ALGAL LABORATORY

POSTAL ADDRESS: Jerusalem, Israel.
EXECUTIVE OFFICER: Dr. I. Friedmann.
YEAR FOUNDED: 1927.
SCOPE OF ACTIVITIES: Unrestricted research on general phycology; graduate and undergraduate instruction.
SEASON OF OPERATION: All year.
PHYSICAL ENVIRONMENT ACCESSIBLE: Mediterranean Sea; sandy and silty beaches.
PROVISIONS FOR VISITING SCIENTISTS: Space for visitors; no fees charged; living quarters available nearby.
MAJOR RESEARCH AND TEACHING FACILITIES: Moderately complete library; facilities for algal cultures; research and identified algal herbarium; machine and wood shop, electrical and electronic shop and skilled shop workman available at the university.
INSTRUCTIONAL PROGRAM: Phycology (introductory and advanced).
SIZE OF STAFF: Three at professional level; 2 technicians.
MAJOR CURRENT RESEARCH PROJECTS AND SCIENTIFIC LEADRES:
The marine algae of Israel (T. Rayss)
Fertilization mechanism in marine algae (I. Friedmann)
Atmophytic algae of the Negev Desert (I. Friedmann)
Zonation and ecology of Mediterranean algae (I. Friedmann)

Hatachana Lecheker Hamidgeh-Dor

THE FISH CULTURE RESEARCH STATION, DOR

POSTAL ADDRESS: Doar Nah Hof HaCarmel, Israel.
LOCATION: Near Haifa.
EXECUTIVE OFFICER: Dr. A. Yashouv, Director.
SPONSORING AGENCY: Machleket Hadaig Sheleyad Misrad Hachaklaut (Department of Fisheries, Ministry of Agriculture).
YEAR FOUNDED: 1940.
SCOPE OF ACTIVITIES: Restricted research on freshwater fisheries and fish culture; instruction.
SEASON OF OPERATION: All year.
PHYSICAL ENVIRONMENT ACCESSIBLE: Kineret (Lake of Tiberias, Sea of Galilee); eutrophic lake, and fish ponds.

PROVISIONS FOR VISITING SCIENTISTS: Space for 1-2 visitors; no fees charged; living quarters available nearby.

MAJOR RESEARCH AND TEACHING FACILITIES: Moderately complete library; biological and chemical laboratories; running sea water planned, large outdoor ponds, small aquarium tanks.

INSTRUCTIONAL PROGRAM: General course in fish culture to fish farmers (in collaboration with the Fish Breeders Association of Israel).

SIZE OF STAFF: Four at professional level; 4 technicians; 8 pond laborers.

MAJOR CURRENT RESEARCH PROJECTS AND SCIENTIFIC LEADERS:

Combined culture of carp and other species of fish (especially *Tilapia and Mugil*) in ponds (A. Yashouv)

Fish pond fertilization; primary production (B. Hepher)

Carp selection and genetics (R. Moav and G. Wohlfarth)

Lake Tiberias fish populations studies (A. Yashouv)

Carp parasite control (especially *Lerneae*) (A. Yashouv)

PUBLICATIONS ISSUED: *Bamidgeh* (regularly published journal)

Hatahana Leheker Hadiag Hayami

SEA FISHERIES RESEARCH STATION

POSTAL ADDRESS: P. O. Box 699, Habankim Street 4, Haifa, Israel.

EXECUTIVE OFFICER: O. H. Oren, Director.

SPONSORING AGENCY: Machleket Hadaig Sheleyad Misrad Hachaklaut (Department of Fisheries, Ministry of Agriculture).

YEAR FOUNDED: 1946.

SCOPE OF ACTIVITIES: Research on control and management of fisheries; dispersal of radioactive materials in the sea, pollution and fouling of ships hulls; undergraduate instruction.

SEASON OF OPERATION: All year.

PHYSICAL ENVIRONMENT ACCESSIBLE: Eastern Mediterranean Sea, Gulf of Elath (Aquaba) on the Red Sea; sandy and silty beaches, rocky and gravelly shores, estuarine conditions, coral reef, and river.

PROVISIONS FOR VISITING SCIENTISTS: Space for 1 visitor; no fees charged.

MAJOR RESEARCH AND TEACHING FACILITIES: Adequate library; small aquarium tanks; research collections of local marine fishes, Mediterranean benthonic fauna; plankton, fish eggs and plankton larvae; identified reference collections of teleosts, crustaceans, polychaetes, mollusks, decapods, echinoderms, tunicates, chaetognaths; one 21 m LOA power vessel shared with local fishing school.

INSTRUCTIONAL PROGRAM: Two week summer course which covers hydrography, algology, plankton, benthonic fauna and ichthyology.

SIZE OF STAFF: Five at professional level; 3 technicians.

MAJOR CURRENT RESEARCH PROJECTS AND SCIENTIFIC LEADERS:

Oceanography of the region (O. H. Oren)

Primary production of the sea (plankton) (O. H. Oren)

Pollution, net preservation, and sea corrosion (B. Kimor [Komarovsky])

Taxonomy, ecology and cultures of plankton (B. Kimor [Komarovsky])

Ecology of benthonic fauna, dynamics of fish populations (E. Gilat [Gottlieb])

Pelagic fisheries (especially sardines and tuna) (A. Ben-Tuvia)

Life history studies and ecology of fish (L. Bograd-Zisman)

Fishing gear and technology (M. Ben-Yami)

PUBLICATIONS ISSUED: *Bulletin of the Sea Fisheries Research Station* (regularly published journal)

ITALY

Acquario "Diacinto Cestoni" e Laboratorio di Biologia Marina

"DIACINTO CESTONI" AQUARIUM AND MARINE BIOLOGICAL LABORATORY

POSTAL ADDRESS: Piazzale Mascagni I, Livorno, Italia (Italy).

EXECUTIVE OFFICER: Professore A. Razzauti, Direttore.

SPONSORING AGENCY: Municipality of Livorno.

YEAR FOUNDED: 1937.

SCOPE OF ACTIVITIES: Unrestricted research on general marine biology.

SEASON OF OPERATION: All year.

ACQUARIO "DIACINTO CESTONI" E LABORATORIO DI BIOLOGIA MARINA, LIVORNO

PHYSICAL ENVIRONMENT ACCESSIBLE: Mare Ligure (North Tyrrhenian and Ligurian Sea).
PROVISIONS FOR VISITING SCIENTISTS: Space for visitors; living quarters available nearby.
MAJOR RESEARCH FACILITIES: Small library; running sea water, small aquarium tanks; small boats and outboard motors.
SIZE OF STAFF: Two at professional level.
IMPORTANT SPECIES AVAILABLE FOR LABORATORY STUDIES:
Echinodermata: *Astropecten, Asterina, Echinaster, Paracentrotus, Sphaerechinus*
Mollusca: *Murex, Trochus, Tapes, Venus, Cardium, Donax, Octopus*
Crustacea: *Palinurus, Homarus, Maia, Carcinus, Eryphia*

Centro Nazionale di Studi Talassografici

ITALIAN CENTER FOR THALASSOGRAPHIC STUDIES

POSTAL ADDRESS: Riva dei Sette Martiri, Venezia, Italia (Venice, Italy).
EXECUTIVE OFFICER: Professore Umberto D'Ancona.
SPONSORING AGENCY: Consiglio Nazionale delle Ricerche (National Research Council).

Laboratorio Centrale di Idrobiologia

CENTRAL HYDROBIOLOGICAL LABORATORY

POSTAL ADDRESS: Piazza Borghese 91, Roma, Italia (Italy).
EXECUTIVE OFFICER: Professore C. M. Maldura, Direttore.
SPONSORING AGENCY: Ministero dell'Agricolture e delle Foreste (Ministry of Agriculture and Forestry).
YEAR FOUNDED: 1927.
SCOPE OF ACTIVITIES: Unrestricted research on fishery biology.
PHYSICAL ENVIRONMENT ACCESSIBLE: Mare Tirreno (Tyrrhenian Sea); sandy and silty beaches, brackish, shallow bays, eutrophic and oligotrophic lakes, and rivers and streams.
PROVISIONS FOR VISITING SCIENTISTS: None.
MAJOR RESEARCH FACILITIES: Very extensive library.
SIZE OF STAFF: Seven at professional level; 3 technicians.
PUBLICATIONS ISSUED: *Bollettino di Pesca, Piscicoltura e Idrobiologia* (regularly published journal)

Istituto Sperimentale Talassografico di Messina

MESSINA INSTITUTE OF EXPERIMENTAL THALASSOGRAPHY

POSTAL ADDRESS: Spianata S. Rainieri, Messina, Italia (Italy).
LOCATION: Sicily.
EXECUTIVE OFFICER: Professore Antonio Sparta, Direttore.
SPONSORING AGENCY: Ministero dell'Agricolture e delle Foreste (Ministry of Agriculture and Forestry).
YEAR FOUNDED: 1916.
SCOPE OF ACTIVITIES: Unrestricted research on marine biology, physics, and chemistry of the sea.
SEASON OF OPERATION: All year.
PHYSICAL ENVIRONMENT ACCESSIBLE: Stretto di Messina (Straits of Messina) and the Mediterranean Sea.
PROVISIONS FOR VISITING SCIENTISTS: Space for 4 visitors; fees charged.
MAJOR RESEARCH FACILITIES: Small library; running sea and fresh-water, small aquarium tanks; research and identified reference collections of principal flora and fauna of the Straits of Messina and the adjacent seas; small boats and outboard motors.
SIZE OF STAFF: Two at professional level; 2 technicians.
IMPORTANT SPECIES AVAILABLE FOR LABORATORY STUDIES: Abundant Mediterranean marine plants and animals easily available to the laboratory.
MAJOR CURRENT RESEARCH PROJECTS:
Eggs and larvae of marine fishes, including abyssal species from the rich fauna of the Straits of Messina
Plankton studies
Physiology, ecology, and biochemistry of marine plants and animals

Istituto Sperimentale Talassografico di Taranto

TARANTO INSTITUTE OF EXPERIMENTAL THALASSOGRAPHY

POSTAL ADDRESS: Via Roma 3, Taranto, Italia (Italy).
EXECUTIVE OFFICER: Aristode Vatova, Direttore.
SPONSORING AGENCY: Ministero dell'Agricolture e delle Foreste (Ministry of Agriculture and Forestry).
YEAR FOUNDED: 1914.
SCOPE OF ACTIVITIES: Unrestricted research on general marine biology.
SEASON OF OPERATION: All year.
PHYSICAL ENVIRONMENT ACCESSIBLE: Gulf of Taranto, Mediterranean and Ionian Seas.
PROVISIONS FOR VISITING SCIENTISTS: None.

ISTITUTO SPERIMENTALE TALASSOGRAFICO DI TARANTO

MAJOR RESEARCH FACILITIES: Moderately complete library; small aquarium tanks; identified reference collections of marine fishes, and algae from the Ionian Sea; small boats and outboard motors; one 10 m LOA power vessel.

SIZE OF STAFF: Four at professional level; 2 technicians.

MAJOR CURRENT RESEARCH PROJECTS AND SCIENTIFIC LEADERS:

Marine biospeleology (Pietro Parenzan)
Bottom fauna (Pietro Parenzan)
Cromatographic analysis (Angelo Strusi)
Analysis of sea water (A. Vatova)
Productivity of sea water (A. Vatova)
Tidal measurements (E. Orlandini)

PUBLICATIONS ISSUED: *Thalassia Jonica* (regularly published journal)

Istituto Sperimentale Talassografico di Trieste

TRIESTE INSTITUTE OF EXPERIMENTAL THALASSOGRAPHY

POSTAL ADDRESS: Viale Romolo Gessi, 2, Trieste, Italia (Italy).

EXECUTIVE OFFICER: Professore Dr. Mario Picotti, Direttore.

SPONSORING AGENCY: Ministero dell'Agricolture e delle Foreste (Ministry of Agriculture and Forestry).

YEAR FOUNDED: 1840.

SCOPE OF ACTIVITIES: Unrestricted research on chemical and physical oceanography, limnology, sedimentology, mareography, spectroscopy, and radioactivity.

SEASON OF OPERATION: All year.

PHYSICAL ENVIRONMENT ACCESSIBLE: Mare Adriatico (Adriatic Sea).

PROVISIONS FOR VISITING SCIENTISTS: Space for 1 visitor; no fees charged.

ISTITUTO SPERIMENTALE TALASSOGRAFICO DI TRIESTE

MAJOR RESEARCH FACILITIES: Moderately complete library; large outdoor ponds and tanks; machine and wood shop; small boats and outboard motors; one 8 m LOA vessel.

SIZE OF STAFF: Eight at professional level; 14 technicians.

Centro Talassografico del Tirreno

TYRRHENIAN CENTER FOR THALASSOGRAPHIC STUDIES

POSTAL ADDRESS: Via Balbi 10, Genova, Italia (Italy).

EXECUTIVE OFFICER: Professore Sergi Conti, Provisionale Presidente e Direttore, Geologia Dipartimento, Universita di Genova, Via Balbi 5, Genova.

SPONSORING AGENCY: Consiglio Nazionale delle Ricerche (National Research Council).

YEAR FOUNDED: 1948.

SCOPE OF ACTIVITIES: Research on general marine biology and geology, sedimentology, plankton, and bottom ecology.

SEASON OF OPERATION: May to October.

PHYSICAL ENVIRONMENT ACCESSIBLE: Mare Ligure, Mare Tirreno, and Mare Taranto; sandy and silty beaches.

PROVISIONS FOR VISITING SCIENTISTS: None.

MAJOR RESEARCH FACILITIES: Small library; small boats and outboard motors, one oceanographic vessel, *Daino,* available from the Marina Militare.

MAJOR CURRENT RESEARCH PROJECTS AND SCIENTIFIC LEADERS:

Benthonic fauna and microplankton of the Ligurian Sea (G. Fierro)
Microfauna and Foraminifera of bottom samples of the north Tyrrhenian Sea (G. Fierro)
Coralline algae of the Gulf of Taranto (V. I. Mastrorilli)

PUBLICATIONS ISSUED: *Pubblicazioni del Centro Talassografico Tirreno* (regularly published journal)

Istituto di Biologia Marina per l'Adriatico

MARINE BIOLOGICAL INSTITUTE OF THE ADRIATIC

POSTAL ADDRESS: Calle San Domenico 1266 A, Venezia, Italia (Venice, Italy).

EXECUTIVE OFFICER: Vacant.

SPONSORING AGENCY: Ministero della Pubblica Istruzione (Ministry of Public Education).

YEAR FOUNDED: 1892.

SCOPE OF ACTIVITIES: Unrestricted research on the hydrography and biology of the Lagoon of Venice and the Adriatic Sea.

SEASON OF OPERATION: All year.

PHYSICAL ENVIRONMENT ACCESSIBLE: Laguna di Venezia (Lagoon of Venice), Mare Adriatico (Adriatic Sea); estuarine conditions, brackish, shallow bays.

PROVISIONS FOR VISITING SCIENTISTS: Space for visitors; living quarters available nearby.
MAJOR RESEARCH FACILITIES: Small library; electrical and electronic shop; small boats and outboard motors.
SIZE OF STAFF: One technician.
IMPORTANT SPECIES AVAILABLE FOR LABORATORY STUDIES:
Crustacea: *Carcinides maenas*
Tunicata: *Mogula* sp.
Pisces: *Mugil* sp., *Gobius* sp.
MAJOR CURRENT RESEARCH PROJECTS AND SCIENTIFIC LEADERS:
Hydrography of the Lagoon of Venice (A. Vatore)
Primary productivity of water with the C-14 method (A. Vatore)
PUBLICATIONS ISSUED: *Nova Thalassia* (occasionally published journal)

Universita di Perugia, Istituto di Idrobiologia e Pescicoltura G. B. Grassi

UNIVERSITY OF PERUGIA, G. B. GRASSI INSTITUTE OF HYDROBIOLOGY AND FISH-CULTURE

POSTAL ADDRESS: Monte del Lago Sul Trasimeno, Italia (Italy).
LOCATION: Near Lago Trasimeno.
EXECUTIVE OFFICER: Professore G. P. Moretti, Direttore.
YEAR FOUNDED: 1956.
SCOPE OF ACTIVITIES: Unrestricted research on limnology, fresh-water biology, water pollution and fish-culture; graduate instruction.
SEASON OF OPERATION: All year.
PHYSICAL ENVIRONMENT ACCESSIBLE: Lago Trasimeno (eutrophic lake); oligotrophic lake, rivers, streams, springs, and hypogean waters.
PROVISIONS FOR VISITING SCIENTISTS: Space for 4 visitors; fees charged; living quarters available nearby.
MAJOR RESEARCH AND TEACHING FACILITIES: Small library; large outdoor tanks, small aquarium tanks; research collections of aquatic birds, Crustacea, Trichoptera, Hydrophyta, and algae; identified reference collections of birds, fishes, and *Anopheles*; skilled shop workman available; 4 boats with outboard motors.
INSTRUCTIONAL PROGRAM: Limnology (physics and chemistry), aquatic botany, invertebrate zoology, water pollution, fish biology, and biospeleology.
SIZE OF STAFF: Five at professional level; 2 technicians.
IMPORTANT SPECIES AVAILABLE FOR LABORATORY STUDIES:
Aquatic plants: *Potamageton pectinatus, Myriophyllum* sp.
Insecta: Plecoptera, Ephemeroptera, Odonata, Trichoptera
Pisces: *Atherina mochon, Rutilus rubilio*

ISTITUTO DI IDROBIOLOGIA E PESCICOLTURA G. B. GRASSI, LAGO TRASIMENO

MAJOR CURRENT RESEARCH PROJECTS AND SCIENTIFIC LEADERS:
Hydrobiology and fish-culture (Giampaolo Moretti)
Genetics (F. S. Gianotti)
PUBLICATIONS ISSUED: *Rivista di Idrobiologia* (quarterly review)

Istituto Italiano di Idrobiologia

ITALIAN INSTITUTE OF HYDROBIOLOGY

POSTAL ADDRESS: Pallanza Verbania, Italia (Italy).
LOCATION: Near Milano (Milan).
EXECUTIVE OFFICER: Professore Vittorio Tonolli, Direttore.
SPONSORING AGENCIES: Ministero della Pubblica Istruzione (Ministry of Public Education) and Consiglio Nazionale delle Ricerche (National Research Council).
SCOPE OF ACTIVITIES: Unrestricted research on limnology, plankton, benthos, biometry and genetics of fresh-water organisms, biochemistry of water and sediments, and primary production.

ISTITUTO ITALIANO DI IDROBIOLOGIA, VERBANIA

SEASON OF OPERATION: All year.

PHYSICAL ENVIRONMENT ACCESSIBLE: Lakes Maggiore, Como, Lugano, Orta, Mergozzo and Varese (eutrophic and oligotrophic lakes); rivers and streams.

PROVISIONS FOR VISITING SCIENTISTS: Research and living space for 5-6 visitors; no fees charged for research space.

MAJOR RESEARCH FACILITIES: Very extensive library; large outdoor ponds and tanks, small aquarium tanks; machine and wood shop; small boats and outboard motors, one 10 m LOA power vessel, *Gardo II.*

SIZE OF STAFF: Nine at professional level; 6 technicians.

MAJOR CURRENT RESEARCH PROJECTS AND SCIENTIFIC LEADERS:

General limnology (Vittorio Tonolli and Livia Tonolli)

Primary production (Rich. A. Vollenweider)

Biochemistry of water and sediments (Domenico Povoledo)

Benthonic communities (Giuliano Bonomi)

Hydrachnida and Halacaridae (Anna Maria Nocentini)

Tardigrada (Giuseppe Ramazzotti)

PUBLICATIONS ISSUED: *Memoire dell'Istituto Italiano di Idrobiologia* (regularly published journal)

Istituto Nazionale di Studi Talassografici

ITALIAN INSTITUTE FOR THALASSOGRAPHIC STUDIES

POSTAL ADDRESS: 1364-A Riva dei Sette Martiri, Venezia, Italia (Venice, Italy).

EXECUTIVE OFFICER: Professore Umberto D'Ancona, Direttore.

SPONSORING AGENCY: Consiglio Nazionale delle Ricerche (National Research Council).

YEAR FOUNDED: 1947.

ISTITUTO NAZIONALE DI STUDI TALASSOGRAFICI, VENICE

SCOPE OF ACTIVITIES: Unrestricted research on general marine biology, oceanography, and plankton.

SEASON OF OPERATION: All year.

PHYSICAL ENVIRONMENT ACCESSIBLE: Mare Adriatico (Adriatic Sea), Laguna di Venezia (Lagoon of Venice); sandy and silty beaches, estuarine conditions, brackish, shallow bays, and rivers and streams.

PROVISIONS FOR VISITING SCIENTISTS: Space for 1-2 visitors; no fees charged; living quarters available nearby.

MAJOR RESEARCH FACILITIES: Moderately complete library; machine and wood shop; small boats and outboard motors.

SIZE OF STAFFS Three at professional level; 4 technicians.

MAJOR CURRENT RESEARCH PROJECTS AND SCIENTIFIC LEADERS:

Plankton in the Italian seas (Umberto D'Ancona)

PUBLICATIONS ISSUED: *Archivio di Oceanografia e Limnologia* (regularly published journal)

Universita di Bologna, Laboratorio di Biologia Marina di Fano

UNIVERSITY OF BOLOGNA, FANO MARINE BIOLOGICAL LABORATORY

POSTAL ADDRESS: Viale Adriatico, Fano (Pesaro), Italia (Italy).

EXECUTIVE OFFICER: Professore Enrico Vannini, Direttore.

YEAR FOUNDED: 1941.

SCOPE OF ACTIVITIES: Unrestricted research on marine and fishery biology.

SEASON OF OPERATION: Summer.

PHYSICAL ENVIRONMENT ACCESSIBLE: Mare Adriatico (Adriatic Sea); sandy and silty beaches, gravelly shores.

PROVISIONS FOR VISITING SCIENTISTS: Space for 2 visitors; no fees charged; living quarters available nearby.

MAJOR RESEARCH FACILITIES: Very extensive library at Istituto di Zoologia; running sea and fresh-water, small aquarium tanks; identified reference collection of local Mollusca; machine and wood shop, electrical and electronic shop, skilled shop workman available; small boats and outboard motors.

IMPORTANT SPECIES AVAILABLE FOR LABORATORY STUDIES:

Mollusca: *Sepia* sp., *Patella* sp., *Littorina* sp.

Echinodermata: *Astropecten* sp.

Crustacea: *Dorippe lanate*

Pisces: *Hippocampus brevirostris*

MAJOR CURRENT RESEARCH PROJECTS AND SCIENTIFIC LEADERS:

Fishery production and environmental conditions (A. Scaccini and M. Scaccini)

Chaetognaths and cuttlefish studies (E. Ghirardelli)

Laboratorio per lo Studio Della Contaminazione Radioattiva del Mare

LABORATORY FOR THE STUDY OF THE RADIOACTIVE CONTAMINATION OF THE SEA

POSTAL ADDRESS: Fiascherino (La Spezia), Italia (Italy).
TEMPORARY LOCATION: Fifteen km southeast of La Spezia.
EXECUTIVE OFFICER: Dr. Michael Bernhard, Direttore.
SPONSORING AGENCY: Comitato Nazionale per l'Energia Nucleare (Italian Atomic Energy Committee), via Belisario 15, Roma.
YEAR FOUNDED: 1959.
SCOPE OF ACTIVITIES: Restricted research on a marine pelagic ecological system with reference to radioactive contamination of the sea.
SEASON OF OPERATION: All year.
PHYSICAL ENVIRONMENT ACCESSIBLE: Golfo La Spezia, Mare Ligure (Ligurian Sea), and Mediterraneo; rocky and gravelly shores.
PROVISIONS FOR VISITING SCIENTISTS: Space for 1 visitor; no fees charged.
MAJOR RESEARCH FACILITIES: Small library; running sea water planned for 1962, small aquarium tanks; planned research and identified reference collections of local fauna and flora; machine and wood shop, skilled shop workman available; small boats and outboard motors.
SIZE OF STAFF: Four at professional level; 14 technicians.
IMPORTANT SPECIES AVAILABLE FOR LABORATORY STUDIES:
Echinodermata: *Arbacia lixula, Sphaerechinus granularis*
Mollusca: *Octopus vulgaris, Sepia* sp.
Siphonales: *Acetabularia mediterranea*
Phytoplankton: Culture collection of pelagic phytoplankton.
MAJOR CURRENT RESEARCH PROJECTS AND SCIENTIFIC LEADERS:
Qualitative and quantitative analysis of marine heterotrophic microorganisms and their function in the marine ecosystem (Ulderico Melchiorri-Santolini)
Qualitative and quantitative analysis of phytoplankton and zooplankton (Leopold Rampi)
Primary production measurements in relation to algal physiology (Michael Bernhard)
Accumulation of radioisotopes by marine organisms (Michael Bernhard)
Distribution of nutrients in the sea (Michael Bernhard)
Development of special oceanographic apparatus for light, depth, temperature, and current measurements (Antonio Benedetti)
PUBLICATIONS ISSUED: *Publicazioni della Divisione Biologica del CNEN* (occasionally published journal)

STAZIONE IDROBIOLOGICA DI CHIOGGIA

Universita di Padova, Stazione Idrobiologica di Chioggia

UNIVERSITY OF PADUA, CHIOGGIA HYDROBIOLOGICAL STATION

POSTAL ADDRESS: Casella Postale 62, Chioggia (Venezia), Italia (Italy).
EXECUTIVE OFFICER: Professore Umberto D'Ancona, Direttore.
YEAR FOUNDED: 1940.
SCOPE OF ACTIVITIES: Unrestricted research on the hydrobiology of the Adriatic lagoons.
SEASON OF OPERATION: All year.
PHYSICAL ENVIRONMENT ACCESSIBLE: Mare Adriatico (Adriatic Sea), Laguna di Venezia (Lagoon of Venice); sandy and silty beaches, estuarine conditions, brackish, shallow bays, and rivers and streams.
PROVISIONS FOR VISITING SCIENTISTS: Research space for 4 and living space for 1 visitor; no fees charged for research space; other living quarters available nearby.
MAJOR RESEARCH FACILITIES: No library; running sea and fresh-water, large outdoor ponds and tanks, small aquarium tanks; small boats and outboard motors.
SIZE OF STAFF: Two at professional level; 1 technician.
MAJOR CURRENT RESEARCH PROJECTS AND SCIENTIFIC LEADERS:
Fish culture in the Adriatic lagoons (Umberto D'Ancona)
Biology of brackish water (Umberto D'Ancona)
Limnology of Lake Garda (Carlo Mozzi)

Stazione Zoologica di Napoli

NAPLES ZOOLOGICAL STATION

POSTAL ADDRESS: Napoli, Italia (Naples, Italy).
EXECUTIVE OFFICER: Dr. Peter Dohrn, Direttore.
SPONSORING AGENCY: Ministero della Pubblica Istruzione (Ministry of Public Education); Fondazione

Anton e Reinhard Dohrn.
YEAR FOUNDED: 1874.
SCOPE OF ACTIVITIES: Unrestricted research on general and experimental marine biology.
SEASON OF OPERATION: All year.
PHYSICAL ENVIRONMENT ACCESSIBLE: Baia di Napoli (Bay of Naples), Mare Tirreno (Tyrrhenian Sea); rocky and gravelly shores.
PROVISIONS FOR VISITING SCIENTISTS: Space for 75 visitors; fees charged.
MAJOR RESEARCH FACILITIES: Very extensive library; running sea and fresh-water, large and small aquarium tanks; research collections of all marine fauna and of algae; machine and wood shop; five power vessels including 14 m LOA, *Rinaldo Dohrn,* 12 m LOA, *Cavolini,* and the 10 m LOA, *Raffaele.*
SIZE OF PERMANENT STAFF: Ten at professional level; 25 technicians. The station exists mainly for visiting scientists.
IMPORTANT SPECIES AVAILABLE FOR LABORATORY STUDIES:
Echinodermata: *Paracentrotus lividus, Sphaerechinus granularis*
Tunicata: *Phallusia mamillata*
Mollusca: *Octopus vulgaris*
Selachii: *Scyllium canicula*
Many other species of plants and animals common to the Italian coast are available.
MAJOR CURRENT RESEARCH PROJECTS OF THE PERMANENT STAFF AND SCIENTIFIC LEADERS:
Hydroid monograph (Anita Brinckmann)
Biochemistry of sea urchin eggs (enzymes) (Eduardo Scarano)
Cephalopod behavior and brain function (John Z. Young)
Many other research projects, too numerous to mention, are conducted by guest scientists.
PUBLICATIONS ISSUED: *Pubblicazioni della Stazione Zoologica di Napoli* (regularly published journal)

STAZIONE ZOOLOGICA DI NAPOLI

Universita di Messina, Istituto di Idrobiologia

UNIVERSITY OF MESSINA, HYDROBIOLOGICAL INSTITUTE

POSTAL ADDRESS: Via Del Verdi 75, Messina, Italia (Italy).
LOCATION: Sicily.
EXECUTIVE OFFICER: Professore Filippo Dulzetto.
YEAR FOUNDED: 1928.
SCOPE OF ACTIVITIES: Unrestricted research on general marine and brackish water biology; instruction.
SEASON OF OPERATION: All year.
PHYSICAL ENVIRONMENT ACCESSIBLE: Stretto di Messina (Strait of Messina).
MAJOR RESEARCH AND TEACHING FACILITIES: Moderately complete library; running sea-water; research collections of benthonic fauna of the Strait of Messina.
INSTRUCTIONAL PROGRAM: Annual courses in hydrobiology and fish culture at the university.
SIZE OF STAFF: One at professional level; 1 assistant.
IMPORTANT SPECIES AVAILABLE FOR LABORATORY STUDIES:
Mollusca: *Mytilus galloprovincialis*
Pisces: *Thunnus thynnus*
MAJOR CURRENT RESEARCH PROJECTS AND SCIENTIFIC LEADERS:
Biology of *Thunnus thynnus* (S. Genovese)
Bacteriology of brackish water (S. Genovese)
Copepods (P. Crisafi)

IVORY COAST

Ministere de la Production Animale. Centre de Recherches Oceanographiques

MINISTRY OF ANIMAL PRODUCTION, CENTER FOR OCEANOGRAPHIC RESEARCH

POSTAL ADDRESS: B. P. 35, Abidjan, Cote d'Ivoire (Ivory Coast).
EXECUTIVE OFFICER: Paul Rancurel, Maitre de Recherches ORSTOM, Chef du Service Oceanographique.
YEAR FOUNDED: 1959.
SCOPE OF ACTIVITIES: Unrestricted research on demersal and pelagic fishes, bottom ecology and general oceanography.
SEASON OF OPERATION: All year.
PHYSICAL ENVIRONMENT ACCESSIBLE: East-tropical Atlantic Ocean; sandy and silty beaches, brackish, shallow bays and mangrove swamps.
PROVISIONS FOR VISITING SCIENTISTS: Research and living space for 2-3 visitors; no fees charged for research space.
MAJOR RESEARCH FACILITIES: Small library; small aquarium tanks; research collections of fishes, Crustacea, Mollusca, Annelida, Echinodermata, plankton;

identified reference collections of local fishes, Crustacea and Mollusca; machine and wood shop, skilled shop workman available; vessels, 11 m LOA, *Pinasse,* and 26 m LOA, *Trawler.*

SIZE OF STAFF: Four at professional level; 4 technicians.

IMPORTANT SPECIES AVAILABLE FOR LABORATORY STUDIES:

Pelecypoda: Teredinae

Pisces: *Sardinella aurita, S. seba, Neothunnus albacora, Parathunnus obesus*

MAJOR CURRENT RESEARCH PROJECTS AND SCIENTIFIC LEADERS:

Biology of tuna and *Sardinella* (E. Marchal)

Bottom ecology and biology of demersal fishes (P. Rancurel)

Biology of Teredinae (P. Rancurel)

PUBLICATIONS ISSUED: *Bulletin du Service Oceanographique de la Cote d'Ivoire* (occasionally published journal).

JAPAN

Geirui Kenkyusho

WHALES RESEARCH INSTITUTE

POSTAL ADDRESS: No. 4, 12-Chome, Nishigashi-Dori, Tsukishima, Chuo-ku, Tokyo, Nippon (Japan).

EXECUTIVE OFFICER: Hideo Omura, Director.

SPONSORING AGENCY: Japan Whaling Association and the Japanese governmental Fisheries Agency.

YEAR FOUNDED: 1947.

SCOPE OF ACTIVITIES: Restricted research on whale biology, particularly population studies.

SEASON OF OPERATION: All year.

PHYSICAL ENVIRONMENT ACCESSIBLE: North Pacific Ocean. Working field consists of coastal water of Japan, the Bering Sea, and the Antarctic Ocean.

GEIRUI KENKYUSHO, TOKYO

PROVISIONS FOR VISITING SCIENTISTS: None.

MAJOR RESEARCH FACILITIES: Small library; research collections of external parasites of whales (including diatoms and Amphipoda), whale food (copepods and euphausiids) and cetacean skeletons; type specimens of beaked whale, *Mesoplodon ginkgodens,* and type specimens of parasitic diatoms *Plumosigma hustedti, P. rimosum,* and *Stauroneis omurai.*

MAJOR CURRENT RESEARCH PROJECTS AND SCIENTIFIC LEADERS:

Population study of large whales (Hideo Omura)

PUBLICATIONS ISSUED: *The Scientific Reports of the Whales Research Institute* (annually published journal)

Hiroshima Daigaku, Mukaishima Rinkai Jikkensho

HIROSHIMA UNIVERSITY, MUKAISHIMA MARINE BIOLOGICAL STATION

POSTAL ADDRESS: Mukaishima-cho (Onomichi Post Office), Hiroshima Prefecture, Nippon (Japan).

LOCATION: Near Onomichi, Inland Sea.

EXECUTIVE OFFICER: Dr. Toshijiro Kawamura, Director of Station and Professor, Hiroshima University, Hiroshima.

YEAR FOUNDED: 1933.

SCOPE OF ACTIVITIES: Unrestricted research on general marine zoology and plankton; graduate and undergraduate instruction.

SEASON OF OPERATION: All year.

PHYSICAL ENVIRONMENT ACCESSIBLE: Setonaikai (Inland Sea of Seto); sandy and silty beaches, rocky and gravelly shores, and brackish, shallow bays.

PROVISIONS FOR VISITING SCIENTISTS: Research and living space for 2-3 visitors and 30 students; no fees charged for research space.

MAJOR RESEARCH FACILITIES: Small library; running sea and fresh-water; small aquarium tanks; research and identified reference collections of Inland Sea fauna; machine and wood shop; vessels, 5 m LOA motorboat, *Venus,* and 10 m LOA power vessel, *Sparus.*

INSTRUCTIONAL PROGRAM: General invertebrate zoology, malacology, ichthyology, marine plankton, developmental and experimental embryology of sea urchins, and general physiology.

SIZE OF STAFF: Two at professional level; 1 technician.

IMPORTANT SPECIES AVAILABLE FOR LABORATORY STUDIES:

Echiuroidea: *Thalassema gogoshimense, Ikeda taenioides*

Mollusca: *Tamanovalva limax*

Brachiopoda: *Lingula unguis*

Echinodermata: *Heliocidaris crassispina*

Xiphosura: *Tachypleus tridentatua*

Enteropneusta: *Glaudiceps hacksi*

MUKAISHIMA RINKAI JIKKENSHO

Cephalochordata: *Branchiostoma japonicum*

MAJOR CURRENT RESEARCH PROJECTS AND SCIENTIFIC LEADERS:

Cytotaxonomic studies of Mollusca (Dr. Akihiko Inaba)

Fauna of the Inland Sea of Seto (Dr. Akihiko Inaba)

Seasonal changes in *Sagitta* (Dr. Reiichiro Hirota)

Plankton fauna of the Inland Sea of Seto (Dr. Reiichiro Hirota)

Hiroshima Daigaku, Sui-Chikusan Gakubu

HIROSHIMA UNIVERSITY, FACULTY OF FISHERIES AND ANIMAL HUSBANDRY

POSTAL ADDRESS: Daimon-cho, Fukuyama, Hiroshima Prefecture, Nippon (Japan).

LOCATION: Fukuyama.

EXECUTIVE OFFICER: Dr. Hisashi Kashima, Dean.

YEAR FOUNDED: 1949.

SCOPE OF ACTIVITIES: Unrestricted research on fisheries, oceanography, aquatic zoology, and phycology, with special emphasis on the problems related to the fisheries and aquiculture in the Seto Inland Sea; undergraduate instruction.

PHYSICAL ENVIRONMENT ACCESSIBLE: Seto Naikai (Inland Sea); sandy and silty beaches, estuarine conditions, brackish, shallow bays, eutrophic lake, and rivers and streams.

PROVISIONS FOR VISITING SCIENTISTS: Space for 2 visitors; fees charged; living quarters available nearby.

MAJOR RESEARCH AND TEACHING FACILITIES: Moderately complete library; running sea and fresh-water, large outdoor tanks, small aquarium tanks; research collections of Cephalopoda, Pisces, and seaweeds; identified reference collections of local fishes, invertebrates, and sea weeds; machine and wood shop, electrical and electronic shop; small boats and outboard motors; 21 m LOA vessel, M/S *Toyoshio Maru.*

INSTRUCTIONAL PROGRAM IN MARINE BIOLOGY: Fisheries, statistics, general oceanography, planktology, limnology, aquatic zoology, animal ecology, animal physiology, animal histology and embroyology, aquatic botany, plant physiology and ecology, embroyology of algae, applied phycology, fish population dynamics, aquiculture, fish embroyology, ichthyology, fish processing, chemistry of nutrition, biochemistry, chemistry of oil and fat, applied microbiology, and food sanitation.

SIZE OF STAFF: Twenty-two at professional level; 39 technicians.

IMPORTANT SPECIES AVAILABLE FOR LABORATORY STUDIES:

Rhodophyeae: *Porphyra tenera*

Phaeophyceae: *Undaria pinnatifida*

Echinodermata: *Temnopleurus toreumaticus*

Mollusca: *Ostrea gigas, Tapes semidecussata, Sepia esculenta, Octopus vulgare*

Pisces: *Fugu rubripes, Lateolabrax japonicus, Anguilla japonica*

MAJOR CURRENT RESEARCH PROJECTS AND SCIENTIFIC LEADERS:

Cytology of *Porphyra* (Rhodophyta) (T. Fujiyama)

Improvement of seaweed culture techniques (T. Fujiyama)

Amino acid composition of muscle extracts of aquatic animals (K. Ito)

Algal flora of the Inland Sea of Japan (S. Inumaru)

Annulus formation in the otolith of fish (T. Irie)

Pound-net fishing in the Inland Sea (S. Kakuda)

Chemical studies on volatile constituents of seaweeds (T. Katayama)

Plankton and primary productivity of the Inland Sea (H. Koyama)

Ecology and culture of marine fishes (D. Kusakabe)

Chemical study of marine suspended matter (Y. Matsudaira and T. Endo)

SUI-CHIKUSAN GAKUBU

Physiology of the laver, *Porphyra tenera* (T. Matsumoto)
Fish pathology (S. Murachi)
Ecology and mass culture of cladocerans (Y. Murakami)
Analysis of fisheries fluctuation in relation to sea conditions (S. Nishikawa)
Electrical fish screens for eels, etc. (I. Takesita)
Ecology of marine tubicolous amphipods (T. Onbe)
Taxonomic studies on the Cephalopoda of Japan (Iwao Taki)

PUBLICATIONS ISSUED: *Journal of the Faculty of Fisheries and Animal Husbandry, Hiroshima University* (regularly published journal)

Hokkaido Daigaku, Rigakubu, Kaiso Kenkyusho

HOKKAIDO UNIVERSITY, FACULTY OF SCIENCE, INSTITUTE OF ALGOLOGICAL RESEARCH

POSTAL ADDRESS: Shintomi-cho, Muroran, Nippon (Japan).
LOCATION: Near Sapporo.
EXECUTIVE OFFICER: Y. Yamada, Director. Department of Botany, Faculty of Science, Hokkaido University, Sapporo, Japan.
YEAR FOUNDED: 1933.
SCOPE OF ACTIVITIES: Unrestricted research on marine phycology.
SEASON OF OPERATION: All year.
PHYSICAL ENVIRONMENT ACCESSIBLE: Oyashio and Tsushima Current; open ocean, rocky and gravelly shores.
PROVISIONS FOR VISITING SCIENTISTS: Research and living space for 1-2 visitors; no fees charged for research space.
MAJOR RESEARCH FACILITIES: Small library, running sea and fresh-water; research collections of seaweeds from vicinity of Hokkaido; identified reference collections of local flora; small boats and outboard motors.
SIZE OF STAFF: Three at professional level.
IMPORTANT SPECIES AVAILABLE FOR LABORATORY STUDIES:

Cholorphyceae: *Monostroma angicava, Chaetomorpha moniligera*
Phaeophyceae: *Pelvetia wrightii, Alaria crassifolia, Laminaria angustata, Leathesia difformis*
Rhodophyceae: *Porphyra variegata, Rhodymenia pertusa, Rhodomela larix*

MAJOR CURRENT RESEARCH PROJECTS AND SCIENTIFIC LEADERS:

Taxonomic study of the marine algae of Hokkaido (Y. Yamada)
Culture studies of the species of Chlorophyceae and Phaeophyceae (Y. Yamada)
Ecological study of Uchiura Bay (Y. Yamada)

HOKKAIDO DAIGAKU, KAISO KENKYUSHO

Hokkaido Daigaku, Akkeshi Rinkai Jikkensho

HOKKAIDO UNIVERSITY, AKKESHI MARINE BIOLOGICAL STATION

POSTAL ADDRESS: Akkeshi, Hokkaido, Nippon (Japan).
EXECUTIVE OFFICERS: Dr. Tohru Uchida, Director. Dr. Fumio Iwata, Resident Director.
YEAR FOUNDED: 1931.
SCOPE OF ACTIVITIES: Unrestricted research on general marine biology; graduate and undergraduate instruction.
SEASON OF OPERATION: All year.
PHYSICAL ENVIRONMENT ACCESSIBLE: Pacific Ocean, Atsukeshi Bay; sandy and silty beaches, rocky and gravelly shores, estuarine conditions, and brackish, shallow bays.
PROVISIONS FOR VISITING SCIENTISTS: Research and living space for 7 visitors.
MAJOR RESEARCH AND TEACHING FACILITIES: Small library; running sea and fresh-water; small aquarium tanks; research collection of nemerteans; identified reference collections of Nemertinea, Gastropoda, Lamellibranchia (Mollusca), Pantopoda, and Crustacea; small boats and outboard motors.
INSTRUCTIONAL PROGRAM: General invertebrate zoology and physiology.
SIZE OF STAFF: Four-five at professional level.
IMPORTANT SPECIES AVAILABLE FOR LABORATORY STUDIES:

Coelenterata: *Tubularia venusta, Polyorchis karafutoensis, Epiactis prolifera*
Nemertinea: *Lineus torquatus, Micrura akkeshiensis*
Polychaeta: *Arenicola claparedii*
Crustacea: *Idotea japonica*
Echinodermata: *Asterias amurensis, Strongylocentrotus intermedius*
Mollusca: *Crassostrea gigas*

AKKESHI RINKAI JIKKENSHO

MAJOR CURRENT RESEARCH PROJECTS AND SCIENTIFIC LEADERS:

Classification and life history of the Coelenterata (Tohru Uchida)

Classification and embryology of the Nemertinea (Fumio Iwata)

Experimental morphology of crustaceans (Chitaru Oguro)

Life history and embryology of hydroids (Zen Nagao)

PUBLICATIONS ISSUED: *Publications from the Akkeshi Marine Biological Station* (regularly published journal)

Hokkaido Daigaku, Suisan Gakubu, Oshoro Rinkai Jikkensho

HOKKAIDO UNIVERSITY, FACULTY OF FISHERIES, OSHORO MARINE BIOLOGICAL STATION

POSTAL ADDRESS: Oshoro-machi, Otaru, Hokkaido, Nippon (Japan).

EXECUTIVE OFFICER: Dr. Hidejiro Niiyama.

YEAR FOUNDED: 1907.

SCOPE OF ACTIVITIES: Unrestricted research on general marine biology, plankton studies, and algology.

SEASON OF OPERATION: All year.

PHYSICAL ENVIRONMENT ACCESSIBLE: Oshoro Bay, Ishikari Bay, Sea of Japan; rocky shores.

PROVISIONS FOR VISITING SCIENTISTS: Research and living space for 2 visitors; fees charged for research space.

MAJOR RESEARCH FACILITIES: No library; running sea and fresh-water; small aquarium tanks; small boats and outboard motors, one small launch, *Sazanami.*

SIZE OF STAFF: Two at professional level; 2 technicians.

IMPORTANT SPECIES AVAILABLE FOR LABORATORY STUDIES:

Algae: *Laminaria, Undaria*

Crustacea: *Hemigrapsus sanguineus*

Echinodermata: *Strongylocentrotus intermedius, Asterina pectinifera, Stichopus japonicus*

Pisces: *Sebastes taczanowskii, Hexagrammus otakii, Myoxocephalus stelleri raninus, Limanda punctatissima, L. herzensteini*

Hokkaido Gakugei Daigaku, Seibutsu Kyoiku Shirikishinai Rinkai Jikkensho

HOKKAIDO GAKUGEI UNIVERSITY, SHIRIKISHINAI MARINE STATION FOR BIOLOGICAL INSTRUCTION

POSTAL ADDRESS: Toyoura, Shirikishinai, Kameda-gun, Hokkaido, Nippon (Japan).

EXECUTIVE OFFICER: Dr. Hideji Yamaguchi, Chief of Station, Biological Laboratory, Hakodate Branch, Hokkaido Gakugei University, Hachiman-cho, 153, Hakodate, Hokkaido.

YEAR FOUNDED: 1954.

SCOPE OF ACTIVITIES: Unrestricted research on general marine biology; undergraduate instruction.

SEASON OF OPERATION: All year.

PHYSICAL ENVIRONMENT ACCESSIBLE: Pacific Ocean; sandy and silty beaches, rocky and gravelly shores.

PROVISIONS FOR VISITING SCIENTISTS: Research and living space for 4 visitors except during the time of undergraduate instruction; no fees charged for research space.

MAJOR RESEARCH AND TEACHING FACILITIES: Small library; small identified reference collections of local fauna and flora; one 7 m LOA vessel.

OSHORO RINKAI JIKKENSHO

INSTRUCTIONAL PROGRAM: General invertebrate zoology, study of plankton, embryology, and study of sea algae.
SIZE OF STAFF: Four at professional level; 1 technician.
MAJOR CURRENT RESEARCH PROJECTS AND SCIENTIFIC LEADERS:
Survey of marine fauna and flora near Shirikishinai (Hideji Yamaguchi)

Hokkaido-Ritsu Suisan Fukajo and Sake Masu Fukajo

HOKKAIDO FISH HATCHERY AND SALMON HATCHERY

POSTAL ADDRESS: Nakanoshima, Toyohiro-chi, Sapporo-gun, Hokkiado, Nippon (Japan).
Branches: Kitami, Nemuro, Tokachi, Teshio, Chitose and Oshima.
LOCATION: Suburb of Sapporo City.
EXECUTIVE OFFICER: Mr. T. Arai, Chief Officer.
SPONSORING AGENCIES: Suisan-cho (Fisheries Agency) and local government of Hokkaido.
YEAR FOUNDED: 1941.
SCOPE OF ACTIVITIES: Unrestricted research on culture of rainbow trout and pond-smelt, etc., and culture of chum, pink and landlocked blueback salmon.
SEASON OF OPERATION: All year.
PHYSICAL ENVIRONMENT ACCESSIBLE: Inland waters and adjacent sea waters in Hokkaido; estuarine conditions, brackish, shallow bays, eutrophic and oligotrophic lakes, rivers and streams.
PROVISIONS FOR VISITING SCIENTISTS: Space for 2 visitors; no fees charged.
MAJOR RESEARCH FACILITIES: Very small library; 43 hatcheries; large outdoor ponds; wood shop; small boats and outboard motors.
IMPORTANT SPECIES AVAILABLE FOR LABORATORY STUDIES:
Pisces: *Oncorhynchus keta, O. masou, O. nerka* (landlocked form), *Cyprinus carpio, Carassius carassius, Salmo irideus, S. gairdneri, Hypomesus olidus*
PUBLICATIONS ISSUED:
Scientific Reports of Hokkaido Salmon Hatchery
Scientific Reports of Hokkaido Fish Hatchery (regularly published journals in Japanese with English summaries)

Ibaraki Daigaku, Hinuma Rinko Jikkensho

IBARAKI UNIVERSITY, HINUMA HYDROBIOLOGICAL STATION

POSTAL ADDRESS: Ibaraki Daigaku, Watari-machi, Mito-shi, Nippon (Japan).
LOCATION: Ishizaki, Ibaraki-machi, Higashi-Ibaraki-gun, Ibaraki-ken.
EXECUTIVE OFFICER: Professor M. Sato, Director of Station, Biological Institute, Ibaraki University, Mito-shi.
YEAR FOUNDED: 1956.
SCOPE OF ACTIVITIES: Unrestricted research on general fresh-water biology, plankton, and bottom ecology.
SEASON OF OPERATION: All year.
PHYSICAL ENVIRONMENT ACCESSIBLE: Hinuma River; eutrophic lake.
PROVISIONS FOR VISITING SCIENTISTS: Research and living space for 3 visitors; no fees charged for living space.
MAJOR RESEARCH FACILITIES: Small library; identified reference collections of Hinuma fishes; small boats and outboard motors.
SIZE OF STAFF: Six at professional level.
IMPORTANT SPECIES AVAILABLE FOR LABORATORY STUDIES:
Coelenterata: *Cordylophora japonica*
Polychaeta: *Tylorrhynchus heterochaetus*
Crustacea: *Neomysis intermedia, Eriocheir japonica*
Mollusca: *Corbicula japonica, Assiminea japonica*
Pisces: *Acanthogobius flavimanus, Anguilla japonica*

HOKKAIDO-RITSU SUISAN FUKAJO AND SAKE MASU FUKAJO

HINUMA RINKO JIKKENSHO

MAJOR CURRENT RESEARCH PROJECTS AND SCIENTIFIC LEADERS:
- Taxonomy and ecology of fresh-water sponges (Taiji Imamura)
- Taxonomy of fishes and water-mites (Taiji Imamura)
- Ecology of Polychaeta (Hisabumi Kikuchi)
- Osmotic regulation in Crustacea (Jutaro Shinozaki)
- Ecology of water plants (Nobuo Nomoto)
- Taxonomy of water plants (Masatomo Suzuki)
- Taxonomy and ecology of algae (Masami Sato)
- Bottom ecology of Lake Hinuma (Yoshio Yamazaki)

Kagawaken Suisan Shikenjo

KAGAWA PREFECTURAL FISHERIES EXPERIMENTAL STATION

KAGAWAKEN SUISAN SHIKENJO

POSTAL ADDRESS: Shido-cho, Okawa-gun, Kagawa-ken, Nippon (Japan).
LOCATION: Near Takamatsu.
EXECUTIVE OFFICER: Kojiro Tanaka, Director.
YEAR FOUNDED: 1900.
SCOPE OF ACTIVITIES: Restricted research on general marine biology.
SEASON OF OPERATION: All year.
PHYSICAL ENVIRONMENT ACCESSIBLE: Seto Inland Sea; brackish, shallow bays, and rivers and streams.
PROVISIONS FOR VISITING SCIENTISTS: None.
MAJOR RESEARCH FACILITIES: Moderately complete library; large outdoor ponds and tanks, small aquarium tanks; research collections of fishes, Crustacea, Cephalopoda, and marine flora including Chlorophyceae and Phaeophyceae; identified reference collections of local fauna and flora; machine and wood shop; one 11 m LOA vessel.
SIZE OF STAFF: One at professional level; 11 technicians.
IMPORTANT SPECIES AVAILABLE FOR LABORATORY STUDIES:
- Algae: *Porphyra tenera, Monostroma* spp.
- Mollusca: *Gryphae gigas, G. denselamellosa, Gardium muticum, Solen gordonis, Sepia subaculeata, Polypus vulgaris, P. fangsiao*
- Crustacea: *Pleuronichtys cornutus, Metapenaeopsis barbatus, M. acelivis, Trachypenaeus curvirostris, Penaeus japonicus, P. monoceros, P. semisulcatus*
- Pisces: *Engraulis japonicus, Ammodytes persontus, Saurida elongata, Conger myriaster, Leiognathus rivulatum, Apogon lineatus, Sillago sihama, Pagrosomus major, Scomberomorus niphonius*

MAJOR CURRENT RESEARCH PROJECTS AND SCIENTIFIC LEADERS:
- Pathology of shellfish (Kojiro Tanaka)
- Experiments on the cultivation of *P. tenella* (Teruo Takasugi and Shigemi Kambara)
- Biological and chemical examination of sea water and bottom mud around oyster beds (Akira Kodo and Chitari Ono)
- Experiments on the cultivation of *C myriaster.* (Tomotada Matsuoka and Tomoyuki Nada)
- Biochemical examination of meat of fishes (Yoshirobu Isa)
- Physiological research of fishes of Seto Inland Sea (Shosaku Tokida and Kozo Takahashi)
- Ecological survey of *Atrina japonica* (Kunio Takinoto and Muneo Takeuchi)

Kagoshima Daigaku, Suisan Gakubu

KAGOSHIMA UNIVERSITY, FACULTY OF FISHERIES

POSTAL ADDRESS: 470 Shimo-arata-cho, Kagoshima, Nippon (Japan).
EXECUTIVE OFFICER: S. Konda, Director.
YEAR FOUNDED: 1949.
SCOPE OF ACTIVITIES: Unrestricted research on general marine biology; undergraduate instruction.
SEASON OF OPERATION: All year.
PHYSICAL ENVIRONMENT ACCESSIBLE: East China Sea; oligotrophic lake.
PROVISIONS FOR VISITING SCIENTISTS: None.
MAJOR RESEARCH AND TEACHING FACILITIES: Very extensive library; large outdoor ponds; research collections of local fishes and marine algae of southern Japan, Formosa, Okinawa, etc.; identified reference collections of Western Pacific flying fishes (life history stages) and local Protoflorideae, Potamogetonaceae and Hydrocalitaceae; small machine and wood shop, small electrical and electronic shop; vessels, 60.5 m LOA, *Kagoshima Maru,* 36 m LOA, *Keiten Maru,* and 14 m LOA, *Shiroyama.*
INSTRUCTIONAL PROGRAM: Aquatic zoology, ichthyology, aquatic botany, plankton, aquatic ecology, physiology of aquatic animals, embryology of aquatic animals, fisheries biology, oceanography, etc.
SIZE OF STAFF: Forty-one at professional level; 15 officers of research-training vessels.

KAGOSHIMA DAIGAKU, SUISAN GAKUBU

MAJOR CURRENT RESEARCH PROJECTS AND SCIENTIFIC LEADERS:
Fertilization in bivalve mollusks (Seiji Wada)
Cultivation of large-sized pearl oysters (Seiji Wada)
Life history of pelagic fishes (Sadahiko Imai)
Cultivation of marine larval fishes (Sadahiko Imai)
Marine algae forms of southern Japan (Takesi Tanaka)
Sea grasses of southern Japan (Koji Nozawa)
Propagation of *Moina macrocopa* (Saburo Murayama)
Circulation of vitamin B-12 in natural waters (Kenichi Kashiwada)

Kisho-Cho, Kaiyokishobu

METEOROLOGICAL AGENCY, MARINE DIVISION

POSTAL ADDRESS:
Headquarters: Otemachi, Chiyoda-ku, Tokyo, Nippon (Japan).
Branch laboratories:
1. Kobe Kaiyo Kishodai (Kobe Marine Observatory)
2. Hakodate Kaiyo Kishodai (Hakodate Marine Observatory)
3. Nagasaki Kaiyo Kishodai (Nagasaki Marine Observatory)

(Descriptions follow.)

EXECUTIVE OFFICERS: K. Wadachi, Director-General of the Agency. K. Terada, Chief of the Marine Division.

SPONSORING AGENCY: Unyu-sho (Ministry of Transportation).

YEAR FOUNDED: 1956.

SCOPE OF ACTIVITIES: Restricted oceanographic research on the seas around Japan.

SEASON OF OPERATION: All year.

PHYSICAL ENVIRONMENT ACCESSIBLE: Northwestern Pacific Ocean.

PROVISIONS FOR VISITING SCIENTISTS: None.

MAJOR RESEARCH FACILITIES: Moderately complete library; research and identified reference collections of diatoms, copepods and chaetognaths; research vessel, *Ryofu Maru* (1200 ton).

SIZE OF BIOLOGICAL STAFF: Two at professional level; 3 technicians for plankton research.

IMPORTANT SPECIES AVAILABLE FOR LABORATORY STUDIES:
Diatomaceae: *Skeletonema costatum*
Copepoda: *Calanus helgolandicus*

MAJOR CURRENT RESEARCH PROJECTS AND SCIENTIFIC LEADERS:
Plankton communities in the adjacent seas of Japan in reference to hydrographic conditions (R. Marumo)
Studies of deep sea plankton (R. Marumo)

PUBLICATIONS ISSUED:
Results of Marine Meteorological and Oceanographical Observations (issued semi-annually)
Oceanographical Magazine (issued semi-annually)

Kobe Kaiyo Kishodai

KOBE MARINE OBSERVATORY

POSTAL ADDRESS: 7-chome, Nakayamate-dori, Kobe, Nippon (Japan).

EXECUTIVE OFFICER: Hiroshi Mano, Director.

YEAR FOUNDED: 1920.

SCOPE OF ACTIVITIES: Restricted research on general oceanography and plankton; instruction.

SEASON OF OPERATION: All year; four voyages per year.

PHYSICAL ENVIRONMENT ACCESSIBLE: Kuroshio region south of Japan; Pacific Ocean.

PROVISIONS FOR VISITING SCIENTISTS: None.

MAJOR RESEARCH AND TEACHING FACILITIES: Moderately complete library; no water supply; research and identified reference collections of diatoms, copepods

KOBE KAIYO KISHODAI

and chaetognaths; machine and wood shop; 33 m LOA vessel, *D. S. Shunpu-Maru.*

INSTRUCTIONAL PROGRAM: Phytoplankton and zooplankton.

SIZE OF STAFF: Two at professional level.

IMPORTANT SPECIES AVAILABLE FOR LABORATORY STUDIES:

Chaetognatha: *Sagitta bedoti, S. enflata*

Crustacea: *Calanus helgolandicus, Mecynocera clausi, Euchaeta marina*

MAJOR CURRENT HYDROBIOLOGICAL RESEARCH PROJECTS AND SCIENTIFIC LEADERS:

Studies on diatoms (Post vacant)

Studies on zooplankton (Kenzo Furuhashi)

Hakodate Kaiyo Kishodai

HAKODATE MARINE OBSERVATORY

POSTAL ADDRESS: 181, Akagawa-dori, Kameda-cho Kameda-gun, Hokkaido, Nippon (Japan).

LOCATION: Near Hakodate City.

EXECUTIVE OFFICER: Zen'ichi Yasui, Director.

YEAR FOUNDED: 1942.

SCOPE OF ACTIVITIES: Restricted research on physical, chemical and biological oceanography, meteorology and weather forecasting.

SEASON OF OPERATION: February-March, May-September and November.

PHYSICAL ENVIRONMENT ACCESSIBLE: Tsugaru Straits, Sea of Japan, North Pacific Ocean, Okhotsk Sea.

PROVISIONS FOR VISITING SCIENTISTS: None.

MAJOR RESEARCH FACILITIES: Small library; research collection of phytoplankton; small machine and wood shop and electrical and electronic shop; one 30 m LOA power vessel.

SIZE OF STAFF: Five at professional level including 3 oceanographers; 18 technicians including 7 in oceanography.

HAKODATE KAIYO KISHODAI

IMPORTANT SPECIES AVAILABLE FOR LABORATORY STUDIES:

Mixed samples of many kinds of zoo- and phytoplankton.

MAJOR CURRENT BIOLOGICAL OCEANOGRAPHIC RESEARCH PROJECTS AND SCIENTIFIC LEADERS:

Vertical distribution of phytoplankton in the northwestern Pacific Ocean, the Okhotsk Sea and the Sea of Japan (Mamoru Owada)

Annual change of the phytoplankton in the Tsugaru Straits since 1950 (Hisanori Kon)

PUBLICATIONS ISSUED: *Marine Meteorological Report of the Hakodate Marine Observatory* (regularly published journal)

Nagasaki Kaiyo Kishodai

NAGASAKI MARINE OBSERVATORY

POSTAL ADDRESS: Minamiyamate-machi 5, Nagasaki, Nippon (Japan).

EXECUTIVE OFFICER: K. Yamada, Director.

YEAR FOUNDED: 1947.

SCOPE OF ACTIVITIES: Restricted research on marine and maritime meteorological observations, including general oceanography and plankton studies.

SEASON OF OPERATION: All year.

PHYSICAL ENVIRONMENT ACCESSIBLE: Amakusa and East China Seas.

PROVISIONS FOR VISITING SCIENTISTS: None.

MAJOR RESEARCH FACILITIES: Moderately complete library; machine and wood shop, electrical and electronic shop; one 37.5 m LOA vessel, *Chofu Maru.*

SIZE OF STAFF: Four at professional level; 39 technicians.

PUBLICATIONS ISSUED: *Kaisho to Kisho* (Oceanography and Meteorology) (regularly published journal)

Kochi Daigaku, Usa Rinkai Jikkensho

KOCHI UNIVERSITY, USA MARINE BIOLOGICAL STATION

POSTAL ADDRESS: Inoshiri, Usa, Tosa-ski, Kochi Prefecture, Nippon (Japan).

EXECUTIVE OFFICER: Professor Toshiji Jamohara, Director of Station, Faculty of Literature and Science, Kochi University, Kochi City, Japan.

YEAR FOUNDED: 1953.

SCOPE OF ACTIVITIES: Unrestricted research on general marine biology; instruction.

SEASON OF OPERATION: All year.

PHYSICAL ENVIRONMENT ACCESSIBLE: Pacific Ocean, Tosa Bay; brackish, shallow bays.

PROVISIONS FOR VISITING SCIENTISTS: Research and living space for 2 visitors; no fees charged for research space.

MAJOR RESEARCH AND TEACHING FACILITIES: Small

library; running sea and fresh-water; research and identified reference collections of Pisces and Echinodermata; small boats and outboard motors.

INSTRUCTIONAL PROGRAM: Zoology and plankton.

SIZE OF STAFF: One at professional level; 1 technician.

IMPORTANT SPECIES AVAILABLE FOR LABORATORY STUDIES:

Protochordata: *Styela plicata, Balanoglossus misakiensis*

Echinodermata: *Echinometra mathaei, Heliocidaris crassispina, Mespilia globulus, Diadema setosum*

MAJOR CURRENT RESEARCH PROJECTS AND SCIENTIFIC LEADERS:

Classification of fishes (Toshiji Kamohara)
Embryology of Crustacea (Tsukoshi Yatsuzuka)

MISAKI RINKAI JIKKENSHO

Kokuritsu Shinju Kenkyusho

NATIONAL PEARL RESEARCH LABORATORY

POSTAL ADDRESS: Kashikojima, Ago, Mie-ken, Nippon (Japan).

LOCATION: Near Toba.

EXECUTIVE OFFICER: Mr. Katsuo Takayama, Director.

SPONSORING AGENCY OR AGENCIES: Department of Agriculture and Forestry, Fishery Agency.

YEAR FOUNDED: 1955.

SCOPE OF ACTIVITIES: Restricted research on pearls and the pearl oyster fishery.

SEASON OF OPERATION: All year.

PHYSICAL ENVIRONMENT ACCESSIBLE: Ise Bay (brackish, shallow bay).

PROVISIONS FOR VISITING SCIENTISTS: None.

MAJOR RESEARCH FACILITIES: Small library; small boats and outboard motors.

SIZE OF STAFF: Eight at professional level; 5 technicians.

IMPORTANT SPECIES AVAILABLE FOR LABORATORY STUDIES:

Lamellibranchia: *Pinctada martensii*

PUBLICATIONS ISSUED: *Bulletin of the National Pearl Research Laboratory* (regularly published journal in Japanese with English summary)

KOKURITSU SHINJU KENKYUSHO

Kyoto Daigaku, Nogakubu Suisangakka Misaki Rinkai Jikkensho

KYOTO UNIVERSITY, DEPARTMENT OF FISHERIES AND MISAKI MARINE BIOLOGICAL INSTITUTE

POSTAL ADDRESS:

Headquarters: Nagahama, Maizuru, Nippon (Japan).
Marine Station: Misaki Marine Biological Institute, Tannawa, Misaki, Sennangun, Osaka Prefecture.

LOCATION: Headquarters near Kyoto on Bay of Maizuru. Misaki Institute on the shore of the Inland Sea of Seto.

EXECUTIVE OFFICER: Professor Kiyomatsu Matsubara, Director.

YEAR FOUNDED: Department in 1947; Institute in 1958.

SCOPE OF ACTIVITIES: Unrestricted research on marine biology, chemistry and microbiology of food products, fisheries technology; graduate and undergraduate instruction.

SEASON OF OPERATION: All year.

PHYSICAL ENVIRONMENT ACCESSIBLE: Japan Sea and Inland Sea of Seto; rocky and gravelly shores.

PROVISIONS FOR VISITING SCIENTISTS: None at the Department; arrangements may be made for some space at the Institute.

MAJOR RESEARCH AND TEACHING FACILITIES: Moderately complete library; extensive research collections of fishes, algae, Cyanophyta, Rhodophyta, Phaeophyta and Chlorophyta; extensive identified reference collections of fishes of Japan and the South China Sea, of algae and flora from Japan, U.S.A., Europe, and Puerto Rico; one 10 m LOA power vessel.

INSTRUCTIONAL PROGRAM: General zoology, plankton, ichthyology, ecology, physiology, science of fishing, algae and fish culture.

SIZE OF STAFF: Four at professional level.

IMPORTANT SPECIES AVAILABLE FOR LABORATORY STUDIES:
Chlorophyceae: *Ulva pertusa*
Phaeophyceae: *Sargassum thunbergii*
Rhodophyceae: *Porphyra pseudolinearis*
Cyclostomata: *Paramyxine atame*
Pisces: *Mustelus manazo, Mugil cephalus, Lateolabrax japonicus*

MAJOR CURRENT RESEARCH PROJECTS AND SCIENTIFIC LEADERS:
Ichthyology (K. Matsubara)
Marine Cyanophyceae and fresh-water algae of Japan (Y. Yonada)

PUBLICATIONS ISSUED: *Memoirs of the College of Agriculture:* Fisheries Series Kyoto University (occasionally published journal)

Kyoto Daigaku, Seto Rinkai Jikkensho

KYOTO UNIVERSITY, SETO MARINE BIOLOGICAL LABORATORY

POSTAL ADDRESS: Seto 3-chome, Shirahama (Town), Wakayama Prefecture, Nippon (Japan).
LOCATION: Near Osaka.
EXECUTIVE OFFICERS: Professor Denzaburo Miyadi, Director of Laboratory, Zoological Institute, Faculty of Science, Kyoto University, Kitasirakawa, Sakyo-ku, Kyoto. Dr. H. Utinomi, Deputy Director.
YEAR FOUNDED: 1922.
SCOPE OF ACTIVITIES: Unrestricted research on general marine biology, ecology and general oceanography; graduate and undergraduate instruction.
SEASON OF OPERATION: All year.
PHYSICAL ENVIRONMENT ACCESSIBLE: Pacific Ocean, Kii Strait, Inland Sea, Kuroshiwo warm current; sandy and silty beaches, rocky and gravelly shores.
PROVISIONS FOR VISITING SCIENTISTS: Research and living space for 3 visitors; no fees charged for research space.

SETO RINKAI JIKKENSHO

MAJOR RESEARCH AND TEACHING FACILITIES: Moderately complete library (probably most complete of similar laboratories in Japan); running sea and fresh-water, large outdoor ponds and tanks, small aquarium tanks; research collections of Cirripedia, Anthozoa, Tunicata, etc. (mostly of Japan); identified reference collections of marine fishes, invertebrates and algae (of Kii province); machine and wood shop, electrical and electronic shop; 3 boats with and without inboard engines and an outboard motor.
INSTRUCTIONAL PROGRAM: General marine biology, invertebrate anatomy, planktology, field ecology, general physiology, oceanography and algology.
SIZE OF STAFF: Six at professional level; 3 technicians.

IMPORTANT SPECIES AVAILABLE FOR LABORATORY STUDIES:
Coelenterata: *Cavernularia obesa*
Phoronida: *Phoronis australis*
Mollusca: *Pinctada martensi, Nodilittorina granularis*
Crustacea: *Tetraclita squamosa, Tigriopus japonicus*
Echinodermata: *Astropecten polyacanthus, Mespilia globulus, Anthocidaris crassispina, Holothuria leucospilota*

MAJOR CURRENT RESEARCH PROJECTS AND SCIENTIFIC LEADERS:
Marine ecology (Denzaburo Miyadi)
Marine invertebrate systematics and littoral faunal survey (Huzio Utinomi and Takasi Tokioka)
Plankton investigations and oceanographical instruments (Isamu Yamazi)
Fisheries biology and productivity of fishing grounds (Shin'ichiro Fuse)

PUBLICATIONS ISSUED: *Publications of the Seto Marine Biological Laboratory* (regularly published journal)

Kyoto Daigaku, Otsu Rinko Jikkensho

KYOTO UNIVERSITY, OTSU HYDROBIOLOGICAL STATION

POSTAL ADDRESS: Kwannonji-machi No. 109, Otsu-shi, Shiga-ken, Nippon (Japan).
LOCATION: Near Kyoto.
EXECUTIVE OFFICER: Professor Mamori Ichikawa.
YEAR FOUNDED: 1914.
SCOPE OF ACTIVITIES: Unrestricted research on fresh-water biology, limnology and lake chronology; graduate and undergraduate instruction.
SEASON OF OPERATION: All year.
PHYSICAL ENVIRONMENT ACCESSIBLE: Lakes Biwa-ko and Yogo-ko, Seta-gawa River; eutrophic and oligotrophic lakes.
PROVISIONS FOR VISITING SCIENTISTS: Research and living space for 2 visitors; no fees charged for research space.
MAJOR RESEARCH AND TEACHING FACILITIES: Very extensive library; research collections of fishes, mollusks,

plankton, etc.; identified reference collections of fresh-water fauna and flora of Lake Biwa-ko and other Japanese inland waters; boats and outboard motors.

INSTRUCTIONAL PROGRAM: Fresh-water fauna and flora, plankton, and limnology.

SIZE OF STAFF: Five at professional level; 1 technician.

MAJOR CURRENT RESEARCH PROJECTS AND SCIENTIFIC LEADERS:

Zooplankton: Taxonomy of Rotatoria, ecology of plankton (Kokichi Yamamoto)

Phytoplankton: Taxonomy of diatoms, ecology of fresh-water algae (Ken-ichiro Negoro)

General ecology of fresh-water organisms (Syuiti Mori)

Paleolimnology and pleistocene ecology (Shoji Horie)

Ecology of fishes (Taiso Miura)

Kyushu Daigaku, Suisangaku Kyoshitsu, Suisan Jikkensho

KYUSHU UNIVERSITY, INSTITUTE OF FISHERIES, FISHERIES RESEARCH LABORATORY

POSTAL ADDRESS:

Main laboratory: Hakozaki-machi, Fukuoka, Nippon (Japan).

Branch laboratory: Tsuyazaki-machi, Fukuoka Prefecture.

EXECUTIVE OFFICERS:

Main laboratory: Professor Tetuo Tomiyama, Chairman.

Branch laboratory: Otohiko Tanaka, Director.

YEAR FOUNDED:

Main laboratory: 1941.

Branch laboratory: 1944.

SCOPE OF ACTIVITIES: Restricted and unrestricted research on aquatic resources (population dynamics), oceanography, plankton, ichthyology, phycology, fishery chemistry and technology, water pollution and marine mycology; graduate and undergraduate instruction.

SEASON OF OPERATION: All year.

PHYSICAL ENVIRONMENT ACCESSIBLE: Hakata Bay (main laboratory), Genkai-Nada (branch laboratory); open ocean, sandy and silty beaches, rocky and gravelly shores, estuarine conditions, and brackish, shallow bays.

FACILITIES FOR VISITING SCIENTISTS: Space for 3 visitors; no fees charged; living quarters nearby.

MAJOR RESEARCH AND TEACHING FACILITIES: Moderately complete library; running sea and fresh-water; extensive research and identified reference collections of fishes and marine algae; machine and wood shop, electrical and electronic shop, skilled shop workman available; one 11.5 m LOA vessel.

INSTRUCTIONAL PROGRAM: Ichthyology, population dynamics, oceanography, plankton, fishery technology, pollution, phycology, marine mycology.

SIZE OF STAFF: Nine at professional level; 8 technicians and research assistants.

IMPORTANT SPECIES AVAILABLE FOR LABORATORY STUDIES:

Phaeophyceae: *Sargassum* spp.

Polychaeta: *Rhizodrilus limasus*

Arthropoda: *Tachypleus tridentatus* Leach

MAJOR CURRENT RESEARCH PROJECTS AND SCIENTIFIC LEADERS:

Fishery biology of bottom fishes; life history of fishes (H. Tsukahara)

Epiphytic algae of the drifting Sargassum (T. Sawada)

Pelagic copepods of the Japanese waters (O. Tanaka)

Reaction of fishes to toxic substances (S. Ishio)

Mineral metabolism of fish by use of radioisotopes (T. Tomiyama)

Quality studies of fish using antibiotics (T. Tomiyama)

Growth-promoting substances in liver (T. Tomiyama)

Antibiotic activity of oxidized oils (M. Toyomizu)

Marine yeasts (Y. Tomiyasu and S. Suehiro)

Mie Kenritsu Daigaku, Suisan Gakubu

PREFECTURAL UNIVERSITY OF MIE, FACULTY OF FISHERIES

POSTAL ADDRESS: Otanichoe, Tsu, Mei Prefecture, Nippon (Japan).

The faculty of Fisheries maintains both a marine biological laboratory and a fresh-water biological laboratory in addition to the headquarters at the university.

LOCATION: Near Nagoya.

EXECUTIVE OFFICER: Professor Yaichiro Okada, Dean and Professor of Marine Zoology and Ichthyology.

YEAR FOUNDED: 1950.

SCOPE OF ACTIVITIES: Unrestricted research on general marine and fresh-water biology; instruction.

SEASON OF OPERATION: All year.

PHYSICAL ENVIRONMENT ACCESSIBLE: Ise Bay, Pacific Ocean; sandy and silty beaches, rocky and gravelly shores, estuarine conditions, brackish, shallow bays,

MIE KENRITSU DAIGAKU, SUISAN GAKUBU

eutrophic and oligotrophic lakes, and rivers and streams.

PROVISIONS FOR VISITING SCIENTISTS: Research and living space for 2-3 visitors; no fees charged for research space.

MAJOR RESEARCH AND TEACHING FACILITIES: Small library; small aquarium tanks; research collections of vertebrates and invertebrates; small boats and outboard motors; one 510 ton oceanographic vessel for student training and research.

INSTRUCTIONAL PROGRAM: General biology, general zoology, animal physiology, animal embryology, animal ecology, fish pathology, limnology, oceanography, animal histology, fish parasitology.

SIZE OF STAFF: Ten at professional level.

MAJOR CURRENT RESEARCH PROJECTS AND SCIENTIFIC LEADERS:

Histochemical studies on pearl formation (Y. Okada and T. Tsujii)
Ichthyological studies (Y. Okada)
Oceanography and phytoplankton (T. Sakamoto and F. Ueno)
Physiology of fishes (N. Kawamoto)
Fish parasites (S. Shiino)
Fouling animals (T. Kawahara)
Limnology (T. Ito)
Seaweeds (N. Segi)

PUBLICATIONS ISSUED:

Report of Faculty of Fisheries, Prefectural University of Mie (regularly published journal)
Journal of Faculty of Fisheries, Prefectural University of Mie (occasionally published journal)

Mie-Ken Suisan Shikenjo

MIE PREFECTURAL FISHERIES EXPERIMENTAL STATION

POSTAL ADDRESS:

Headquarters: Hamajima-cho, Shima-gun, Mie-ken, Nippon (Japan).
Branches: Owase and Ise-wan.

EXECUTIVE OFFICER: Ichiro Nomoto, Director.

YEAR FOUNDED: 1899.

SCOPE OF ACTIVITIES: Unrestricted research on general marine biology, with emphasis on species of economic importance including pearl oyster fisheries.

SEASON OF OPERATION: All year.

PHYSICAL ENVIRONMENT ACCESSIBLE: Pacific Ocean; sandy and silty beaches.

PROVISIONS FOR VISITING SCIENTISTS: None.

MAJOR RESEARCH FACILITIES: Small library; large outdoor ponds and tanks; small aquarium tanks; identified reference collections of local fauna and flora; skilled shop workman available; vessels, 158 ft LOA, *Taisei Maru,* 65 ft LOA, *Asama Maru,* and the 40 ft LOA, *Urakaze.*

Taisei Maru OF THE MIE-KEN SUISAN SHIKENJO

SIZE OF STAFF: About 30 at professional and technical level.

IMPORTANT SPECIES AVAILABLE FOR LABORATORY STUDIES:

Algae: *Undaria pinnatifida, Gelidium amansii*
Mollusca: *Octopus vulgaris, Haliotis gigantea, Pteria martensii*
Crustacea: *Panulirus japonicus, Penaeus japonicus*
Pisces: *Engraulis japonica, Katsuwonus pelamis, Seriola quinqueradiata*

MAJOR CURRENT RESEARCH PROJECTS AND SCIENTIFIC LEADERS:

Migration studies of shipjack, *Katsuwonus pelamis,* and yellowtail, *Seriola quinqueradiata* (Takeo Ozaki)
Production and management studies of various fry and spat (abalone, prawns, mullet, yellowtail) (Saburo Kimura)
Studies on management of shore fisheries (Ichiro Fujii)

PUBLICATIONS ISSUED: *Report of the Fisheries Experimental Station of the Mie Prefecture* (regularly published journal)

Nagasaki Daigaku, Suisan Gakabu

NAGASAKI UNIVERSITY, FISHERIES INSTITUTE

POSTAL ADDRESS:

Headquarters: No. 200, Ohashi-machi, Nagasaki, Nagasaki Prefecture, Nippon (Japan).
Branch laboratories:

1. Nomo Rinkai Jikkensho (Nomo Marine Laboratory) Nomoskai-machi, Nagaski Prefecture.
2. Suisan Jikkenjissyujo (Fisheries Experimental Laboratory) Aba, Nagaski, Nagaski Prefecture.

EXECUTIVE OFFICER: M. Tsuchiya, Director.

YEAR FOUNDED: Headquarters, 1949; Marine Laboratory, 1933; Experimental Laboratory, 1961.

SCOPE OF ACTIVITIES: Research on general marine biology, including plankton, benthos, fisheries and oceanography; undergraduate instruction.

NAGASAKI DAIGAKU

SEASON OF OPERATION: All year.
PHYSICAL ENVIRONMENT ACCESSIBLE: Tusima Current (branch of Kuroshiwo—Japanese Warm Current), Yellow and East China Seas; sandy and silty beaches.
PROVISIONS FOR VISITING SCIENTISTS: Research and living space for 1-2 visitors at Aba; no fees charged for research space.
MAJOR RESEARCH AND TEACHING FACILITIES: Small library; large outdoor ponds and tanks; small aquarium tanks; research collections of fishes and algae; identified reference collections of local gobioid fishes and marine shells; small boats and outboard motors; vessels, 22 m LOA vessel, *Nagasaki Maru,* and 8 m LOA vessel, *Asagiri*
INSTRUCTIONAL PROGRAM: Ichthyology, marine mammals, fish physiology, ecology and embryology, science of fish populations, plankton, general invertebrate zoology, fisheries biology, phycology, microbiology, oceanography, aquiculture, fishery processing.
SIZE OF STAFF: Twenty three at professional level.
IMPORTANT SPECIES AVAILABLE FOR LABORATORY STUDIES:

Phaeophyceae: *Undaria pinnulifida, Hijikiya fusiformis*
Mollusca: *Pinctada martensi*
Crustacea: *Panulirus japonicus*
Pisces: *Trachurus japonicus, Scomber japonicus, Taius tumifrons, Seriola* spp.

MAJOR CURRENT RESEARCH PROJECTS AND SCIENTIFIC LEADERS:

Marine biology (Tetuo Yamada)
Plankton and oceanography (Haruhiko Irie)
Fish physiology (Osamu Tamura)
Phycology (Yosikazu Okada)
Microbiology (Buhei Zenitani)
Life history of Cephalopoda (Syuro Hayasi)
Marine algae (Seiji Migita)
Conchology (Yosio Ko)
Science of fish populations (Masao Oka)
Marine mammals (Kazuhiro Mizue)
Life history of fishes (Yosie Dotu)

PUBLICATIONS ISSUED: *Bulletin of the Faculty of Fisheries, Nagasaki University* (regularly published journal)

Nagoya Daigaku, Suisangaku-Kyoshitsu

NAGOYA UNIVERSITY, FISHERIES LABORATORY

POSTAL ADDRESS: Anjo, Aichi Prefecture, Nippon (Japan).
LOCATION: Near Nagoya.
EXECUTIVE OFFICER: Professor T. Tamura.
YEAR FOUNDED: 1951.
SCOPE OF ACTIVITIES: Unrestricted research on the physiology and ecology of fishes; graduate and undergraduate instruction.
SEASON OF OPERATION: All year.
PHYSICAL ENVIRONMENT ACCESSIBLE: Ise Bay (brackish, shallow bay) and Kiso River.
PROVISIONS FOR VISITING SCIENTISTS: None.
MAJOR RESEARCH AND TEACHING FACILITIES: Small library; small aquarium tanks.
SIZE OF STAFF: Four at professional level; 1 technician.

Nagoya Daigaku, Sugashima Rinkai Jikkensho

NAGOYA UNIVERSITY, SUGASHIMA MARINE BIOLOGICAL STATION

POSTAL ADDRESS: Sugashima, Toba-shi, Mie Perfecture, Nippon (Japan).
LOCATION: Near Nagoya.
EXECUTIVE OFFICER: M. Sugiyama, Director.
YEAR FOUNDED: 1939.
SCOPE OF ACTIVITIES: Unrestricted research on developmental physiology of marine organisms; graduate and undergraduate instruction.
SEASON OF OPERATION: All year.

NAGOYA DAIGAKU, SUGASHIMA RINKAI JIKKENSHO

PHYSICAL ENVIRONMENT ACCESSIBLE: Ise Bay; sandy and silty beaches, and gravelly shores.

PROVISIONS FOR VISITING SCIENTISTS: Research and living space for visitors; no fees charged for research space.

MAJOR RESEARCH AND TEACHING FACILITIES: Small library; running sea and fresh-water; small motor boats.

INSTRUCTIONAL PROGRAM: General marine invertebrate zoology, physiology of marine animals, and embryology of marine animals.

SIZE OF STAFF: Three at professional level; 2 technicians.

IMPORTANT SPECIES AVAILABLE FOR LABORATORY STUDIES:

Echinodermata: *Anthocidaris crassispina, Temnopleurus toreumaticus, Pseudocentrotus depressus, Hemicentrotus pulcherrimus, Clypeaster japonicus*

MAJOR CURRENT RESEARCH PROJECTS AND SCIENTIFIC LEADERS:

Physiology of fertilization in sea urchin eggs (Masao Sugiyama)

Biochemical studies of activation in sea urchin eggs (Masaru Ishikawa)

Experimental studies of cleavage in eggs of marine animals (Manabu Kojima)

Nihon Daigaku, Rinkai Jikkensho

JAPAN UNIVERSITY, MARINE BIOLOGICAL STATION

POSTAL ADDRESS: Mabori, Yokosuka-shi, Kanagawa Prefecture, Nippon (Japan).

EXECUTIVE OFFICER: Professor Seiji Kokubo, Director.

YEAR FOUNDED: 1951.

SCOPE OF ACTIVITIES: Unrestricted research on general marine biology; instruction.

SEASON OF OPERATION: All year, but most activities are from late June to early September.

PHYSICAL ENVIRONMENT ACCESSIBLE: Tokyo Bay; sandy and silty, partly rocky shores, and estuarine conditions.

PROVISIONS FOR VISITING SCIENTISTS: Research and living space for 2-3 visitors; no fees charged for research space.

MAJOR RESEARCH AND TEACHING FACILITIES: No library; running sea and fresh-water, small aquarium tanks; research collections of almost all neritic fishes and invertebrates; shop facilities available in Yokosuka City.

INSTRUCTIONAL PROGRAM: Marine biology for high school teachers.

IMPORTANT SPECIES AVAILABLE FOR LABORATORY STUDIES:

Polychaeta: *Sabellastarte indica, Anthopleura stella, Reniera japonica*

Mollusca: *Mactra sulcataria, Thais clavigera*

Echinodermata: *Asterina pectinifera, Heliocidaris crassispina*

Crustacea: *Hemigrapsus sanguinus*

Tunicata: *Styela clava*

Pisces: *Sebastodes tokionis*

MAJOR CURRENT RESEARCH PROJECTS AND SCIENTIFIC LEADERS:

Studies on the development of *Porphyra tenera* (M. Arazaki)

Studies on the condition of the sea off Mabori (H. Hosoya)

NIHON DAIGAKU, RINKAI JIKKENSHO

Niigata Daigaku, Rigakubu Fuzoku Rinkai Jikkensho

NIIGATA UNIVERSITY, SADO MARINE BIOLOGICAL STATION

POSTAL ADDRESS: Aikawa, Sado Island, Niigata Prefecture, Nippon (Japan).

EXECUTIVE OFFICERS: Dr. Mitsuzo Noda, Director. Dr. Hisaaki Iwasawa, Resident Director.

YEAR FOUNDED: 1954.

SCOPE OF ACTIVITIES: Unrestricted research on general marine biology; graduate instruction.

SEASON OF OPERATION: All year.

PHYSICAL ENVIRONMENT ACCESSIBLE: Sea of Japan; sandy and silty beaches, and rocky shores.

PROVISIONS FOR VISITING SCIENTISTS: Research and living space for 10 visitors; fees charged for research space.

MAJOR RESEARCH AND TEACHING FACILITIES: Small library; running sea and fresh-water, small aquarium tanks; one 2 ton vessel.

INSTRUCTIONAL PROGRAM: General zoology and plankton.

SIZE OF STAFF: Two at professional level; 3 technicians.

IMPORTANT SPECIES AVAILABLE FOR LABORATORY STUDIES:

Pelecypoda: *Mytilus crassitesta, Septifer virgatus*

NIIGATA DAIGAKU, RIGAKUBU FUZOKU RINKAI JIKKENSHO

OKAYAMA DAIGAKU, RIGAKUBU FUZOKU RINKAI JIKKENSHO

Crustacea: *Mitella mitella, Tetraclita squamosa, Chthamalus challengeri*
Echinodermata: *Paracaudina chilensis, Anthocidaris crassispina, Ophiothrix japonicus*
Pisces: *Chasmichthys dolichognathus*
Note: A list of species found near the laboratory has been published in the *Journal of Faculty Science Niigata University*, Ser. II, Vol. 2, No. 2, pp. 61-71, April, 1955.

MAJOR CURRENT RESEARCH PROJECTS AND SCIENTIFIC LEADERS:
Life history studies of Pelecypoda and Cirripedia (Shigeo Emura)
Comparative endocrinology (Hisaaki Iwasawa)

Okayama Daigaku, Rigakubu Fuzoku Rinkai Jikkensho

OKAYAMA UNIVERSITY, TAMANO MARINE LABORATORY

POSTAL ADDRESS: 888 Shibukawa, Tamano, Okayama Prefecture, Nippon (Japan).
LOCATION: Near Okayama.
EXECUTIVE OFFICER: Dr. Shumpei Inoh, Director. Biological Institute, Faculty of Science, Okayama University, Okayama.
YEAR FOUNDED: 1953.
SCOPE OF ACTIVITIES: Unrestricted research on general marine biology; graduate and undergraduate instruction.
SEASON OF OPERATION: All year.
PHYSICAL ENVIRONMENT ACCESSIBLE: The Inland Sea; sandy and silty beaches, rocky and gravelly shores.
PROVISIONS FOR VISITING SCIENTISTS: Research and living space for 5 visitors; fees charged for research space.
MAJOR RESEARCH AND TEACHING FACILITIES: Small library; running sea and fresh-water, small aquarium tanks; skilled shop workman available from Okayama University; small boats and outboard motors.
INSTRUCTIONAL PROGRAM: Zoo- and phytoplankton, taxonomy of marine algae, marine invertebrate zoology, comparative physiology.
SIZE OF STAFF: Two at professional level; one technician.
IMPORTANT SPECIES AVAILABLE FOR LABORATORY STUDIES:
Chlorophyceae: *Acetabularia calyculus*
Phaeophyceae: *Sargassum* sp.
Rhodophyceae: *Martensia denticulata*
Coelenterata: *Spirocodon saltatrix, Dactylometra pacifica, Paracondylactis hertwigi*
Annelida: *Thalassema gogoshimense* (Echiuroidea)
Mollusca: *Mactra veneriformis*
Echinodermata: *Peronella japonica*
Protochordata: *Halocynthia roretzi*

MAJOR CURRENT RESEARCH PROJECTS AND SCIENTIFIC LEADERS:
Cytology of algae (Shumpei Inoh)
Taxonomy of algae (Hiroyuki Hirose)
Electron microscopy of muscle (Siro Kawaguti)
Photosensitivity in marine invertebrates (Masao Yoshida)
Neurosecretion in crustaceans (Kunio Matsumoto)
Physiology of the melanophore (Kiyotugu Seizi Iwata)

Suisan-Cho

FISHERIES AGENCY

POSTAL ADDRESS:
Headquarters: 2-1 Kasumigaseki, Chiyoda-ku, Tokyo, Nippon (Japan).
Branch laboratories:
1. Hokkaido-Ku Suisan Kenkyusho (Hokkaido Regional Fisheries Research Laboratory)
2. Naikai-Ku Suisan Kenkyusho (Naikai Regional Fisheries Research Laboratory)
3. Nankai-Ku Suisan Kenkyusho (Nankai Regional

Fisheries Research Laboratory)
4. Nihon kai-Ku Suisan Kenkyusho (Japan Sea Regional Fisheries Research Laboratory)
5. Seikaiku Suisan Kenkyusho (Seikai Regional Fisheries Research Laboratory)
6. Tansui-Ku Suisan Kenkyujo (Fresh-water Fisheries Research Laboratory)
7. Tohoku kai-Ku Suisan Kenkyusho (Tohoku Regional Fisheries Research Laboratory)
8. Tokai-Ku Suisan Kenkyusho (Tokai Regional Fisheries Research Laboratory)

(Descriptions follow.)

EXECUTIVE OFFICER: G. Shono, Director.

SPONSORING AGENCY: Norin-sho (Ministry of Agriculture and Forestry).

Hokkaido-Ku Suisan Kenkyusho

HOKKAIDO REGIONAL FISHERIES RESEARCH LABORATORY

POSTAL ADDRESS: Hamanaka, Yoichi, Hokkaido, Nippon (Japan).

LOCATION: Near Otaru.

EXECUTIVE OFFICER: Kiyoshi Uchihashi, Director.

YEAR FOUNDED: 1902.

SCOPE OF ACTIVITIES: Restricted research on fishery resources of Hokkaido and the North Pacific; instruction.

SEASON OF OPERATION: All year.

PHYSICAL ENVIRONMENT ACCESSIBLE: Japan Sea.

PROVISIONS FOR VISITING SCIENTISTS: None.

MAJOR RESEARCH AND TEACHING FACILITIES: Small library; running sea and fresh-water, small aquarium tanks; machine and wood shop, electrical and electronic shop; skilled workman available; vessels 220 ton, *Hokko Maru,* and 69 ton, *Tankai Maru.*

INSTRUCTIONAL PROGRAM: Hydrography, population dynamics, ecology of marine algae, handling and processing of marine products, water pollution.

SIZE OF STAFF: Five at professional level; 75 technicians.

HOKKAIDO-KU SUISAN KENKYUSHO

IMPORTANT SPECIES AVAILABLE FOR LABORATORY STUDIES:
- Algae: *Laminaria angustata, L. religiosa*
- Mollusca: *Pecten yessoensis, Ommastrephes sloani pacificus*
- Crustacea: *Paralithodes camtschatica*
- Pisces: *Theragra chalcogramma, Pleurogrammus azonus, Cololabis saira, Oncorhynchus keta, O. nerka, O. gorbuscha, O. mason, Clupea pallasii, Pneumatophorus japonicus*

MAJOR CURRENT RESEARCH PROJECTS AND SCIENTIFIC LEADERS:
- Coastal and offshore fisheries resources (Sakae Sato)
- High seas fisheries resources (Junsuke Soeda)
- Propagation of fishes (Toraichiro Kinoshita)
- Utilization of fishes (Hikomi Igarashi)

PUBLICATIONS ISSUED: *Bulletin of the Hokkaido Regional Fisheries Research Laboratory* (occasionally published journal)

Naikai-Ku Suisan Kenkyusho

NAIKAI REGIONAL FISHERIES RESEARCH LABORATORY

POSTAL ADDRESS: Ujina, Hiroshima, Japan.
Branch Laboratory: Kasaoka, Okayama Prefecture.
Field Laboratory: Onomichi, Hiroshima Prefecture.

EXECUTIVE OFFICER: Dr. Tasuku Hanaoka, Director.

YEAR FOUNDED: 1949.

SCOPE OF ACTIVITIES: Restricted research on fisheries resources, productivity, marine and estuarine pollution.

SEASON OF OPERATION: All year.

PHYSICAL ENVIRONMENT ACCESSIBLE: Seto Inland Sea, sandy and silty beaches, rocky and gravelly shores, estuarine conditions, and brackish, shallow bays.

PROVISIONS FOR VISITING SCIENTISTS: Space for 1-2 visitors; living quarters nearby.

MAJOR RESEARCH FACILITIES: Small library; running sea and fresh-water, small aquarium tanks, indoor tanks with running sea and fresh-water; research collections of fishes and Crustacea from the Inland Sea; identified skeleton reference collection (about 400 species) of fishes from the Inland Sea; vessels, 18 m, 10 m, and 9 m LOA.

SIZE OF STAFF: Thirty at professional level; 10 technicians.

IMPORTANT SPECIES AVAILABLE FOR LABORATORY STUDIES:
- Chlorophyceae: *Ulva pertusa*
- Rhodophyceae: *Porphyra tenera*
- Pelecypoda: *Crassostrea laperousei, Mytilus edulis*
- Crustacea: *Tachypleus tridentatus, Penaeus japonicus, Penaeopsis* spp.
- Pisces: *Lateolabrax japonicus, Sparus longispinis, Trachurus trachurus*

MAJOR CURRENT RESEARCH PROJECTS AND SCIENTIFIC LEADERS:

- Prey-predator relationships (Tomoo Hayashi)
- Statistical research on fisheries biology (Yoshio Fukuda)
- Fisheries biology of shrimps and prawns (Jisburo Yasuda)
- Suspended matter in the sea (Atsushi Furukawa)
- Oyster-culture and its biology (Yoshimitsu Ogasawara)
- Marine pollution (Tadao Nitta)

Nankai-Ku Suisan Kenkyusho

NANKAI REGIONAL FISHERIES RESEARCH LABORATORY

POSTAL ADDRESS:
Headquarters: 2, 6 chome, Sanbashi-dori, Kochi-shi, Kochi Ken, Nippon (Japan).
Branches: Nobeoka, Aburatsu and Kushimoto in Wakayama Prefecture.

EXECUTIVE OFFICER: Mr. H. Nakamura,Chief Officer.

YEAR FOUNDED: 1949.

SCOPE OF ACTIVITIES: Restricted research on fish populations, especially of tuna.

SEASON OF OPERATION: All year.

PHYSICAL ENVIRONMENT ACCESSIBLE: Kuroshio (Japan Current), Pacific Ocean.

PROVISIONS FOR VISITING SCIENTISTS: Research and living space for 2-3 visitors; no fees charged.

MAJOR RESEARCH FACILITIES: Small library; machine and wood shop, electrical and electronic shop, skilled shop workman available; vessels, 32 m LOA and 12. 5 m LOA.

SIZE OF STAFF: Twenty at professional level; 36 technicians.

Nihon kai-Ku Suisan Kenkyusho

JAPAN SEA REGIONAL FISHERIES RESEARCH LABORATORY

POSTAL ADDRESS:
Headquarters: Bandaijima, Niigata, Nippon (Japan).

EXECUTIVE OFFICER: Dr. Kiyoshi Uchihashi, Laboratory Director.

YEAR FOUNDED: 1949.

SCOPE OF ACTIVITIES: Restricted research on the fisheries resources in the Sea of Japan; marine fisheries biology, fisheries oceanography and food technology of fish.

SEASON OF OPERATION: All year.

PHYSICAL ENVIRONMENT ACCESSIBLE: Sea of Japan; Shinano River; estuarine conditions.

PROVISIONS FOR VISITING SCIENTISTS: Space for visitors; living quarters available nearby.

MAJOR RESEARCH FACILITIES: Moderately complete library; research and identified reference collections of fishes of the Sea of Japan; one 20 m LOA vessel.

SIZE OF STAFF: Twenty-six at professional level; 26 technicians including crews.

NIHON KAI-KU SUISAN KENKYUSHO

IMPORTANT SPECIES AVAILABLE FOR LABORATORY STUDIES:
Cephalopoda: *Watsenia scintellans*
Cyclostomata: *Paramyxine atami*

MAJOR CURRENT RESEARCH PROJECTS AND SCIENTIFIC LEADERS:

- Biological study of sardines and related fishes (Sukekata Ito)
- Biological study of bottom fishes (Akira Ouchi)
- Study of the nervous system and ecology of fishes (Kiyoshi Uchihashi)
- Population dynamics of fishes (Ichiro Yamanaka)
- Biological study of pink salmon in the Sea of Japan (Genji Katoh)
- Study of hydrography and fishing conditions (Shunichi Nagata)
- Exploitation of new fishing grounds (Toshimasa Shimomura)

PUBLICATIONS ISSUED: *Bulletin of the Japan Sea Regional Fisheries Research Laboratory* (occasionally published journal)

Seikaiku Suisan Kenkyusho

SEIKAI REGIONAL FISHERIES RESEARCH LABORATORY

POSTAL ADDRESS:
Headquarters: 5 Maruo-machi, Nagasaki-shi, Nagasaki Prefecture, Nippon (Japan).
Branch: Hama-machi, Fujitsu-gun, Saga Prefecture.
Field Stations: Shimonoseki-shi, Yamaguchi Prefecture. Fukuoka-shi, Fukuoka Prefecture.

EXECUTIVE OFFICER: Mr. T. Ito, Chief Officer.

YEAR FOUNDED: 1950.

SCOPE OF ACTIVITIES: Unrestricted research on fish resources and fish utilization.

SEASON OF OPERATION: All year.

PHYSICAL ENVIRONMENT ACCESSIBLE: China and Ariake Seas; sandy and silty beaches.

PROVISIONS FOR VISITING SCIENTISTS: None.

SEIKAIKU SUISAN KENKYUSHO

MAJOR RESEARCH FACILITIES: Small library; small aquarium tanks; small boats and outboard motors.
SIZE OF STAFF: Four at professional level; 19 technicians.
IMPORTANT SPECIES AVAILABLE FOR LABORATORY STUDIES:
Pisces: *Sardinia melanosticta, Etrumeus microps, Engraulis japonicus, Scomber japonicus, S. tapeinocephalus, Trachurus japonicus, Taius tumifrons, Muraenesox cinereus, Trichiurus haumela, Pseudosciaena manchurica, Nibea nibe, N. mitsukrii, Lepidotrigla microptera, Saurida undosquamis*
Pelecypoda: *Paphia philippinarum, Ostrea laperousei*
MAJOR CURRENT RESEARCH PROJECTS AND SCIENTIFIC LEADERS:
Investigations on the bottom fish resources in the China Sea (Shiro Murakami)
Investigation on the pelagic fish resources (Tokimi Tsujita)
Studies on the utilization of the fishes (Kisaku Yamada)
PUBLICATIONS ISSUED: *Bulletin of the Seikai Regional Fisheries Research Laboratory* (occasionally published journal)

Tansui-Ku Suisan Kenkyusho

FRESH-WATER FISHERIES RESEARCH LABORATORY

POSTAL ADDRESS: 399, Miya, Hino Machi, Minamitama-gun, Tokyo, Nippon (Japan).
EXECUTIVE OFFICER: N. Nakamura, Director.
YEAR FOUNDED: 1949.
SCOPE OF ACTIVITIES: Restricted research on the improvement and development of fish production in natural bodies of fresh-water and in ponds.
SEASON OF OPERATION: All year.
PHYSICAL ENVIRONMENT ACCESSIBLE: Tama-gawa River; eutrophic and oligotrophic lakes, fish ponds and reservoirs.
PROVISIONS FOR VISITING SCIENTISTS: Space for 1-2 visitors; no fees charged; living quarters available nearby.
MAJOR RESEARCH FACILITIES: Small library; large outdoor ponds, small aquarium tanks; small boats and outboard motors at the Lake Sagami Branch Station.
SIZE OF STAFF: Eight at professional level; 20 technicians.
IMPORTANT SPECIES AVAILABLE FOR LABORATORY STUDIES:
Pisces: *Cyprinus carpio, Carassinus carassius, Salmo gairdnerii, Plecoglossus altivelis, Tilapia mossambica, Tribolodon hakonensis*
MAJOR CURRENT RESEARCH PROJECTS AND SCIENTIFIC LEADERS:
Studies on fish-production in rivers and streams (K. Onodera)
Studies on fish-production in lakes and reservoirs (Y. Shiraishi)
Studies on water pollution (Y. Matida)
Studies on fish-production in farm ponds (K. Nakamura)
Studies on pond-fish culture (T. Shimazu)
Biology of cyprinid fishes with reference to their fisheries (T. Kafuku)
PUBLICATIONS ISSUED: *Bulletin of the Fresh-water Fisheries Research Laboratory* (regularly published journal)

Tohoku kai-Ku Suisan Kenkyusho

TOHOKU REGIONAL FISHERIES RESEARCH LABORATORY

POSTAL ADDRESS:
Headquarters: Suginoiriomote, Shiogama-shi, Miyagi Prefecture, Nippon (Japan).
One branch.
LOCATION: Near Sendai.
EXECUTIVE OFFICER: Mr. Kinosuke Kimura, Chief Officer.
YEAR FOUNDED: 1949.

TANSUI-KU SUISAN KENKYUSHO

TOHOKU KAI-KU SUISAN KENKYUSHO

SCOPE OF ACTIVITIES: Restricted research on fisheries biology, aquiculture, and utilization of marine products.

SEASON OF OPERATION: All year.

PHYSICAL ENVIRONMENT ACCESSIBLE: Pacific Ocean, Matsushima Bay (brackish, shallow bay).

PROVISIONS FOR VISITING SCIENTISTS: Space for 2 visitors.

MAJOR RESEARCH FACILITIES: Small library; small aquarium tanks; one 23 m LOA vessel.

SIZE OF STAFF: Four at professional level; 19 technicians.

IMPORTANT SPECIES AVAILABLE FOR LABORATORY STUDIES:

Mollusca: *Crassostrea gigas*

MAJOR CURRENT RESEARCH PROJECTS AND SCIENTIFIC LEADERS:

Oceanographical investigations (Kinosuke Kimura)
Population study of the Pacific saury (Kinosuke Kimura)
Population study of the skipjack (Kinosuke Kimura)
Studies on oyster culture (Senji Tanita)
Studies on the propagation of benthonic shellfishes (Senji Tanita)
Studies on marine algae, especially on the culture of useful seaweeds (Munenao Kurogi)
Investigations on the environmental factors of shallow seas (Takashi Sano)

PUBLICATIONS ISSUED: *Bulletin of the Tohoku Regional Fisheries Research Laboratory* (regularly published journal)

Tokai-Ku Suisan Kenkyusho

TOKAI REGIONAL FISHERIES RESEARCH LABORATORY

POSTAL ADDRESS:

Headquarters: 12-2, Nishigashi-dori, Tsukishima, Chuo-ku, Tokyo, Nippon (Japan).

Branch: Hachijo Island.

LOCATION: Near Yokohama.

EXECUTIVE OFFICER: Ichitaro Gensho, Director.

YEAR FOUNDED: 1949.

SCOPE OF ACTIVITIES: Promotion of development of Japanese fisheries through research on fishery biology, plankton and oceanography; instruction.

SEASON OF OPERATION: All year.

PHYSICAL ENVIRONMENT ACCESSIBLE: Tokyo Bay, Pacific Ocean, sandy and silty beaches, estuarine conditions.

PROVISIONS FOR VISITING SCIENTISTS: Space for 10 visitors; fees charged; living quarters available nearby.

MAJOR RESEARCH AND TEACHING FACILITIES: Very extensive library; small aquarium tanks, indoor tanks for fishing gear experiments; vessels, 36 m LOA, *Tenyo Maru,* 36 m LOA, *Soyo Maru,* and 13 m LOA, *Taka Maru.*

INSTRUCTIONAL PROGRAM: Instruction in fishery biology, fishing technology and food technology are given under approved technical assistance programs.

SIZE OF STAFF: Twenty at professional level; 135 including senior scientists, officers and crew.

IMPORTANT SPECIES AVAILABLE FOR LABORATORY STUDIES:

Pisces: *Sardinops melanosticta, Engraulis japonica, Scomber japonica*
Mollusca: *Venerupis semidecussata, Meretrix meretrix lusoria*
Algae: *Porphyra tenera*

MAJOR CURRENT RESEARCH PROJECTS AND SCIENTIFIC LEADERS:

Investigations on *iwashi* resources (sardine, anchovy and round herring (Zinziro Nakai)
Fishery biology of mackerels (Tokiharu Abe)
Marine plankton and other related organisms (Zinziro Nakai)
Distribution of fur seals off Japan (Fukuzo Nagasaki)
Population dynamics (Susumu Kurita)
Oceanography related to fisheries (Nobuo Watanabe)

TOKAI-KU SUISAN KENKYUSHO

Ecological study of important shellfish (Takashi Ino)
Propagation of commercial seaweeds (Takeshi Kawana and Shunzo Suto)
Studies on fishing gear and method (Shigene Takayama)
Studies on chemistry and utilization of marine products (Hideo Higashi)
Radioactivity relevant to fisheries (Rinnosuke Fukai and Keishi Amano)

PUBLICATIONS ISSUED: *Bulletin of Tokai Regional Fisheries Research Laboratory* (regularly published journal)

Tohoku Daigaku Nogakubu Suisan Gakka, Onagawa Suisan Jikkensho

TOHOKU UNIVERSITY, FACULTY OF AGRICULTURE, DEPARTMENT OF FISHERIES AND ONAGAWA FISHERIES LABORATORY

POSTAL ADDRESS:
Department of Fisheries, Kita 6-bancho, Sendai, Nippon (Japan).
Onagawa Fisheries Laboratory: Onagawa, Oshika-gun, Miyagi Prefecture.

EXECUTIVE OFFICER: Professor Yasuhiko Tsuchiya, Chief.

YEAR FOUNDED: Department, 1947; Fisheries Laboratory, 1935.

SCOPE OF ACTIVITIES: Unrestricted research on biological oceanography, fisheries biology, aquiculture, utilization of fishery products, and fisheries chemistry; graduate instruction.

SEASON OF OPERATION: All year.

PHYSICAL ENVIRONMENT ACCESSIBLE: Tohoku Sea, Pacific Ocean; rocky and gravelly shores, brackish, shallow bays.

PROVISIONS FOR VISITING SCIENTISTS: Space for 2-3 visitors at the department and at the fisheries laboratory; no fees charged; living quarters available nearby.

MAJOR RESEARCH AND TEACHING FACILITIES: Moderately complete library at the department, small library at the fisheries laboratory; running sea and fresh-water at the fisheries laboratory, small aquarium tanks at both locations, with large outdoor breeding pools at the fishery laboratory; small boats and outboard motors at both locations.

INSTRUCTIONAL PROGRAMS Fisheries biology, aquiculture, population ecology, biological oceanography, fish physiology, marine products technology and biochemistry.

SIZE OF STAFF: Twenty at professional level; 16 technicians.

IMPORTANT SPECIES AVAILABLE FOR LABORATORY STUDIES:
Algae: *Porphyra tenera, Ulva pertusa*
Mollusca: *Crassostrea gigas, Haliotis gigantea, Mactra sachalinensis*
Echinodermata: *Stichopus japonicus, Helioidaris crassispina*
Pisces: *Oncorhynchus keta, O. mason, Salmo gairdneri, Plecoglossus altivelis Cololabus saira, Katsuwonus bagaus, Limanda augustrirostris, Pneumatophorus, japonicus, Engraulis japonica, Seriola quinqueradiata, Trachurus japonicus*

CURRENT RESEARCH PROJECTS AND SCIENTIFIC LEADERS:
Oyster breeding and genetics (Takeo Imai)
Conservation of chum salmon (Ryukai Sato)
Natural production of fish populations (Masayoshi Hatanaka)
Marine fertility and plankton physiology (Chikayoshi Matsudaira)
Fish physiology (Teiji Kariya)
Marine products technology (Yasuhiko Tsuchiya)
Vitamin-A metabolism in fish (Mitsuo Hata)
Toxins of marine animals (Motokazu Asano)

PUBLICATIONS ISSUED: *The Tohoku Journal of Agricultural Research* (regularly published journal)

Tohoku Daigaku, Rigakubu Fuzoku Rinkai Jikkensho

TOHOKU UNIVERSITY, MARINE BIOLOGICAL STATION

POSTAL ADDRESS: Asamushi, Aomori Prefecture, Nippon (Japan).

EXECUTIVE OFFICER: Dr. Eturo Hirai, Director.

YEAR FOUNDED: 1924.

SCOPE OF ACTIVITIES: Restricted research on general marine biology; graduate and undergraduate instruction.

SEASON OF OPERATION: All year.

PHYSICAL ENVIRONMENT ACCESSIBLE: Mutsu Bay; open ocean, rocky and gravelly shores.

PROVISIONS FOR VISITING SCIENTISTS: Research and living space for about 20 visitors; fees charged for research space.

TOHOKU DAIGAKU, RIGAKUBU FUZOKU RINKAI JIKKENSHO

MAJOR RESEARCH AND TEACHING FACILITIES: Small library; running sea and fresh-water, large outdoor ponds and tanks, small aquarium tanks; identified reference collections of Lamellibranchia of Mutsu Bay; machine and wood shop, skilled shop workman available; one 8.5 m LOA vessel.

INSTRUCTIONAL PROGRAM: General zoology, plankton, zoophysiology, and embryology.

SIZE OF STAFF: Six at professional level; 2 technicians.

IMPORTANT SPECIES AVAILABLE FOR LABORATORY STUDIES:

Hydrozoa: *Cladonema uchidai*
Pelecypoda: *Caecella chinensis*
Brachiopoda: *Terebratalia oceanica*
Holothuroidea: *Paracaudina chilensis ransonnetii*
Echinoidea: *Strongylocentrotus pulcherrimus, S. nudus*
Ascidiacea: *Halocynthia roretzi, Chelyosoma siboja*

MAJOR CURRENT RESEARCH PROJECTS AND SCIENTIFIC LEADERS:

Experimental investigations on the early development of marine animals (Isao Motomura)
Physiology of marine animals (Kiyoshi Aoki)
Synecological investigation of the tidal zone (Mutsuo Kato)
Investigations of the life cycles of invertebrate marine animals (Eturo Hirai)

PUBLICATIONS ISSUED: *The Bulletin of the Marine Biological Station of Asamushi* (regularly published journal)

Tokyo Daigaku, Nogakubu Fuzoku, Suisan Jikkensho

TOKYO UNIVERSITY, FACULTY OF AGRICULTURE, FISHERIES LABORATORIES

POSTAL ADDRESS:

Two laboratories are described here:

1. Shinmaiko, Chita-machi, Chita-gun, Aichi-ken, Nippon (Japan).
2. Ikawazu, Atsumi-machi, Atsumi-gun, Aichi-ken, Nippon (Japan).

EXECUTIVE OFFICER: Professor Dr. Yoshio Hiyama, Director, Shinmaiko Laboratory.

YEAR FOUNDED: 1936.

SCOPE OF ACTIVITIES: Restricted research on biological and chemical oceanography, general marine biology, fish conservation, and fish culture.

SEASON OF OPERATION: All year.

PHYSICAL ENVIRONMENT ACCESSIBLE: Ise and Mikawa Bays; open sea; estuarine conditions, brackish, shallow bays, and fresh- and brackish-water fish ponds.

PROVISIONS FOR VISITING SCIENTISTS: Space for 1-2 visitors at each laboratory; no fees charged; living space at Ikawazu and near the Shinmaiko laboratory.

MAJOR RESEARCH FACILITIES: Small library; running sea and fresh-water, large outdoor ponds and tanks,

IKAWAZU FISHERIES LABORATORY

small aquarium tanks; identified reference collection of young fishes gathered in littoral *Zostera* zone; small boats and outboard motors; one 11 mm LOA vessel.

SIZE OF STAFF: Three at professional level.

IMPORTANT SPECIES AVAILABLE FOR LABORATORY STUDIES:

Pelecypoda: *Venerupis philippinarum*
Crustacea: *Penaeus japonicus*
Pisces: *Cyprinus carpio, Carassius auratus, Anguilla japonica, Mugil cephalus*

CURRENT RESEARCH PROJECTS AND SCIENTIFIC LEADERS:

A study on the phenomenon of the Tobi-Koi or shoot carp (N. Nakamura)
A study on the productivity of eel culture ponds (N. Nakamura)
A study on the anchor worm (*Lernaea*) parasitizing the eel (S. Kasahara)
An ecological study on *Undaria pinnatifida* (Y. Saito)

Tokyo Daigaku, Rigakubu Fuzoku, Misaki Rinkai Jikkensho

TOKYO UNIVERSITY, FACULTY OF SCIENCE, MISAKI MARINE BIOLOGICAL STATION

POSTAL ADDRESS: Misaki, Kanagawa Prefecture, Nippon (Japan).

LOCATION: Near Yokosuka.

EXECUTIVE OFFICER: Dr. Itiro Tomiyama, Director.

YEAR FOUNDED: 1887.

SCOPE OF ACTIVITIES: Unrestricted research on general marine biology; undergraduate instruction.

SEASON OF OPERATION: All year.

PHYSICAL ENVIRONMENT ACCESSIBLE: Sagami and Tokyo Bays; open ocean, sandy and silty beaches, rocky and gravelly shores.

PROVISIONS FOR VISITING SCIENTISTS: Space for 8 or more visitors; fees charged; living space for 2 at the station, other living quarters available nearby.

MISAKI RINKAI JIKKENSHO

MAJOR RESEARCH AND TEACHING FACILITIES: Small library; running sea and fresh-water; machine and wood shop, electrical and electronic shop; small boats and outboard motors.

INSTRUCTIONAL PROGRAM: General invertebrate zoology, embryology, physiology, and physiological chemistry.

SIZE OF STAFF: Four at professional level; 3 collectors.

IMPORTANT SPECIES AVAILABLE FOR LABORATORY STUDIES:

Hydrozoa: *Spirocodon saltatrix*
Pelecypoda: *Mytilus edulis*
Asteroidea: *Asterias amurensis, Asterina pectinifera*
Echinoidea: *Pseudocentrotus depressus, Hemicentrotus pulcherrimus, Anthocidaris crassispina, Clypeaster japonicus*
Pisces: *Chasmichthys gulosus*

MAJOR CURRENT RESEARCH PROJECTS AND SCIENTIFIC LEADERS:

Taxonomy of fishes (Itiro Tomiyama)
Cell physiology (Yukio Hiramoto)
Embryological studies of echinoderms (Katsuma Dan)
Fertilization studies (Jean Clark Dan)
Biochemical studies of spermatozoa and eggs of echinoderms (Takashi Fujii and Juro Ishida)

Tokyo Kyoiku Daigaku, Shimoda Rinkai Jikkensho

TOKYO KYOIKU UNIVERSITY, SHIMODA MARINE BIOLOGICAL STATION

POSTAL ADDRESS: Shimoda, Shizuoka Prefecture, Nippon (Japan).

LOCATION: Near Ito, on Shimoda Bay.

EXECUTIVE OFFICER: Dr. Hidemichi Oka, Professor of Zoology, Zoological Institute, Faculty of Science, Tokyo Kyoiku University, Bunkyo-ku, Tokyo, Japan.

YEAR FOUNDED: 1933.

SCOPE OF ACTIVITIES: Unrestricted research on general marine biology, plankton, physiology and oceanography; graduate and undergraduate instruction.

SEASON OF OPERATION: All year.

PHYSICAL ENVIRONMENT ACCESSIBLE: Pacific Ocean; sandy and silty beaches, rocky and gravelly shores; estuarine conditions, brackish, shallow bays, rivers and streams.

PROVISIONS FOR VISITING SCIENTISTS: Space for 1-2 visitors; fees charged; living quarters available nearby.

MAJOR RESEARCH AND TEACHING FACILITIES: Small library; running sea and fresh-water, large outdoor ponds and tanks, small aquarium tanks; identified reference collections of local Crustacea (Decapoda and Cumacea), Tunicata, Pisces (marine) and algae; machine and wood shop, electrical and electronic shop, skilled shop workman available; one 7 m LOA vessel, *R. V. Sagitta.*

INSTRUCTIONAL PROGRAM: Invertebrate zoology, comparative physiology, general algology, and general marine biology.

SIZE OF STAFF: Four at professional level; 3 technicians.

IMPORTANT SPECIES AVAILABLE FOR LABORATORY STUDIES:

Coelenterata: *Cymbactis actionostoides, Staurocladia acuminata*
Echinodermata: *Strongylocentrotus pulcherrinus, Echinometra mathaei, Heliocidaris crassispina, Comanthus japonica*
Crustacea: *Panulirus japonicus, Balanus* spp., *Cypridina hilgendorfi*
Mollusca: *Dolabella* sp., *Ostrea* spp.
Tunicata: Compound ascidians (many species)

MAJOR CURRENT RESEARCH PROJECTS AND SCIENTIFIC LEADERS:

Studies on compound ascidians (Hidemichi Oka)
Systematic studies on Cumacea (Isokichi Harada)

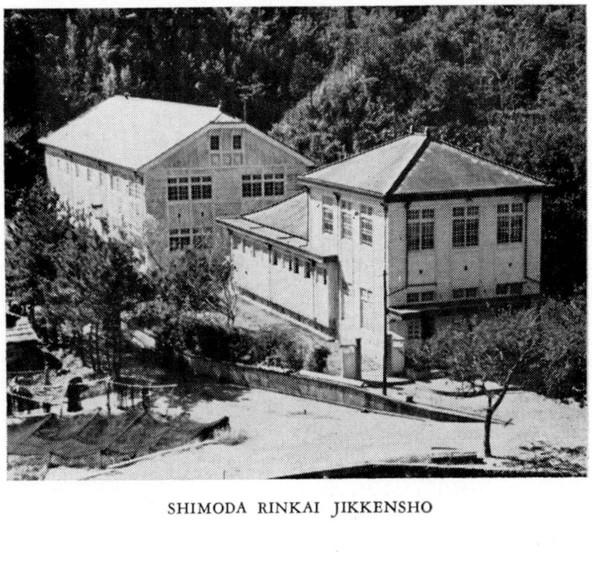

SHIMODA RINKAI JIKKENSHO

Life-history of Hydrozoa (Eleutheriidae) (Isokichi Harada)
Life-history of green algae (Mitsuo Chihara)
Ecology of marine chironomids (Hiroshi Hashimoto)

Tokyo Suisan Daigaku

TOKYO UNIVERSITY OF FISHERIES

POSTAL ADDRESS: 6 Chome, Shibakaigandori, Minato-ku, Tokyo, Nippon (Japan).
EXECUTIVE OFFICER: Sekine Yutaka, President.
SPONSORING AGENCY: Ministry of Education.
SCOPE OF ACTIVITIES: Unrestricted research on fisheries biology and technology, fish culture, and oceanography; instruction.
SEASON OF OPERATION: All year.
PHYSICAL ENVIRONMENT ACCESSIBLE: Pacific Ocean.
PROVISIONS FOR VISITING SCIENTISTS: None.
MAJOR RESEARCH FACILITIES: Very extensive library; machine and wood shop; vessels, 72 m LOA, *Umitaka Maru,* 36 m LOA, *Shinyo Maru,* and 29 m LOA, *Hayabusa Maru.*
INSTRUCTIONAL PROGRAM IN BIOLOGY: Marine zoology, marine botany, animal ecology, animal physiology, fishery resources, fish-culture (marine and fresh-water), culture of marine plants, histology, embryology, limnology, fish nutrition, fish diseases, plankton, and genetics.
SIZE OF STAFF: Eighty-two at professional level; 62 technicians.
MAJOR CURRENT BIOLOGICAL RESEARCH PROJECTS AND SCIENTIFIC LEADERS:
Study of behavior of fish schools affected by the intensity of illumination and color condition of sea water (Takeharu Kumagori)
Studies on the behavior of fish schools towards fishing gear (Kenji Kanda)
A population study of *Sardinia melanosticta* (Hideaki Yasuda)
Long term fluctuations of the ocean and fisheries in relation to weather (Michitaka Uda)

Umitaka Maru, RESEARCH VESSEL OF THE TOKYO SUISAN DAIGAKU

Studies of oceanographic conditions in the Indian and Antarctic Oceans in relation to fisheries (Makoto Ishino)
Mathematical studies of the fluctuation of fish populations (Tomokichi Yoshihara)
Study on the bottom configuration and bottom deposits of fisheries ground (Hiroshi Niino)
Improvement of artificial propagation in trout culture (Densabro Inaba and Minoru Nomura)
Studies on the increase of fish production by means of aeration and filtration of pond water (Densabro Inaba)
Ecological studies of "Ame" a variety of *Oncorhynchus rhodurus,* propagated in Lake Suwa (Minoru Nomura)
Ecological studies of grass carp propagated in the River Tone (Densabro Inaba)
Studies on complete diets for trout culture (Densabro Inaba and Minoru Nomura)
Haemotological studies of cultured fish (Tokuo Sano)
Studies on *Porphyra* cultivation in Japan (Saburo Ueda)
Studies on the utilization of algae (Saburo Ueda)
Systematic and ecological studies on cultivating *Porphyra* species (Akio Miura)
Nutrition of Rainbow trout (Chinkichi Ogino)
Biochemical studies on chemical composition of the eggs of Rainbow trout (Chinkichi Ogino)
Studies of fish disease, especially of disease due to bacteria and parasites (Toshikazu Hoshima)
Studies on collections by the *Umitaka Maru* on a voyage to and from the Antarctic Ocean, especially on Pisces (Ken-ichi Ebina)
Studies on collections by the *Umitaka Maru* on a voyage to and from the Antarctic Ocean, especially plankton and the invertebrates (Jiro Seno)
Diurnal rhythm of the shell formation in the Japanese top-shell, *Turbo cornutus* (Yutaka Uno)
Rate of growth in *Turbo cornutus* as a function of latitude (Yutaka Uno)
Fishery biology of marine animals. Taxonomic studies of decapod Crustacea (Macurura) (Itsuo Kubo)
Fishery biology of marine fishes. Taxonomic studies on marine fishes, especially on the gobioid fishes (Kazunori Takagi)
PUBLICATIONS ISSUED: *Journal of Tokyo University of Fisheries* (regularly published journal)

Tokyo Suisan Daigaku, Kominato Jikkensho

TOKYO UNIVERSITY OF FISHERIES, KOMINATO MARINE BIOLOGICAL LABORATORY

POSTAL ADDRESS: No. 1, Uchi-ura, Awa-Kominato, Chiba Prefecture, Nippon (Japan).
LOCATION: Near Chiba.
EXECUTIVE OFFICER: Professor I. Kubo, Director.
YEAR FOUNDED: 1932.

TOKYO SUISAN DAIGAKU, KOMINATO JIKKENSHO

SCOPE OF ACTIVITIES: Unrestricted research on general marine biology; graduate and undergraduate instruction.
SEASON OF OPERATION: All year.
PHYSICAL ENVIRONMENT ACCESSIBLE: Pacific Ocean, Kuroshiwo (Japan Current); rocky and gravelly shores.
PROVISIONS FOR VISITING SCIENTISTS: Research and living space for 1-2 visitors from October to March; no fees charged for research space.
MAJOR RESEARCH AND TEACHING FACILITIES: Small library; running sea and fresh-water, large outdoor ponds and tanks, small aquarium tanks; research collections of Mollusca (gastropods and bivalves), Pisces, and algae; machine and wood shop, electrical and electronic shop, skilled shop workman available; small boats and outboard motors.
INSTRUCTIONAL PROGRAM: Fishery biology, ichthyology, embryology (Pisces and Echinodermata), and algology.
SIZE OF STAFF: Two at professional level; 1 technician.
IMPORTANT SPECIES AVAILABLE FOR LABORATORY STUDIES:
Rhodophyceae: *Gelidium amansii, Gloiopeltis* sp.
Phaeophyceae: *Hijikia* spp.
Echinodermata: *Heliocidaris crassispina*
Mollusca: *Polypus vulgaris, Haliotis gigantea, Turbo cornutus, Babylonia japonica*
Crustacea: *Panulirus japonicus*
Pisces: *Paralichthys olivaceus, Girella punctata, Scomber japonicus*
MAJOR CURRENT RESEARCH PROJECTS AND SCIENTIFIC LEADERS:
On the dispersion of the stock, and estimating the abundance of the population of the spiny lobster, *Panulirus japonicus* (Itsuo Kubo)
Biological studies on the population of a flatfish, *Paralichthys olivaceus* (Tomokichi Yoshihara)
Population studies on the Japanese ivory shell, *Babylonia japonica* (T. Yoshihara)
Taxonomic and ecological study on the young fishes found in Japanese waters (Tatsu Yoshi Masuda)
Studies on a collection of coastal plankton from Prov. Boshu, Chiba Prefecture (Tatsu Yoshi Masuda)
Ecological studies of the sea-weed, *Hijikia fusiforme* (Sargassaceae) (M. Katada)

Yokohama Kokuritsu Daigaku, Fuzoku Rika Kyoiku Manazuru Jikkensho

YOKOHAMA NATIONAL UNIVERSITY, MANAZURU MARINE LABORATORY FOR SCIENCE EDUCATION

POSTAL ADDRESS: Iwa, Manazuru-machi, Kangawa Prefecture, Nippon (Japan).
LOCATION: Near Yokohama.
EXECUTIVE OFFICER: Dr. T. Sakai, Director.
YEAR FOUNDED: 1954.
SCOPE OF ACTIVITIES: Unrestricted research in marine biology and oceanography for scientists and science teachers; graduate and undergradaute instruction.
SEASON OF OPERATION: All year.
PHYSICAL ENVIRONMENT ACCESSIBLE: Tokyo Bay, Pacific Ocean; rocky and gravelly shores.
PROVISIONS FOR VISITING SCIENTISTS: None.
MAJOR RESEARCH AND TEACHING FACILITIES: No library; running sea and fresh-water; research and identified reference collections of local flora and fauna in preparation; small boats and outboard motors.
INSTRUCTIONAL PROGRAM: General marine biology.
SIZE OF STAFF: One at professional level; 2 technicians.
IMPORTANT SPECIES AVAILABLE FOR LABORATORY STUDIES:
Echinodermata: *Heliocidaris crassispina*
Crustacea: *Panulirus* sp.
Mollusca: *Turbo, Haliotis, Ommastrephes* spp.
MAJOR CURRENT RESEARCH PROJECTS AND SCIENTIFIC LEADERS:
Decapod crustaceans (T. Sakai)
Isopods and amphipods (M. Iwasa)
Pisces (S. Abe)

KENYA

Kenya Ministry of Forest Development, Game and Fisheries, Inland Fishery Research Station

POSTAL ADDRESS: P. O. Box 147, Fort Hall, Kenya.
LOCATION: Sagana, Kenya, 7 miles from Fort Hall.
EXECUTIVE OFFICER: Mr. C. E. P. Watson, Chief Fisheries Officer, c/o Ministry of Forest Development, Game and Fisheries, P. O. Box 30027, Nairobi, Kenya.
YEAR FOUNDED: 1952.
SCOPE OF ACTIVITIES: Restricted research on the culture

INLAND FISHERY RESEARCH STATION, KENYA

of *Tilapia* spp. in ponds, river fishes and fisheries.

SEASON OF OPERATION: All year.

PHYSICAL ENVIRONMENT ACCESSIBLE: Sagana and Ragati Rivers, tributaries of the Tana River, shallow 1/50th–4 acre ponds.

PROVISIONS FOR VISITING SCIENTISTS: Research and living space for 2 visitors; no fees charged for research space.

MAJOR RESEARCH FACILITIES: Small library; small aquarium tanks, artificial stream in laboratory with specially constructed underwater glass windows for observation of fish behavior and spawning; small research and identified reference collections of fresh-water fishes of Kenya, Uganda and Tanganyika, as well as local flora; small boats and outboard motors.

SIZE OF STAFF: Two at professional level; 2 technicians.

IMPORTANT SPECIES AVAILABLE FOR LABORATORY STUDIES:

Pisces: *Tilapia nigra, T. mossambica, Anguilla nebulosa labiata, Barbus tanesis, Labeo cylindricus*

MAJOR CURRENT RESEARCH PROJECTS AND SCIENTIFIC LEADERS:

Pond culture studies on *Tilapia nigra, T. niloticus* and *Labeo niloticus*

PUBLICATIONS ISSUED: *Report on Kenya Fisheries* (annual report).

KOREA

Chung Ang Soo San Si Hum Jang

KOREA CENTRAL FISHERIES EXPERIMENTAL STATION

POSTAL ADDRESS: #16-2 Ka, Namhang Dong, Pusan, South Korea.

EXECUTIVE OFFICER: Bong Nae Lee, So-Jang.

SPONSORING AGENCY: Office of Marine Affairs.

YEAR FOUNDED: 1921.

SCOPE OF ACTIVITIES: Restricted research on the biology and ecology of fishes; oceanography.

SEASON OF OPERATION: All year.

PHYSICAL ENVIRONMENT ACCESSIBLE: Tsushima Current, Yellow Sea, Sea of Japan; sandy and silty beaches, rocky and gravelly shores, estuarine conditions, brackish, shallow bays, rivers and streams.

PROVISIONS FOR VISITING SCIENTISTS: Space for visitors; no fees charged; living quarters available nearby.

MAJOR RESEARCH FACILITIES: Moderately complete library; running sea and fresh-water, large outdoor ponds and tanks, small aquarium tanks; research collections of fishes and other marine fauna; identified reference collections of marine and fresh-water fishes, mollusks and others; machine and wood shop; 12 vessels, including the 23 m LOA, *Buk Han San Ho,* 23 m LOA, *Jin Yang Ho,* and 22 m LOA, *Kae Rim Ho.*

SIZE OF STAFF: Thirty-four at professional level; 250 technicians.

IMPORTANT SPECIES AVAILABLE FOR LABORATORY STUDIES:

Mollusca: *Ommatostrephes sloani pacificus, Tapes japonica, Ostrea gigas*

Pisces: *Trachurus japonicus, Engraulis japonicus, Pseudosciaena manchurica, Theragra chalcograma, Scomber japonicus, Cololabis saira, Cyprinus carpio*

MAJOR CURRENT RESEARCH PROJECTS AND SCIENTIFIC LEADERS:

Biochemistry (Bong Nae Lee and Hee Un Chang)
Sectional oceanographic observation (Tong Hwan Bae)
Fisheries resource investigation (Tong Hwan Bae)
Marine ecology (Tong Hwan Bae)
Tidal flats development (Won Tack Yang)

Pusan-Soosan-Daehak, Chung-Shik-Kwa

PUSAN FISHERIES COLLEGE, DEPARTMENT OF SEA PRODUCE

POSTAL ADDRESS: 599-1 Daeyundong, Pusan, South Korea.

EXECUTIVE OFFICER: Kyoh-Soo Taeyung Chung, Kwa-Jang.

CHUNG ANG SOO SAN SI HUM JANG

YEAR FOUNDED: 1941.

SCOPE OF ACTIVITIES: Research on general marine and fresh-water biology; graduate and undergraduate instruction.

SEASON OF OPERATION: All year.

PHYSICAL ENVIRONMENT ACCESSIBLE: Korea Strait; open ocean and sandy beaches.

PROVISIONS FOR VISITING SCIENTISTS: Research and living space for 3 visitors; no fees charged.

MAJOR RESEARCH AND TEACHING FACILITIES: Small library; small aquarium tanks; research collections of fishes, marine algae, shells of Mollusca; wood shop; small boats and outboard motors; vessels, 24 m and 21 m LOA.

INSTRUCTIONAL PROGRAM: General zoology, general botany, parasitology, phycology, ichthyology, general invertebrate zoology, plankton, fresh-water propagation, salt water propagation, and fishery resources.

SIZE OF STAFF: Seven at professional level; 1 technician.

PUSAN-SOOSAN-DAEHAK

IMPORTANT SPECIES AVAILABLE FOR LABORATORY STUDIES:

- Algae: Rhodophyceae (*Gelidium* spp.)
- Platyhelminthes: *Chlonorchis sinensis, Metagonimus yokogawai*
- Pisces: *Misgurnus anguillicaudatus*

MAJOR CURRENT RESEARCH PROJECTS AND SCIENTIFIC LEADERS:

- Local marine algae (Jae-Won Kang)
- An epidemiological survey of *Metagonimus yokogawai* in the Naktong River (Se-Kyu Chun)
- Studies on the trematodes of the genus *Metagonimus*, and the life cycle of *Exorchis oviformis* (Seh-Kyu Chun)
- Studies on the trematodes, intermediate hosts of which are brackish water fishes (Seh-Kyu Chun)

PUBLICATIONS ISSUED: *Bulletin of Pusan Fisheries College* (regularly published journal)

Laboratories about Which No Detailed Information Was Available:

Marine Products Experimental Station, Pusan, South Korea

Director: Mr. Im Do Lee.

MADAGASCAR

Institut de Recherche Scientifique a Madagascar, Station Oceanographique et des Peches

MADAGASCAR INSTITUTE OF SCIENTIFIC RESEARCH, OCEANOGRAPHIC AND FISHERY STATION

POSTAL ADDRESS: B.P. 68, Nossi Be, Malagasy Republic (Nosy-Be, Madagascar).

LOCATION: Near Diego-Suarez.

EXECUTIVE OFFICER: Professeur Jacques Millot, Directeur de l'Institut, B.P. 434, Tananarive, Malagasy Republic.

SPONSORING AGENCY: Office de la Recherche scientifique et technique Outre-Mer (Office of Overseas Scientific Research and Technology), 20, rue Monsieur, Paris VII, France.

YEAR FOUNDED: 1954.

SCOPE OF ACTIVITIES: Unrestricted research on general marine biology, plankton and physical oceanography.

SEASON OF OPERATION: All year.

PHYSICAL ENVIRONMENT ACCESSIBLE: Indian Ocean, Mozambique Channel; sandy and silty beaches, estuarine conditions, brackish, shallow bays, coral reefs, and crater lakes.

PROVISIONS FOR VISITING SCIENTISTS: Research and living space for 2-4 visitors; no fees charged for research space.

MAJOR RESEARCH FACILITIES: Small library; running sea and fresh-water, small aquarium tanks; research collections of marine fauna; identified reference collections of Pisces, Crustacea, Gastropoda, Pelecypoda, Echinodermata; machine and wood shop, skilled shop workman available; one outboard motorboat; 15 m LOA vessel, *Maran-atha.*

SIZE OF STAFF: Three at professional level; 2 technicians.

MAJOR CURRENT RESEARCH PROJECTS AND SCIENTIFIC LEADERS:

- Study of the fishes of the Mozambique Channel (Fourmanoir)
- Studies on the feasibility of shrimp and spiny lobster fisheries (Crosnier)
- Biology of shrimp and spiny lobsters (Crosnier)
- Brachyuran decapod fauna of Madagascar (Crosnier)
- Studies on the Mozambique Channel water (Menache)

PUBLICATIONS ISSUED: *Memoires de l'Institut de Recherche Scientifique de Madagascar, Serie F; Oceanographie; Naturaliste Malgache* (regularly published journals)

MALI

Laboratoire d'Hydrobiologie de Mopti

MOPTI HYDROBIOLOGICAL LABORATORY

POSTAL ADDRESS: B.P. 91, Mopti, Mali.

EXECUTIVE OFFICER: Jacques Daget, Chef.

SPONSORING AGENCY: Service des Eaux et Forets de la Republique du Mali (Mali Water and Forestry Service).

YEAR FOUNDED: 1949.

SCOPE OF ACTIVITIES: Unrestricted research on limnology and ichthyology.

SEASON OF OPERATION: All year.

PHYSICAL ENVIRONMENT ACCESSIBLE: Niger River; swamps of the Niger.

PROVISIONS FOR VISITING SCIENTISTS: None.

MAJOR RESEARCH AND TEACHING FACILITIES: Small library; research and identified reference collections of fresh-water Pisces and Mollusca; small boats and outboard motors.

INSTRUCTIONAL PROGRAM: General ichthyology.

SIZE OF STAFF: Two at professional level; 2 technicians.

MAJOR CURRENT RESEARCH PROJECTS AND SCIENTIFIC LEADERS:

Biology and anatomy of fishes (J. Daget)
Systematics of Mollusca (J. Daget)
Fishery techniques (A. Tembely)

MARSHALL ISLANDS

Eniwetok Marine Biological Laboratory

POSTAL ADDRESS: University of Hawaii, Honolulu, Hawaii, USA.

LOCATION: Eniwetok Atoll, Marshall Islands.

EXECUTIVE OFFICER: Dr. Robert W. Hiatt, Director.

SPONSORING AGENCY: U. S. Atomic Energy Commission, Division of Biology and Medicine, Washington 25, D.C., USA.

YEAR FOUNDED: 1952.

SCOPE OF ACTIVITIES: Unrestricted research on general tropical marine biology, both field and experimental.

SEASON OF OPERATION: All year.

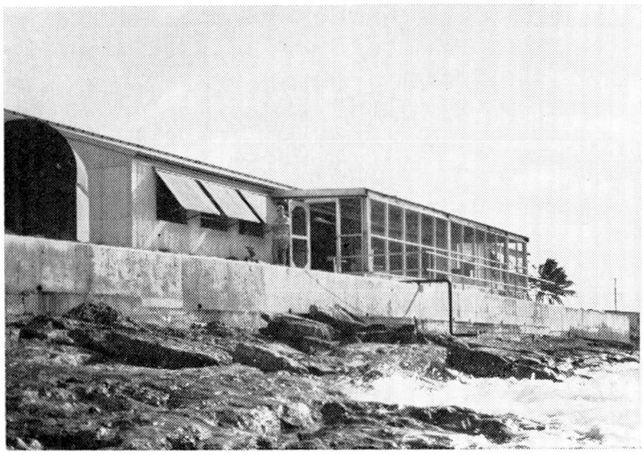

ENIWETOK MARINE BIOLOGICAL LABORATORY

PHYSICAL ENVIRONMENT ACCESSIBLE: Coral reefs.

PROVISIONS FOR VISITING SCIENTISTS: The Laboratory exists only for visiting scientists. Fifteen-20 persons can be accommodated at once. Use restricted to U. S. citizens.

MAJOR RESEARCH FACILITIES: Small library; running sea and fresh-water, large indoor tank, small aquarium tanks; identified reference collections of Eniwetok fishes, coelenterates, polychaetes, echinoderms, crustaceans, insects, foraminiferans, radiolarians, pelecypods, gastropods and cephalopods, marine algae and terrestrial plants; machine and wood shop, electrical and electronic shop, skilled workmen available; small boats and landing craft.

SIZE OF STAFF: No permanent professional staff.

IMPORTANT SPECIES AVAILABLE FOR LABORATORY STUDIES: All tropical central Pacific coral reef organisms.

MAJOR CURRENT RESEARCH PROJECTS AND SCIENTIFIC LEADERS:

Research projects vary with the visiting scientists.

MAURITIUS

Mauritius Institute

POSTAL ADDRESS: B.P. 54, Port Louis, Ile Maurice (Mauritius).

EXECUTIVE OFFICER: J. Vinson, Director.

SPONSORING AGENCY: Government of Mauritius.

YEAR FOUNDED: 1880.

SCOPE OF ACTIVITIES: Unrestricted research on the ecology of marine invertebrates and algae.

SEASON OF OPERATION: All year.

PHYSICAL ENVIRONMENT ACCESSIBLE: Indian Ocean; sandy and silty beaches, rocky and gravelly shores, estuarine conditions, brackish, shallow bays, and coral reefs.

PROVISIONS FOR VISITING SCIENTISTS: Space for 2 visitors; no fees charged; living quarters available nearby.

MAJOR RESEARCH FACILITIES: Moderately complete library; small aquarium tanks; research collections of Pisces, Crustacea, Mollusca, Annelida, Coelenterata and algae; identified reference collections of local Echinodermata, Mollusca, Crustacea and algae.

SIZE OF STAFF: Two at professional level; 2 technicians.

MAJOR CURRENT RESEARCH PROJECTS AND SCIENTIFIC LEADERS:

General ecology of marine invertebrates (Claude Michel)

Algal taxonomy and ecology (R. E. Vaughan)

MEXICO

Secretaria de Agricultura y Ganaderia, Campana Nacional de Piscicultura Agricola

DEPARTMENT OF AGRICULTURE AND ANIMAL INDUSTRY, NATIONAL PROGRAM OF AGRICULTURAL FISH-CULTURE

POSTAL ADDRESS: Uruguay 55-411, Mexico 1, D. F., Mexico.

EXECUTIVE OFFICER: Dr. Fernando Obregon Fernandez, Director.

YEAR FOUNDED: 1954.

SCOPE OF ACTIVITIES: Restricted research on fish-culture.

SEASON OF OPERATION: All year.

PHYSICAL ENVIRONMENT ACCESSIBLES: Nearly 100,000

CAMPANA NACIONAL DE PISCICULTURA AGRICOLA, CENTRO PRODUCTOR PISCICOLA DE CHAPINGO

ponds as well as rivers, streams, and lakes throughout Mexico.

PROVISIONS FOR VISITING SCIENTISTS: Space for 2-3 visitors.

MAJOR RESEARCH FACILITIES: No library; large outdoor ponds, 7 fresh-water fish hatcheries; small boats and outboard motors.

MAJOR CURRENT RESEARCH PROJECTS AND SCIENTIFIC LEADERS:

Research on *Cyprinus carpio v. specularis* relating to pond culture (Staff members)

Direccion General de Pesca e Industrial Conexas, Laboratorios de Biologia Marina y de Agua Dulce

FISHERIES DEPARTMENT AND ALLIED INDUSTRIES, MARINE AND FRESH-WATER BIOLOGICAL LABORATORIES

POSTAL ADDRESS:

Headquarters: Aquiles Serdan 28, 4° piso, Mexico 1 D. F., Mexico.

Branch laboratories:

Marine: (Descriptions follow.)

1. Estacion de Biologia Marina de Mazatlan (Mazatlan Marine Biological Station)
2. Sub-Estacion de Biologia Marina de Guaymas (Guaymas Sub-station of Marine Biology)

Fresh-water: (Not described in the *Directory.*)

1. Estacion Limnologica de Patzcuaro (Limnological Station of Patzcuaro), Michoacan
2. Estacion Piscicola "El Zarco" ("El Zarco" Fishery Station), Estado de Mexico

EXECUTIVE OFFICERS: Lic. Jose Landero Samano, Subdirector de Pesca. Rodolfo Ramirez Granados, Jefe de Estuido Biologico.

SPONSORING AGENCY: Secretaria de Industria y Comercio (Department of Industries and Commerce).

YEAR FOUNDED: 1952.

SCOPE OF ACTIVITIES: Restricted research on marine and fresh-water fisheries.

SEASON OF OPERATION: All year.

MAJOR RESEARCH FACILITIES: Moderately complete library; research and identified reference collections of local fauna and flora; small boats and outboard motors.

SIZE OF STAFF: Twenty at professional level; 20 technicians.

MAJOR CURRENT RESEARCH PROJECTS AND SCIENTIFIC LEADERS:

Marine biology (R. Ramirez)

Oyster culture (M. Sevilla)

Carcinology and marine ecology (P. Mercado)

Fresh-water fishes (A. Solorzano)

Biology of lakes and swamps (E. Ramirez)

Fresh-water biology (M. Flores)

Estacion de Biologia Marina de Mazatlan

MAZATLAN MARINE BIOLOGICAL STATION

POSTAL ADDRESS: Casa del Marino, Paseo Claussen, Colonia los Pinos, Mazatlan, Sinaloa, Mexico.
EXECUTIVE OFFICER: Eduardo Hernandez Bello, Encargado.
YEAR FOUNDED: 1954.
SCOPE OF ACTIVITIES: Fisheries investigations of the Pacific Ocean.
SEASON OF OPERATION: All year.
PHYSICAL ENVIRONMENT ACCESSIBLE: Gulf of California, Pacific Ocean; sandy and silty beaches, estuarine conditions, and brackish, shallow bays.
PROVISIONS FOR VISITING SCIENTISTS: Space for 4 visitors.
MAJOR RESEARCH FACILITIES: Small library; research collection of local fauna and flora; small boats and outboard motors.

Sub-Estacion de Biologia Marina de Guaymas

GUAYMAS SUBSTATION OF MARINE BIOLOGY

POSTAL ADDRESS: Victor Salazar 14, Guaymas, Sonora, Mexico.
LOCATION: Near Hermosillo.
EXECUTIVE OFFICER: Biologo Roberto Mercado Fuentes, Encargado.
SCOPE OF ACTIVITIES: Restricted research on oyster culture, fishery exploration, marine biology, and ecology.
SEASON OF OPERATION: All year.
PHYSICAL ENVIRONMENT ACCESSIBLE: Open ocean, sandy and silty beaches, rocky and gravelly shores, estuarine conditions.
PROVISIONS FOR VISITING SCIENTISTS: None.
MAJOR RESEARCH FACILITIES: Small boats and outboard motors.

Escuela Nautica Mercante "Fernando Siliceo"

"FERNANDO SILICEO" MERCHANT MARINE SCHOOL

POSTAL ADDRESS: Boulevard Manuel Avila Camacho, Apgo. Postal 317, Veracruz, Veracruz, Mexico.
EXECUTIVE OFFICERS: Capitan de Altura de la Marina Mercante Mexicana Marcelino Tuero y Molina, Director. Dr. Moises Quiroga, Professor de Biologia Maritima.
SPONSORING AGENCIES: Gobier no Federal y la Universisad Veracruzana (Federal Government of Mexico and the University of Veracruz).
YEAR FOUNDED: 1919.
SCOPE OF ACTIVITIES: Instruction in marine biology, studies on industrial fishing and plankton; classification of fresh-water, marine, and lacustrine species; statistics, etc.

Instituto Tecnologico de Veracruz, Estacion de Biologia Marina

TECHNOLOGIC INSTITUTE OF VERACRUZ, MARINE BIOLOGICAL STATION

POSTAL ADDRESS: Bulevar Manuel Avila Camacho y muro Sur., Veracruz, Veracruz, Mexico.
EXECUTIVE OFFICER: Professor Jorge Carranza, Director.
SPONSORING AGENCY: Secretaria de Educacion Publica (Department of Public Education).
YEAR FOUNDED: 1958.
SCOPE OF ACTIVITIES: Restricted research on marine biology, fisheries, food technology, and oceanography; graduate and undergraduate instruction.
SEASON OF OPERATION: All year.
PHYSICAL ENVIRONMENT ACCESSIBLE: Gulf of Mexico, Laguna de Alvarado; open ocean, sandy and silty beaches, estuarine conditions, coral reefs, rivers and streams.
PROVISIONS FOR VISITING SCIENTISTS: Space for 4 visitors; no fees charged; living quarters available nearby.
MAJOR RESEARCH AND TEACHING FACILITIES: Moderately complete library; running sea and fresh-water, small aquarium tanks, a 706 m^3 public marine aquarium tank; research collection of fishes of the Gulf of Mexico, small collection of crustaceans and other invertebrates; identified reference collection of fish and algae is being enlarged; machine and wood shop, electrical shop, skilled shop workman available; 32 ft LOA vessel with sail and diesel engine.
INSTRUCTIONAL PROGRAM: Economic zoology (vertebrate and invertebrate), fishery biology, general oceanography, food technology, fishing methods and gear, sanitation of fishery products.
SIZE OF STAFF: Six at professional level; 1 technician.

INSTITUTO TECNOLOGICO DE VERACRUZ

MAJOR CURRENT RESEARCH PROJECTS AND SCIENTIFIC LEADERS:
- Biology, taxonomy, and fishery of the snooks of the genus *Centropomus* (H. Chavez)
- Oysters of Laguna de Alvarado (C. Garcia)
- Biology and fishery of yellow-fin tuna (J. Carranza)
- New methods of fishing (experimental fishing) (L. Navarro)

Universidad Autonoma de Baja California, Centro de Investigaciones Marinas, Escuela Superior de Ciencias Marinas

AUTONOMOUS UNIVERSITY OF BAJA CALIFORNIA, MARINE RESEARCH CENTER, COLLEGE OF MARINE SCIENCE

POSTAL ADDRESS: Calle Primera 1838, Entre Rayon y Aldama, Ensenada, Baja California, Mexico.

EXECUTIVE OFFICER: Biologo Pedro Mercado Sanchez, Director.

YEAR FOUNDED: 1961.

SCOPE OF ACTIVITIES: Unrestricted research on general marine oceanography, biology, and technology; undergraduate instruction.

SEASON OF OPERATION: All year.

PHYSICAL ENVIRONMENT ACCESSIBLE: Pacific Ocean; sandy and silty beaches, rocky and gravelly shores, and brackish, shallow bays.

PROVISIONS FOR VISITING SCIENTISTS: None at present.

MAJOR RESEARCH AND TEACHING FACILITIES: Small library; other facilities in the planning stage; small boats and outboard motors.

INSTRUCTIONAL PROGRAM: Biology, biochemistry, technology and marine geology.

IMPORTANT SPECIES AVAILABLE FOR LABORATORY STUDIES:
- Typical Pacific Coast southern fauna and flora.

MAJOR CURRENT RESEARCH PROJECTS AND SCIENTIFIC LEADERS:
- Marine biology (P. Sanchez)
- Oceanography (G. del Villar)

MONACO

Musee Oceanographique de Monaco

OCEANOGRAPHIC MUSEUM OF MONACO

POSTAL ADDRESS: Avenue Saint-Martin, Monaco-ville, Monaco.

EXECUTIVE OFFICER: Commandant Jaques-Yves Cousteau, Directeur.

SPONSORING AGENCY: Institut Oceanographique, 195 rue Saint Jacques, Paris V^{e}, France.

YEAR FOUNDED: 1910.

SCOPE OF ACTIVITIES: Unrestricted research on general oceanography.

SEASON OF OPERATION: All year.

PHYSICAL ENVIRONMENT ACCESSIBLE: Mediterranean Sea; rocky and gravelly shores.

PROVISIONS FOR VISITING SCIENTISTS: Research and living space for 6 visitors; no fees charged for research space.

MAJOR RESEARCH FACILITIES: Very extensive library; running sea and fresh-water, small aquarium tanks; research collections of all marine flora and fauna of the Atlantic and Mediterranean Seas; catalogs of identified reference collections available; machine and wood shop, electrical and electronic shop, skilled shop workman available; oceanographic vessels, 20 m LOA, *Winnaretta-Singer,* and 10 m LOA, *Physalie.*

SIZE OF STAFF: Eight at professional level; 16 technicians.

IMPORTANT SPECIES AVAILABLE FOR LABORATORY STUDIES:
- Mollusca: *Aplysia,* spp., *Sepia officinalis, Octopus vulgaris*
- Pisces: *Scyliorhinus canicula, Scyllium stellare*

MAJOR CURRENT RESEARCH PROJECTS AND SCIENTIFIC LEADERS:
- Oceanographic underwater research (J. Y. Cousteau)
- Scientific underwater research (J. Alinat)
- Diology (G. Belloc)
- Electrophysiology (Dr. Chalazonitis)
- Marine physiology (R. Motais)
- Dating and natural radioactivity (Mr. Thommeret)
- Hydrology using C^{14} technique (J. Brouardel)
- Benthonic ecology (Ch. Carpine)

PUBLICATIONS ISSUED:
- *Bulletin de l'Institut Oceanographique*
- *Annales de l'Institut Oceanographique* (both regularly published journals)

MOROCCO

Institut des Peches Maritimes du Maroc

MARINE FISHERIES INSTITUTE OF MOROCCO

POSTAL ADDRESS: Rue de Tiznit, Casablanca, Maroc (Morocco).

EXECUTIVE OFFICER: Jean Collignon, Directeur scientifique.

SPONSORING AGENCIES: Direction de la Marine marchande (Gouvernement marocain); Office Francais de la Recherche scientifique et technique Outre-Mer (Moroccan Merchant Marine Department; French Office of Overseas Scientific Research and Technology).

YEAR FOUNDED: 1946.

SCOPE OF ACTIVITIES: Restricted research on oceanography as applied to marine fisheries.

SEASON OF OPERATION: All year.

PHYSICAL ENVIRONMENT ACCESSIBLE: Atlantic and Mediterranean Oceans.

PROVISIONS FOR VISITING SCIENTISTS: Research and living space for 4 visitors.

INSTITUT DES PECHES MARITIMES DU MAROC

MAJOR RESEARCH FACILITIES: Small library; running sea and fresh-water, large outdoor ponds and tanks, small aquarium tanks; research collections of Pisces, Mollusca, and decapod Crustacea; vessels, 25 m and 17 m LOA.

SIZE OF STAFF: Six at professional level; 2 technicians.

MAJOR CURRENT RESEARCH PROJECTS AND SCIENTIFIC LEADERS:
- Oceanography applied to marine fisheries (Henri Aloncle and Jean Collignon)
- Physico-chemical oceanography (Pierre Erimesco)
- Aquarium techniques (Jean Collignon)

PUBLICATIONS ISSUED: *Bulletin de l'Institut des Peches Maritimes du Maroc* (published semiannually)

Institut Scientifique Cherifien

CHERIFIEN SCIENTIFIC INSTITUTE

POSTAL ADDRESS: Avenue Biarnay, Rabat, Maroc (Morocco).

EXECUTIVE OFFICER: Professeur Louis Pasqualini, Directeur de l'Institut et Doyen de la Faculte des Sciences.

SPONSORING AGENCY: Faculte des Sciences de Rabat.

YEAR FOUNDED: 1920.

SCOPE OF ACTIVITIES: Unrestricted research on intertidal marine biology and faunistics; general and systematic limnology.

SEASON OF OPERATION: All year.

PHYSICAL ENVIRONMENT ACCESSIBLE: Atlantic Ocean, Oued Bou Regreg (river); sandy and silty beaches, rocky and gravelly shores, estuarine conditions, and eutrophic lake.

PROVISIONS FOR VISITING SCIENTISTS: Space for 2-3 visitors; no fees charged; living quarters available nearby.

MAJOR RESEARCH AND TEACHING FACILITIES: Large tank with artificial tides and sea water for algology only, small aquarium tanks, marine tank with artificial tides (algology only); research and identified reference collections of algae and local fauna as well as fresh-water algal cultures; machine and wood shop, electrical and electronic shop, all available in Physics Department of the Faculty of Sciences; small boats and outboard motors for rivers and lakes.

INSTRUCTIONAL PROGRAM: At the Faculty of Sciences: general and systematic botany and zoology, general biology, and animal physiology.

SIZE OF STAFF: Eight at professional level; 5 technicians.

IMPORTANT SPECIES AVAILABLE FOR LABORATORY STUDIES:
- Algae: Ulvaceae, Dictyotaceae, *Sphaeroma serratum*
- Crustacea: *Palaemon serratus, P. squilla, Pachygrapsus marmoratus, Uca tangeri*

MAJOR CURRENT RESEARCH PROJECTS AND SCIENTIFIC LEADERS:
- Marine and fresh-water algae (Paulette Gayral)
- Ecology and culture of unicellular fresh-water algae (Paulette Gayral)
- Biology and culture of Ulvaceae (Paulette Gayral)
- Biology of intertidal fauna (Jean Panouse)
- Ecology and faunistics of lakes and temporary ponds (Jean Panouse)

Station Piscicole d'Azrou

D'AZROU FISHERIES STATION

POSTAL ADDRESS:
- *Headquarters:* Azrou, Province de Meknes, Morocco.
- *Fish Hatcheries:* Ras, Ma and Arkbal.

EXECUTIVE OFFICER: Berrada Abdeslam, Chef et Ingenieur des eaux et forets.

SPONSORING AGENCY: Moroccan Government.

YEAR FOUNDED: 1925.

SCOPE OF ACTIVITIES: Restricted research on biology and pathology of fishes, benthos and plankton.

SEASON OF OPERATION: All year.

PHYSICAL ENVIRONMENT ACCESSIBLE: Eutrophic and oligotrophic lakes, rivers and streams and artificial bodies of water.

PROVISIONS FOR VISITING SCIENTISTS: Space for visitors; no fees charged for research space; living quarters available nearby.

MAJOR RESEARCH FACILITIES: Small library; small aquarium tanks; research collection of marsh plant life; identified reference collections of fresh-water fish, benthos, zooplankton, algae, mosses, marsh plants, and larvae of fresh-water insects.

SIZE OF STAFF: Three at professional level; 2 technicians.

MAJOR CURRENT RESEARCH PROJECTS AND SCIENTIFIC LEADERS: Many projects on fish culture (especially *Tilapia* sp.), diseases and parasites of fresh-water fishes, ecology of lakes and reservoirs, artificial propagation of fishes, introductions and acclimatization of exotic salmon and trout, etc.

MOZAMBIQUE

Direccaeo dos Servicos de Marinha, Estacaeo de Biologia Maritima

MARITIME DEPARTMENT, MARINE BIOLOGICAL STATION

POSTAL ADDRESS: Direccaeo dos Servicos de Marinha, C. P. 262, Lourenco Marques, Mozambique.

EXECUTIVE OFFICER: Contra-Almirante J. Moreira Rato, Director dos Servicos de Marinha.

YEAR FOUNDED: 1951.

SCOPE OF ACTIVITIES: Unrestricted research on general marine biology.

SEASON OF OPERATION: All year, but greater activity in July and December.

PHYSICAL ENVIRONMENT ACCESSIBLE: Baia de Lourenco Marques, Indian Ocean; sandy and silty beaches, rocky and gravelly shores, estuarine conditions, brackish, shallow bays, and coral reef.

DIRECCAEO DES SERVICOS DE MARINHA, ESTACAEO DE BIOLOGIA MARITIMA, MOZAMBIQUE

PROVISIONS FOR VISITING SCIENTISTS: Research and living space for 6 visitors; no fees charged for research space.

MAJOR RESEARCH FACILITIES: Small library; running sea and fresh-water, small aquarium tanks; identified reference collections of corals, marine algae, and incomplete collections of other marine fauna; small boats and outboard motors.

IMPORTANT SPECIES AVAILABLE FOR LABORATORY STUDIES:

Anthozoa: *Madreporaria* spp.
Crustacea: *Dotilla fenestrata, Uca* spp.
Mollusca: *Littorina* spp., *Donax* spp.
Protochordata: *Balanoglossus* spp.
Pisces: *Periophthalmus sobrinus*

HYDROBIOLOGISCH INSTITUT, NIEUWERSLUIS

NETHERLANDS

Koninklijke Nederlandse Akademie van Wetenschappen, Hydrobiologisch Instituut

ROYAL NETHERLANDS ACADEMY OF SCIENCES, HYDROBIOLOGICAL INSTITUTE

POSTAL ADDRESS: Rijksstraatweg 6, Nieuwersluis, Nederland (Netherlands).

EXECUTIVE OFFICER: Vacant.

YEAR FOUNDED: 1957.

SCOPE OF ACTIVITIES: Unrestricted research on general fresh-water biology, biochemistry, and microbiology.

PHYSICAL ENVIRONMENT ACCESSIBLE: Vecht-plassen (shallow eutrophic lake).

PROVISIONS FOR VISITING SCIENTISTS: Research and living space for visitors; no fees charged for research space.

MAJOR RESEARCH FACILITIES: Small library; large outdoor ponds and tanks, small aquarium tanks; machine and wood shop; small boats and outboard motors, larger vessels in planning stage.

SIZE OF STAFF: Four at professional level; 3 technicians.

MAJOR CURRENT RESEARCH PROJECTS AND SCIENTIFIC LEADERS:

Biochemistry—cycle of elements in fresh water (H. L. Golterman)
Parasites in snails; zooplankton (B. Z. Salome)

Koninklijke Nederlandse Akademie van Wetenschappen, Hydrobiologisch Instituut, Afdeling Delta-Onderzoek

ROYAL NETHERLANDS ACADEMY OF SCIENCES, HYDROBIOLOGICAL INSTITUTE, DEPARTMENT FOR ESTUARINE RESEARCH

POSTAL ADDRESS: Vierstraat 28, Ierseke, Zeeland, Nederland (Netherlands).

EXECUTIVE OFFICER: Dr. K. F. Vaas, Directeur.
YEAR FOUNDED: 1959.
SCOPE OF ACTIVITIES: Restricted research on the biology of estuaries resulting from the construction of new dikes.
SEASON OF OPERATION: All year.
PHYSICAL ENVIRONMENT ACCESSIBLE: Estuaries of the Rhine, Meuse, Eastern and Western Scheldt; sandy and silty beaches, and brackish, shallow bays.
PROVISIONS FOR VISITING SCIENTISTS: Research and living space for 2 visitors; no fees charged.
MAJOR RESEARCH FACILITIES: Small library; running sea and fresh-water, small aquarium tanks; small research collection of local fauna and flora; small boats and outboard motors.
SIZE OF STAFF: Five at professional level; 5 technicians.
IMPORTANT SPECIES AVAILABLE FOR LABORATORY STUDIES:
Polychaeta: *Nereis diversicolor*
Crustacea: *Orchestia cavimana, O. gamarella, Gammarus locusta, Sphaeroma rugicauda*
Mollusca: *Limapontia depressa*
Phaeophyceae: *Fucus vesiculosus, F. serratus*
Chlorophyceae: *Codium fragile*
Rhodophyceae: *Ceramium rubrum*
MAJOR CURRENT RESEARCH PROJECTS AND SCIENTIFIC LEADERS:
Hydrography of local estuarine waters (J. M. Hoekman)
Littoral fauna (C. den Hartog)
Plant sociology of mud flats (W. G. Beeftink)
Plankton (C. Bakker)
Fish fauna (K. F. Vaas)

Laboratorium Voor de Bestrijding Van Scheepsaangroei

LABORATORY FOR ANTI-FOULING RESEARCH

POSTAL ADDRESS: Buitenhaven 27, Den Helder, Nederland (Netherlands).
EXECUTIVE OFFICER: P. de Wolf, Wetenschappelijk Onderzoek.
SPONSORING AGENCY: Toegepast Natuurwetenschappelijk Onderzoek (Organization for Applied Research).
YEAR FOUNDED: 1958.
SCOPE OF ACTIVITIES: Restricted anti-fouling research.
SEASON OF OPERATION: All year.
PHYSICAL ENVIRONMENT ACCESSIBLE: North Sea, Wadden Zee.
MAJOR RESEARCH FACILITIES: Small library; running sea water, small aquarium tanks; skilled shop workman available; small boats and outboard motors.
SIZE OF STAFF: Two at professional level; 4 technicians.

LABORATORIUM VOOR DE BESTRIJDING VAN SCHEEPSAANGROEI, DEN HELDER

IMPORTANT SPECIES AVAILABLE FOR LABORATORY STUDIES:
Cirripedia: *Balanus balanoides, Elminius modestus, Balanus crenatus*
MAJOR CURRENT RESEARCH PROJECTS AND SCIENTIFIC LEADERS:
Culture of barnacles (P. de Wolf)
Toxicity experiments on barnacles (P. de Wolf)
Paint testing (A. M. van Londen)

Nederlands Instituut voor Onderzoek der Zee

NETHERLANDS INSTITUTE OF SEA RESEARCH

POSTAL ADDRESS: Buitenhaven 27, Den Helder, Nederland (Netherlands).
EXECUTIVE OFFICER: Dr. J. Verwey, Directeur.
SPONSORING AGENCY: Ministerie van Onderwijs, Kunsten en Wetenschappen (Ministry of Education, Arts and Sciences); administered by Nederlandse Dierkundige Vereniging (Netherlands Zoological Society).
YEAR FOUNDED: 1876.
SCOPE OF ACTIVITIES: Unrestricted research on ecology, and hydrography; graduate and undergraduate instruction.
SEASON OF OPERATION: All year.
PHYSICAL ENVIRONMENT ACCESSIBLE: Marsdiep Channel, North Sea, and Wadden Zee; sandy and silty beaches, estuarine conditions, and brackish, shallow bays.
PROVISIONS FOR VISITING SCIENTISTS: Research and living space for visitors; no fees charged for research space.
MAJOR RESEARCH AND TEACHING FACILITIES: Extensive library; running sea water, large tanks, small aquarium tanks; identified reference collection of marine algae and fauna from the southern North Sea; machine and wood shop, skilled shop workman

available; small boats and outboard motors; 40 ft LOA, *Max Weber.*

INSTRUCTIONAL PROGRAM: Summer courses of about two weeks length in marine ecology and hydrography; courses at Den Helder in comparative physiology and general invertebrate zoology; thesis research for students of Dutch universities.

SIZE OF STAFF: Nine or 10 at professional level; 12 technicians.

IMPORTANT SPECIES AVAILABLE FOR LABORATORY STUDIES:

Coelenterata: Five species of medusae
Polychaeta: Thirty-five species of polychaetes
Crustacea: *Carcinus maenas, Cancer pagurus, Eupagurus bernhardus, Crangon* sp.
Cephalopoda: *Sepia officinalis*
Echinodermata: *Asterias rubens, Psammechinus miliaris*

MAJOR CURRENT RESEARCH PROJECTS AND SCIENTIFIC LEADERS:

Chemical hydrography (K. Postma)
Dissolved organic matter (E. K. Duursma)
Periodicity (J. W. de Blok)
Migration problems (F. Creutzberg)
Underwater sound (W. H. Dudok van Heel)
Population dynamics (J. Westenberg)
Physiology of molluscan pumping (A. Dral)
Ecology and behavior of invertebrates (J. Verwey)

PUBLICATIONS ISSUED: None directly. Annual reports of the station appear in *Archives Neerlandaises de Zoologie.* From 1961 results of research at the station appear in *The Netherlands Journal of Sea Research.*

Rijksinstituut voor Visserijonderzoek

NETHERLANDS INSTITUTE FOR FISHERY INVESTIGATIONS

POSTAL ADDRESS:

Headquarters: Postbus 68, IJmuiden, Nederland (Netherlands).
Field Station: Wemeldinge (Zeeland), Reepweg, Stormezandepolder.

EXECUTIVE OFFICER: Professor Dr. P. Korringa, Directeur.

SPONSORING AGENCY: Ministerie van Landbouw en Visserij (Ministry of Agriculture and Fisheries).

YEAR FOUNDED: 1888.

SCOPE OF ACTIVITIES: Restricted research on fisheries including biological, microbiological, chemical, and hydrographical investigations.

SEASON OF OPERATION: All year.

PHYSICAL ENVIRONMENT ACCESSIBLE: North Sea (sandy beaches), Wadden Zee (high salinity, tidal flats and creeks, strong currents), IJsselmeer (eutrophic lake); estuarine conditions at Zeeland Field Station, eutrophic slightly brackish canals and smaller lakes.

PROVISIONS FOR VISITING SCIENTISTS: Space for 1-2 visitors at headquarters, 1 at Zeeland Field Station; fees not usually charged; living quarters available nearby.

MAJOR RESEARCH FACILITIES: Moderately complete library; running sea and fresh-water, small aquarium tanks, direct supply of high salinity seawater and large outdoor oyster pond at Zeeland Field Station; research collections of fauna and flora available at Rijksmuseum Van Natuurlyk Historic, Leiden (State Museum of Natural History, Leiden); machine and wood shop, electrical and electronic shop, skilled shop workman available; vessels, 34 m LOA, *Willem Beukelsz,* and 12 m LOA dredge boat as well as various inspection vessels on the IJsselmeer and Wadden Zee.

SIZE OF STAFF: Thirteen at professional level; 20 technicians.

IMPORTANT SPECIES AVAILABLE FOR LABORATORY STUDIES:

Crustacea: *Crangon vulgare*
Mollusca: *Mytilus edulis, Ostrea edulis*
Pisces: *Esox lucius, Anguilla vulgaris, Solea vulgaris, Pleuronectes platessa, Clupea harengus, Ammodytus marinus*

MAJOR CURRENT RESEARCH PROJECTS AND SCIENTIFIC LEADERS:

Herring stock versus herring fishery (J. J. Zijlstra)
Herring behavior and herring fishery (K. Postuma)
Herring larvae and herring stock (J. J. Zijlstra and K. Postuma)
Plaice stock fluctuations and plaice fishery (L. K. Boerema and J. de Veen)
Whiting stock and whiting fishery (M. Roessingh)
Serological background of fish populations (W. de Ligny)
Eel stock and eel fishery and production biology (C. Deelder)
Hatchery problems in pike and pike-perch (J. Willemse)
Shrimp stock and shrimp fishery (R. Boddeke)
Productivity of fresh water bodies and fish stock (R. Th. Roskam and J. Willemse)

RIJKSINSTITUUT VOOR VISSERIJONDERZOEK, IJMUIDEN

Mesh size and net material versus fish stock and selectivity (M. Roessingh)
Industrial fishery (especially sand eels) (M. Roessingh)
Sole stock and sole fishery (J. de Veen)
The future of the oyster industry (Delta project) (A. Drinkwaard and A. Vlasblom)

NETHERLANDS ANTILLES

Caraibisch Marien-Biologisch Instituut

CARIBBEAN MARINE BIOLOGICAL INSTITUTE

POSTAL ADDRESS: Piscaderabaai, Curacao, Nederlandse Antillen (Netherlands Antilles).
LOCATION: Near Willemstad.
EXECUTIVE OFFICER: Dr. Ingvar Kristensen, Directeur.
SPONSORING AGENCY: Curacao Regering (Government).
YEAR FOUNDED: 1955.
SCOPE OF ACTIVITIES: Unrestricted research in tropical marine ecology, physiology, systematics, and anatomy.
SEASON OF OPERATION: All year.
PHYSICAL ENVIRONMENT ACCESSIBLE: Caribbean Sea; sandy and silty beaches, rocky and gravelly shores, brackish, shallow bays (in the autumn rainy season), coral reefs, eutrophic lake (dries up after the rainy season), land locked lagoons with normal sea water and hypersalinic lagoons.
PROVISIONS FOR VISITING SCIENTISTS: Research and living space for 8 visitors; no fees charged for research space; visiting scientists are very welcome.
MAJOR RESEARCH FACILITIES: Moderately complete library; running sea and fresh-water, small aquarium tanks, small outdoor tanks and large fish pens; identified reference collections of corals, mollusks, fishes and some smaller groups of invertebrates; two small motor vessels.

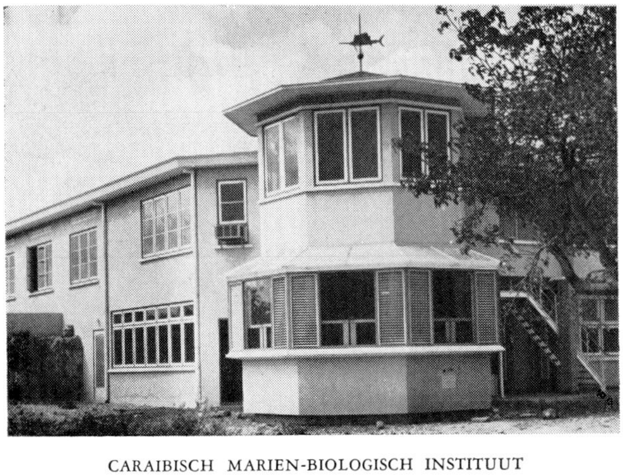

CARAIBISCH MARIEN-BIOLOGISCH INSTITUUT

SIZE OF STAFF: One at professional level; 5 technicians. ostracods, and phyllopods.
IMPORTANT SPECIES AVAILABLE FOR LABORATORY STUDIES: Typical tropical Atlantic fauna and flora with abundant coral reef types; brackish, shallow bays and fresh-water lakes provide large fauna of bryozoans, ostracods, and phyllopods.
MAJOR CURRENT RESEARCH PROJECTS AND SCIENTIFIC LEADERS:
Ecology of corals (I. Kristensen)
Ethology of coral fish (I. Kristensen)
Osmoregulation of fish, decapods, and snails (I. Kristensen)
Biology of *Molliensia vandepolli* (I. Kristensen)
Ecology of *Artemia* (I. Kristensen)

NEW CALEDONIA

Aquarium de Noumea, Station de Biologie Marine

NOUMEA AQUARIUM, BIOLOGICAL MARINE STATION

POSTAL ADDRESS: B. P. 15, Noumea, Nouvelle-Caledonie (New Caledonia).
EXECUTIVE OFFICER: Dr. Rene Catala.
SPONSORING AGENCY: Private foundation.
YEAR FOUNDED: 1956.
SCOPE OF ACTIVITIES: Unrestricted research on general marine biology.
SEASON OF OPERATION: All year.
PHYSICAL ENVIRONMENT ACCESSIBLE: Mer de Corail (Coral Sea); coral reefs. Exceptional environment for zoologists who are skin divers and aqualung divers.
PROVISIONS FOR VISITING SCIENTISTS: Space for 1-2 visitors; fees charged for research space; living quarters available nearby.
MAJOR RESEARCH FACILITIES: Small library; running sea and fresh-water, large outdoor ponds and tanks, small aquarium tanks; important identified collection of algae; small boats and outboard motors; 5 m glass bottom raft, *Pedalo*.
SIZE OF STAFF: Two at professional level; 1 technician.
IMPORTANT SPECIES AVAILABLE FOR LABORATORY STUDIES:
Organisms permanently established in aquaria.
Coelenterata:
- Actinians (from shallow and deep water)
- Hexacorals (from shallow and deep water)
- Octocorals (gorgonians, alcyonarians, pennatulids)

Echinodermata:
- Asteroidea (especially *Oreaster, Nardoa, Linckia*)
- Crinoidea (especially *Comatula, Antedon*)
- Ophiuroidea (especially *Ophiarachna incrassata*)
- Echinoidea (several genera)
- Holothuroidea (*Holothuria, Synapta*)

Annelida: Sedentary Polychaeta (*Serpula,* etc.)

Mollusca:
Amphineura (several species)
Pelecypoda (*Pinna, Pecten,* etc.)
Cephalopoda (several species)
Gastropoda (several species)
Crustacea: Lobsters, crabs, *Squilla,* pagurids, etc.
Protochordata: Several shallow water ascidians
Vertebrata:
Pisces (85 species maintained)
Reptilia: Marine turtles and snakes
Note: Hundreds of other species can be maintained for research purposes.

MAJOR CURRENT RESEARCH PROJECTS AND SCIENTIFIC LEADERS:
General biology of neritic organisms (R. L. A. Catala and Stucki Catala)
Fluorescent corals (R. L. A. Catala and Stucki Catala)

Centre d'Oceanographie de l'Institut Francais d'Oceanie

OCEANOGRAPHIC LABORATORY OF THE INSTITUTE OF FRENCH OCEANIA

POSTAL ADDRESS: B. P. 4, Noumea, Nouvelle-Caledonie (New Caledonia).

EXECUTIVE OFFICER: Monsieur M. P. Legand, Chef du Centre d'Oceanographie.

SPONSORING AGENCY: Office de la Recherche scientifique et technique Outre-Mer, (Office of Overseas Scientific and Technical Research), Paris, France.

YEAR FOUNDED: 1948.

SCOPE OF ACTIVITIES: Unrestricted research on general biological and physical oceanography.

SEASON OF OPERATION: All year.

PHYSICAL ENVIRONMENT ACCESSIBLE: Mer de Corail (Coral Sea), coral reefs, sandy and silty beaches, and estuarine conditions.

PROVISIONS FOR VISITING SCIENTISTS: Space for 2-3 visitors; no fees charged; living quarters available nearby.

MAJOR RESEARCH FACILITIES: Small research collections of bathypelagie fishes and zooplankton; small machine and wood shop and electrical and electronic shop; 23 m LOA vessel, *ORSOM III.*

SIZE OF STAFF: Five at professional level; 6 technicians; 3 ship's officers and 9 seamen.

IMPORTANT SPECIES AVAILABLE FOR LABORATORY STUDIES:
Most Indo-Pacific fauna and flora readily available.

MAJOR CURRENT RESEARCH PROJECTS AND SCIENTIFIC LEADERS:
Primary productivity (Bruno Wauthy)
Phytoplankton (Roger Desrosieres)
Quantitative zooplankton and biology of tunas (Michel Legand)
Physicochemistry of sea water with emphasis on plant nutrients (Henri Rotschi and Bruno Wauthy)
Applied fishery biology (Bruno Wauthy and Michel Legand)

NEW ZEALAND

Auckland University, Marine Biological Station

A new marine biological station for teaching and research has been proposed by the University of Auckland, to be situated at Leigh, New Zealand, north of the Hauraki Gulf on the North Island. Plans are to operate the Station all year and there will be space for one or more visitors. At Leigh there is access to a wide variety of marine conditions, including open oceanic shore, sandy beach, estuarine mud flats and sheltered reefs. Information about the Station may be had by writing to Professor J. E. Morton, Department of Zoology, University of Auckland, P. O. Box 2175, Auckland, New Zealand.

New Zealand Marine Department, Fisheries Laboratory

POSTAL ADDRESS:
Headquarters: 27 Wingfield Street, Wellington, New Zealand.
Branches:
1. Fisheries Laboratory, Te Wairoa Road, Rotorua, N. Z. (ecology of rainbow trout in lakes).
2. Fisheries Laboratory, Kyle Street, Riccarton, Christchurch, N. Z. (inter-relations of brown trout and eels in rivers).
3. Marine Department, P. O. Box 18, Bluff, N. Z. (ecology of oysters, *Ostrea sinuata*).

EXECUTIVE OFFICER: Mr. G. L. O'Halloran, Secretary for Marine Department, Box 2395, Wellington, New Zealand.

YEAR FOUNDED: 1925.

SCOPE OF ACTIVITIES: Restricted research presently on the life history, ecology and commercial production of tarakihi and snapper; fresh-water ecology, particularly of brown and rainbow trout; local management investigations.

SEASON OF OPERATION: All year.

PHYSICAL ENVIRONMENT ACCESSIBLE: Wellington Harbour, Cook Strait, Hutt River; open ocean, sandy and silty beaches, rocky and gravelly shores, and estuarine conditions.

PROVISIONS FOR VISITING SCIENTISTS: Space for visitors; no fees charged; living quarters available nearby.

MAJOR RESEARCH FACILITIES: Small library; small aquarium tanks; limited research collections of fauna and flora; small boats and outboard motors at Rotorua; 63 ft LOA vessel, *Ikatere,* based at Auckland.

SIZE OF STAFF: Thirteen at professional level; 10 technicians. (Staff being substantially increased.)

IMPORTANT SPECIES AVAILABLE FOR LABORATORY STUDIES: (at Wellington)

Gastropoda: *Haliotis iris*

Crustacea: *Jasus lalandii*

Pisces. *Galeorhinus australis, Cheilodactylus macropterus, Chrysophrys auratus, Coridodax pullus, Salmo trutta, Carassus auratus*

MAJOR CURRENT RESEARCH PROJECTS AND SCIENTIFIC LEADERS:

Fresh-water angling statistics, expenditure surveys and stream bottom fauna investigation (Kenneth Radway Allen)

Tarakihi and snapper investigation (Margaret Kemp McKenzie)

Management investigations, Rotorua lakes, Lake Taupo, Lake Alexandrina, etc. (Brian Turnbull Cunningham)

Ecology of rainbow trout in the lakes (Rotorua Laboratory) (Geoffrey Robert Fish)

Interrelations and ecology of eels and brown trout in rivers (Christchurch Laboratory) (Alfred Maxwell Ralph Burnet)

Ecology of oysters, *Ostrea sinuata* (David Henry Stead)

Investigations into ecology of flatfish; feeding habits of seals; whale marking (work carried out from Lyttelton) (Terence Brian Simpson Gorman and Robert John Street)

New Zealand Oceanographic Institute

POSTAL ADDRESS: P. O. Box 8009, 177 Thorndon Quay, Wellington C.1, New Zealand.

EXECUTIVE OFFICER: James W. Brodie, Director.

SPONSORING AGENCY: Department of Scientific and Industrial Research.

YEAR FOUNDED: 1954.

SCOPE OF ACTIVITIES: Restricted research on general marine biology, geology and physical oceanography.

SEASON OF OPERATION: All year.

PHYSICAL ENVIRONMENT ACCESSIBLE: Southwest Pacific Ocean, Tasman Sea, Wellington Harbour; sandy and silty beaches, rocky and gravelly shores, and brackish, shallow bays.

PROVISIONS FOR VISITING SCIENTISTS: Space for 2 visitors; no fees charged; living quarters available nearby.

MAJOR RESEARCH FACILITIES: Very extensive library; research collections of benthos, plankton and sediment microfauna from New Zealand region, tropical southwest Pacific, Southern Ocean and Ross Sea; extensive reference collections of local fauna and flora available at nearby Dominion Museum; machine and wood shop, electrical and electronic shop, skilled shop workman available; vessels, 220 ft LOA, M.V. *Taranui,* and 18 ft LOA, motor launch, *Taihoa.*

SIZE OF STAFF: Thirteen at professional level; 13 technicians.

NEW ZEALAND OCEANOGRAPHIC INSTITUTE

IMPORTANT SPECIES AVAILABLE FOR LABORATORY STUDIES:

Phaeophyceae: *Macrocystis pyrifera, Carpophyllum maschalocarpum*

Rhodophyceae: *Gigartina* spp.

Mollusca: *Amphibola* sp., *Amphidesma* sp., *Haliotis* spp.

Coelenterata: *Phylactenactis* sp.

MAJOR CURRENT RESEARCH PROJECTS AND SCIENTIFIC LEADERS:

Ocean circulation in Southern Ocean

Deep currents (A. E. Gilmour)

Regional circulation studies (D. M. Garner)

Benthonic ecology of shelf regions (D. E. Hurley)

Benthonic ecology of Ross Sea (J. S. Bullivant)

Phytoplankton distribution, systematics and ecology (U. V. Cassie)

Microdistribution of plankton (R. M. Cassie)

Amphipod and isopod systematics (D. E. Hurley)

Ecology of marine bacteria (T. M. Skerman)

Recent Foraminifera, distribution, systematics and ecology

Distribution of shelf sediments (H. M. Pantin)

Deep sea sediments

Regional bathymetry and interpretation (J. W. Brodie)

PUBLICATIONS ISSUED:

New Zealand Journal of Science (D.S.I.R. regularly published journal which includes papers from the Oceanographic Institute)

New Zealand Oceanographic Institute Memoirs (occasionally published)

Portobello Marine Biological Station

POSTAL ADDRESS: Box 8, Portobello, New Zealand.

LOCATION: Near Dunedin.

EXECUTIVE OFFICER: Dr. Elizabeth Batham, Senior Lecturer in Marine Biology.

SPONSORING AGENCY: University of Otago.

YEAR FOUNDED: 1904.

SCOPE OF ACTIVITIES: Unrestricted research on general marine biology with emphasis on live animal studies.

SEASON OF OPERATION: All year.

PHYSICAL ENVIRONMENT ACCESSIBLE: Otago Harbour, Pacific Ocean; sandy and silty beaches, rocky and gravelly shores, and estuarine conditions.

PROVISIONS FOR VISITING SCIENTISTS: Research and living space for about 3 visitors; fees charged for research space.

MAJOR RESEARCH AND TEACHING FACILITIES: Small library; running sea and fresh-water (latter limited), large outdoor ponds and tanks, small aquarium tanks, small public, teaching and research aquarium; limited research collections of East Otago fauna and flora; identified reference collections of East Otago algae and marine invertebrates; wood shop, semi-skilled shop workman available; small boats and outboard motors.

PORTOBELLO MARINE BIOLOGICAL STATION

INSTRUCTIONAL PROGRAM: Two weeks' course for undergraduates in marine ecology, invertebrate zoology and physiology.

SIZE OF STAFF: One at professional level; 2 technicians.

IMPORTANT SPECIES AVAILABLE FOR LABORATORY STUDIES:

Coelenterata: *Mimetridium cryptum*
Brachiopoda: *Terebratella inconspicua*
Mollusca: *Solemya parkinsoni*
Pisces: *Squalus lebruni*

MAJOR CURRENT RESEARCH PROJECTS AND SCIENTIFIC LEADERS:

Nervous system of sea anemones (E. J. Batham)
Electronmicroscopy of sea anemones (E. J. Batham)
Neurophysiology and respiration of dogfish (G. Satchell)
Ecological survey of E. Otago shore and bottom habitats (E. J. Batham)

NORWAY

Fiskeridirektoratets Havforskningsinstitutt

THE DIRECTORATE OF FISHERIES, INSTITUTE OF MARINE RESEARCH

POSTAL ADDRESS: Nordnesparken, Bergen, Norge (Norway).

EXECUTIVE OFFICER: Gunnar Rollefsen, Direktoer.

SPONSORING AGENCY: Det Kongelige Norske Fiskeridepartement (The Royal Norwegian Ministry of Fisheries).

YEAR FOUNDED: 1900.

SCOPE OF ACTIVITIES: General fisheries biology and oceanography of a very broad scope; graduate and undergraduate instruction in collaboration with the Universities of Oslo and Bergen.

SEASON OF OPERATION: All year.

PHYSICAL ENVIRONMENT ACCESSIBLE: The North, Norwegian, and Barents Seas; brackish, shallow bays, fjords, coral reefs, eutrophic and oligotrophic lakes, rivers and streams.

PROVISIONS FOR VISITING SCIENTISTS: Research and living space for 5-10 visitors; no fees charged for research space.

MAJOR RESEARCH AND TEACHING FACILITIES: Very extensive library; running sea and fresh-water, large outdoor ponds and tanks, small aquarium tanks, one 16 m diameter circular tank divisible into compartments for different salinities with central observation room containing 20 windows; research and identified reference collections of local fauna and flora accessible at the Universities of Bergen and Oslo; machine and wood shop, electrical and electronic shop, skilled shop workman available; small boats and outboard motors; power vessels, 170 ft LOA, *G. O. Sars,* 171 ft LOA, *Johan Hjort,* and the 80 ft LOA, *Peder Roennestad.*

INSTRUCTIONAL PROGRAM: The institute provides for student-scientists on ships and in laboratories; special courses arranged through Norwegian universities.

FISKERIDIREKTORATETS HAVFORSKNINGSINSTITUTT, BERGEN

THE *Johan Hjort,* RESEARCH SHIP OF THE FISKERIDIREKTORATETS HAVFORSKNINGSINSTITUTT, BERGEN

SIZE OF STAFF: Twenty-five at professional level; 40 technicians.

MAJOR CURRENT RESEARCH PROJECTS AND SCIENTIFIC LEADERS:

Physical oceanography (J. Eggvin)
Plankton (Kr. F. Wiborg)
Herring (population dynamics; scanning) (Finn Devold)
Gadoid fishes (population dynamics; scanning) (Gunnar Saetersdal)
Scombriform fishes and sharks (Olav Aasen)
Sebastes and seals (Birger Rasmussen)
Physiology and behavior (Gunnar Sundnes)
Hatching and rearing (Gunnar Rollefsen)

PUBLICATIONS ISSUED:

Fiskeridirektoratets Skrifter, series Teknologiske undersoekelser (reports on technological research concerning Norwegian fishing industry) (regularly published journal)
Fiskeridirektoratets Skrifter, serie Havundersoekelser (report on Norwegian Fishery and Marine Investigations) (regularly published journal)

Norsk Institutt for Tang-og Tareforskning

NORWEGIAN INSTITUTE OF SEAWEED RESEARCH

POSTAL ADDRESS: N. T. H., Trondheim, Norge (Norway).

EXECUTIVE OFFICER: Arne Haug, Styrer.

SPONSORING AGENCY: Norwegian Council for Industrial and Scientific Research.

YEAR FOUNDED: 1949.

SCOPE OF ACTIVITIES: Research aimed at increased utilization of seaweed resources.

SEASON OF OPERATION: All year.

PHYSICAL ENVIRONMENT ACCESSIBLE: Rocky and gravelly shores, estuarine conditions, fjords.

PROVISIONS FOR VISITING SCIENTISTS: Space for 1-2 visitors; no fees charged.

MAJOR RESEARCH FACILITIES: Small library at the institute (extensive library at Trondheim); research collection of brown and red algae from the Norwegian coast; machine and wood shop, skilled shop workman available; small boats and outboard motors.

SIZE OF STAFF: Seven at professional level; 3 technicians.

MAJOR CURRENT RESEARCH PROJECTS AND SCIENTIFIC LEADERS:

Mapping of seaweed resources (Birger Grenager)
Anatomy of brown algae (Egil Baardseth)
General chemistry of brown and red algae (Arne Jensen, Bjorn Larsen, Arne Haug)
Industrial exploitation of seaweed (Sverre Myklestad)

Statens Biologiske Stasjon Floedevigen

THE FLOEDEVIGEN BIOLOGICAL STATION

POSTAL ADDRESS: Arendal, Norge (Norway).

EXECUTIVE OFFICER: Gunnar Dannevig, Styrer.

SPONSORING AGENCY: Fiskeridirektoratets Havforskningsinstitutt, Bergen (Directorate of Fisheries, Institute of Marine Research, Bergen).

YEAR FOUNDED: 1882.

SCOPE OF ACTIVITIES: Officially restricted research on commercial fishery investigations; hatching and rearing of fish larvae.

SEASON OF OPERATION: All year.

PHYSICAL ENVIRONMENT ACCESSIBLE: Skagerak and North Sea; rocky and gravelly shores.

PROVISIONS FOR VISITING SCIENTISTS: Space for 1-2 visitors; no fees charged; living quarters available nearby.

MAJOR RESEARCH FACILITIES: Moderately complete library; running sea and fresh-water, large outdoor ponds and tanks, small aquarium tanks, apparatus for hatching fish eggs and for rearing lobster larvae; identified reference collections of eggs and larvae of fishes; machine and wood shop, skilled shop workman available; small boats and outboard motors; vessels,

NORSK INSTITUTT FOR TANG-OG TAREFORSKNING, TRONDHEIM

STATENS BIOLOGISKE STASJON FLOEDEVIGEN, ARENDAL

65 ft LOA, R/V *G. M. Dannevig,* and 23 ft LOA motorboat.

SIZE OF STAFF: Three at professional level; 7 technicians.

IMPORTANT SPECIES AVAILABLE FOR LABORATORY STUDIES:

Pisces: *Gadus morrhua, Pleuronectes platessa, P. flesus, P. limanda, Clupea harengus*

Crustacea: *Homarus vulgaris*

MAJOR CURRENT RESEARCH PROJECTS AND SCIENTIFIC LEADERS:

Fluctuations in the abundance of fishes (Gunnar Dannevig)

Techniques for hatching and rearing fish larvae (Gunnar Dannevig)

Influence of environmental factors on fish (Gunnar Dannevig)

Hydrography (Gunnar Dannevig)

Liberation of cod larvae in an attempt to increase local stock in the fjords (Gunnar Dannevig)

Chromatography as a means for identifying population units of fishes (Gunnar Dannevig)

Tromsoe Museum, Marinbiologiske Stasjon

TROMSOE MUSEUM, MARINE BIOLOGICAL STATION

POSTAL ADDRESS: Tromsoe, Norge (Norway).

EXECUTIVE OFFICERS: Bengt Christiansen, Styrer and Konservator of Zoology at Tromsoe Museum. Per T. Hognestad, Research Officer.

YEAR FOUNDED: 1959 (Tromsoe Museum founded 1872).

SCOPE OF ACTIVITIES: Unrestricted research on general marine biology, ichthyology and hydrography.

SEASON OF OPERATION: All year.

PHYSICAL ENVIRONMENT ACCESSIBLE: Atlantic and Arctic Oceans, Norwegian and Barents Seas; sandy and silty beaches, rocky and gravelly shores, rivers and streams, fjords.

PROVISIONS FOR VISITING SCIENTISTS: Space for 3-5 visitors; no fees charged; living quarters nearby.

MAJOR RESEARCH FACILITIES: Very extensive library in Tromsoe Museum; running sea and fresh-water, small aquarium tanks, indoor large tanks; research and identified reference collections of local flora and fauna at Tromsoe Museum; machine and wood shop, electrical and electronic shop located in Tromsoe; small boats and outboard motors; one 70 ft LOA ocean going research vessel, R/V *Asterias.*

SIZE OF STAFF: Two at professional level; 1 technician.

MAJOR CURRENT RESEARCH PROJECTS AND SCIENTIFIC LEADERS:

Herring investigations (Per Hognestad)

Ecology of microfauna in deep water, especially Foraminifera (Bengt Christiansen)

Recent changes in arctic marine fauna (Bengt Christiansen)

On the general fish-fauna of northern Norway (Per Hognestad)

Fish-fauna of Spitsbergen (Per Hognestad)

Hydrography of the fjords in northern Norway (Per Hognestad)

Shore fauna of Spitsbergen (Carlos Christophersen)

Growth investigations on algae (Ove Sundene)

Investigations on *Pandalus borealis* (Bengt Christiansen)

PUBLICATIONS ISSUED: *Tromsoe Museums Skrifter, Acta Borealia, A. Scientia, Astrate* (all occasionally published)

Trondheim Biologiske Stasjon

TRONDHEIM BIOLOGICAL STATION

POSTAL ADDRESS: Trondheim, Norge (Norway).

EXECUTIVE OFFICER: Cand. real. Ditlef Rustad, Bestyrer.

SPONSORING AGENCY: Det Kongelige Norske Videnskabers Selskab. Museet (Royal Norwegian Society of Sciences and Letters. The Museum).

TROMSOE MUSEUM, MARINBIOLOGISKE STASJON

TRONDHEIM BIOLOGISKE STASJON

UNIVERSITETET I BERGEN BIOLOGISKE STASJON

YEAR FOUNDED: 1900.
SCOPE OF ACTIVITIES: Unrestricted research on marine biology; hatching of plaice.
SEASON OF OPERATION: All year.
PHYSICAL ENVIRONMENT ACCESSIBLES: Trondheimsfjorden (Trondheim Fjord), Troendelagskysten (Troendelag Coast); open sea, sandy and silty beaches, rocky and gravelly shores, coral reef.
PROVISIONS FOR VISITING SCIENTISTS: Space for 2-3 visitors; fees charged for expensive collecting work; living quarters available nearby.
MAJOR RESEARCH FACILITIES: Very extensive library at the D.K.N.V.S. Bibliotek, Trondheim, small library at the station; running sea and fresh-water, one outdoor and one indoor tank, small aquarium tanks, plaice hatchery and small public aquarium; research collections at the Museum as follows: Anthozoa, Bryozoa, Echinodermata, Teleostei, calcareous algae (identified), Crustacea, Mollusca (partly identified); Porifera, Coelenterata, Annelida (mostly unidentified); shop facilities in Trondheim; small boats; vessels of 64 ft, and 19 ft.
SIZE OF STAFF: One at professional level; 3 technicians.
MAJOR CURRENT RESEARCH PROJECTS AND SCIENTIFIC LEADERS:
Plaice hatching and stocking (D. Rustad)
Use of antibiotics in laboratory cultures (D. Rustad)
Intertidal ecology (D. Rustad)

Universitetet i Bergen Biologiske Stasjon

UNIVERSITY OF BERGEN BIOLOGICAL STATION

POSTAL ADDRESS: Espegrend, Norge (Norway).
LOCATION: Espegrend is about 20 km south of Bergen.
EXECUTIVE OFFICER: Professor Hans Brattstroem.
YEAR FOUNDED: 1892. New laboratory opened in 1957.
SCOPE OF ACTIVITIES: Unrestricted research on general marine biology; graduate and undergradaute instruction.
SEASON OF OPERATION: All year.
PHYSICAL ENVIRONMENT ACCESSIBLE: North Sea, West Norwegian fjords; rocky and gravelly shores, brackish, shallow bays, and coral reefs.
PROVISIONS FOR VISITING SCIENTISTS: Research and living space for about 20 visitors; no fees charged for research space.
MAJOR RESEARCH AND TEACHING FACILITIES: Very extensive library at the university, rather complete marine library at the station; running sea and freshwater, small aquarium tanks, larger concrete tanks; identified reference collections of local fauna and flora; small machine and wood shop; small boats and outboard motors; vessels, 63 ft LOA, R/V *Fridtjof Nansen,* and the 30 ft LOA motorboat, *Knurr.*
INSTRUCTIONAL PROGRAM: Elementary courses in marine zoology and botany, graduate course in marine biology, Nordic special courses with topics varying from year to year, e.g., marine biological instruments and methods, shore ecology, fishery biology.
SIZE OF STAFF: Four at professional level; 8 technicians and crew.
IMPORTANT SPECIES AVAILABLE FOR LABORATORY STUDEIS: All species characteristic of fjords of west coast of Norway are present.
MAJOR CURRENT RESEARCH PROJECTS: Marine biological studies involving taxonomy, natural history, ecology, physiology, anatomy, embryology and development, and microbiology.
PUBLICATIONS ISSUED: *Sarsia* (occasionally published journal)

Universitetet i Oslo, Institutt for Marin Biologi, Avd. A.

UNIVERSITY OF OSLO, INSTITUTE OF MARINE BIOLOGY, SECTION A

POSTAL ADDRESS: Frederiksgate 3, Oslo, Norge (Norway).
EXECUTIVE OFFICER: Professor Johan T. Ruud, Styrer.
YEAR FOUNDED: 1920.

SCOPE OF ACTIVITIES: Unrestricted research on general marine biology, plankton studies, bottom ecology, general oceanography, pollution problems; graduate instruction.
SEASON OF OPERATION: All year.
PHYSICAL ENVIRONMENT ACCESSIBLE: Oslofjorden, Dramsfjord; brackish, shallow bays.
PROVISIONS FOR VISITING SCIENTISTS: Space for 2-3 visitors; no fees charged.
MAJOR RESEARCH AND TEACHING FACILITIES: Moderately complete library; 42 ft LOA vessel, R/V *Gunnar Knudsen.*
INSTRUCTIONAL PROGRAM: Chemical oceanography, zooplankton, microbiology, fisheries biology and marine ecology.
SIZE OF STAFF: Five at professional level; 1 technician.
MAJOR CURRENT RESEARCH PROJECTS AND SCIENTIFIC LEADERS:
Hydrography, zooplankton and benthos of the Oslofjord (F. Beyer)
Pollution problems in the Oslofjord (Ernst Foeyn)
Bacteria in the Oslofjord (O. M. Soemme)
Paper chromotography in taxonomic studies (K. Enge)
PUBLICATIONS ISSUED: *Hvalradets Skrifter* (occasionally published journal)

Universitetet i Oslo, Institutt for Marin Biologi, Avd. B.

UNIVERSITY OF OSLO, INSTITUTE OF MARINE BIOLOGY, SECTION B

POSTAL ADDRESS: Universitetet i Oslo, Blindern, Norge (Norway).
EXECUTIVE OFFICER: Professor T. Braarud, Styrer.
YEAR FOUNDED: 1947.
SCOPE OF ACTIVITIES: Unrestricted research on marine botany; graduate instruction.
SEASON OF OPERATION: All year.
PHYSICAL ENVIRONMENT ACCESSIBLE: Oslofjord.
PROVISIONS FOR VISITING SCIENTISTS: No research space for visitors at this time.
MAJOR RESEARCH AND TEACHING FACILITIES: Small library; 42 ft LOA vessel, R/V *Gunnar Knudsen.*
INSTRUCTIONAL PROGRAM: Marine phytoplankton, marine benthonic algae.
SIZE OF STAFF: Five at professional level; 3 technicians.
MAJOR CURRENT RESEARCH PROJECTS AND SCIENTIFIC LEADERS:
Field ecological survey of the phytoplankton of the Norwegian Sea and the Hardangerfjord (T. Braarud)
Electron microscope studies of marine coccolithrophorids (K. Gaarder)
Experimental studies of marine benthonic algae (Ove Sundene)
Survey of the benthonic algal vegetation of the Hardangerfjord (Ingerid Jorde and Nils Klavestad)
Phytoplankton of the Pacific portion of the Antarctic (G. R. Hasle)
Life cycle and physiology of coccolithophorids (E. Paasche)
Benthonic algae of Spitsbergen (P. Svendsen)

Universitetet i Oslo, Limnologisk Institutt

UNIVERSITY OF OSLO, DEPARTMENT OF LIMNOLOGY

POSTAL ADDRESS: Blindern, Norge (Norway).
EXECUTIVE OFFICER: Professor Kaare Stroem, Styrer.
YEAR FOUNDED: 1946.
SCOPE OF ACTIVITIES: Unrestricted research on limnology; land-locked waters of the sea; graduate instruction.
SEASON OF OPERATION: All year.
PHYSICAL ENVIRONMENT ACCESSIBLE: Eutrophic and oligotrophic lakes, rivers and streams, fjords.
PROVISIONS FOR VISITING SCIENTISTS: None.
MAJOR RESEARCH AND TEACHING FACILITIES: Moderately complete library.
INSTRUCTIONAL PROGRAM: Limnology, sediments, ecology of fresh-water animals, geomorphology, land-locked waters.
SIZE OF STAFF: Four at professional level; 1 technician.
MAJOR CURRENT RESEARCH PROJECTS AND SCIENTIFIC LEADERS:
Lake Tokke (K. Stroem)
Limnological survey of Norway (K. Stroem)
Fresh-water ecology (animals) (Elgmork)
PUBLICATIONS ISSUED: *Folia Limnologica Scandinavica* (occasionally published journal)

Universitetet i Oslo, Statens Institutt for Hvalforskning

UNIVERSITY OF OSLO, THE STATE INSTITUTE OF WHALE RESEARCH

POSTAL ADDRESS: Frederiksgate 3, Oslo, Norge (Norway).
EXECUTIVE OFFICER: Professor Dr. Johan T. Ruud.
SPONSORING AGENCIES: Universitetet i Oslo (University of Oslo) and Det kongelige norske fiskeridepartement (the Royal Norwegian Ministry of Fisheries).
YEAR FOUNDED: 1934.
SCOPE OF ACTIVITIES: Restricted research on whale biology.
SEASON OF OPERATION: All year.
PHYSICAL ENVIRONMENT ACCESSIBLE: Area of operation for this institute is in the Arctic and Antarctic.
PROVISIONS FOR VISITING SCIENTISTS: Space for 2-3 visitors; no fees charged; living quarters available nearby.
MAJOR RESEARCH FACILITIES: Moderately complete library; cooperative use of whaling fleet.

SIZE OF STAFF: Three at professional level; 3 technicians.

PUBLICATIONS ISSUED: *Hvalraedets Skrifter* (occasionally published journal)

Universitetet i Oslo, Universitetets Biologiske Stasjon

UNIVERSITY OF OSLO, BIOLOGICAL STATION

POSTAL ADDRESS: 2 Biologveien, Droebak, Norge (Norway).

EXECUTIVE OFFICER: Professor Bjoern Foeyn, Styrer.

YEAR FOUNDED: 1894.

SCOPE OF ACTIVITIES: Unrestricted research on general marine biology including cytology, genetics, sexuality, embryology, histology and anatomy of marine fauna and flora; instruction.

SEASON OF OPERATION: All year.

PHYSICAL ENVIRONMENT ACCESSIBLE: Open ocean, sandy and silty beaches, rocky and gravelly shores, estuarine conditions, brackish, shallow bays, fjord (Oslofjorden), eutrophic lakes, rivers and streams.

PROVISIONS FOR VISITING SCIENTISTS: Space for visitors; no fees charged; living quarters available nearby.

MAJOR RESEARCH AND TEACHING FACILITIES: Small library; running sea and fresh-water, small aquarium tanks; research collections of bottom fauna of the Oslofjorden; small boats and outboard motors; power vessels, 36 ft LOA R/V *Kristine Bonnevie,* and the 24 ft LOA, *Gobius.*

INSTRUCTIONAL PROGRAM: Courses in general marine invertebrate and vertebrate biology, phytoplankton, algae.

SIZE OF STAFF: Two at professional level; 1 technician.

IMPORTANT SPECIES AVAILABLE FOR LABORATORY STUDIES:

Crustacea: *Palaemon fabricii, Crangon vulgaris, Carcinus maenas*
Cyclostomata: *Myxine glutinosa*
Pisces: *Gadus callarias*
Chlorophyceae: *Ulva* sp.
Phaeophyceae: *Laminaria saccharina, L. digitata*
Rhodophyceae: *Antithamnion plumula, A. boreale*

UNIVERSITETET I OSLO, BIOLOGISKE STASJON

PAKISTAN

Pakistan Ministry of Food and Agriculture, Marine Fisheries Department

POSTAL ADDRESS: Fish Harbour, West Wharf Road, Karachi, Pakistan.

EXECUTIVE OFFICER: Dr. M. R. Qureshi, Director.

YEAR FOUNDED: 1951.

SCOPE OF ACTIVITIES: Development of biological and technological aspects of marine fisheries in Pakistan.

SEASON OF OPERATION: All year.

MAJOR RESEARCH FACILITIES: Vessels, 67 ft LOA, M.F.T. *Machhera,* and 38 ft LOA, M.F.T. *New Hope.*

SIZE OF STAFF: Twenty-four at professional level.

Zoological Survey Department, Marine Biological Research Laboratory

POSTAL ADDRESS: Ispahani Building, 183, McLeod Road, Karachi-1, Pakistan.

EXECUTIVE OFFICER: Dr. A. R. Ranjha, Officer-in-Charge.

SPONSORING AGENCY: Pakistan Ministry of Food and Agriculture.

YEAR FOUNDED: 1948.

SCOPE OF ACTIVITIES: Restricted research on general marine biology and plankton.

SEASON OF OPERATION: All year; some problems, such as faunistic surveys, are suspended from May to September, the monsoon season.

PHYSICAL ENVIRONMENT ACCESSIBLE: Arabian Sea, Indus River delta, Manchar Lake; open ocean, sandy and silty beaches, rocky and gravelly shores, estuarine conditions, brackish, shallow bays, and rivers.

PROVISIONS FOR VISITING SCIENTISTS: Space for visitors; no fees charged.

MAJOR RESEARCH FACILITIES: Extensive library; running sea water, large outdoor ponds and tanks, small aquarium tanks; research collections of Porifera, Coelenterata, marine fishes, Crustacea, Echinodermata, Mollusca, etc.; identified reference collections of local fishes, Crustacea, Mollusca, and plankton; one motor boat, one 45 ft LOA marine launch under construction.

SIZE OF STAFF: Ten at professional level; numerous technicians.

PAKISTAN ZOOLOGICAL SURVEY DEPARTMENT, MARINE BIOLOGICAL RESEARCH LABORATORY

IMPORTANT SPECIES AVAILABLE FOR LABORATORY STUDIES:

Mollusca: *Ostrea gryphoides, O. discoides, Lithophaga* sp., *Placuna placenta*

Crustacea: *Penaeus* spp.

MAJOR CURRENT RESEARCH PROJECTS AND SCIENTIFIC LEADERS:

Taxonomic study of marine Gastropoda (A. R. Ranjha)

Biology and culture of edible oysters (S. A. Hasan)

Biology of marine borers (A. R. Ranjha)

Taxonomic study of plankton and their seasonal variations (Mr. Nooruddin)

PERU

Compania Administradora del Guano

GUANO COMPANY

POSTAL ADDRESS: Casilla 2147, Lima, Peru.

EXECUTIVE OFFICER: Ing. Victor E. Ostolaza, Gerente de la Compania.

SPONSORING AGENCY: Semi-governmental.

SCOPE OF ACTIVITIES: Although the Department of Oceanography and Ichthyology and the Isla Don Martin Station no longer exist, the company remains an important source of information about marine birds and fishes, especially Anchovetta (*Engraulis ringens*).

SEASON OF OPERATION: All year.

PHYSICAL ENVIRONMENT ACCESSIBLE: Peruvian current, Guano Islands.

PROVISIONS FOR VISITING SCIENTISTS: Space can probably be arranged for visitors who wish to work in the Guano Islands.

IMPORTANT SPECIES AVAILABLE FOR LABORATORY STUDIES:

Pinnepedia: *Otaria, Artocephalus australis*

Pisces: *Engraulis ringens*

Aves: *Phalacrocorax bougainvillie, Sula variegata, S. nevoxi, Pelecanus thagus*

PUBLICATIONS ISSUED: *Boletin de la Compania del Guano* (regularly published journal)

Peru Ministerio de Agricultura, Direccion de Pesqueria y Caza, Division de Investigacion Pesquera, Laboratorio de Hidrobiologia

PERU MINISTRY OF AGRICULTURE, DEPARTMENT OF FISH AND GAME, DIVISION OF FISHERIES RESEARCH, HYDROBIOLOGICAL LABORATORY

POSTAL ADDRESS: Edificio Ministerio de Educacion, Piso 18, Lima, Peru.

EXECUTIVE OFFICER: Felipe Ancieta C., Jefe de la Division y del Laboratorio.

YEAR FOUNDED: 1949.

SCOPE OF ACTIVITIES: Unrestricted research on marine and fresh-water ichthyology.

SEASON OF OPERATION: All year.

PHYSICAL ENVIRONMENT ACCESSIBLE: Pacific Ocean.

MAJOR RESEARCH FACILITIES: Small library; small aquarium tanks; research collections of marine and fresh-water fishes and aquatic invertebrates; small boats and outboard motors, one 30 ft LOA vessel.

SIZE OF STAFF: Six at professional level.

MAJOR CURRENT RESEARCH PROJECTS AND SCIENTIFIC LEADERS:

Life history and population research on bonito (*Sarda chilensis*) (Felipe Ancieta C. and Marcelino Verastegui)

Biology of mollusks (Daniel Cordova)

Fish taxonomy and zoogeography (Norma Chirichigno)

Reproduction in fishes (Aurora Chirinos de Vildoso)

PUBLICATIONS ISSUED: *Pesca y Caza* (regularly published journal)

Instituto de Investigacion de los Recursos Marinos

MARINE RESOURCES RESEARCH INSTITUTE

POSTAL ADDRESS: Av. Bolognesi 24, La Punta, Callao, Peru; or P.O. Box 3734, Lima, Peru.

LOCATION: Near Lima.

EXECUTIVE OFFICER: Dr. Trygve Sparre, Director.

SPONSORING AGENCY: Consejo de Investigaciones Hidrobiologicas (Hydrobiological Research Council), Apartado 3734, Lima, Peru.

YEAR FOUNDED: 1960.

SCOPE OF ACTIVITIES: Research on marine resources, general marine biology, general oceanography, plankton, studies in fishery economics and technology.

SEASON OF OPERATION: All year.

PHYSICAL ENVIRONMENT ACCESSIBLE: Pacific Ocean and the Humboldt Current.

PROVISIONS FOR VISITING SCIENTISTS: None at present.

MAJOR RESEARCH FACILITIES: Well equipped laboratories in temporary building; small specialized library; two, 75 ft and 145 ft, research vessels, in reconditioning; plans for permanent building ready.

SIZE OF STAFF: Fifteen at professional level; 10 technicians; total staff of 79.

INSTITUTO DE INVESTIGACION DE LOS RECURSOS MARINOS, CALLAO

MAJOR CURRENT RESEARCH PROJECTS AND SCIENTIFIC LEADERS:
- Fishery biology (Hermann Einarssen)
- Population dynamics of the anchovetta (Gunnar Saetersdal)
- Zooplankton (Blanca Rojas de Mendiola)
- Ornithology (Romulo Jordan)
- Bonito (Aurora de Vildoso)
- Whales (Obla Ramirez)
- Oceanography (Zacarias Popovici)
- Economics of marine resources (Wilbert F. Doucet)
- Technological studies (Erling Arnesen)

PUBLICATIONS ISSUED:
- *Informes del Instituto de Investigacion de los Recursos Marinos*
- *Boletin del Instituto de Investigacion de los Recursos Marinos*

PHILIPPINES

Philippine Department of Agriculture and Natural Resources, Bureau of Fisheries

POSTAL ADDRESS:
Headquarters: Diliman, Quezon City, Filipinas (Philippines).
Branch laboratories:
1. Dagat-dagatan Salt-Water Fishery Experimental Station
2. Tanay Fresh-Water Fishery Experimental Station
3. Limnological Station

(Descriptions follow.)

EXECUTIVE OFFICER: Jose R. Montilla, Director of Fisheries.

YEAR FOUNDED: 1947.

SCOPE OF ACTIVITIES: Research on the biology, capture, culture, processing, and preservation of fish.

FISHING VESSELS: 110 ton, M/V *Malasugui,* 30 ton, M/V *David Starr Jordon,* and 9 ton, M/B *Tanguingue.*

SIZE OF STAFF: About 24 at professional level; 24 technicians (in the three branches).

PUBLICATIONS ISSUED:
- *Philippine Journal of Fisheries* (published biannually)
- *Fisheries Statistics of the Philippines* (issued annually)

Dagat-Dagatan Salt-Water Fishery Experimental Station

POSTAL ADDRESS: BAE Building, Diliman, Quezon City.

LOCATION: Dagat-dagatan Lagoon, Malabon, Rizal Province.

EXECUTIVE OFFICER: Jose R. Montilla, Director of Fisheries.

YEAR FOUNDED: 1936.

SCOPE OF ACTIVITIES: Restricted research on general marine biology and the hydrology of inland bays and waters.

SEASON OF OPERATION: All year.

PHYSICAL ENVIRONMENT ACCESSIBLE: Manila Bay; open ocean, estuarine conditions, brackish, shallow bays, rivers and streams.

PROVISIONS FOR VISITING SCIENTISTS: None.

MAJOR RESEARCH FACILITIES: Small library; running sea, brackish, and fresh-water, large outdoor ponds, small aquarium tanks; research collections of fish and higher plants from fish ponds, local plankton and algae; identified reference collections of commercially important local fishes, algae and marine invertebrates; machine and wood shop; small boats with inboard motors.

SIZE OF STAFF: Twenty at professional level; 20 technicians.

IMPORTANT SPECIES AVAILABLE FOR LABORATORY STUDIES:

DAGAT-DAGATAN SALT-WATER FISHERY EXPERIMENTAL STATION

Algae: *Gracilaria confervoides, G. compressa, Corallopsis opunta*
Crustacea: *Penaeus* spp., *Scylla serrata*
Pisces: *Chanos chanos, Mugil* sp.

MAJOR CURRENT RESEARCH PROJECTS AND SCIENTIFIC LEADERS:

Operation of small trawls in Manila Bay (C. Martin and staff)
Biology of important fishes of Manila Bay (I. Ronquillo and staff)
Hydrology of Manila Bay (M. Llorca)
Plankton composition of Manila Bay (E. Bernabe)
Bottom fauna of Manila Bay (J. Ordonez)

Tanay Fresh-Water Fishery Experimental Station

POSTAL ADDRESS: Tanay, Rizal Province.
LOCATION: Near Manila.
EXECUTIVE OFFICER: Sergio S. Felix, Fish Farm Manager.
YEAR FOUNDED: 1939.
SCOPE OF ACTIVITIES: Unrestricted research on fish culture and propagation; instruction.
SEASON OF OPERATION: All year.
PHYSICAL ENVIRONMENT ACCESSIBLE: Laguna de Bay; eutrophic lake.
PROVISIONS FOR VISITING SCIENTISTS: None.
MAJOR RESEARCH AND TEACHING FACILITIES: No library; large outdoor ponds; research and identified reference collections of various fishes.
INSTRUCTIONAL PROGRAM: Fresh-water fish culture.
SIZE OF STAFF: Two at professional level; 4 technicians.
IMPORTANT SPECIES AVAILABLE FOR LABORATORY STUDIES:

Pisces: *Cyprinus carpio, Tilapia mossambica, Arius manilensis, Ophicephalus striatus, Clarias batrachus*

MAJOR CURRENT RESEARCH PROJECTS AND SCIENTIFIC LEADERS:

Breeding of common carp (golden, red, and puncten varieties) under Philippine conditions (Sergio S. Felix)
Bangos (*Chanos chanos*) culture in fresh-water ponds (Pedro A. Acosta and Sergio S. Felix)
Application of organic fertilizer in fresh-water ponds (Sergio S. Felix)
Fish culture in rice paddies (Sergio S. Felix and Pedro A. Acosta)
Toxicity studies of Endrin on fresh-water fishes under cultivation (Sergio S. Felix)

Limnological Station

A new Limnological Station is being built by the Bureau of Fisheries at Los Banos, Laguna. Information about the station may be obtained by writing Mr. Pedro A. Acosta, Supervising Fishery Technologist, Bureau of Fisheries, Diliman, Quezon City, Philippines.

University of the Philippines College of Fisheries, Department of Inland Fisheries

POSTAL ADDRESS: Diliman, Quezon City, Philippines.
EXECUTIVE OFFICER: Assistant Professor Alfonso R. Sebastian, Head of Department.
YEAR FOUNDED: 1959.
SCOPE OF ACTIVITIES: Unrestricted research on fresh- and brackish-water fish culture, plankton, inland fisheries management and limnology; undergraduate instruction.
SEASON OF OPERATION: All year.
PHYSICAL ENVIRONMENT ACCESSIBLE: Manila, Nasugbu, Batangas, and Laguna Bays, Sampaloc and Taal Lakes, Dagatdagatan Lagoon, Pasig and Navotas Rivers; open ocean, estuarine conditions, brackish, shallow bays.
PROVISIONS FOR VISITING SCIENTISTS: None at present.
MAJOR RESEARCH AND TEACHING FACILITIES: Small library; large outdoor ponds and tanks, small aquarium tanks; research and identified reference collections of Philippine fishes, commercial aquatic invertebrates, and seaweeds; machine and wood shop, skilled shop workman available; small boats and outboard motors.
INSTRUCTIONAL PROGRAM: General zoology, ichthyology, general botany, aquatic botany (phycology), limnology, fish diseases, aquatic invertebrates, ecology of fishes, fresh- and brackish-water fish culture, early life history of fishes, fish pond construction and management, general fisheries.
SIZE OF STAFF: Four at professional level; 2 technicians.
IMPORTANT SPECIES AVAILABLE FOR LABORATORY STUDIES:

Algae: *Oscillatoria, Enteromorpha, Padina, Coscinodiscus, Gracillaria*
Pisces: *Tilapia mossambica, Glossogobius giurus, Chanos chanos, Clarias batracus, Cyprinus carpio*

MAJOR CURRENT RESEARCH PROJECTS AND SCIENTIFIC LEADERS:

Identification and preservation of the algae of Nasugbu, Batangas (Zosima T. Vicencio)

University of the Philippines College of Fisheries, Department of Marine Fisheries

POSTAL ADDRESS: Boston and 23rd Streets, Port Area, Manila, Filipinas (Philippines).
EXECUTIVE OFFICER: Professor Teodoro G. Megia, Head of Department.
YEAR FOUNDED: 1958.
SCOPE OF ACTIVITIES: Restricted research on general oceanography; undergraduate instruction.
SEASON OF OPERATION: All year.
PHYSICAL ENVIRONMENT ACCESSIBLE: Manila Bay, South China Sea; sandy and silty beaches, rocky and gravelly shores, estuarine conditions, brackish, shallow bays, and coral reefs.

PROVISIONS FOR VISITING SCIENTISTS: Space for 2 visitors by arrangement; no fees charged; living quarters available nearby.

MAJOR RESEARCH AND TEACHING FACILITIES: Small library; machine and wood shop, skilled shop workman available; one 31 m LOA vessel.

INSTRUCTIONAL PROGRAM: General oceanography, fisheries oceanography, marine machinery, navigation and seamanship.

SIZE OF STAFF: One at professional level; 3 technicians.

IMPORTANT SPECIES AVAILABLE FOR LABORATORY STUDIES: No experimental work done. Laboratory devoted primarily to oceanographic studies.

MAJOR CURRENT RESEARCH PROJECTS AND SCIENTIFIC LEADERS:

A general oceanographic survey of important Philippine fishing grounds (Teodoro G. Megia)
Marine productivity studies (Teodoro G. Megia)
An oceanographic model of Manila Bay (Romeo O. Villarta)

University of the Philippines, Marine Biological Station

POSTAL ADDRESS: Puerto Galera, Oriental Mindoro, Filipinas (Philippines).

LOCATION: Near Calapan.

EXECUTIVE OFFICER: Chairman, Division of Natural Sciences, College of Arts and Sciences, University of the Philippines, Diliman, Rizal, Philippines.

YEAR FOUNDED: 1925.

SCOPE OF ACTIVITIES: Unrestrcted research on general marine biology; graduate and undergraduate instruction.

SEASON OF OPERATION: April and May.

PHYSICAL ENVIRONMENT ACCESSIBLE: Verde Island Passage, South China Sea; sandy and silty beaches, rocky and gravelly shores, coral reefs, rivers and streams.

UNIVERSITY OF THE PHILIPPINES, MARINE BIOLOGICAL LABORATORY

PROVISIONS FOR VISITING SCIENTISTS: None.

MAJOR RESEARCH AND TEACHING FACILITIES: No library at the station, but library materials from the university are brought to the station; small boats and outboard motors.

INSTRUCTIONAL PROGRAM: Phycology and field zoology.

IMPORTANT SPECIES AVAILABLE FOR LABORATORY STUDIES:

Marine algae: several groups
Coelenterata: many species of stony and soft corals, *Cassiopea medusa*
Echinoidea: *Centrechinus setosus*
Asteroidea: *Archaster typicus*
Holothoroidea: *Stichopus chloronotus, Holothuria* sp.
Gastropoda: *Dolobella gigas*
Crustacea: *Remipes testudinarius*

MAJOR CURRENT RESEARCH PROJECTS AND SCIENTIFIC LEADERS:

Algae (G. T. Velasquez)
Scleractinians (F. Nemenzo)
Fish systematics (J. V. Yapchiongco)

PUBLICATIONS ISSUED: *University of Philippines Natural and Applied Science Bulletin* (occasionally published journal)

POLAND

Instytut Biologii Doswiadczalnej im. M. Nenckiego

M. NENCKI INSTITUTE OF EXPERIMENTAL BIOLOGY

POSTAL ADDRESS:

Headquarters: ul. Pasteura, 3, Warszawa, 22, Polska (Warsaw, Poland).
Department of Experimental Hydrobiology: ul. Pasteura 3, Warszawa.
Hydrobiological Station: Mikolajki kolo Mragowa. (Descriptions follow.)

EXECUTIVE OFFICER: Professor Dr. Jan Dembowski, Dyrektor Instytutu.

SPONSORING AGENCY: Polska Akademia Nauk (Polish Academy of Sciences).

PUBLICATIONS ISSUED: *Polskie Archiwum Hydrobiologii* (regularly published journal)

Zaklad Hydrobiologii Eksperymentalnej

DEPARTMENT OF EXPERIMENTAL HYDROBIOLOGY

POSTAL ADDRESS: ul. Pasteura, 3, Warszawa 22.

EXECUTIVE OFFICER: Romuald Klekowski, Chief of Department.

YEAR FOUNDED: 1954.

SCOPE OF ACTIVITIES: Unrestricted research on the limnology of intermittent and periodic, natural and artificial water bodies.

SEASON OF OPERATION: All year.

PHYSICAL ENVIRONMENT ACCESSIBLE: Intermittent and periodic, natural and artificial bodies of water.

PROVISIONS FOR VISITING SCIENTISTS: Space for 4 visitors; no fees charged; living quarters available nearby.

MAJOR RESEARCH FACILITIES: Very extensive library; small aquarium tanks; machine and wood shop, skilled shop workman available.

SIZE OF STAFF: Ten at professional level; 6 technicians.

IMPORTANT SPECIES AVAILABLE FOR LABORATORY STUDIES:

- Chlorophyceae: *Coleochaete* spp. and other periphyton algae
- Annelida: *Hirudo medicinalis, Haemopsis sanguisuga*
- Gastropoda: *Planorbis planorbis, Coretus corneus, Limnaea stagnalis*
- Insecta: *Lestes sponsa* larvae, *Lestes nympha* larvae, *Coenagrion hastulatum* larvae (Odonata), *Culex* sp., *Mochlonyx* (Diptera)

MAJOR CURRENT RESEARCH PROJECTS AND SCIENTIFIC LEADERS:

- Hydrophysiology (metabolism and dessication) of Invertebrata (Romuald Klekowski)
- Environmental factors (hydrochemistry and hydrophysics) (J. Paschalski)
- Hydromicrobiology (E. Fischer)
- Biology of dragon fly larvae (Z. Fischer)
- Biology of Nematodes (W. Chodorowska)
- Biology of Copepoda (M. Wierzbicka)
- Biology of Trematoda, ecology of water stages of parasites (E. Styczynska-Jurewicz)
- Biocoenology (succession); biology of Turbellaria (A. Chodorowski)
- Algology, biology of periphyton (H. Wysocka-Bujalska)
- Biochemistry of organic matter in water (A. Dowgiallo)

Stacja Hydrobiologiczna

HYDROBIOLOGICAL STATION AT MIKOLAJKI

POSTAL ADDRESS: Mikolajki kolo Mragowa.

EXECUTIVE OFFICER: Andrzej Szczepanski, Chief of Station.

YEAR FOUNDED: 1951.

SCOPE OF ACTIVITIES: Unrestricted research on general limnology of the Masurian Lakes district.

SEASON OF OPERATION: All year.

PHYSICAL ENVIRONMENT ACCESSIBLE: Research and living space for 10 visitors; no fees charged for research space.

MAJOR RESEARCH FACILITIES: Very extensive library at the institute in Warsaw; small aquarium tanks; machine and wood shop; vessels, 11 m and 21 m LOA.

SIZE OF STAFF: Four at professional level; 5 technicians.

IMPORTANT SPECIES AVAILABLE FOR LABORATORY STUDIES:

- Lamellibranchiata: *Dreissena polymorpha*
- Gastropoda: *Viviparus fasciatus*
- Diptera: *Claoborus crystallinus*
- Trichoptera: *Molanna angustata*
- Crustacea: *Mysis relicta*
- Pisces: *Alburnus alburnus, Perca fluviatilis,* and other fishes

MAJOR CURRENT RESEARCH PROJECTS AND SCIENTIFIC LEADERS:

- Energy balance of lakes (Andrzej Szczepanski)
- Regional limnology (Andrzej Szczepanski)
- Diatomic and Si-balance (Z. Malanowski)
- Stability of water bodies in lakes (W. Szczepanska)
- Phytosociology of waterplants (B. Solinska)

Instytut Rybactwa Srodladowego

INSTITUTE OF INLAND WATER FISHERIES

POSTAL ADDRESS:

Headquarters: Olsztyn-Kortowo, Polska (Poland).

Biological Stations:

1. Gizycko (Masurian Lakes District)
2. Warszawa (Vistula River)
3. Zabieniec (Experimental ponds)
4. Oliwa near Gdansk (hatchery)

EXECUTIVE OFFICER: Professor Dr. Stanislaw Sakowicz, Dyrektor.

SPONSORING AGENCY: Ministerstwo Rolnictwa (Ministry of Agriculture).

YEAR FOUNDED: 1951.

SCOPE OF ACTIVITIES: Restricted research on the biological productivity of inland water as a basis of fishery management of lakes, rivers, and carp-trout ponds. Aquatic chemistry, plankton studies, aquatic plants, biology of fishes, breeding of pond fishes, fishing gear and fishing economics.

SEASON OF OPERATION: All year.

PHYSICAL ENVIRONMENT ACCESSIBLE: Masurian Lake

INSTYTUT RYBACTWA SRODLADOWEGO

district (eutrophic lakes), Vistula River, and carp and trout ponds.

PROVISIONS FOR VISITING SCIENTISTS: Research and living space for 6 visitors; no fees charged for research space.

MAJOR RESEARCH FACILITIES: Extensive library; large outdoor ponds, small aquarium tanks; machine and wood shop, skilled shop workman available; small boats and outboard motors; vessels 9 m and 13 m LOA.

SIZE OF STAFF: Fifty-four at professional level; 25 technicians.

IMPORTANT SPECIES AVAILABLE FOR LABORATORY STUDIES:

Pisces: *Cyprinus carpio, Coregonus albula, Salmo gairdneri, S. trutta*

MAJOR CURRENT RESEARCH PROJECTS AND SCIENTIFIC LEADERS:

Native stock of Lake Trout, *Salmo trutta*; an attempt towards its acclimation into the sea and various lakes (Stanislaw Sakowicz)

Methods of fishery management of lakes (J. Zawisza)

Biological productivity of lakes (K. Patalas)

Methods of fishery management of streams, rivers, and reservoirs (T. Backiel)

Biological bases of carp culture (P. Wolny)

Aquatic plants; biology of some coregonid fishes (S. Bernatowicz)

Improvement of fishing methods (W. Dembinski)

Economics of inland water fisheries (B. Dabrowski)

Morski Instytut Rybacki

SEA FISHERIES INSTITUTE

POSTAL ADDRESS:

Headquarters: Aleja Zjednoczenia 1, Gdynia, Polska (Poland).

Branches:

1. Kolobrzeg
2. Swinoujscie

EXECUTIVE OFFICER: Jerzy Kukucz, Deputy Professor.

SPONSORING AGENCY: Ministerstwo Zeglugi i Gospodarki Wodnej (Ministry of Shipping).

YEAR FOUNDED: 1923.

SCOPE OF ACTIVITIES: Restricted research on ichthyology, oceanography, fisheries technology, sea fisheries industry economy, and fishing gear and techniques.

SEASON OF OPERATION: All year.

PHYSICAL ENVIRONMENT ACCESSIBLE: Gulf of Gdansk (Danzig), Baltic Sea; estuarine conditions, brackish, shallow bays.

PROVISIONS FOR VISITING SCIENTISTS: Space for 2 visitors; no fees charged.

MAJOR RESEARCH FACILITIES: Very extensive library; small aquarium tanks, machine and wood shop; small boats and outboard motors; vessels, 30 m LOA, 24 m LOA, *Michal Siedlecki II,* and 18 m LOA, *Ewa.*

MORSKIEGO INSTYTUT RYBACTWA, GDYNIA

SIZE OF STAFF: Sixty-four at professional level; 25 technicians.

PUBLICATIONS ISSUED: *Biuletyn Informacyjny Morskiego Instytutu Rybackiego* (occasionally published journal)

Polska Akademia Nauk, Zaklad Biologii Wod

POLISH ACADEMY OF SCIENCES, HYDROBIOLOGICAL LABORATORY

POSTAL ADDRESS:

Headquarters: ul. Slawkowska 17, Krakow, Polska (Cracow, Poland).

Branches:

1. Stacja Hydrobiologiczna w Goczalkowicach (Goczalkowice Hydrobiological Station).
2. Doswiadczalne Gospodarstwa Stawowe a Ochabach (Ochaby Experimental Pond Farms).

EXECUTIVE OFFICER: Professor Dr. Karol Starmach, Dyrektor.

SPONSORING AGENCY: Wydzial II-Nauk Biologicznych, Polska Akademia Nauk (Section II-Biological Sciences, Polish Academy of Sciences).

YEAR FOUNDED: 1953.

SCOPE OF ACTIVITIES: Unrestricted research on the hydrobiology of rivers, reservoirs, and fish ponds.

SEASON OF OPERATION: All year.

PHYSICAL ENVIRONMENT ACCESSIBLE: Zbiornik Goczalkowicki, reservoirs, Wisla and Vistula Rivers, oligotrophic lake.

PROVISIONS FOR VISITING SCIENTISTS: None at Krakow, but research and living space for 2 visitors at Goczalkowice and also 2 at Ochaby; no fees charged for living space.

MAJOR RESEARCH FACILITIES: Moderately complete library; large outdoor ponds in Ochaby; small aquarium tanks in Goczalkowice and Ochaby; research collections in Ochaby of fresh-water fishes from southern Poland; bibliography of algal flora of Poland; machine and wood shop, electrical and electronic shop, skilled shop workman available in Krakow; one motorboat and 2 boats with outboard motors in Goczalkowice.

SIZE OF STAFF: Thirty at professional level; 11 technicians.

IMPORTANT SPECIES AVAILABLE FOR LABORATORY STUDIES:

Species inhabiting fish-ponds and rivers immediately available for study.

MAJOR CURRENT RESEARCH PROJECTS AND SCIENTIFIC LEADERS:

Dynamics of biocoenoses of Carpathian rivers (Karol Starmach and Jadwiga Sieminska)

Formation of biocoenoses and of environment in barrage reservoirs (Anna Rumek)

Polish carp, *Cyprinus carpio,* and its rearing in ponds of the upper Wisla River basin (Edward Rudzinski and Jan Wlodek)

Environment and biocoenoses of the fish ponds in the river basin of the upper Wisla and their change in relation to farming types (Karol Starmach and Stanislaw Wrobel)

PUBLICATIONS ISSUED: *Acta Hydrobiologica* (regularly published journal)

Pracownia Ekologii Wodnej Zakladu Ekologii (PAN)

INSTITUTE OF ECOLOGY (PAN), LABORATORY OF WATER ECOLOGY

POSTAL ADDRESS: Nowy Swiat 72, Warsaw, Poland.

EXECUTIVE OFFICER: Kajak Zdzislaw, Chief of Laboratory.

SPONSORING AGENCY: Polish Academy of Science.

YEAR FOUNDED: 1952.

SCOPE OF ACTIVITIES: Unrestricted research on dynamics and interrelations of aquatic populations and biocoenoses; plankton studies, bottom ecology, ecology of periphyton, productivity of fresh-water ecosystems.

SEASON OF OPERATION: All year.

PHYSICAL ENVIRONMENT ACCESSIBLE: Eutrophic and oligotrophic lakes, rivers, streams, and fish ponds.

PROVISIONS FOR VISITING SCIENTISTS: Space available for two visitors; no fees charged; living quarters available in the city.

MAJOR RESEARCH FACILITIES: Very extensive library; running fresh-water and aquaria; all types of mechanical shops available in the city; small boats; one vessel 55 m LOA.

SIZE OF STAFF: Seven at professional level, 1 technician.

IMPORTANT SPECIES AVAILABLE FOR LABORATORY STUDIES:

Mollusca: *Viviparus fasciatus, Coretus corneus, Limnaea stagnalis, Dreissensia polymorpha.*

Tendipedidae: *Tendipes plumosus, Pelopia kraatzi, Procladius* sp.

MAJOR CURRENT RESEARCH PROJECTS AND SCIENTIFIC LEADERS:

Ecology of benthos, especially benthonic Tendipedidae (Kajak Zdzislaw)

Ecology of planktonic Rotatoria (Anna Hillbricht-Ilkowska)

Problems of succession (Anna Hillbricht-Ilkowska)

Ecology of periphyton, especially periphytonic Nematoda (Eva Pieczynska)

Ecology of Hydracarina (Eligiusz Pieczynska)

Ecology of Mollusca (Anna Stanczykowska)

Ecology of Algae (Irena Spodniewska)

PUBLICATIONS ISSUED: *Ekologia Polska,* ser. A and B; *Polish Ecological Bibliography* (regularly published journal)

Pracownia Higieny i Sanitarej Ochrony Wod Powierzchniowych, Zakladu Higieny Komunalnej

INVESTIGATION AND SANITARY PROTECTION OF SURFACE WATERS LABORATORY, COMMUNAL HYGIENE DEPARTMENT

POSTAL ADDRESS: Chocimska 24, Warsaw, Poland.

EXECUTIVE OFFICER: Doc. Dr. Irena Cabejszek, Chief of Laboratory.

SPONSORING AGENCY: State Institute of Hygiene.

YEAR FOUNDED: 1935.

SCOPE OF ACTIVITIES: Unrestricted research on plankton and river bottoms relating to pollution and purification; graduate instruction.

SEASON OF OPERATION: All year.

PHYSICAL ENVIRONMENT ACCESSIBLE: Rivers; biocoenose of trinklink filter in the sewage purification process.

PROVISION FOR VISITING SCIENTISTS: None.

MAJOR RESEARCH FACILITIES: Extensive library; running fresh-water, small aquarium tanks; small boats and outboard motors.

SIZE OF STAFF: Six at professional level.

IMPORTANT SPECIES AVAILABLE FOR LABORATORY STUDIES:

Chlorophyceae: *Stigeoclonium* sp., *Clado phora* sp.

Protozoa: *Paramecium caudatum*

Crustacea: *Daphnia magna*

MAJOR CURRENT RESEARCH PROJECTS AND SCIENTIFIC LEADERS:

Hydrobiology, algology, biological plankton and periphyton (Irena Cabejszek)

Hydrology, protozoology, microbiology (Janina Stanislawska)

Hydrology, ecology, Cladocera, Copepoda, Tendipedidae (Jan Igor Rybak)

Hydrobiology, Tendipedidae (Bohdan Styczynski)

Hydrochemistry (Jerzy Luczak)

PUBLICATIONS ISSUED: *Roczniki Panstwowego Zakladu Higieny* (regularly published journal).

Stacja Biologiczna Gorki Wschodnie

BIOLOGICAL STATION GORKI WSCHODNIE

POSTAL ADDRESS: Sobieszewo via Gdansk, Polska (Sobieszewo via Danzig, Poland).

EXECUTIVE OFFICER: Professor Dr. Fryderyk Pautsch, Dyrektor.

SPONSORING AGENCIES: Akademia Medyczna w Gdansku (Danzig Medical School) and Societas Scientiarium Gedanensis (Danzig Society of Arts and Sciences).

YEAR FOUNDED: 1955.

SCOPE OF ACTIVITIES: Unrestricted research on zoology, comparative physiology, and brackish-water biology; graduate and undergraduate instruction.

SEASON OF OPERATION: All year.

PHYSICAL ENVIRONMENT ACCESSIBLE: Baltic Sea; sandy and silty beaches, estuarine conditions, and brackish, shallow bays.

PROVISIONS FOR VISITING SCIENTISTS: Research and living space for 12 visitors; no fees charged for research space.

MAJOR RESEARCH AND TEACHING FACILITIES: Small library; small aquarium tanks; skilled shop workman available; small boats and outboard motors.

INSTRUCTIONAL PROGRAM: Marine and brackish-water invertebrates; marine and brackish-water fish, algae, and crustaceans, and endocrinology.

SIZE OF STAFF: Three at professional level; 3 technicians.

IMPORTANT SPECIES AVAILABLE FOR LABORATORY STUDIES:

Hydrozoa: *Cordylophora caspia*
Scyphomedusae: *Aurelia aurita*
Polychaeta: *Nereis diversicolor*
Crustacea: *Idothea baltica* (Isopoda), *Crangon crangon* (Decapoda), *Palaemonetes varians* (Decapoda), *Rhithropanopeus harrisi* (Brachyura)
Lamellibranchia: *Mya arenariais*

STACJA BIOLOGICZNA GORKI WSCHODNIE

MAJOR CURRENT RESEARCH PROJECTS AND SCIENTIFIC LEADERS:

Embryonic and larval development of the crab, *Rhithropanopeus harrisi* (L. Lawinski)
Chromatophores of *Rhithropanopeus* (Fryderyk Pautsch)
Hormonal regulation of the color change of *Rhithropanopeus* (Fryderyk Pautsch)
Neurosecretory cells of *Rhithropanopeus* (Fryderyk Pautsch)
Diabetogenic hormone of *Rhithropanopeus* (Fryderyk Pautsch)

PUBLICATIONS ISSUED: *Societas Scientiarium Gedanensis, Acta Biologica et Medica* (occasionally published journal)

Uniwersytet Jagiellonski, Katedra Hydrobiologii

JAGIELLONIAN UNIVERSITY, DEPARTMENT OF HYDROBIOLOGY

POSTAL ADDRESS: Oleandry Krakow, Polska (Poland).

EXECUTIVE OFFICER: Professor Dr. Karol Starmach, Dyrektor.

YEAR FOUNDED: 1957.

SCOPE OF ACTIVITIES: Unrestricted research on the ecology of bottom fauna and flora of streams and barrage reservoirs; graduate and undergraduate instruction.

SEASON OF OPERATION: All year.

PHYSICAL ENVIRONMENT ACCESSIBLE: Wisla and Vistula Rivers; oligotrophic lake, and barrage reservoirs.

PROVISIONS FOR VISITING SCIENTISTS: None at present; after 1963, space for visitors is anticipated in new facilities.

MAJOR RESEARCH AND TEACHING FACILITIES: Small library; research collections of Ephemeroptera, Plecoptera, plankton of barrage reservoirs; machine and wood shop, electrical and electronic shop, skilled shop workman available.

INSTRUCTIONAL PROGRAM: General limnology, limnology of rivers.

SIZE OF STAFF: Three at professional level; 1 technician.

MAJOR CURRENT RESEARCH PROJECTS AND SCIENTIFIC LEADERS:

Biocoenoses of the Carpathian streams (Karol Starmach)

Uniwersytet Mikolaja Kopernika, Stacja Limnologiczna

COPERNICUS UNIVERSITY LIMNOLOGICAL STATION

POSTAL ADDRESS: 10, Sienkiewicza Street, Ilawa, Polska (Poland).

EXECUTIVE OFFICER: Professor Dr. Joseph St. Mikulski, Director, Department of Ecology and Nature Conservation, Copernicus University, 30-32 Sienkiewicza Str., Torun, Polska.

YEAR FOUNDED: 1958.

SCOPE OF ACTIVITIES: Unrestricted research on general fresh-water biology of the Masurian lakes; graduate and undergraduate instruction.

SEASON OF OPERATION: All year.

PHYSICAL ENVIRONMENT ACCESSIBLE: Lake Jeziorak (eutrophic lake).

PROVISIONS FOR VISITING SCIENTISTS: Research and living space for 1-2 visitors; no fees charged for research space.

MAJOR RESEARCH AND TEACHING FACILITIES: Small library under construction; small aquarium tanks; two small boats and outboard motors; vessels, 4 m and 6 m LOA.

INSTRUCTIONAL PROGRAM: Summer course in general fresh-water biology.

SIZE OF STAFF: Two at professional level; 2 technicians.

MAJOR CURRENT RESEARCH PROJECTS AND SCIENTIFIC LEADERS:
- The history of lake deposits (Joseph St. Mikulski)
- Phytoplankton (R. Bohr)
- Zooplankton (L. Bittel)
- Horizontal plankton distribution (S. Ochocki)
- Ecology of Tendipedidae in small basins of Ilawa district (A. K. Gizinski)

PUBLICATIONS ISSUED: *Papers from the Limnological Station in Ilawa* (regularly published journal)

Wyzsza Szkola Rolnicza, Wydzial Rybacki

HIGHER SCHOOL OF AGRICULTURE, FACULTY OF FISHERIES

POSTAL ADDRESS: Olsztyn-Kortowo, Polska (Poland). Marine Research Center: Wladyslawowo.

EXECUTIVE OFFICER: Prof. Dr. Wladyslaw Mankowski, Dean of the Faculty.

SPONSORING AGENCY: Polish Ministry of Higher Education.

YEAR FOUNDED: 1951.

SCOPE OF ACTIVITIES: A five-year course leading to the Master of Sciences in Fisheries is offered to both Polish and foreign students. The faculty has seven departments, four of which perform research associated with marine biology.

SEASON OF OPERATION: All year.

PHYSICAL ENVIRONMENT ACCESSIBLE: Various lakes and rivers, Vistula Bay, and Baltic Sea.

MAJOR RESEARCH AND TEACHING FACILITIES: Lecture rooms, laboratories, biological and technical museums, aquaria; fish ponds and lakes; small boats and outboard motors; ocean going vessels.

INSTRUCTIONAL PROGRAM: General chemistry, general botany, general zoology, plant physiology ichthyoanatomy, ichthyoembryology, biochemistry, microbiology, statistics, inland waters biology, ichthyophysiology, marine biology, fish diseases, preservation of fish, fish processing, and management of ponds, lakes, and rivers.

SIZE OF STAFF: Exact size is not known, but there are 15 lecturers in the major subjects plus other technical assistants.

MAJOR CURRENT RESEARCH PROJECTS:
- Department of Oceanography and Marine Biology:
  - Biology of the Baltic Sea and Vistula Bay
- Department of Limnology:
  - Thermical rebuilding of lakes as a method of intensification of their productivity
  - Benthal sediments as fertilizers
  - Migration of plankton
  - Benthal fauna of lakes
- Department of Ichthyology:
  - Vascularity of various organs
  - Annual histo-physiological changes in endocrine glands
  - Physiology of embryonic development, particularly respiration of embryos
  - Growth, feeding, and migration of marine and fresh-water fishes
  - Epizootics among fishes
  - Pathogenesis of diseases
- Department of Fisheries:
  - Dynamics of Baltic sprat shoals
  - Productivity of Baltic fishing grounds
  - Methods of lake husbandry

PORTUGAL

Junta de Investigacoes do Ultramar, Centro de Biologia Piscatoria

COUNCIL FOR OVERSEAS INVESTIGATIONS, CENTER FOR FISHERIES BIOLOGY

POSTAL ADDRESS:

Headquarters:

R. Dr. Antonio Candido No. 9, Lisboa (Lisbon) 1, Portugal.

Branch laboratory:

Baia Farta, Angola.

CENTRO DE BIOLOGIA PISCATORIA, LISBON

EXECUTIVE OFFICER: Dr. Pedro da Franca, Director.

YEAR FOUNDED: 1951.

SCOPE OF ACTIVITIES: Restricted and unrestricted research on general marine biology, especially fisheries biology; graduate instruction.

SEASON OF OPERATION: All year.

PHYSICAL ENVIRONMENT ACCESSIBLE: Atlantic and Indian Oceans; sandy and silty beaches, rocky and gravelly shores, estuarine conditions, brackish, shallow bays, and coral reefs.

PROVISIONS FOR VISITING SCIENTISTS: Space for 2 visitors in Lisbon and 2 in Angola.

MAJOR RESEARCH FACILITIES: Small library; research collections of Pisces, Crustacea, Mollusca, algae and plankton; identified reference collections of local fauna and flora from Cape Verde, Guinee, Angola and Mozambique; small boats and outboard motors; 50 m LOA vessel, *Baldaque da Silva.*

SIZE OF STAFF: Sixteen at professional level; 10 technicians.

MAJOR CURRENT RESEARCH PROJECTS AND SCIENTIFIC LEADERS:

- Fishery biology and ichthyology (P. da Franca, Pissaro, F. Correia da Costa, J. Goncalves Sanches)
- Fishery biology and malacology (M. L. Paes da Franca)
- Fishery biology and technology (D. Draganca Gil, M. Sousa Vasconcelos)
- Ichthyology (Rui Monteiro)
- Foraminifera (Jaime Martins Ferreira)
- Zooplankton (Chaetognaths) (Teresa Soares Neto)
- Zooplankton (Copepoda) (Inacia Paiva)
- Phytoplankton (Jorge Falcao Paredes)
- Algology (Francisco Palminha)
- Carcinology (A. Ribeiro)
- Oceanography (G. Soares)
- Technology of fisheries products (L. M. Torres, R. Romana, L. Manso)

PUBLICATIONS ISSUED: *Trabalhos do Centro de Biologia Piscatoria* (occasionally published journal)

LABORATORY AT BAIA FARTA, ANGOLA

ESTACAO AQUICOLA, VILA DO CONDE

Estacao Aquicola

WATER RESEARCH STATION

POSTAL ADDRESS: Avenida Dr. Bernardino Machado, Vila do Conde, Portugal.

EXECUTIVE OFFICER: Dr. Joaquim Antonio Soares Soeiro, Director.

SPONSORING AGENCY: Direccao Geral dos Servicos Florestais e Aquicolas (General Office of Forestry and Agricultural Services).

YEAR FOUNDED: 1886.

SCOPE OF ACTIVITIES: Stocking of inland waters and restricted research on limnology and fresh-water fishery biology, river pollution, and acclimatization.

SEASON OF OPERATION: All year.

PHYSICAL ENVIRONMENT ACCESSIBLE: Rivers and streams.

PROVISIONS FOR VISITING SCIENTISTS: None at present.

MAJOR RESEARCH FACILITIES: Small library; well water.

SIZE OF STAFF: Five at professional level; 3 technicians.

MAJOR CURRENT RESEARCH PROJECTS AND SCIENTIFIC LEADERS:

- Industrial effluent problems and recovery studies (Joaquim Soeiro)
- Plankton studies (Antonio Castro)
- Acclimatization of fishes, especially *Micropterus salmoides, M. dolomieu* and *Esox lucius* (Eduardo Lencastre)

Ministerio da Marinha, Instituto de Biologica Maritima

MINISTRY OF THE NAVY, MARINE BIOLOGICAL INSTITUTE

POSTAL ADDRESS: Cais do Sodre, Lisboa (Lisbon) 2, Portugal.

EXECUTIVE OFFICER: Dr. Herculano Vilela, Director.

YEAR FOUNDED: 1950.

SCOPE OF ACTIVITIES: Unrestricted research on general marine biology.
SEASON OF OPERATION: All year.
PHYSICAL ENVIRONMENT ACCESSIBLE: Atlantic Ocean, Rio Telo (River Tagus); sandy and silty beaches, rocky and gravelly shores, and estuarine conditions.
PROVISIONS FOR VISITING SCIENTISTS: None.
MAJOR RESEARCH FACILITIES: Small library. A new building is to be located near the fishing dock in Lisbon.
SIZE OF STAFF: Five at professional level; 4 technicians. (Staff to be increased to 8 at professional level; 7 technicians.)
IMPORTANT SPECIES AVAILABLE FOR LABORATORY STUDIES:
Pisces: *Sardina pilchardus, Trachurus trachurus, Thunnus thynnus*
Mollusca: *Gryppaea angulata, Mytilus edulis*
MAJOR CURRENT RESEARCH PROJECTS AND SCIENTIFIC LEADERS:
Biology of tunas (Herculano Vilela)
Biology of Clupeidae and Carangidae (Jaime don Santos Pinto)
Biology of Gadoid fish (Maria Ruivo)
Phytoplankton (systematics and ecology) (Estela de Sousa e Silva)
Biology of oysters and clams (Herculano Vilela)
PUBLICATIONS ISSUED: *Notas e Estudos do Instituto de Biologia Maritima* (occasionally published journal)

Instituto de Zoologia e Estacao de Zoologia Maritima "Dr. Augusto Nobre"

ZOOLOGICAL INSTITUTE AND MARINE ZOOLOGICAL STATION "DR. AUGUST NOBRE"

POSTAL ADDRESS: Faculdade de Ciencias, Campo dos Martires de Patria, Oporto, Portugal.
EXECUTIVE OFFICER: Professor Dr. Amilcar Mateus, Director.
SPONSORING AGENCY: Universidade do Porto.
YEAR FOUNDED: 1916.
SCOPE OF ACTIVITIES: Unrestricted research on general marine and fresh-water biology; instruction.
SEASON OF OPERATION: All year.
PHYSICAL ENVIRONMENT ACCESSIBLE: Atlantic Ocean, Douro River; brackish, shallow bays.
PROVISIONS FOR VISITING SCIENTISTS: Space for 4 visitors; no fees charged; living quarters available.
MAJOR RESEARCH AND TEACHING FACILITIES: Moderately complete library; running sea and fresh-water, small aquarium tanks; research and identified reference collections of Crustacea, Mollusca, Echinodermata, Pisces and Amphibia; small boats and outboard motors.
INSTRUCTIONAL PROGRAM: General zoology, systematic zoology, animal ecology, comparative anatomy, and physiology.
SIZE OF STAFF: Three at professional level; 3 technicians.
IMPORTANT SPECIES AVAILABLE FOR LABORATORY STUDIES:
Echinodermata: *Asterias rubens, Marthasterias glacialis*
Crustacea: *Portunus puber*
Mollusca: *Octopus vulgaris*
Pisces: *Barbus bocagei, Sardina pilchardus, Scyllium canicula*
Amphibia: *Rana esculenta, Triturus marmoratus, T. (Pleurodeles) waltli*
MAJOR CURRENT RESEARCH PROJECTS AND SCIENTIFIC LEADERS:
Systematics of Amphipoda (Amilcar Mateus and Emilia de Oliveira Mateus)
Systematics of Isopoda (fresh-water) (Jose Braga)
Ichthyophthology (Joao Machado Cruz)

REPUBLIC OF GUINEA

Ministere de l'Economie Rurale, Section Technique des Peches Maritimes

MINISTRY OF RURAL ECONOMICS, MARINE FISHERIES TECHNOLOGY SECTION

POSTAL ADDRESS: B. P. 559, Conakry, Guinee (Guinea).
YEAR FOUNDED: 1955.
SCOPE OF ACTIVITIES: Physical oceanography, research on clupeids, tuna, and crustaceans.
MAJOR RESEARCH FACILITIES: Small boats and outboard motors; 18 m LOA vessel, CV *Pyrrhus.*
SIZE OF STAFF: Three at professional level; 10 crew.

REPUBLIC OF PANAMA

Comision Interamericana del Atun Tropical

INTER-AMERICAN TROPICAL TUNA COMMISSION, PANAMA LABORATORY

POSTAL ADDRESS: P. O. Box 3665, Balboa, Canal Zone. No detailed description of this branch was available, but see LaJolla, California, USA *Headquarters,* page 209.

REPUBLIC OF SOUTH AFRICA

Jonkershoek Trout Hatchery

POSTAL ADDRESS: Private Bag 14, Stellenbosch, Republic of South Africa.
LOCATION: Near Cape Town.
EXECUTIVE OFFICER: Mr. G. F. van Wyk, Senior Professional Officer (Inland Fisheries).
SPONSORING AGENCY: Cape Provincial Administration, Department of Nature Conservation.
YEAR FOUNDED: 1944.
SCOPE OF ACTIVITIES: Restricted research on estuarine surveys and stream improvement.
SEASON OF OPERATION: All year.
PHYSICAL ENVIRONMENT ACCESSIBLE: Eerste River; estuarine conditions, brackish, shallow bays, and farm dams.
PROVISIONS FOR VISITING SCIENTISTS: Space for 2 visitors; no fees charged; living quarters available nearby.
MAJOR RESEARCH FACILITIES: Small library; large outdoor ponds and tanks, small aquarium tanks; research and identified reference collections of fresh-water fish of the Cape Province and estaurine fauna (bait organisms); machine and wood shop; small boats and outboard motors; one 12 ft LOA power vessel.
SIZE OF STAFF: Two at professional level; 7 technicians.
IMPORTANT SPECIES AVAILABLE FOR LABORATORY STUDIES:
Crustacea: *Callianassa kraussi, Upogebia africana*
Amphibia: *Xenopus laevis*
Pisces: *Sandelia capensis, Galaxias zebratus* and miscellaneous fresh-water species.
MAJOR CURRENT RESEARCH PROJECTS AND SCIENTIFIC LEADERS:
Fertilization of fish ponds (D. J. van Schoor)
Survey of Cape estuaries (G. F. van Wyk)

Natal Parks, Game and Fish Preservation Board, Fisheries Laboratory

POSTAL ADDRESS: P. O. Box 662, Pietermaritzburg, Natal, Republic of South Africa.
EXECUTIVE OFFICER: Colonel J. Vincent, Director of Wildlife Conservation.
SPONSORING AGENCY: Province of Natal; affiliation with the University of Natal.
YEAR FOUNDED: 1952.
SCOPE OF ACTIVITIES: Restricted research on freshwater fish biology, systematics and management.
SEASON OF OPERATION: All year.
PHYSICAL ENVIRONMENT ACCESSIBLE: Rivers, streams and artificial impoundments.
MAJOR RESEARCH FACILITIES: Small library; small aquarium tanks; research and identified collection of indigenous fresh-water fish; identified reference collection of Ephemeroptera; small boats and outboard motors.
SIZE OF STAFF: Two at professional level; 2 technicians.
MAJOR CURRENT RESEARCH PROJECTS AND SCIENTIFIC LEADERS:
Systematics and ecology of fresh-water fish in Natal River systems (R. S. Crass)
Biology of *Salmo trutta* and *S. gairdneri* in Natal (R. S. Crass)
Pond management research (Mrs. R. E. Hutchison)

The National Institute for Water Research

POSTAL ADDRESS: P. O. Box 395, Pretoria, Republic of South Africa.
EXECUTIVE OFFICER: Dr. G. J. Stander, Director of the Institute.
SPONSORING AGENCY: South African Council for Scientific and Industrial Research.
SCOPE OF ACTIVITIES: The Institute concentrates on hydrobiological research, chemistry and bacteriology, relating to treating and disposing of industrial and domestic wastes, water treatment and supply problems.
SEASON OF OPERATION: All year.
PHYSICAL ENVIRONMENT ACCESSIBLE: Vaal-Orange River System, Limpopo River System, Hartebeestpoort Dam; eutrophic lake.
PROVISIONS FOR VISITING SCIENTISTS: None at present.
MAJOR RESEARCH FACILITIES: Extensive Institute library but small hydrobiological section; small aquarium tanks; research collections of fresh-water invertebrates and diatoms; identified reference collections of diatoms, Chironomidae, Trichoptera and others; machine and wood shop, electrical and electronic shop, skilled shop workman available; small boats and outboard motors.
SIZE OF STAFF: Twenty-two at professional level; 1 technician.

THE NATIONAL INSTITUTE FOR WATER RESEARCH, PRETORIA

MAJOR CURRENT RESEARCH PROJECTS AND SCIENTIFIC LEADERS:

Hydrobiological surveys of the Tugela River System, Natal (W. D. Oliff)
Hydrobiological survey of the Umgeni River System, Natal (H. J. Schoonbee)
Systematic and special ecological studies on Trichoptera (K. M. F. Scott)
Systematic and special ecological studies on diatoms (B. J. Cholnoky)
Physiological tolerances of aquatic animals (including fish toxicity work), in conjunction with Transvaal Department of Nature Conservation (B. R. Allanson and R. G. Noble)
Studies on the processes of natural self-purification in natural waters (W. A. Lombard)
Nutritional requirements of algae in pure culture with special reference to nitrogen (N. O. van Gylswyk)
Nutritional requirements of organisms in aerobic effluent purification processes (W. H. Hattingh)
Laboratory studies on the bacteriology of the water zone and bottom sediments (W. A. Pretorius)
Aerobic bacteria as indicators of faecal pollution of water (T. Pretorius)
Ecology and habitat of coliforms, including studies on natural waters (T. Pretorius)
Ecology and habitat of faecal Streptococci, including studies on natural waters (T. Pretorius)
The effect of industrial effluents on the bacteriology of natural waters (O. J. Coetzee)
Sewage effluent pollution of the sea (O. J. Coetzee)
Bacteriophage as an indicator of pollution (O. J. Coetzee)

Potchefstroom University, Institute for Zoological Research

POSTAL ADDRESS: c/o Potchefstroom University, Potchefstroom, Transvaal, Republic of South Africa.
EXECUTIVE OFFICER: Dr. J. A. van Eeden, Director.
YEAR FOUNDED: 1958.
SCOPE OF ACTIVITIES: Unrestricted research on taxonomy, distribution, and ecology of fresh-water Mollusca; graduate instruction.
SEASON OF OPERATION: All year.
PHYSICAL ENVIRONMENT ACCESSIBLE: Mooi, Schoonspruit and Vaal Rivers, and Strydom Dam.
PROVISIONS FOR VISITING SCIENTISTS: Space for 2-3 visitors; living quarters available nearby.
MAJOR RESEARCH AND TEACHING FACILITIES: Small library; small aquarium tanks; research and identified reference collections of Basommatophora; research collection of fresh-water invertebrates to be built up; machine and wood shop, skilled shop workman available.
INSTRUCTIONAL PROGRAM: General zoology.
SIZE OF STAFF: Three at professional level.
MAJOR CURRENT RESEARCH PROJECTS AND SCIENTIFIC LEADERS:

Distribution of fresh-water Mollusca in South Africa (J. A. van Eeden)
Morphology of *Physopsis africanus* (J. A. van Eeden)
Ecology of *Physopsis africanus* (J. A. van Eeden)
Hydrobiology of rivers in western Transvaal (J. A. van Eeden and P. A. J. Ryke)
Hydrobiology of the source of the Mooi River (J. A. van Eeden and P. A. J. Ryke)

Rhodes University, Department of Ichthyology

POSTAL ADDRESS: Grahamstown, Republic of South Africa.
LOCATION: Near Port Elizabeth.
EXECUTIVE OFFICER: Professor J. L. B. Smith, Head, Department of Ichthyology.
SPONSORING AGENCIES: Rhodes University and South African Council for Scientific and Industrial Research.
YEAR FOUNDED: 1946.
SCOPE OF ACTIVITIES: Unrestricted research on fishes of southern and eastern Africa and of the western Indian Ocean.
SEASON OF OPERATION: All year.
PHYSICAL ENVIRONMENT ACCESSIBLE: Atlantic and Indian Oceans; sandy and silty beaches, rocky and gravelly shores, estuarine conditions, brackish, shallow bays, coral reefs, eutrophic and oligathropic lakes, and rivers.
PROVISIONS FOR VISITING SCIENTISTS: Space for 2 visitors; no fees charged, living quarters available (often with difficulty) nearby.
MAJOR RESEARCH AND TEACHING FACILITIES: Moderately complete library; small aquarium tanks; research and identified reference collections of marine and fresh-water fishes of southern Africa and of the western Indian Ocean; small boats and outboard motors.
INSTRUCTIONAL PROGRAM: General systematics for graduate students.
SIZE OF STAFF: Three at professional level; 2 technicians.
MAJOR CURRENT RESEARCH PROJECTS AND SCIENTIFIC LEADERS:

Fishes of the western Indian Ocean (J. L. B. Smith)
Marine fishes of southern Africa (J. L. B. Smith)

PUBLICATIONS ISSUED: *Rhodes University Ichthyological Research Bulletin* (occasionally published journal)

Transvaal Provincial Administration, Department of Nature Conservation, Hydrobiological Laboratory

POSTAL ADDRESS: Private Bag, Pretoria, Republic of South Africa.
EXECUTIVE OFFICER: Brian Robert Allanson, Officer in Charge.
YEAR FOUNDED: 1955.

SCOPE OF ACTIVITIES: Restricted research on the effects of industrial pollution on the biology and chemistry of rivers and lakes.

SEASON OF OPERATION: All year.

PHYSICAL ENVIRONMENT ACCESSIBLE: Jukskei-Crocodile river system, Olifants river system, Hartebeestpoort and Loskop Dams; eutrophic lake.

PROVISIONS FOR VISITING SCIENTISTS: Space for 2 visitors; no fees charged; living quarters available nearby.

MAJOR RESEARCH FACILITIES: Small library; small aquarium tanks, supply of nearly chemically constant water; catalogued collections of river fauna from two major river systems in the Transvaal; identified reference collections of local Chironomidae, aquatic Hemiptera, Ephemeroptera, Cladocera, aquatic Hirudinea; skilled shop workman available; small boats and outboard motors.

SIZE OF STAFF: Three at professional level.

IMPORTANT SPECIES AVAILABLE FOR LABORATORY STUDIES:

Ephemeroptera: *Baetis harrisoni*

Pisces: *Tilapia sparmanni, Barbus trimaculatus*

MAJOR CURRENT RESEARCH PROJECTS AND SCIENTIFIC LEADERS:

Investigations into the ecology of polluted inland waters in the Transvaal: The Jukskei-Crocodile River (Brian Robert Allanson)

Limnology of Hartebeestpoort Dam (Brian Robert Allanson)

Oliphants river system (Gabriel Venter)

The Limnology of Loskop Dam (Brian Robert Allanson and Gabriel Venter)

Investigations into the toxicity of industrial effluents to fresh-water fish (Brian Robert Allanson)

Lowveld Fisheries Research Station

POSTAL ADDRESS: Private Bag Nature Conservation, Marble Hall, Northern Transvaal, Republic of South Africa.

LOCATION: 120 miles from Pretoria.

EXECUTIVE OFFICER: Geoffrey L. Lombard, Senior Professional Officer.

SPONSORING AGENCY: Nature Conservation Section of Transvaal Provincial Administration.

YEAR FOUNDED: 1955.

SCOPE OF ACTIVITIES: Restricted research on pisciculture, particularly on *Tilapia mossambica.*

SEASON OF OPERATION: All year.

PHYSICAL ENVIRONMENT ACCESSIBLE: Olifants River, Loskop Dam; variety of outdoor ponds.

PROVISIONS FOR VISITING SCIENTISTS: Research and living space for 1 visitor; no fees charged for research space.

MAJOR RESEARCH FACILITIES: Small library; well equipped laboratory; small aquarium tanks; identified reference collections of aquatic invertebrates and fresh-water fishes; machine and wood shop, skilled shop workman available; small boats and outboard motors.

SIZE OF STAFF: Two at professional level; 2 technicians; total staff 29.

IMPORTANT SPECIES AVAILABLE FOR LABORATORY STUDIES:

Mollusca: *Limnaea* and *Bulinus* spp.

Pisces: *Tilapia mossambica, T. melanopleura, Cyprinus carpio* (Aisch. var.), *Micropterus salmoides*

MAJOR CURRENT RESEARCH PROJECTS AND SCIENTIFIC LEADERS:

Fish spawning experimental studies (G. L. Lombard)

Fish culture; field experiments and production in ponds and exploitation of natural waters (G. L. Lombard)

Biological control of fish parasites, particularly Trematoda (G. L. Lombard)

Plankton and dietetic studies and production in ponds (J. D. Venter)

Oceanographic Research Institute, University of Natal

POSTAL ADDRESS: P. O. Box 736, 2 West Street, Durban, Natal, Republic of South Africa.

EXECUTIVE OFFICER: Professor David H. Davies, Director.

SPONSORING AGENCIES: The South African Association for Marine Biological Research and the University of Natal.

YEAR FOUNDED: 1960.

SCOPE OF ACTIVITIES: Unrestricted research on general oceanography with particular emphasis on marine biology; graduate instruction.

SEASON OF OPERATION: All year.

PHYSICAL ENVIRONMENT ACCESSIBLE: Indian Ocean; sandy beach, rocky shore and brackish, shallow bays.

PROVISIONS FOR VISITING SCIENTISTS: Space and facilities for 2 visitors is available in the Research Institute.

MAJOR RESEARCH AND TEACHING FACILITIES: Small library; running sea and fresh-water; 2 large outdoor marine tanks or oceanaria; research and identified reference collection of sharks from Natal coast; skilled shop workman available; small boats and outboard motors.

INSTRUCTIONAL PROGRAM: General course for M.Sc. Oceanography to be drawn up in 1963.

SIZE OF STAFF: Eight at professional level; 2 technicians.

MAJOR CURRENT RESEARCH PROJECTS AND SCIENTIFIC LEADERS:

Survey of sharks of the Natal region (D. H. Davies and J. d'Aubrey)

Study of the behavior of sharks (D. H. Davies and J. d'Aubrey)

Studies on shark attack (D. H. Davies and G. D. Campbell)

Study of the biology of the seventy-four, *Polysteganus undulosus* (R. A. Ahrens)

Primary production studies in the Indian Ocean (E. Mitchell-Innes)

REPUBLIC OF SOUTH AFRICA DEPARTMENT OF COMMERCE AND INDUSTRIES, DIVISION OF SEA FISHERIES

Republic of South Africa Department of Commerce and Industries, Division of Sea Fisheries

POSTAL ADDRESS: Beach Road, Sea Point, Cape Town, Republic of South Africa.
EXECUTIVE OFFICER: Mr. C. C. du Plessis, Director.
YEAR FOUNDED: 1895.
SCOPE OF ACTIVITIES: Research on pelagic fisheries and general fisheries oceanography.
SEASON OF OPERATION: All year.
PHYSICAL ENVIRONMENT ACCESSIBLE: Atlantic and Indian Oceans.
PROVISIONS FOR VISITING SCIENTISTS: Space for 1 visitor.
MAJOR RESEARCH FACILITIES: Library; running sea water, small aquarium tanks; research collections of phytoplankton, zooplankton, fish eggs and larvae; machine shop, skilled shop workman available; vessels, two 70 ft, one 120 ft and one 205 ft LOA.
SIZE OF STAFF: Twenty-three at professional level; 7 technicians.
MAJOR CURRENT RESEARCH PROJECTS AND SCIENTIFIC LEADERS:
Pelagic fisheries program (C. G. du Plessis and staff)
Rock lobsters (C. G. du Plessis and staff)
General oceanography (C. G. du Plessis and staff)
Experimental fishing (C. G. du Plessis and staff)
PUBLICATIONS ISSUED: *Fisheries Bulletins* (occasionally published journal)

Transvaal Provincial Administration, Department of Nature Conservation, Transvaal Provincial Fisheries Institute

POSTAL ADDRESS: P. O. Box 45, Lydenburg, Transvaal, Republic of South Africa.
EXECUTIVE OFFICER: Mr. S. S. du Plessis, Chief Professional Officer.
YEAR FOUNDED: 1949.
SCOPE OF ACTIVITIES: Research on improvement of sport fisheries, and general conservation as applied to inland waters.
SEASON OF OPERATION: All year.
PHYSICAL ENVIRONMENT ACCESSIBLE: Reservoirs, dams, rivers and streams.
PROVISIONS FOR VISITING SCIENTISTS: Space for 1 visitor; living quarters available nearby.
MAJOR RESEARCH FACILITIES: Library; laboratories; large outdoor ponds and tanks, small aquarium; identified reference collections of local fishes; work shop; small boats and outboard motors.
SIZE OF STAFF: Three at professional level; 2 technicians; total staff 9.
IMPORTANT SPECIES AVAILABLE FOR LABORATORY STUDIES:
Pisces: Trout, bass, and all indigenous species.
MAJOR CURRENT RESEARCH PROJECTS AND SCIENTIFIC LEADERS:
Population studies (A. A. Groenewald)
Age and growth studies (C. C. Straub)

University of Cape Town, Department of Oceanography

POSTAL ADDRESS: Rondebosch, Cape of Good Hope, Republic of South Africa.
LOCATION: Near Cape Town.
EXECUTIVE OFFICERS: Prof. J. H. Day (Zoology). Prof. J. Darbyshire (Oceanography).
YEAR FOUNDED: 1958.
SCOPE OF ACTIVITIES: Research on general marine biology and oceanography; graduate instruction.
SEASON OF OPERATION: All year.
PHYSICAL ENVIRONMENT ACCESSIBLE: Indian and Atlantic Oceans, sandy and silty beaches, rocky and gravelly shores.
PROVISIONS FOR VISITING SCIENTISTS: Space for 1 visitor in each field; no fees charged; living quarters available nearby.
MAJOR RESEARCH AND TEACHING FACILITIES: Very extensive library, including extensive collection of standard works on marine algae; small aquarium tanks; research collections of marine algae from South Africa and general marine collections of entire South African coast; extensive named collections available; machine and wood shop, skilled shop workman available in Department of Physics workshop; one 75 ft LOA vessel.
INSTRUCTIONAL PROGRAM: Advanced marine botany, marine biology, graduate training in oceanography.
SIZE OF STAFF: Twelve at professional level; 2 technicians.
IMPORTANT SPECIES AVAILABLE FOR LABORATORY STUDIES:
Algae (Rhodophyceae): *Porphyra capensis*

Crustacea (Macrura): *Jasus lalandii*
Crustacea (Brachyura): *Potamon perlatus, Cyclograpsus punctatus*
Gastropoda: *Bullia laevissima, Littorina knysnaensis*
Pelecypoda: *Mytilus meridionalis*
Echinoidea: *Parechinus angulosus*
Tunicata: *Pyura stolonifera, Ciona intestinalis*

MAJOR CURRENT RESEARCH PROJECTS AND SCIENTIFIC LEADERS:
Marine flora and marine vegetation of southern Africa (W. E. Isaac)
Physiology of marine animals (B. J. Krijgsman and A. C. Brown)
Estuarine ecology (J. H. Day)
Distribution of benthonic marine animals in South African Seas (J. H. Day)
Taxonomy of Polychaeta (J. H. Day)
Taxonomy of Hydrozoa (N. A. H. Millard)
Plankton of Agulhas Current (P. Zoutendyk)
Hydrology of Agulhas Current (L. Trotti)

PUBLICATIONS ISSUED: *Publications of the Oceanography Department* (published biannually)

REPUBLIC OF VIETNAM

Hai Hoc Vien Nhatrang

OCEANOGRAPHIC INSTITUTE OF NHATRANG (WITH MARINE BIOLOGICAL, PHYSICAL AND GEOPHYSICAL LABORATORIES)

POSTAL ADDRESS: Hai Hoc Vien Nhatrang, South Vietnam.
EXECUTIVE OFFICERS: Nguyen Dinh Hu'ng, Director. Nguyen Hai, Vice Director.
SPONSORING AGENCY: Government of South Vietnam.
YEAR FOUNDED: 1922.
SCOPE OF ACTIVITIES: Unrestricted research on general marine biology, plankton, algology, bottom ecology, and marine physics and chemistry.
SEASON OF OPERATION: All year.
PHYSICAL ENVIRONMENT ACCESSIBLE: China Sea, western Pacific Ocean; sandy and silty beaches, rocky and gravelly shores, estuarine conditions, brackish, shallow bays, and coral reefs.
PROVISIONS FOR VISITING SCIENTISTS: Research and living space for 18 visitors; no fees charged for research space.
MAJOR RESEARCH AND TEACHING FACILITIES: Very extensive library; running sea and fresh-water, small aquarium tanks; research and identified reference collections of Seaweeds, Mollusca, Pisces, Crustacea, Fish, Corals; machine and wood shop, skilled shop workman available; one 10 m motor boat.
INSTRUCTIONAL PROGRAM: UNESCO training courses in general invertebrates, plankton and fish.
SIZE OF STAFF: Four at professional level; 6 technicians.
IMPORTANT SPECIES AVAILABLE FOR LABORATORY STUDIES: An abundant Indo-Pacific fauna and flora is available.

ROUMANIAN PEOPLE'S REPUBLIC

Laboratories about Which No Detailed Information Was Available:

Marine biological laboratories:

Acvarium Public "Prof. Ioan Borcea"

POSTAL ADDRESS: Republicii, Constanta, Romania.
EXECUTIVE OFFICER: Ing. I. Stanciu, Director.
SPONSORING AGENCY: Sfatul Popular al Orasului Constanta (Public Council of Constanta).

Statiunea de Cercetari Marine

MARINE RESEARCH STATION

POSTAL ADDRESS: Bd. V. I. Lenin Nr. 304, Constanta, Romania.
EXECUTIVE OFFICER: Nicolae Ionescu, Director, Institutul de Cercetari Piscicole al Republica Populara Romina.
SPONSORING AGENCY: Institutul de Cercetari Piscicole al Republica Populara Romina (Institute of Fishery Research), Bd. Ana Ipatescu Nr. 42, Bucuresti (Bucharest), Romania.

Statiunea de Cercetari Marine—Sulina

SULINA MARINE RESEARCH STATION

POSTAL ADDRESS: Sulina, Romania.
EXECUTIVE OFFICER: Prof. Nicolai Gavrilescu, Director.
SPONSORING AGENCY: Centrul de Cercetari Biologice al Academiei Republica Populara Romina (Biological Research Center of the Roumanian People's Republic).

Statiunea Zoologica Marina "Prof. Ioan Borcea"

MARINE ZOOLOGICAL STATION "PROF. IOAN BORCEA"

POSTAL ADDRESS: Agigea, Reg., Constanta, Rominia.
EXECUTIVE OFFICER: Prof. Paul Borcea, Director.
SPONSORING AGENCY: Universitatea "Al. I. Cuza."

PUBLICATIONS ISSUED:
Lucrarile Statiunei Zoologice Marine Agigea (occasionally published)
Analele Stiintifice ale Universitatii "Al. I. Cuza"

Fresh-water biological stations:

Institutul de Cercetari Piscicole al Republicii Populare Romine

ROUMANIAN PEOPLE'S REPUBLIC INSTITUTE OF FISHERY RESEARCH

POSTAL ADDRESS:
Headquarters: Bd. Ana Ipatescu 42, Bucuresti (Bucharest), Romania.
Branch laboratories:

1. Statiunea de Cercetari Piscicole—Tulcea
Piata Republicii Nr. 1, Tulcea. Dr. Rodica Leonte, Director.
2. Statiunea de Cercetari Piscicole—Braila
Str. Vapoarelor Nr. 9, Braila. Ing. Anghel Cristea, Director.
3. Statiunea de Cercetari Piscicole—Nucet
Raion Tirgoviste, Reg. Ploiesti. Ing Paul Grozavu, Director.
4. Statiunea de Cercetari Pisciole—Tarcau
Raion Piatra Neamt, Reg. Bacau. Ing. Dumitru Matei, Director.

EXECUTIVE OFFICER: Ing. G. Mirica, Director.
SPONSORING AGENCY: Ministerul Industriel Alimentare.

Statiunea Hidrobiologica—Braila

BRAILA HYDROBIOLOGICAL STATION

POSTAL ADDRESS: Str. Vapoarelor, Braila, Romania.
EXECUTIVE OFFICER: Dimitrie Radu, Director.
SPONSORING AGENCY: Universitatea "C. I. Parhon."

Statiunea Biologica—Stejarul

STEJARUL BIOLOGICAL STATION

POSTAL ADDRESS: Pingarati, Raion Piatra Neamt, Reg. Bacau, Romania.
EXECUTIVE OFFICER: Ion Boistean, Director.
SPONSORING AGENCY: Universitatea "Al. I. Cuza."

Statiunea Experimentala Stuficola, Delta Dunarii

DANUBE DELTA EXPERIMENTAL RUSH-GRASS STATION

POSTAL ADDRESS: Raion Tulcea, Maliuc, Romania.
EXECUTIVE OFFICER: Ing. I. Gisca, Director.
SPONSORING AGENCY: Ministerul Chimiei si Petrolului (Ministry of Chemistry and Petroleum).

Statiunea Zoologica—Sinaia

SINAIA ZOOLOGICAL STATION

POSTAL ADDRESS: Str. Stefan Gheorghiu (Cumpatul), Sinaia, Romania.
EXECUTIVE OFFICER: Dr. Mircea Ienistea, Director.
SPONSORING AGENCY: Universitatea "C. I. Parhon."
SCOPE OF ACTIVITIES: Study of mountain streams and alpine-like fauna.

SENEGAL

Institut Francais d'Afrique Noire (IFAN), Section de Biologie Marine

FRENCH AFRICAN INSTITUTE, MARINE BIOLOGY DEPARTMENT

POSTAL ADDRESS: B.P. 206, Dakar, Senegal.
EXECUTIVE OFFICERS: Professeur Th. Monod, Directeur de l'IFAN, Mr. J. Cadenat, Chef de Section.
SPONSORING AGENCY: IFAN is attached to the Universite de Dakar.
YEAR FOUNDED: 1938 (IFAN); 1946 (Section de Biologie Marine).
SCOPE OF ACTIVITIES: Unrestricted research on general marine biology, particularly ichthyology.
SEASON OF OPERATION: All year.
PHYSICAL ENVIRONMENT ACCESSIBLE: Atlantic Ocean; sandy and silty beaches, rocky and gravelly shores.
PROVISIONS FOR VISITING SCIENTISTS: Space for 3 visitors; no fees charged for research space.
MAJOR RESEARCH FACILITIES: Laboratoire de Biologie Marine on island of Goree at Dakar; Laboratoire de Zoologie—Invertebres within main building; moderately complete library; running sea and fresh-water; research collections of many groups of fauna and flora; identified reference collections of local Pisces, Mollusca and Crustacea; machine and wood shop; small boat.
SIZE OF STAFF: Three at professional level.

INSTITUT FRANCAIS D'AFRIQUE NOIRE

LABORATOIRE DE BIOLOGIE MARINE, GOREE

PUBLICATIONS ISSUED: *Bulletin de l'Institut Francais d'Afrique Noire, Serie A, Sciences Naturelles* (regularly published journal)

Centre d'Etudes des Peches de Joal

FISHERIES RESEARCH CENTER, JOAL

POSTAL ADDRESS: Joal, Senegal.
LOCATION: Near Dakar.
EXECUTIVE OFFICER: A. Blanc, Directeur.
SPONSORING AGENCY: Service de l'Oceanographie et des Peches Maritimes du Senegal (Oceanographic and Marine Fisheries Service of Senegal).
YEAR FOUNDED: 1947.
SCOPE OF ACTIVITIES: Restricted research on marine fisheries and oyster culture.
SEASON OF OPERATION: All year.
PHYSICAL ENVIRONMENT ACCESSIBLE: Atlantic Ocean; sandy and silty beaches, and estuarine conditions.
PROVISIONS FOR VISITING SCIENTISTS: Research and living space for 2-3 visitors; no fees charged for research space.
MAJOR RESEARCH FACILITIES: Small library; small boats and outboard motors; one 13 m LOA power vessel.

Laboratoire d'Oceanographie de Tiaroye/Mer-Senegal

OCEANOGRAPHIC LABORATORY OF TIAROYE/MER-SENEGAL

POSTAL ADDRESS: B.P. 289, Dakar, Senegal.
EXECUTIVE OFFICER: Dr. Jean Gousset.
SPONSORING AGENCY: Service d'Oceanographie et des Peches Maritimes du Senegal (Oceanographic and Marine Fisheries Service of Senegal).
YEAR FOUNDED: 1960.
SCOPE OF ACTIVITIES: Unrestricted research on general oceanography and plankton.
SEASON OF OPERATION: All year.
PHYSICAL ENVIRONMENT ACCESSIBLE: Estuaries of the Atlantic Ocean.
PROVISIONS FOR VISITING SCIENTISTS: None.
MAJOR RESEARCH FACILITIES: Small library; small research collections of fauna and flora; machine and wood shop, small boats and outboard motors; 18 m LOA vessel, *Gerard Treca*.
SIZE OF STAFF: One at professional level.
IMPORTANT SPECIES AVAILABLE FOR LABORATORY STUDIES:
Pisces: *Temnodon saltator, Sardinella eba, S. aurita, Dentex filosus, Ethmalosa fimbriata*
MAJOR CURRENT RESEARCH PROJECTS AND SCIENTIFIC LEADERS:
Oceanography of the Atlantic Ocean along the Senegal coasts to 500 meters depth (J. Gousset)
Variations of plankton near Dakar (J. Gousset)
Hydrological conditions of Saloum and Casamance estuaries of Senegal (J. Gousset)

CENTRE D'ETUDES DES PECHES DE JOAL

LABORATOIRE D'OCEANOGRAPHIE DE TIAROYE/MER-SENEGAL

SIERRA LEONE

Ministry of Natural Resources, Fisheries Division

POSTAL ADDRESS: Private postal bag, Freetown, Sierra Leone.
EXECUTIVE OFFICER: Dr. J. C. D. Watts, Scientist in Charge.
YEAR FOUNDED: 1957.
SCOPE OF ACTIVITIES: Restricted research on fisheries biology and technology.
SEASON OF OPERATION: All year.
PHYSICAL ENVIRONMENT ACCESSIBLE: Atlantic Ocean, Sierra Leone River Estuary; sandy and silty beaches, rocky and gravelly shores, estuarine conditions, and mangrove swamps.
PROVISIONS FOR VISITING SCIENTISTS: Space for 2 visitors; no fees charged; living quarters available nearby.
MAJOR RESEARCH FACILITIES: Small library; running sea and fresh-water; identified reference collections of marine and fresh-water fish is being built up; machine and wood shop, skilled shop workman available; small boats and outboard motors; one 28 ft LOA vessel, one 50 ft patrol vessel.
SIZE OF STAFF: Three at professional level; 2 technicians.
MAJOR CURRENT RESEARCH PROJECTS AND SCIENTIFIC LEADERS:
Bionomics of demersal fish important commercially (A. R. Longhurst)
Spoilage and preservation of demersal fish (J. C. D. Watts)

SPAIN

Instituto Espanol de Oceanografia

SPANISH INSTITUTE OF OCEANOGRAPHY

POSTAL ADDRESS:
Headquarters: Laboratorio Central, Alcala 27, 4°, Madrid, Espana (Spain)
Branch laboratories:
1. Laboratorio de Malaga, Malaga.
2. Laboratorio Oceanografico de Palma de Mallorca, Palma de Mallorca.
3. Laboratorio Oceanografico de Canarias (Santa Cruz de Tenerife), Santa Cruz de Tenerife, Islas Canarias.
4. Laboratorio Oceanografico de Santander, Santander.
5. Laboratorio Oceanografico de Vigo, Vigo.
6. Laboratorio Oceanografico de San Sebastian, San Sebastian. (Not described in the *Directory.*)

(Descriptions follow.)

EXECUTIVE OFFICER: Almirante Arturo Genova, Director General.
SPONSORING AGENCY: Ministerio de Marina (Ministry of Marine).
YEAR FOUNDED: 1914.
SCOPE OF ACTIVITIES: General oceanography, including marine biology as it relates to fisheries, marine fouling, corrosion, etc.
SEASON OF OPERATION: All year.
PHYSICAL ENVIRONMENT ACCESSIBLE: Mediterranean Sea, Atlantic Ocean.
PROVISIONS FOR VISITING SCIENTISTS: Space for visitors; no fees charged.
MAJOR RESEARCH FACILITIES: Very extensive library; well equipped laboratories; 700 ton, 500 horsepower *Xauen.*
SIZE OF STAFF: Forty at professional level.
PUBLICATIONS ISSUED:
Boletin del Instituto Espanol de Oceanografia (occasionally published journal)
Trabajos (occasionally published journal)

Laboratorio de Malaga

MALAGA LABORATORY

POSTAL ADDRESS: Paseo de la Farola, 27, Malaga.
EXECUTIVE OFFICER: Fernando Lozano, Director.
YEAR FOUNDED: 1909.
SCOPE OF ACTIVITIES: General oceanography.
SEASON OF OPERATION: All year.
PHYSICAL ENVIRONMENT ACCESSIBLE: Sea of Alboran, Straits of Gibraltar, and waters of Morocco.
PROVISIONS FOR VISITING SCIENTISTS: Several visitors can be accommodated; no fees charged; living quarters available nearby.
MAJOR RESEARCH FACILITIES: Small, select library; well equipped laboratories for biological oceanography; collections of fauna and flora in process; home port of the *Xauen.*
SIZE OF STAFF: Three at professional level; 4 technicians.

Laboratorio Oceanografico de Palma de Mallorca

PALMA DE MALLORCA OCEANOGRAPHIC LABORATORY

POSTAL ADDRESS: P. O. Box 291, Paseo Maritimo, Palmo de Mallorca.
EXECUTIVE OFFICER: Miguel Oliver, Director.
YEAR FOUNDED: 1906.
SCOPE OF ACTIVITIES: Unrestricted research on general marine biology and plankton.
SEASON OF OPERATION: All year.
PHYSICAL ENVIRONMENT ACCESSIBLE: Mediterranean Sea.
PROVISIONS FOR VISITING SCIENTISTS: Space for 3 visitors; no fees charged.
MAJOR RESEARCH FACILITIES: Small library; running sea and fresh-water, small aquarium tanks; research

collections of plankton from western Mediterranean and Straits of Gibraltar; small boats and outboard motors.

SIZE OF STAFF: Four at professional level; 1 Patron de Pesca.

MAJOR CURRENT RESEARCH PROJECTS AND SCIENTIFIC LEADERS:

Biology of commercial fishes (Miguel Oliver)
Phytoplankton (Pedro Balle)
Distribution of Chaetognatha (Miguel Massuti)
Biology of deep-sea Penaeidae (Miguel Massuti)
Distribution of pelagic Copepoda (Miguel Massuti)

Laboratoria Oceanografico de Canarias

CANARY ISLAND OCEANOGRAPHIC LABORATORY

POSTAL ADDRESS: Mendez Nunez 54-4° B, Santa Cruz de Tenerife, Islas Canarias.

EXECUTIVE OFFICER: Ramon Carmelo Garcia Cabrera, Director Accidental (temporary).

YEAR FOUNDED: 1928; buildings are presently being rebuilt.

SCOPE OF ACTIVITIES: Restricted research on general marine biology.

SEASON OF OPERATION: All year.

PHYSICAL ENVIRONMENT ACCESSIBLE: Atlantic Ocean; rocky and gravelly shores.

PROVISIONS FOR VISITING SCIENTISTS: Space for visitors; living quarters now under construction.

MAJOR RESEARCH FACILITIES: Under construction. Plans for library, experimental aquarium, and running sea and fresh-water.

Laboratorio Oceanografico de Santander

SANTANDER OCEANOGRAPHIC LABORATORY

POSTAL ADDRESS: Lealtad, 13, Santander.

EXECUTIVE OFFICER: Dr. J. Cuesta Urcelay, Director.

YEAR FOUNDED: 1886.

SCOPE OF ACTIVITIES: Unrestricted research on fisheries and shell-fish culture, general marine biology, and plankton studies.

SEASON OF OPERATION: All year.

PHYSICAL ENVIRONMENT ACCESSIBLE: Cantabrique Sea, Bay of Vizcay; sandy and silty beaches, rocky and gravelly shores, estuarine conditions, brackish, shallow bays.

PROVISIONS FOR VISITING SCIENTISTS: Space for 4 visitors; no fees charged; living quarters available nearby.

MAJOR RESEARCH FACILITIES: Small but rich library; running seawater, large outdoor ponds and tanks; identified reference collections of all regional taxonomic groups; small boats and outboard motors; one 12 m LOA vessel.

SIZE OF STAFF: Three at professional level.

IMPORTANT SPECIES AVAILABLE FOR LABORATORY STUDIES:

Crustacea: *Mytilicola intestinalis, Palinurus vulgaris*
Mollusca: *Griphaea angulata, Ostrea edulis, Mytilus edulis*
Pisces: *Clupea pilchardus, Engraulis encrasicholus*

MAJOR CURRENT RESEARCH PROJECTS AND SCIENTIFIC LEADERS:

The biology of *Clupea pilchardus* and *Engraulis encrasicholus* (J. Cuesta Urcelay)
Regional phytoplankton (J. Cuesta Urcelay)
Shellfish culture (J. Cuesta Urcelay)

Laboratorio Oceanografico de Vigo

VIGO OCEANOGRAPHIC LABORATORY

POSTAL ADDRESS: Calle de Felipe Sanchez, 18, Vigo.

EXECUTIVE OFFICER: D. Rafael Lopez Costa, Director.

YEAR FOUNDED: 1936.

SCOPE OF ACTIVITIES: Study of fish and fish products.

SEASON OF OPERATION: All year.

PHYSICAL ENVIRONMENT ACCESSIBLE: Atlantic Ocean.

PROVISIONS FOR VISITING SCIENTISTS: None.

MAJOR RESEARCH FACILITIES: Small library, chemical and biological laboratories, small boats.

SIZE OF STAFF: Three at professional level.

Instituto de Investigaciones Pesqueras

INSTITUTE OF FISHERY RESEARCH

POSTAL ADDRESS:

Headquarters and Laboratorio Central:
Paseo Nacional, Barcelona 3, Espana (Spain).
Regional laboratories:
1. Blanes (Gerona).
2. Cadiz.
3. Castellon.
4. Vigo.

(Descriptions follow.)
Small field station:
Vinaroz. (Not described in the *Directory.*)

EXECUTIVE OFFICER: Francisco Garcia del Cid, Director.

SPONSORING AGENCY: Consejo Superior de Investiga-

INSTITUTO DE INVESTIGACIONES PESQUERAS, BARCELONA

ciones Cientificas; Patronato "Juan de la Cierva" de Investigacion Tecnica (Superior Council of Scientific Investigations; "Juan de la Cierva," Patronage of Technical Investigations).

YEAR FOUNDED: 1951.

SCOPE OF ACTIVITIES: Unrestricted research on fisheries and marine resources, and basic marine biology.

SEASON OF OPERATION: All year.

PHYSICAL ENVIRONMENT ACCESSIBLE: Mediterranean Sea; sandy and silty beaches.

PROVISIONS FOR VISITING SCIENTISTS: Space for 3 visitors; no fees charged; living quarters available nearby.

MAJOR RESEARCH AND TEACHING FACILITIES: Small library; running sea and fresh-water (with and without chlorine), small aquarium tanks, small research and identified reference collections of fauna and flora in formation; spectophotometer equipment for measuring primary production with C^{14}, general chemistry laboratory; cultures of algae; limited shop facilities; small boats.

INSTRUCTIONAL PROGRAM: A program is in preparation in collaboration with the University of Barcelona.

SIZE OF STAFF: Twenty at professional level.

IMPORTANT SPECIES AVAILABLE FOR LABORATORY STUDIES:

Echinodermata: *Strongylocentrotus lividus*
Mollusca: *Patella* spp., *Mytilus* spp.
Crustacea: *Nephrops norvegicus*

MAJOR CURRENT RESEARCH PROJECTS AND SCIENTIFIC LEADERS:

Dynamics of phytoplankton populations (Ramon Margalef and Francisco Vives)
Growth and morphogenesis (Carlos Bas)
Bacteriology (Josefina Castellvi)
Sardine biology (J. J. Lopez)
Octopus biology (Enrique Morales)
Fouling (Enrique Arias)

PUBLICATIONS ISSUED: *Investigacion Pesquera* (regularly published journal)

Laboratorio de Blanes

BLANES LABORATORY

POSTAL ADDRESS: 15 Puerto Pesquero, Blanes.

EXECUTIVE OFFICER: Mr. Manuel Rubio, Director.

PROVISIONS FOR VISITING SCIENTISTS: Space for 2 visitors; no fees charged; living quarters available nearby.

MAJOR RESEARCH FACILITIES: Small library; running sea and fresh-water.

SIZE OF STAFF: One at professional level.

IMPORTANT SPECIES AVAILABLE FOR LABORATORY STUDIES:

Crustacea: *Tigriopus brevicornis* and abyssal crustaceans
Pisces: Abyssal species

MAJOR CURRENT RESEARCH PROJECTS AND SCIENTIFIC LEADERS:

Fishing gear technology (Manuel Rubio Lois)

INSTITUTO DE INVESTIGACIONES PESQUERAS, BLANES

Laboratorio de Cadiz

CADIZ LABORATORY

POSTAL ADDRESS: Puerto Pesquero, Cadiz.

EXECUTIVE OFFICER: Dr. Julio Rodriguez-Roda Compaired, Director.

YEAR FOUNDED: 1955.

PROVISIONS FOR VISITING SCIENTISTS: Space for 3 visitors; no fees charged; living quarters available nearby.

MAJOR RESEARCH FACILITIES: Small library; running fresh-water; general chemistry laboratory.

SIZE OF STAFF: Four at professional level.

IMPORTANT SPECIES AVAILABLE FOR LABORATORY STUDIES:

Crustacea: *Uca tangeri*

MAJOR CURRENT RESEARCH PROJECTS AND SCIENTIFIC LEADERS:

Biology of tuna (migrations, growth, and fluctuations) (Julio Rodriguez-Roda)
Ecology and distribution of littoral algae (Juan Seoane Camba)

INSTITUTO DE INVESTIGACIONES PESQUERAS, CADIZ

INSTITUTO DE INVESTIGACIONES PESQUERAS, CASTELLON

Laboratorio de Castellon

CASTELLON LABORATORY

POSTAL ADDRESS: 2 Monturiol, Castellon.

EXECUTIVE OFFICER: Manuel Gomez Larraneta, Director.

YEAR FOUNDED: 1949.

PROVISIONS FOR VISITING SCIENTISTS: Space for 1 visitor; no fees charged; living quarters available nearby.

MAJOR RESEARCH FACILITIES: Small library; running fresh-water; limited shop facilities; small boats and outboard motors; 12 m LOA vessel, *Nika.*

SIZE OF STAFF: Four at professional level.

IMPORTANT SPECIES AVAILABLE FOR LABORATORY STUDIES:

Pisces: *Valencia hispanica, Aphanius iberus*

MAJOR CURRENT RESEARCH PROJECTS AND SCIENTIFIC LEADERS:

Dynamics of sardine populations (Manuel Gomez Larraneta)
Chemistry of sediments (Felipe Munz)
Hydrography and plankton (Jose M. SanFelio)
Experimental fishing (Pedro Suan)

Laboratorio de Vigo

VIGO LABORATORY

POSTAL ADDRESS: 39 Orillamar, Vigo.

EXECUTIVE OFFICER: Buenaventura Andreu Morera, Director.

PROVISIONS FOR VISITING SCIENTISTS: Space for 3 visitors; no fees charged; living quarters available nearby.

MAJOR RESEARCH FACILITIES: Small library; running fresh-water; limited shop facilities; small boats and outboard motors; 11 m LOA vessel, *Lampadena.*

SIZE OF STAFF: Five at professional level.

IMPORTANT SPECIES AVAILABLE FOR LABORATORY STUDIES:

Mollusca: *Ostrea edulis, Mytilus edulis, Tapes* spp., *Solen* spp.
Polychaeta: *Arenicola* sp.
Dinoflagellata: *Gonyaulax* sp.

MAJOR CURRENT RESEARCH PROJECTS AND SCIENTIFIC LEADERS:

Ecology of mussels and oysters; problems related to commercial exploitation (Buenaventura Andreu Morera)
Glucids of Bifurcaria (algae) (Fernando Saiz Martinez)
Organic cycles in the sea, especially nitrogen (Fernando Fraga Rodriguez)

SUDAN

Sudan Inland Fisheries Research Institute

POSTAL ADDRESS: Ministry of Animal Resources, P. O. Box 336, Khartoum, Sudan.

EXECUTIVE OFFICER: Yousif I. Medani, Fisheries Hydrobiologist.

SPONSORING AGENCY: Sudan Government.

YEAR FOUNDED: 1956.

SCOPE OF ACTIVITIES: Restricted research on fresh-water fisheries.

SEASON OF OPERATION: All year.

PHYSICAL ENVIRONMENT ACCESSIBLE: River Nile, White Nile and Blue Nile.

PROVISIONS FOR VISITING SCIENTISTS: Space for 2 visitors; no fees charged; living quarters available nearby.

MAJOR RESEARCH FACILITIES: Small library; large outdoor ponds and tanks, small aquarium tanks; good research collection of Sudanese fresh-water fishes;

INSTITUTO DE INVESTIGACIONES PESQUERAS, VIGO

SUDAN INLAND FISHERIES RESEARCH INSTITUTE

identified reference collections of fishes of the Nile and Sudanese fresh-water fishes; machine and wood shop; small boats and outboard motors.

SIZE OF STAFF: Two at professional level.

IMPORTANT SPECIES AVAILABLE FOR LABORATORY STUDIES:

Pisces: *Tilapia nilotica, Lates niloticus, Labeo* spp.

MAJOR CURRENT RESEARCH PROJECTS AND SCIENTIFIC LEADERS:

Fertilization of Tilapia ponds (Y. I. Medani)

Sudan Ministry of Animal Resources, Marine Research Laboratory

A laboratory concerned with the management of marine fisheries is planned by the Ministry of Animal Resources. It will be located at Port Sudan on the Red Sea and will be able to accommodate two visiting scientists. Inquiries may be addressed to Yousif I. Medani, Fisheries Hydrobiologist, Ministry of Animal Resources, P. O. Box 336, Khartoum, Sudan.

University of Khartoum, Hydrobiological Research Unit

POSTAL ADDRESS: P. O. Box 321, University of Khartoum, Khartoum, Sudan.

EXECUTIVE OFFICER: Dr. L. Berry, Hydrobiological Research Officer.

YEAR FOUNDED: 1953.

SCOPE OF ACTIVITIES: Unrestricted research on the hydrobiology of the Nile and other inland waters of the Sudan.

SEASON OF OPERATION: All year.

PHYSICAL ENVIRONMENT ACCESSIBLE: River Nile (Main, White and Blue).

PROVISIONS FOR VISITING SCIENTISTS: Space for 1 visitor by previous arrangement; no fees charged.

MAJOR RESEARCH FACILITIES: Small library; small aquarium tanks, machine and wood shop, skilled shop workman available; 1 small boat with outboard motor; 66 ft LOA motor launch.

SIZE OF STAFF: One full time and 3 part time at professional level; 1 technician.

MAJOR CURRENT RESEARCH PROJECTS AND SCIENTIFIC LEADERS:

Research on food requirements of Nile fish (J. L. Cloudsley-Thompson)

Effect of *Eichhornia crassipies* on Nile waters and fish (H. M. Bishai)

Conductivity and physical characteristics of Nile waters (L. Berry and H. M. Bishai)

Characteristics of Nile bottom sediments (L. Berry)

SWEDEN

Abisko Naturvetenskapliga Station

ABISKO SCIENTIFIC STATION

POSTAL ADDRESS: Abisko, Sverige (Sweden).

LOCATION: Near Kiruna, Sverige and Narvik, Norge (in Swedish Lappland, 68° 21′ N, 18° 49′ E).

EXECUTIVE OFFICER: Dr. G. A. Sandberg, Laborator. Address from October 15 to May 31: Linnegatan 11, Uppsala, Sverige (Sweden).

SPONSORING AGENCY: Kungl. Vetenskapsakademien (Royal Swedish Academy of Science).

YEAR FOUNDED: 1903 at Vassijaure; 1912 moved to Abisko.

SCOPE OF ACTIVITIES: Unrestricted ecological and limnological research in mountain area north of the Polar Circle; graduate and undergraduate instruction. (The Station also sponsors geological, bioclimatical and terrestrial biological research).

ABISKO NATURVETENSKAPLIGA STATION, LAPPLAND

SEASON OF OPERATION: All year.
PHYSICAL ENVIRONMENT ACCESSIBLE: Lake Tornetrask (317 km^2, 168 m deep); eutrophic and oligotrophic lakes, rivers and streams, and mountain waters undisturbed by man.
PROVISIONS FOR VISITING SCIENTISTS: Space for 25 visitors; no fees charged; living quarters available nearby.
MAJOR RESEARCH AND TEACHING FACILITIES: Small library; electrical and electronic shop, skilled shop workman available; small boats and outboard motors.
INSTRUCTIONAL PROGRAM: Plant ecology (summer course).
SIZE OF STAFF: Two at professional level; 2 (4-5 in summer) technicians.
MAJOR CURRENT RESEARCH PROJECTS AND SCIENTIFIC LEADERS:
Limnological investigations (S. Ekman, G. Lohammar, B. Pejler, W. Rodhe, H. Skuja)

Goeteborgs Universitet, Marinbotaniska Institutionen

GOTHENBURG UNIVERSITY, MARINE BOTANICAL INSTITUTE

POSTAL ADDRESS: Froelundgagtan 22, Goeteborgs, Sverige (Gothenburg, Sweden).
EXECUTIVE OFFICER: Dr. Tore Levring, Director and Professor of Marine Botany.
YEAR FOUNDED: 1948.
SCOPE OF ACTIVITIES: General marine botany; systematics, distribution, ecology, and physiology of marine algae, cytology, culture methods.
SEASON OF OPERATION: All year.
PHYSICAL ENVIRONMENT ACCESSIBLE: Kattegat, Skagerrak; fjords, rocky and gravelly shores, sandy and silty beaches, and brackish, shallow bays.
MAJOR RESEARCH FACILITIES: Small library; small aquarium tanks; research and identified reference collections of local marine algae.
SIZE OF STAFF: Two at professional level.

GOETEBORG UNIVERSITET, MARINBOTANISKA INSTITUTIONEN

Kungl. Fiskeristyrelsen

THE ROYAL BOARD OF FISHERIES

POSTAL ADDRESS:
Headquarters: Fack, Goteborg 5, Sverige (Gothenburg, Sweden).
Laboratories:
1. Havsfiskelaboratoriet
2. Sotvattenslaboratoriet
(Descriptions follow.)
EXECUTIVE OFFICER: Dr. Joran Hult, Director-in-Chief.

Havsfiskelaboratoriet

INSTITUTE FOR MARINE RESEARCH

POSTAL ADDRESS: Lysekil, Sverige.
EXECUTIVE OFFICER: Dr. Hans Hoglund, Senior Officer.
YEAR FOUNDED: 1929.
SCOPE OF ACTIVITIES: Restricted marine fishery research.
SEASON OF OPERATION: All year.

HAVSFISKELABORATORIET, GOTEBORG

PHYSICAL ENVIRONMENT ACCESSIBLE: North and Baltic Seas, Skagerrak and Kattegat, the Sound; inshore archipelagoes.
PROVISIONS FOR VISITING SCIENTISTS: Space for 2 visitors; no fees charged; living quarters available nearby.
MAJOR RESEARCH FACILITIES: Small library; running sea and fresh-water; small aquarium tanks; vessels, 45.8 m LOA, *Skagerrak,* and 20.4 m LOA, *Eystrasalt.*
SIZE OF STAFF: Four at professional level; 8 technicians.
PUBLICATIONS ISSUED: *Institute of Marine Research Lysekil, Ser. Biology, Report* (occasionally published journal)

Soetvattenslaboratoriet

INSTITUTE OF FRESH-WATER RESEARCH

POSTAL ADDRESS: Drottningholm, Sverige.
EXECUTIVE OFFICER: Professor Sven Runnstrom, Senior Officer.
YEAR FOUNDED: 1932.

SOEVATTENSLABORATORIET, DROTTNINGHOLM

SCOPE OF ACTIVITIES: Restricted research on general biological problems of fresh-water fisheries.

SEASON OF OPERATION: All year.

PHYSICAL ENVIRONMENT ACCESSIBLE: Lake Malaren (oligotrophic lake).

PROVISIONS FOR VISITING SCIENTISTS: None.

MAJOR RESEARCH FACILITIES: Moderately complete library; large outdoor ponds and tanks, small aquarium tanks; machine and wood shop; small boats and outboard motors.

SIZE OF STAFF: Ten biologists; 10 fishery asssistants; 15 laboratory and office assistants.

MAJOR CURRENT RESEARCH PROJECTS AND SCIENTIFIC LEADERS:

- Population dynamic studies in salmonids (S. Runnstrom, K.-J. Gustafson, G. Svardson, and Th. Lindstrom)
- Speciation in coregonids (G. Svardson)
- Biology of whitefish young (Th. Lindstrom)
- Ecology of the fauna of flowing water (T. Roos)
- Behavior and competition in salmonid fish (H. Kalleberg)
- Effect of artificial lake level fluctuations on bottom fauna and feeding habits and growth of fish (U. Grimas, M. Stube, N. A. Nilsson, and S. Runnstrom)
- Interactive segregation in the feeding habits of salmonids (N.-A. Nilsson)

PUBLICATIONS ISSUED: *Reports of the Institute of Freshwater Research* (regularly published journal)

Kristinebergs Zoologiska Station

MARINE ZOOLOGICAL STATION AT KRISTINEBERG

POSTAL ADDRESS: Fiskebackskil, Sverige (Sweden).

LOCATION: Near Lysekil.

EXECUTIVE OFFICER: Dr. Bertil Swedmark.

SPONSORING AGENCY: Kungl. Svenska Vetenskapsakademien (Royal Swedish Academy of Science).

YEAR FOUNDED: 1877.

SCOPE OF ACTIVITIES: Unrestricted marine biological research; undergraduate instruction.

SEASON OF OPERATION: All year, but most work done in summer.

PHYSICAL ENVIRONMENT ACCESSIBLE: Skagerrak, Gullmar Fjord; rocky and gravelly shores.

PROVISIONS FOR VISITING SCIENTISTS: Research and living space for 30 visitors; no fees charged for research space.

MAJOR RESEARCH AND TEACHING FACILITIES: Small library; running surface and bottom water (differing salinities); small aquarium tanks; machine and wood shop; small boats and outboard motors; vessels, 42 ft LOA, *Sven Loven,* and 32 ft LOA, *Nereis.*

INSTRUCTIONAL PROGRAM: Marine zoology and comparative physiology.

SIZE OF STAFF: Three at professional level; 7 technicians.

IMPORTANT SPECIES AVAILABLE FOR LABORATORY STUDIES:

- Echinodermata: *Psammechinus miliaris, Echinus esculentus*
- Crustacea: *Pandalus borealis*
- Cyclostomata: *Myxine glutinosa*

MAJOR CURRENT RESEARCH PROJECTS AND SCIENTIFIC LEADERS: Most research is carried out by visiting scientists.

Lunds Universitets Limnologiska Institutionen, Laboratoriet i Aneboda

LIMNOLOGICAL INSTITUTE OF THE UNIVERSITY OF LUND, ANEBODA LABORATORY

POSTAL ADDRESS: Aneboda, Sverige (Sweden).

LOCATION: Near Vaxjo.

EXECUTIVE OFFICER: Professor Sven G. Thunmark, Direktor, Limnologiska institutionen, Magle Stora Kyrkogata 12 B, Lund, Sverige (Sweden).

YEAR FOUNDED: 1928.

SCOPE OF ACTIVITIES: Unrestricted research on regional limnology, plankton ecology and ecology of macro-

LIMNOLOGISKA LABORATORIET I ANEBODA

phytic communities; graduate and undergraduate instruction.

SEASON OF OPERATION: June 15 to October 15 at Aneboda.

PHYSICAL ENVIRONMENT ACCESSIBLE: The oligotrophic lakes Fiolen, Allgunnen, Straken, Skarshultsjon and Frejen; rivers, streams, and peat bogs.

PROVISIONS FOR VISITING SCIENTISTS: Research and living space for visitors; no fees charged for research space.

MAJOR RESEARCH AND TEACHING FACILITIES: Small library; small aquarium tanks; identified reference collections of plankton samples, algae and invertebrates; small boats and outboard motors.

INSTRUCTIONAL PROGRAM: General limnology (three weeks' course).

SIZE OF STAFF: Five at professional level; 1 technician.

IMPORTANT SPECIES AVAILABLE FOR LABORATORY STUDIES:

Crustacea: *Daphnia magna*
Gramineae: *Phragmites communis*

MAJOR CURRENT RESEARCH PROJECTS AND SCIENTIFIC LEADERS:

Theoretical and applied limnology (Sven G. Thunmark)

PUBLICATIONS ISSUED: *Acta Limnologica* (occasionally published journal)

Soedra Sveriges Fiskerifoerening

FISHERY SOCIETY OF SOUTHERN SWEDEN

POSTAL ADDRESS: Aneboda, Lammhult, Sverige (Sweden).

LOCATION: Near Vaxjo.

EXECUTIVE OFFICER: Dr. B. Berzins, Direktor.

YEAR FOUNDED: 1906.

SCOPE OF ACTIVITIES: Restricted research on fresh-water fishery biology including plankton, cultivation of fish in ponds and lakes, management of lakes; training of inland fisheries workers.

SEASON OF OPERATION: All year.

PHYSICAL ENVIRONMENT ACCESSIBLE: Eutrophic and oligotrophic lakes, rivers and streams, and fish ponds.

PROVISIONS FOR VISITING SCIENTISTS: Space for 2-3 visitors; no fees charged; living quarters available in alternate years.

MAJOR RESEARCH AND TEACHING FACILITIES: Small library; large outdoor ponds and tanks, small aquarium tanks; small boats and outboard motors.

INSTRUCTIONAL PROGRAM: For fishery instructors: limnology, zooplankton, management of fish ponds and lakes, applied botany, etc.

SIZE OF STAFF: One at professional level; 3 technicians.

MAJOR CURRENT RESEARCH PROJECTS AND SCIENTIFIC LEADERS:

Zooplankton and production of fingerlings in ponds (B. Berzins)
Taxonomy and ecology of rotifers in southern Sweden (B. Berzins)
Biology of pike-perch fry (B. Berzins)
Inundations fauna in pike-ponds (B. Berzins)
Management of lakes with rotenone (B. Berzins)
Toxicity of aquatic herbicides on fish (B. Berzins, Andersson, Carlgren)

SOEDRA SVERIGES FISKERIFOERENING

Uppsala Universitet, Institutionen for Fysiologisk Botanik

UPPSALA UNIVERSITY, INSTITUTE FOR PHYSIOLOGICAL BOTANY

POSTAL ADDRESS: Uppsala, Sverige (Sweden).

EXECUTIVE OFFICER: Professor Nils Fries.

YEAR FOUNDED: 1939.

SCOPE OF ACTIVITIES: Unrestricted research on the physiology of marine plants in pure (axenic) culture; graduate and undergraduate instruction.

SEASON OF OPERATION: All year.

PROVISIONS FOR VISITING SCIENTISTS: Space for about 6 visitors; no fees charged; living quarters available nearby.

MAJOR RESEARCH AND TEACHING FACILITIES: Moderately complete library; machine and wood shop, skilled shop workman available.

INSTRUCTIONAL PROGRAM: Morphology and taxonomy of marine and fresh-water algae.

SIZE OF STAFF: Thirty-five at professional level; 16 technicians.

MAJOR CURRENT RESEARCH PROJECTS AND SCIENTIFIC LEADERS:

Physiology of Rhodohyta (Lisbeth Fries)
Nutrition of Phaeophyta (Marianne Hielm)
Phototaxis and photosynthesis in marine Chlorophyta (Bjorn Lindahl)
Physiology and morphogenesis in Charophyta (Curt Forsberg)

Exudation of organic material by *Nostoc* sp. (Elisabeth Henriksson)
PUBLICATIONS ISSUED: *Symbolae Botanicae Upsaliensis* (occasionally published journal)

Uppsala Universitet, Klubbans Biologiska Station

UPPSALA UNIVERSITY, KLUBBANS BIOLOGICAL STATION

POSTAL ADDRESS: Fiskebackskil, Sverige (Sweden).
LOCATION: Near Goteborg (Gothenburg) on the Gullmar Fjord.
EXECUTIVE OFFICER: Professor Gosta Jagersten, Direktor, and Professor of Zoology and Comparative Anatomy, Uppsala University, Uppsala, Sweden.
SPONSORING AGENCY: Uppsala Universitet (University of Uppsala).
YEAR FOUNDED: 1915.
SCOPE OF ACTIVITIES: Devoted primarily to summer instruction in general marine biology; research on plankton, bottom ecology, and morphology.
SEASON OF OPERATION: Summer.
PHYSICAL ENVIRONMENT ACCESSIBLE: Skagerrak; open ocean, sandy and silty beaches, rocky and gravelly shores and fjord.
PROVISION FOR VISITING SCIENTISTS: None.
MAJOR RESEARCH AND TEACHING FACILITIES: Small library; running sea water.

Uppsala Universitet, Limnologiska Institutionen

UNIVERSITY OF UPPSALA, INSTITUTE OF LIMNOLOGY

POSTAL ADDRESS:
Headquarters: Limnologiska Institutionen, Uppsala, Sverige, (Sweden)
Branch laboratory: Erkenlaboratoriet, Norrtaelje.
LOCATION: Lake Erken is 50 km east of Uppsala and 65 km northeast of Stockholm.
EXECUTIVE OFFICER: Dr. C. O. W. Rodhe, Director and Professor of Limnology.
YEAR FOUNDED: Uppsala, 1949, Erkenlaboratoriet, 1944.
SCOPE OF ACTIVITIES: Unrestricted limnological research; graduate and undergraduate instruction.
SEASON OF OPERATION: All year.
PHYSICAL ENVIRONMENT ACCESSIBLE: Lake Erken (eutrophic lake); rivers and streams.
PROVISION FOR VISITING SCIENTISTS: Research and living space for 5-10 visitors at Erken; no fees charged for research space.
MAJOR RESEARCH AND TEACHING FACILITIES: At Uppsala: laboratories for waterchemistry, radioactivity, microbiology, hydrobiology and applied limnology. At Erken laboratory: laboratory for water-chemistry and hydrobiology. Boats and outboard motors.

LIMNOLOGISKA LABORATORIET VID ERKEN

INSTRUCTIONAL PROGRAM: At Uppsala: theoretical and applied limnology. At Erken laboratory: field classes.
SIZE OF STAFF: One at professional level; 4 assistants; 4 technicians.
MAJOR CURRENT RESEARCH PROJECTS AND SCIENTIFIC LEADERS:
Primary production and its conditions (W. Rodhe)
Fish ecology and fisheries in Lake Erken (T. Anderson)
Bottom fauna in Lake Erken (G. Sandberg)
Zooplankton in Lapland lakes (J. Axelson)
Chemical conditions in the River Fyris (O. Lindgren)
Chemical composition of lake waters (T. Ahl)
Phosphorous and nitrogen budget in a polluted lake (I. (Ahlgren)
Production in a salmon-breeding pond (R. Arnemo)
Production of epiphytic algae in Lake Erken (L. Kronborg)
Trophic relations between phyto- and zooplankton (A. Nauwerck)

Laboratories for Which No Detailed Information Was Available:

Biologiska Station i Annsjon, Ann, Sverige

Lector Lars Faxen, Linkoping.
Sponsoring agency: Uppsala Universitet.

Vaxtfysiologiska Institutionen, Uppsala, Sverige

Professor Einar du Rietz.
Sponsoring agency: Uppsala Universitet.

INSTITUTE OF FISHERY BIOLOGY, TAIPEI

TAIWAN

National Taiwan University, Institute of Fishery Biology

POSTAL ADDRESS: Roosevelt Road Sec. III, Taipei Taiwan.
EXECUTIVE OFFICER: Dr. Fah-hsuen Liu, Director.
SPONSORING AGENCIES: Ministry of Economic Affairs and National Taiwan University.
YEAR FOUNDED: 1954.
SCOPE OF ACTIVITIES: Unrestricted research on general marine and fresh-water biology, bottom ecology, general oceanography and fish culture with particular emphasis on fisheries development.
SEASON OF OPERATION: All year.
PHYSICAL ENVIRONMENT ACCESSIBLE: South China and Yellow Seas; estuarine conditions, fish ponds and inland waters.
PROVISIONS FOR VISITING SCIENTISTS: Space for 1-2 visitors; no fees charged; living quarters available nearby.
MAJOR RESEARCH AND TEACHING FACILITIES: Very extensive library; large outdoor ponds, small aquarium tanks, research collections of fish, shells of Mollusca, and corals; one 30 m LOA vessel.
INSTRUCTIONAL PROGRAM: General invertebrate zoology, plankton, fish culture, fishery biology, fish diseases, ecology, limnology, oceanology, introduction to fishery products. (Program closely associated with the University's Department of Zoology).
SIZE OF STAFF: Two at professional level; 12 technicians.
MAJOR CURRENT RESEARCH PROJECTS AND SCIENTIFIC LEADERS:
Studies on the resources of bottom fishes (F. H. Liu)
Studies on the resources and biology of Wen-fish (herring-like fishes) (F. H. Liu)
Spawning of some important fresh-water culture fishes in Taiwan (F. H. Liu)
Oceanographic investigations of coastal waters (T. Y. Chu)
PUBLICATIONS ISSUED: *Report of the Institute of Fishery Biology* (occasionally published journal)

Taiwan Fisheries Research Institute

POSTAL ADDRESS: 125 Hou-i Road, Chilung (Keelung), Taiwan.
LOCATION: Near Taipei.
EXECUTIVE OFFICER: Huo-Tu Teng, Director.
SPONSORING AGENCY: Department of Agriculture and Forestry.
YEAR FOUNDED: 1945.
SCOPE OF ACTIVITIES: Unrestricted research on general marine biology.
SEASON OF OPERATION: All year.
PHYSICAL ENVIRONMENT ACCESSIBLE: Taiwan Strait, Pacific Ocean; sandy and silty beaches, rocky and gravelly shores, estuarine conditions, brackish, shallow bays, coral reefs, rivers and streams.
PUBLICATIONS ISSUED: None.
MAJOR RESEARCH FACILITIES: Moderately complete library; large outdoor ponds and tanks; research collections of fish from Taiwan Strait and adjacent waters; skilled shop workman available; one 104 ft LOA vessel.
SIZE OF STAFF: Forty-six at professional level; 31 technicians.
IMPORTANT SPECIES AVAILABLE FOR LABORATORY STUDIES:
Algae: *Gelidium* sp.
Coelenterata: *Metridium* sp.
Echinodermata: *Echinometra* sp.
Crustacea: *Portunus* sp.
Mollusca: *Loligo* sp.
Pisces: *Scoliodon* sp., *Gambusia patruelis, Cyprinus carpio*
Amphibia: *Rana* sp.
MAJOR CURRENT RESEARCH PROJECTS AND SCIENTIFIC LEADERS:
Studies on the elasmobranchs of Taiwan (Huo-Tu Teng)

TAIWAN FISHERIES RESEARCH INSTITUTE

THAILAND

Thai Ministry of Agriculture, Department of Fisheries

POSTAL ADDRESS:
Headquarters: Bangkok, Muang Tai (Thailand).
Branch fresh-water stations:

1. Bangkhen Inland Fisheries Experimental Station, Kasetsart University, Bangkhen
2. Bung Borapet Fisheries Station, Bung Borapet, Nakorn Serwan Province
3. Chai Nart Fisheries Station, Chai Nart Province
4. Kwan Payao Fisheries Station, Chiengrai
5. Nong Harn Fisheries Station, Sakorn Nakorn

Branch brackish water stations:

6. Bang Chun Shrimp Fisheries Station, Bang Chun District, Chundhaburi Province
7. Klong Wan Brackish Water Fish Culture Station, Prachuab Kirikhan
8. Patalung Fisheries Station, Patalung

Branch marine station:

9. Ban Phae Fishery Station, Ban Phae, Rayong

(Descriptions follow.)

EXECUTIVE OFFICERS: Nai Boon Indrambarya, Director-General. Nai Wit Yorsaengrat, Deputy Director-General.

YEAR FOUNDED: 1926.

PUBLICATIONS ISSUED: *Thai Fisheries Gazette* (regularly published journal)

Bangkhen Inland Fisheries Experimental Station

POSTAL ADDRESS: Kasetsart University, Bangkhen, Bangkok.

EXECUTIVE OFFICER: Pairoj Sibikorn, Head.

YEAR FOUNDED: 1938.

SCOPE OF ACTIVITIES: Restricted research on fresh-water fish culture in ponds; graduate and undergraduate instruction, training courses.

PHYSICAL ENVIRONMENT ACCESSIBLE: Bangkhen Canal, a tributary of the Chao Phya River.

SEASON OF OPERATION: All year.

PROVISIONS FOR VISITING SCIENTISTS: Space for about 30 visitors; no fees charged; living quarters available nearby.

MAJOR RESEARCH AND TEACHING FACILITIES: Moderately complete library; identified reference collection of commercial fresh-water fish; skilled shop workman available.

INSTRUCTIONAL PROGRAM: Pond construction, hatcheries management, general fish cultures for fisheries officers, civil officers, and shool teachers.

SIZE OF STAFF: Two technicians.

IMPORTANT SPECIES AVAILABLE FOR LABORATORY STUDIES:
Pisces: *Cyprinus carpio, Trichogaster pectoralis, Clarias macrocephalus, C. batrachus, Tilapia mossambica, Osphronemus goramy, Pangasius sutchi*

MAJOR CURRENT RESEARCH PROJECTS AND SCIENTIFIC LEADERS:
Production of *Tilapia mossambica* in an experimental pond (Umbol Pongsuwana)
Breeding of *Clarias macrocephalus* by pituitary gland injection (Snith Tongsanga)
The combination of Plachon (*Ophicephalus striatus*) and Tilapia (*Tilapia mossambica*) in a pond (Snith Tongsanga)

Bung Borapet Fisheries Station

POSTAL ADDRESS: Bung Borapet, Nakorn Serwan Province.

LOCATION: On the Central Plain.

EXECUTIVE OFFICER: Ariya Sidhimunka, Head.

YEAR FOUNDED: 1929.

SCOPE OF ACTIVITIES: Restricted research on general fisheries biology, with emphasis on the spawning and rearing grounds of *Pangasius* sp. and other fishes suitable for culture.

SEASON OF OPERATION: All year.

PHYSICAL ENVIRONMENT ACCESSIBLE: Nan and Chao Phya Rivers; large swamp near the Nan River.

PROVISIONS FOR VISITING SCIENTISTS: Space for 5 visitors; living quarters available nearby.

MAJOR RESEARCH FACILITIES: No library; water supply by pump from the swamp; small boats and outboard motors.

SIZE OF STAFF: Two technicians.

IMPORTANT SPECIES AVAILABLE FOR LABORATORY STUDIES:
Pisces: *Catlocarpio siamensis, Pangasius sutchi, P. largnaudii, Leptobarbus hoevenii, Trichogaster pectoralis*

MAJOR CURRENT RESEARCH PROJECTS AND SCIENTIFIC LEADERS:
Fish population in Bung Borapet Swamp (Ariya Sidhimunka)
Report on the yield of *Claris* breeding by natural methods (Ariya Sidhimunka and P. Ekuru)

Chai Nart Fisheries Station

POSTAL ADDRESS: Chai Nart Province.

EXECUTIVE OFFICER: Prasit Ekuru, Head.

YEAR FOUNDED: 1958.

SCOPE OF ACTIVITIES: Restricted research on the biology of river fishes.

SEASON OF OPERATION: All year.

PHYSICAL ENVIRONMENT ACCESSIBLE: Chao Phya River.

PROVISIONS FOR VISITING SCIENTISTS: None.

MAJOR RESEARCH FACILITIES: No library; small boats

and outboard motors.

SIZE OF STAFF: One technician.

IMPORTANT SPECIES AVAILABLE FOR LABORATORY STUDIES:

Pisces: *Dasyatis bleekeri, Cryptopterus cryptopterus, Pangasius sutchi, Cirrhinus jullieni*

MAJOR CURRENT RESEARCH PROJECTS AND SCIENTIFIC LEADERS:

Physical, chemical, and biological conditions of the Chao Phya River (Prasit Ekuru)

Kwan Payao Fisheries Station

POSTAL ADDRESS: Chiengrai.

LOCATION: Payao District.

EXECUTIVE OFFICER: Promot Vanichkorn, Head.

YEAR FOUNDED: 1941.

SCOPE OF ACTIVITIES: Restricted research on fisheries biology of the Payao Swamp and nearby rivers.

SEASON OF OPERATION: All year.

PHYSICAL ENVIRONMENT ACCESSIBLE: Payao Swamp and the Ing River.

PROVISIONS FOR VISITING SCIENTISTS: Space for 5 visitors; living quarters available nearby.

MAJOR RESEARCH FACILITIES: No library; small boats and outboard motors.

SIZE OF STAFF: One technician.

IMPORTANT SPECIES AVAILABLE FOR LABORATORY STUDIES:

Pisces: *Crossocheilus* spp., *Pristolepis fasciatus, Trichogaster pectoralis, Notopterus chitala*

MAJOR CURRENT RESEARCH PROJECTS AND SCIENTIFIC LEADERS:

Fish population in Payao Swamp (Promot Vanichkorn)

Nong Harn Fisheries Station

POSTAL ADDRESS: Sakorn Nakorn.

EXECUTIVE OFFICER: Wai Pinyo, Head.

YEAR FOUNDED: 1942.

SCOPE OF ACTIVITIES: Restricted research on fisheries biology; emphasis on fishes of rivers, swamps, and irrigation reservoirs.

SEASON OF OPERATION: All year.

PHYSICAL ENVIRONMENT ACCESSIBLE: Nong Harn Swamp, Kram River, a tributary of the Mae Kong River; oligotrophic lake.

PROVISIONS FOR VISITING SCIENTISTS: Space for 5 visitors; living quarters available nearby.

MAJOR RESEARCH FACILITIES: No library; large outdoor ponds and tanks; research collections of local freshwater fishes, skilled shop workman available; small boats and outboard motors; one 6 m LOA vessel.

SIZE OF STAFF: One at professional level; 1 technician.

IMPORTANT SPECIES AVAILABLE FOR LABORATORY STUDIES:

Pisces: *Aloza kanagurta, Osteochilus hasseltii, Puntius gonionotus, Anabas testudineus, Setipinna melanochir*

MAJOR CURRENT RESEARCH PROJECTS AND SCIENTIFIC LEADERS:

Fish population in Nong Harn Swamp (Wai Pinyo)

Bang Chun Shrimp Fisheries Station

POSTAL ADDRESS: Bang Chun District, Chundhaburi Province.

EXECUTIVE OFFICER: Vanich Varikul, Head.

SCOPE OF ACTIVITIES: Restricted research on shrimp biology and culture.

SEASON OF OPERATION: All year.

PHYSICAL ENVIRONMENT ACCESSIBLE: Gulf of Thailand; sandy and silty beaches.

PROVISIONS FOR VISITING SCIENTISTS: None.

MAJOR RESEARCH FACILITIES: No library; running sea water; research collections of shrimp and brackish water fishes; small boats and outboard motors.

SIZE OF STAFF: Two technicians.

IMPORTANT SPECIES AVAILABLE FOR LABORATORY STUDIES:

Crustacea: *Penaeus indicus, P. merguiensis, P. monodon, Metapenaeus monoceros, Palaemon* spp., *Leander* spp.

MAJOR CURRENT RESEARCH PROJECTS AND SCIENTIFIC LEADERS:

Shrimp culture and biology (Vanich Varikul)

Klong Wan Brackish Water Fish Culture Station

POSTAL ADDRESS: Prachuab Kirikhan.

EXECUTIVE OFFICER: Uthai Sundharothok, Head.

SCOPE OF ACTIVITIES: Restricted research on the biology of milk fish and shrimps.

SEASON OF OPERATION: All year.

PHYSICAL ENVIRONMENT ACCESSIBLE: Klong Wan (tidal stream), Gulf of Thailand.

PROVISIONS FOR VISITING SCIENTISTS: None.

MAJOR RESEARCH FACILITIES: No library; small boats and outboard motors.

SIZE OF STAFF: One technician.

IMPORTANT SPECIES AVAILABLE FOR LABORATORY STUDIES:

Pisces: *Chanos chanos, Mugil* spp.

Crustacea: *Penaeus indicus, Metapenaeus monoceros*

MAJOR CURRENT RESEARCH PROJECTS AND SCIENTIFIC LEADERS:

Culture of *Chanos chanos* fry (Uthai Sundharotok)

Patalung Fisheries Station

POSTAL ADDRESS: Patalung.

EXECUTIVE OFFICER: Swasdi Boonthai, Head.

YEAR FOUNDED: 1955.

SCOPE OF ACTIVITIES: Restricted research on brackish water fishery biology.

SEASON OF OPERATION: All year.
PHYSICAL ENVIRONMENT ACCESSIBLE: Songkhla Lake (eutrophic lake).
PROVISIONS FOR VISITING SCIENTISTS: None.
MAJOR RESEARCH FACILITIES: No library; water supplied by machine pump; small boats and outboard motors.
SIZE OF STAFF: One technician.
IMPORTANT SPECIES AVAILABLE FOR LABORATORY STUDIES:
Algae: *Gracillaria confervoides*
Crustacea: *Penaeus indicus*
Pisces: *Nematlosa nasus, Osphronemus goramy, Prophagorus nieuhofii*
MAJOR CURRENT RESEARCH PROJECTS AND SCIENTIFIC LEADERS:
Electrical fishing methods (Swasdi Boonthai)

Ban Phae Fishery Station

POSTAL ADDRESS: Ban Phae, Rayong.
LOCATION: Near Satahee Naval Base.
EXECUTIVE OFFICER: Prakob Rodpothong, Head.
YEAR FOUNDED: 1950.
SCOPE OF ACTIVITIES: Restricted research on general fishery biology and technology.
SEASON OF OPERATION: All year.
PROVISIONS FOR VISITING SCIENTISTS: Research and living space for 5-10 visitors; no fees charged for research space.
MAJOR RESEARCH FACILITIES: Small library; rain water available; machine and wood shop, skilled shop workman available; small boats and outboard motors; six power vessels of which the largest is about 35 ft LOA.
SIZE OF STAFF: Six at professional level.
PHYSICAL ENVIRONMENT ACCESSIBLE: Gulf of Thailand; sandy and silty beaches.

Kasetsart University, College of Fisheries

POSTAL ADDRESS: Bangkhen, Bangkok, Muang Tai (Thailand).
EXECUTIVE OFFICER: Nai Boon Indrambarya, Dean.
YEAR FOUNDED: 1943.
SCOPE OF ACTIVITIES: Unrestricted research; undergraduate instruction.
SEASON OF OPERATION: All year.
PHYSICAL ENVIRONMENT ACCESSIBLE: Bangkhen Canal (tributary of Chao Phya River); central plain.
PROVISIONS FOR VISITING SCIENTISTS: None.
MAJOR RESEARCH AND TEACHING FACILITIES: Moderately complete library; water supply controlled by university pump.
INSTRUCTIONAL PROGRAM: Zoology, botany, fishery biology, fish culture, fish technology, and oceanography.
IMPORTANT SPECIES AVAILABLE FOR LABORATORY STUDIES:
Pisces: *Cyprinus carpio, Ctenopharyngodon idellus, Hypophthalmichthys molitrix, Pangasius sutchi*

TUNISIA

Station Oceanographique de Salammbo

SALAMMBO OCEANOGRAPHIC STATION

POSTAL ADDRESS: Salammbo, Tunisia.
LOCATION: Near Carthage.
EXECUTIVE OFFICER: Brahim Douik, Directeur.
SPONSORING AGENCY: Secretariat d'etat a l'Industrie et aux Transports (State Department of Industry and Transportation).
YEAR FOUNDED: 1924.
SCOPE OF ACTIVITIES: Unrestricted research on general marine biology and general oceanography; exploratory fisheries research.
SEASON OF OPERATION: All year.
PHYSICAL ENVIRONMENT ACCESSIBLE: Mediterranean Sea; sandy and silty beaches, rocky and gravelly shores, estuarine conditions, and eutrophic lake.

STATION OCEANOGRAPHIQUE DE SALAMMBO

PROVISIONS FOR VISITING SCIENTISTS: Research and living space for 2 visitors; fees charged for research space.
MAJOR RESEARCH AND TEACHING FACILITIES: Very extensive library; running sea and fresh-water; large outdoor ponds and tanks, small aquarium tanks; research collections of Pisces, Echinodermata and Mollusca; machine and wood shop, electrical and electronic shop; small boats and outboard motors; vessels, 12 m, 20 m, and 3 m LOA.
INSTRUCTIONAL PROGRAM: General invertebrate zoology, phytoplankton, and zooplankton.
SIZE OF STAFF: One at professional level.
PUBLICATIONS ISSUED: *Annales et Bulletin de la Station Oceanographique de Salmmbo* (regularly published journal).

TURKEY

Et ve Balik Kurumu, Balikcilik Mueduerluegue, Besiktas, Istanbul

FISHERIES DIRECTORATE OF THE MEAT AND FISH OFFICE

POSTAL ADDRESS: Besiktas, Istanbul, Tuerkiye (Turkey)
EXECUTIVE OFFICER: Mr. Dogan Akaguenduez, Direktor.
YEAR FOUNDED: 1959.
SCOPE OF ACTIVITIES: Experimental fishing methods, fish preservation, fishery trade, transport.
SEASON OF OPERATION: All year.
PHYSICAL ENVIRONMENT ACCESSIBLE: Bosporus, Sea of Marmara and Black Sea.
MAJOR RESEARCH FACILITIES: Small library; research vessels, *Arar, Gezer, Goeruer, Bulur,* and 8 fishing boats of 9 to 45 tons.

RESEARCH VESSEL OF THE ISTANBUL FISHERIES DIRECTORATE OF THE MEAT AND FISH OFFICE

SIZE OF STAFF OF FISHERY BIOLOGY BRANCH: Three at professional level.
MAJOR CURRENT RESEARCH PROJECTS AND SCIENTIFIC LEADERS:
Biology of pelagic and demersal fish (I. Artuz)
Hydrography (B. Turgutcan)
Plankton (N. Gurturk)
Age analysis of pelagic and demersal species (N. Kutaygill)

Hidrobioloji Arastirma Enstitusu

HYDROBIOLOGICAL RESEARCH INSTITUTE

POSTAL ADDRESS:
Headquarters: Baltalimani Caddesi No. 80, Istanbul-Emirgan, Tuerkiye (Turkey).
Branch laboratories:
1. Trabzon on eastern Black Sea coast of Anatolia
2. Canakkal on the Dardanelles

HIDROBIOLOJI ARASTIRMA ENSTITUSU, ISTANBUL

EXECUTIVE OFFICER: Professor Dr. Recai Ermin, Direktor
SPONSORING AGENCIES: Istanbul Universitesi; financial support from the Ministry of Commerce and Balikcilik Mueduerluegue Besiktas (Meat and Fish Office).
YEAR FOUNDED: 1951.
SCOPE OF ACTIVITIES: Restricted research on general marine and fresh-water biology research projects vary according to the source of operating funds.
SEASON OF OPERATION: All year.
PHYSICAL ENVIRONMENT ACCESSIBLE: Black Sea, Bosporus, Sea of Marmara, Lagoons of Cek mece; open ocean, sandy and silty beaches, rocky and gravelly shores, estuarine conditions, brackish, shallow bays, eutrophic and oligotrophic lakes, rivers and streams.
PROVISIONS FOR VISITING SCIENTISTS: Research and living space for 2 visitors for short periods.
MAJOR RESEARCH FACILITIES: Moderately complete library; running sea and fresh-water, small aquarium tanks; incomplete identified reference collections of local fresh-water and marine fishes, invertebrates, benthos, and plankton; machine and wood shop; skilled shop workman available; small boats and outboard motors; vessels, 11.7 m LOA, *Bulur,* 11.7 m LOA, *Gezer,* and 11.7 m LOA, *Gorur.*
SIZE OF STAFF: Eight at professional level; 7 technicians.
IMPORTANT SPECIES AVAILABLE FOR LABORATORY STUDIES:
Crustacea: *Sphaeroma* sp.
Pisces: *Lepadogaster* sp., *Aphanius* sp., *Blennius* sp., *Gasterosteus* sp., *Mugil* sp.
MAJOR CURRENT RESEARCH PROJECTS AND SCIENTIFIC LEADERS:
Biology of sardines (F. Erman and M. Atli)
Biology of mullets (F. Erman)
Biology of eels and taxonomy of fishes (F. Aksiray)
Propagation of fish in lakes (F. Aksiray)
Plankton and benthos of the Black Sea, Sea of Mar-

mara and the Agean Sea (M. Demir, N. Demir, and U. Demirhindi)

Hydrographic research in the Bosporus, Sea of Marmara, and the Black Sea (A. Acara)

Quantitative analysis of the fish meal and oil of economic important fishes (A. Acara)

PUBLICATIONS ISSUED:

Hidrobiologi Serie B (in international languages)

Hidrobiologi Serie A (in Turkish)—both are regularly published journals

UGANDA

East African Freshwater Fisheries Research Organization

POSTAL ADDRESS: P. O. Box 343, Nile Crescent, Jinja, Uganda.

EXECUTIVE OFFICER: P. B. N. Jackson, Director.

SPONSORING AGENCY: East African Common Services Organization.

EAST AFRICAN FRESHWATER FISHERIES RESEARCH ORGANIZATION LABORATORY

YEAR FOUNDED: 1947.

SCOPE OF ACTIVITIES: Unrestricted research on the hydrobiology of tropical lakes with emphasis on the management of inland fisheries.

SEASON OF OPERATION: All year.

PHYSICAL ENVIRONMENT ACCESSIBLE: Lake Victoria and other eutrophic as well as oligotrophic lakes of East Africa; Nile River.

PROVISIONS FOR VISITING SCIENTISTS: Research and living space for 2 visitors; no fees charged for research space.

MAJOR RESEARCH FACILITIES: Moderately complete library; small aquarium tanks; research and identified reference collections of local fish and aquatic insects; machine and wood shop, skilled shop workman available; small boats and outboard motors; two motor launches.

SIZE OF STAFF: Six at professional level; 2 technicians.

IMPORTANT SPECIES AVAILABLE FOR LABORATORY STUDIES:

Pisces: *Tilapia* spp., *Bagrus* sp., *Clarias* sp., *Mormyrus* sp., *Protopterus* sp., *Haplochromis* sp.

MAJOR CURRENT RESEARCH PROJECTS:

Hydrological studies on Lake Victoria

Phytoplankton of Lake Victoria

Food and feeding habits of commercially important fish of Lake Victoria

Aquatic insect studies

Snail vectors of *Bilharzia*

Fish and fisheries of Lake Victoria

Uganda Fisheries Department, Kajansi Fish Farm

POSTAL ADDRESS: P. O. Box 530, Kampala, Uganda.

EXECUTIVE OFFICERS: D. H. Rhodes, Chief Fisheries Officer, Uganda Fisheries Department, P. O. Box 4, Entebbe, Uganda. C. J. H. Simpson, Fisheries Officer, Kajansi Fish Farm.

YEAR FOUNDED: 1953.

SCOPE OF ACTIVITIES: Restricted research on fish culture and fish farming; small ad hoc courses of instruction on fish culture.

SEASON OF OPERATION: All year.

PHYSICAL ENVIRONMENT ACCESSIBLE: Lake Victoria and other eutrophic lakes; streams and ponds.

PROVISIONS FOR VISITING SCIENTISTS: Research and living space for 1-2 visitors; no fees charged.

MAJOR RESEARCH FACILITIES: Very extensive library available at University College of E. Africam Makerere, small library at Department headquarters at Entebbe; large and small outdoor ponds, small aquarium tanks; research and identified reference collections of fauna and flora available at Makerere; small boats and outboard motors; 42 ft LOA power vessel.

SIZE OF STAFF: One at professional level; 3 technicians.

IMPORTANT SPECIES AVAILABLE FOR LABORATORY STUDIES:

Pisces: *Tilapia* spp., *Cyprinus carpio, Lates albertianus, Protopterus ethiopicus, Polypterus senegalensis*

Insecta: *Anopheles gambiae, A. funestus.*

MAJOR CURRENT RESEARCH PROJECTS:

Use of *Tilapia* and various large predators as culture fish

Hybridization and selection of *Tilapia*

Testing suitability of other indigenous fish for fish culture

UNION OF SOVIET SOCIALIST REPUBLICS

Scientific Foundations of the Academy of Sciences of the USSR

1. *Institute of Zoology, AS USSR*

POSTAL ADDRESS: Universitetskaya nab. 1, Leningrad.
EXECUTIVE OFFICER: E. N. Pavlovsky, Director.
YEAR FOUNDED: 1930.
SCOPE OF ACTIVITIES: The institute performs research on marine fauna.
PUBLICATIONS ISSUED:
Science of the USSR
Determinants on Fauna USSR

2. *Institute for Biology of Reservoirs, AS USSR*

POSTAL ADDRESS: p. o. Verkhne-Nikolskoye, Yaroslavsk obl.
EXECUTIVE OFFICER: I. D. Papanin, Director.

3. *Institute of Microbiology, AS USSR*

POSTAL ADDRESS: Leninsky prospekt 33, Moscow.
EXECUTIVE OFFICER: A. A. Imshenetsky, Director.
YEAR FOUNDED: 1930.
SCOPE OF ACTIVITIES: General marine microbiology.

4. *Institute of Animal Morphology, AS USSR*

POSTAL ADDRESS: Leninsky prospekt 33, Moscow.
EXECUTIVE OFFICER: G. K. Krushchov, Director.

5. *Institute of Oceanology, AS USSR*

POSTAL ADDRESS: pr. Vladimirova 3, Moscow.
EXECUTIVE OFFICER: V. G. Kort, Director.
YEAR FOUNDED: 1945.
SCOPE OF ACTIVITIES: Research in physical oceanography, marine chemistry, marine geology, and marine biology.
PHYSICAL ENVIRONMENT ACCESSIBLE: Antarctica; the Atlantic, Indian, and Pacific Oceans, Mediterranean Sea.
VESSELS: *Vitiaz,* and the *Academic Vavilov.*

6. *Institute of Physiology, AS USSR*

POSTAL ADDRESS: Tuchkova nab. 2a, Leningrad.
EXECUTIVE OFFICER: K. M. Bykov, Director.

7. *Institute of Botany, AS USSR*

POSTAL ADDRESS: U1. Popova 2, Leningrad.
EXECUTIVE OFFICER: P. A. Baranov.

8. *Institute of Hydrobiology, AS USSR*

POSTAL ADDRESS:
Headquarters: Kiev.
Odessa Biological Station: Odessa.
YEAR FOUNDED: 1939.
SCOPE OF ACTIVITIES: Study of the estuaries of the north-western part of the Black Sea.
VESSELS: *Miklukha Maklai, Academic Zernov, Nauchniy.*

ODESSA BIOLOGICAL STATION

POSTAL ADDRESS: Odessa.
YEAR FOUNDED: 1954.
SCOPE OF ACTIVITIES: Research on the hydrobiology of the Black Sea.
VESSELS: *Miklukha Maklai.*

9. *Institute of Scientific Information, AS USSR*

POSTAL ADDRESS: Baltiiskii pos. 42b, Moscow.

10. *Laboratory of Helminthology, AS USSR*

POSTAL ADDRESS: Pogodinskaya 10, Moscow.
EXECUTIVE OFFICER: K. I. Skryabin, Director.

11. *Laboratory of Limnology, AS USSR*

POSTAL ADDRESS: Nab. Makarova 2, Leningrad.
EXECUTIVE OFFICER: S. V. Kalesnik, Director.

12. *Sevastopol Biological Research Station, AS USSR*

POSTAL ADDRESS: Sevastopol.
EXECUTIVE OFFICER: V. A. Vodyanitsky, Director.
YEAR FOUNDED: 1871-1872.
SCOPE OF ACTIVITIES: The hydrobiology and ichthyology of the Black and Mediterranean Seas.
PHYSICAL ENVIRONMENT ACCESSIBLE: Black and Mediterranean Seas.
VESSEL: *Academic Kovalevski.*

13. *Siberian Division of the Academy of Sciences, AS USSR*

POSTAL ADDRESS: Novosibirsk.
East Siberian Branch.
Postal address: Irkutsk.
Branches:
(1) Institute of Biology
(2) Baykal Limnological Station
Sakhalin Research Institute,
Postal address: Tuzhno- Sakhalinsk.

Branches of the Academy of Sciences of the USSR.

1. *Daghestan Branch, AS USSR*

POSTAL ADDRESS: Makhach-kala.
BRANCH: Ichthyological Laboratory.

2. *Karelian Branch, AS USSR*

POSTAL ADDRESS: Petrozavodsk.
BRANCHES:
(1) Institute of Biology.
(2) White Sea Biological Station.

3. *Kola Branch, AS USSR*

POSTAL ADDRESS:
Headquarters: Kirovsk, Murmansk obl.
Institute of Marine Biology: Kirovsk, Murmansk obl.

Institute of Marine Biology

YEAR FOUNDED: 1936.
SCOPE OF ACTIVITIES: Studies of laws regulating the number of fish taken, the migration of game fish in the littoral zone of Murmansk in connection with biological, hydrobiological and hydrochemical processes.
VESSEL: *Deanna.*

4. *Komi Branch, AS USSR*

POSTAL ADDRESS: Syktykvar, Komi USSR.
BRANCH: Division of Biology.

5. *Moldavian Branch, AS USSR*

POSTAL ADDRESS: Kishinev.
BRANCH: Institute of Biology.

6. *Yakutsk Branch, AS USSR*

POSTAL ADDRESS: Yakutsk, Siberia.
BRANCH: Institute of Biology.

Institutes and Stations Sponsored by Academies of Sciences of the Union Republics

1. *AS Armenian SSR*

POSTAL ADDRESS: Erevan.
BRANCH: Sevang Hydrobiological Station.

2. *AS Azerbaijan SSR*

POSTAL ADDRESS: Baku.
BRANCH: Institute of Zoology.

3. *AS Byelorussian SSR*

POSTAL ADDRESS: Minsk.
BRANCH: Institute of Biology.

4. *AS Estonian SSR*

POSTAL ADDRESS: Tallinn.
BRANCH: Institute of Zoology and Botany, Marine Ichthyological Laboratory.

5. *AS Georgian SSR*

POSTAL ADDRESS: Tbilisi.
BRANCH: Institute of Zoology.

6. *Yakutsk Branch, AS USSR*

POSTAL ADDRESS: Alma-alta.
BRANCHES:
(1) Altai Ichythyological Station.
(2) Institute of Ichthyology and Fish Industry
  a. Aral Sea Ichthyological Department (see description below).
  b. Balkhash Ichthyological Division.

Aral Sea Ichthyological Department

POSTAL ADDRESS: Aralsk. Kazakh SSR.
YEAR FOUNDED: 1929.
SCOPE OF ACTIVITIES: Studies of commercial stocks of the Aral Sea; feeding and breeding conditions of commercial fishes in connection with hydrotechnical construction.
MAJOR RESEARCH FACILITIES: Laboratories equipped with optical, hydrochemical, and hydrobiological apparatus; seine boat and cutter.

7. *AS Kirghiz SSR*

POSTAL ADDRESS: Frunze.
BRANCH: Institute of Zoology and Parasitology.

8. *AS Latvian SSR*

POSTAL ADDRESS: Riga.
BRANCH: Institute of Biology.

9. *AS Lithuanian SSR*

POSTAL ADDRESS: Vilnius.
BRANCH: Institute of Biology.

10. *AS Tajik SSR*

POSTAL ADDRESS: Stalinabad.
BRANCH: Institute of Zoology and Parasitology.

11. *AS Turkmen SSR*

POSTAL ADDRESS: Ashkhabad.
BRANCH: Institute of Biology.

12. *AS Ukrainian SSR*

POSTAL ADDRESS:
Headquarters: Kiev.
Institute of Hydrobiology: Kiev.
Karadagsk Biological Station: Province of Krimsk, Region of Sudaksk.

Karadagsk Biological Station:

YEAR FOUNDED: 1914.
SCOPE OF ACTIVITIES: Hydrobiology of the Black Sea.
VESSEL: *Viazemski.*

13. *AS Uzbek SSR*

POSTAL ADDRESS: Tashkent.
BRANCHES:
(1) Institute of Zoology and Parasitology.
(2) Karakalpak Complex Institute.

Fisheries Department of the State Planning Committee of the USSR

The All-Union Research Institute of Marine Fisheries and Oceanography (VNIRO).

POSTAL ADDRESS: Moscow.
BRANCH: Algal Laboratory, Arkhangelsk.
YEAR FOUNDED: 1933.
SCOPE OF ACTIVITIES: Oceanography, assessment of stocks, regulation of fisheries, fishing techniques, reproduction of stocks, acclimatization, physiology, fisheries biology, economics, and technology.
MAJOR RESEARCH FACILITIES: Library and museum; sections of scientific information, international fisheries and economics; biological laboratories.

The All-Russian Council of National Economy

1. *The Pacific Research Institute of Fisheries and Oceanography (TINRO).*

POSTAL ADDRESS: Vladivostok.
BRANCHES:
(1) Amur Branch, Khabarovsk.
(2) Kamchatka Branch (Description follows.)
(3) Magadan Branch, Magadan.
(4) Sakhalin Branch (Description follows.)
(5) Okhotsk Ichthyological Laboratory, Okhotsk.

YEAR FOUNDED: 1925.
SCOPE OF ACTIVITIES: Studies on the fish, faunal, and floral resources of the seas, lakes, and rivers of the Far East and the Pacific Ocean; investigations on applied ichthyology, commercial fisheries technique, hydrobiology, oceanography, mammal and crab fisheries, technology of production.

Kamchatka Branch

POSTAL ADDRESS: Petropavlovsk-Kamchatskii.
YEAR FOUNDED: 1932.
SCOPE OF ACTIVITIES: Commercial ichthyology, reproduction of fish, food supply, oceanography, mechanization of fishery and fishery processing.

Sakhalin Branch

POSTAL ADDRESS: P/O Antonovo, Chekhovsky Region, Sakhalinskaya Oblast.
YEAR FOUNDED: 1945.
SCOPE OF ACTIVITIES: Studies of stock conditions, distribution and behavior of fish in the Okhotsk and Japan Seas; designs and modernization of fishing gear; mechanization of fish processing including shellfish and algae.
MAJOR RESEARCH FACILITIES: Technical library and museum; well equipped laboratories; vessels are provided by TINRO for research needs.

2. *The State Research Institute of Lake and River Fisheries (GOSNIORH).*

POSTAL ADDRESS: Leningrad.
BRANCHES:
(1) Velikiye Luki Branch, Velikiye Luki.
(2) Karelian Branch, Petrozavodsk.
(3) Novgorod Branch, Novgorod.
(4) Novosibirsk Branch, Novosibirsk.
(5) Ob-Tazovsk Branch, Khanty-Mansiysk.
(6) Saratov Branch, Saratov.
(7) Siberian Branch, Krasnoyarsk.
(8) Stalingrad Branch, Stalingrad.
(9) Tatar Branch, Kazan.
(10) Ural Branch, Sverdlovsk.
(11) Yakutsk Branch, Yakutsk.

3. *Astrakhan Economic Administrative Region*

The Caspian Research Institute of Marine Fisheries and Oceanography (KASPNIRO).

POSTAL ADDRESS: Astrakhan.
YEAR FOUNDED: 1898.
SCOPE OF ACTIVITIES: Fishery biology and oceanography; fishery technology and processing.
MAJOR RESEARCH FACILITIES: Laboratories and workshops; vessels, 5 river motor boats, and 4

sea going vessels, SRT *Lomonosov,* RS *Opit, Issledoyatel, Pochin.*

4. *Kaliningrad Economic Administrative Region*

The Baltic Research Institute of Marine Fisheries and Oceanography (BALTNIRO).

POSTAL ADDRESS: Kaliningrad.
YEAR FOUNDED: 1949.
SCOPE OF ACTIVITIES: Biological and fisheries investigations in the Baltic and North Seas and the central Atlantic; technology and fish processing; gear design.
MAJOR RESEARCH FACILITIES: Laboratories; vessels, SRT, *Lomonosov,* SRT *Artemovsk,* SRT *Alazan,* SRT-129, SRT-4576, and the *Mazirbe.*

5. *Murmansk Economic Administrative Region*

The Polar Research and Designing Institute of Marine Fisheries and Oceanography (PINRO).

POSTAL ADDRESS: Murmansk.
YEAR FOUNDED: 1933.
SCOPE OF ACTIVITIES: The hydrological, hydrochemical, and hydrobiological regimes of the Barents Sea and the Atlantic Ocean; construction and design of fishing gear; fishery and processing technology.
MAJOR RESEARCH FACILITIES: Library and museum; laboratories; vessels, *Sevastopol, Toonets, Persei II, Prof. Mesiatsev, Academic Berg.*

6. *Rostov Economic Administrative Region*

The Azov Fisheries Research Institute (AZNIIRH).

POSTAL ADDRESS: Rostov/Don.
YEAR FOUNDED: 1922.
SCOPE OF ACTIVITIES: Reproduction of stocks, commercial ichthyology, hydrology and hydrobiology, fish culture, and fishery economics.
MAJOR RESEARCH FACILITIES: Laboratories; experimental hatchery on the Don River; vessels, *Issledovatel, Prof. Vasnetsov.*

The Council of National Economy for Various Union Republics

1. *Azerbaijan SSR*

The Azerbaijan Fisheries Research Laboratory (AZERNIRL).

POSTAL ADDRESS: Baku.
YEAR FOUNDED: 1912.
SCOPE OF ACTIVITIES: Fishery biology; stock preservation, population dynamics; fishery economics.
MAJOR RESEARCH FACILITIES: Library; ichthyological, oceanographical, fishery biology laboratories; experimental hatchery on lower Kura River; sea going vessel for marine biological and oceanographical studies.

2. *Byelorussian SSR*

The Byelorussian Fisheries Research Institute

POSTAL ADDRESS: Minsk.

3. *Daghestan ASSR*

The Research Institute of Food Industry

POSTAL ADDRESS: Makjach-Kala.

4. *Georgia SSR*

The Fisheries Research Station

POSTAL ADDRESS: Batumi.

5. *Latvia SSR*

The Latvian Fisheries Research Institute.

POSTAL ADDRESS: Riga.
YEAR FOUNDED: 1945.
SCOPE OF ACTIVITIES: The regime of the Baltic Sea, stock conditions of the main commercial species, their population dynamics and distribution, fishery biology, modernization of hydroacoustic devices, reproduction of anadromous fishes, and fish processing.

6. *Turkmenryga Trust SSR*

The Turkmen Ichthyological Laboratory

POSTAL ADDRESS: Krasnovodsk.

7. *Ukrainia SSR*

The Azov and Black Sea Research Institute of Marine Fisheries and Oceanography (AZCHERNIRO).

POSTAL ADDRESS: Kerch.
YEAR FOUNDED: 1921.
SCOPE OF ACTIVITIES: Ichthyology, hydrobiology, and hydrochemistry of the Azovski and Black Seas.
MAJOR RESEARCH FACILITIES: Laboratories; vessels

equipped with hydroacoustic devices and other fishing gear, SRT-4509, SRT *Grot,* SRT *Gonets,* VCHS *Danilevski.*

Ministry of Agriculture of the RSFSR.

The All-Russian Research Institute of Pond Fisheries

POSTAL ADDRESS: 9 Khlebnikov Pereulok, Moscow.

Moscow State University

1. *Faculty of Biology*

Institute for Hydrobiology
Institute for Ichthyology

2. *Faculty of Biology and Pedology*

3. *The Zoological Museum*

Moscow Technical Institute of Fisheries and the Fish Industry

Department of Hydrobiology

POSTAL ADDRESS: Pryanshnikova 2a, Moscow.

UNITED ARAB REPUBLIC

Alexandria Institute of Hydrobiology

POSTAL ADDRESS: Kayed Bay, Alexandria, United Arab Republic.
EXECUTIVE OFFICER: Mr. A. Rifaat, Director.
SPONSORING AGENCY: Ministry of Agriculture, Hydrobiological Department.
YEAR FOUNDED: 1931.
SCOPE OF ACTIVITIES: Restricted fisheries and limnological research; pond culture.
SEASON OF OPERATION: All year.
PHYSICAL ENVIRONMENT ACCESSIBLE: Mediterranean Sea, Lakes Elkou and Mariout (eutrophic lakes); estuarine conditions.
PROVISIONS FOR VISITING SCIENTISTS: Space for 2 visitors; no fees charged; living quarters available nearby.

ALEXANDRIA INSTITUTE OF HYDROBIOLOGY

MAJOR RESEARCH FACILITIES: Small library; running sea and fresh-water, large outdoor ponds and tanks, small aquarium tanks; research collections of flabellid and turbinoid corals, copepods and other crustaceans; 20 m LOA vessel, S.S. *Mabahiss.*
SIZE OF STAFF: Seventeen at professional level; 3 technicians.
IMPORTANT SPECIES AVAILABLE FOR LABORATORY STUDIES:
Phytoplankton: *Nitzschia* spp.
Aquatic flowering plants: *Ceratophyllum demersum, Potamogeton crispus*
Crustacea: *Pneus* spp., *Neptunus pelagicus, Gammarus* spp.
Pisces: *Tilapia zillii, T. galilaea, Mugil capito, M. cephalus, Sardinella* spp.
MAJOR CURRENT RESEARCH PROJECTS AND SCIENTIFIC LEADERS:
Fishing gear (Samy Gorgy)
Oceanographic research (Samy Gorgy)
Phytoplankton (M. Salah)
Fisheries biology (lakes) (S. El-Zarka)
Fresh-water fisheries biology and fish farms (R. Koura)
PUBLICATIONS ISSUED: *Notes and Memoires* (occasionally published journal)

Egyptian Ministry of Agriculture, Hydrobiological Department, Institute of Freshwater Biology

POSTAL ADDRESS: P. O. Gizira, 10, Hassam Sabry Street, Cairo, United Arab Republic.
EXECUTIVE OFFICER: Mr. Riad Qura, Director.
YEAR FOUNDED: 1955.
SCOPE OF ACTIVITIES: Restricted research on fish biology and pond culture.
SEASON OF OPERATION: All year.
PHYSICAL ENVIRONMENT ACCESSIBLE: River Nile; canals, and fish farm ponds.
PROVISIONS FOR VISITING SCIENTISTS: None.

INSTITUTE OF FRESHWATER BIOLOGY, CAIRO

MAJOR RESEARCH FACILITIES: Very small library; 12 outdoor ponds (Nile water supply), small aquarium tanks; 6 m LOA launch.

SIZE OF STAFF: Four at professional level.

IMPORTANT SPECIES AVAILABLE FOR LABORATORY STUDIES:

Pisces: *Mormyrus* spp., *Schilbe* spp., *Clarias* spp., *Bagras* spp., *Chrysichthys* spp., *Tilapia* spp.

MAJOR CURRENT RESEARCH PROJECTS AND SCIENTIFIC LEADERS:

Studies on the anatomy and biology of Nile fishes of commercial value (Riad Qura and staff)

Selective action of gear and nets (Riad Qura and staff)

Experimental studies on carp, *Tilapia* and mullet (Riad Qura and staff)

PUBLICATIONS ISSUED: *Notes and Memoires of the Hydrobiological Department* (occasionally published journal)

University of Alexandria, Department of Oceanography

POSTAL ADDRESS: Faculty of Science, University of Alexandria, Moharrem Bay, Alexandria, United Arab Republic.

EXECUTIVE OFFICER: Dr. A. A. Aleem, Head of the Department and Professor of Biological Oceanography.

YEAR FOUNDED: 1948.

SCOPE OF ACTIVITIES: Unrestricted research on fisheries, general marine biology, plankton and bottom ecology; graduate instruction.

SEASON OF OPERATION: All year.

PHYSICAL ENVIRONMENT ACCESSIBLE: Eastern Mediterranean region, brackish water lakes (Lakes Maryut, Idku, Manzala, Qarun); sandy and silty beaches, rocky and gravelly shores, estuarine conditions, brackish, shallow bays, and eutrophic lake.

PROVISIONS FOR VISITING SCIENTISTS: Upon arrangement.

MAJOR RESEARCH AND TEACHING FACILITIES: Small library; small aquarium tanks; research collections of diatoms, peridinians, marine algae, sea grasses, marine and brackish bottom fauna and various marine invertebrates; machine and wood shop available at University; vessel, 28 ft LOA, *Bahith.*

INSTRUCTIONAL PROGRAM: Biological oceanography and fisheries, marine ecology, classification of marine invertebrates, sea grasses and algae, brackish water ecology, phytoplankton, comparative physiology, economic oceanography, fisheries and fish biology, zooplankton, history of oceanography, instruments and methods of research, submarine sediments.

SIZE OF STAFF: Six at professional level; 1 technician.

IMPORTANT SPECIES AVAILABLE FOR LABORATORY STUDIES:

Rhodophyceae: *Pterocladia capillacea*

Pisces: *Sardinella aurita, Mugil, Tilapia* spp.

MAJOR CURRENT RESEARCH PROJECTS AND SCIENTIFIC LEADERS:

Marine algae and phytoplankton of Alexandria (A. A. Aleem)

Dinoflagellata (Y. Halim)

Primary production in Lake Maryut (A. A. Aleem and A. Samaan)

Fouling organisms (A. A. Aleem and A. Dowidar)

Biology of Egyptian sardines (El-Maghraby and Girguis)

Lake sediments (El Wakeel)

Hydrography of the Suez Canal (Anton-Morcos)

UNIVERSITY OF CAIRO, HYDROBIOLOGICAL INSTITUTE

University of Cairo, Hydrobiological Institute

POSTAL ADDRESS: Ataqa, United Arab Republic.

EXECUTIVE OFFICER: Professor Hamed A. F. Gohar, Director.

YEAR FOUNDED: 1960.

SCOPE OF ACTIVITIES: Unrestricted research on marine biology, plankton ecology, physiology and general oceanography; graduate and undergraduate instruction.

SEASON OF OPERATION: All year.

PHYSICAL ENVIRONMENT ACCESSIBLE: Gulf of Suez, Suez Canal and lakes, Ismailia Canal (fresh-water); sandy and silty beaches, rocky and gravelly shores, brackish, shallow bays, rivers and streams.

PROVISIONS FOR VISITING SCIENTISTS: Research and

living space for 4 or more visitors; fees charged for research space.

MAJOR RESEARCH AND TEACHING FACILITIES: Running sea and fresh-water, large indoor concrete aquarium tanks; small boats and outboard motors; one 11.5 m LOA vessel.

INSTRUCTIONAL PROGRAM: Practical training in general oceanography, marine biology, ecology, general invertebrate zoology, embryology of marine invertebrates, biology of fishes, plankton, physiology, algae and marine phanerogams.

SIZE OF STAFF: Three at professional level; 3 technicians.

IMPORTANT SPECIES AVAILABLE FOR LABORATORY STUDIES:

Coelentrata: *Cassiopea* sp.
Turbellaria: *Cryptophallus* sp.
Polychaeta: *Nereis* sp.
Crustacea: *Squilla* sp., *Leander* sp., *Neptunus* sp.
Echinodermata: *Synapta* sp., *Astropecten* sp., *Echinometra* sp.
Mollusca: *Pinctada* sp., *Sepia* sp., *Sirce* sp., *Tridacna* sp.
Pisces: *Rhynobatus* sp., *Sardinella* sp., *Saurus* sp., *Carcharinus* sp., *Rhynchobatus* sp.

MAJOR CURRENT RESEARCH PROJECTS AND SCIENTIFIC LEADERS:

General marine biology (H. A. F. Gohar)
Physical oceanography (El-sayed M. Hassam)
Invertebrate physiology (H. Roushdy)
Fish physiology and biochemistry (A. A. Latif)

University of Cairo, Institute of Oceanography

POSTAL ADDRESS: University of Cairo, Cairo, United Arab Republic.

EXECUTIVE OFFICER: Professor Hamed A. F. Gohar, Director.

YEAR FOUNDED: 1950.

SCOPE OF ACTIVITIES: Unrestricted marine research; graduate and undergraduate instruction.

SEASON OF OPERATION: All year.

PHYSICAL ENVIRONMENT ACCESSIBLE: Red Sea, Gulf of Suez, River Nile and its branches.

PROVISIONS FOR VISITING SCIENTISTS: None.

MAJOR RESEARCH AND TEACHING FACILITIES: The Institute is located at the University and its facilities are almost exclusively devoted to instruction. The field laboratories at Ataqa and Al-Ghardaqa contain the research facilities.

INSTRUCTIONAL PROGRAM: General oceanography, marine ecology, general invertebrate zoology, embryology of marine invertebrates, coral reef problems, biology of fishes, marine mammals, plankton, physiology, algae and marine phanerogams and limnology.

SIZE OF STAFF: Eleven at professional level.

UNIVERSITY OF CAIRO, MARINE BIOLOGICAL STATION, AL-GHARDAQA

University of Cairo, Marine Biological Station

POSTAL ADDRESS: Al-Ghardaqa, Red Sea, United Arab Republic.

LOCATION: Near Hurghada.

EXECUTIVE OFFICER: Professor Hamed A. F. Gohar, Director.

SPONSORING AGENCY: Institute of Oceanography of the University of Cairo.

YEAR FOUNDED: 1931.

SCOPE OF ACTIVITIES: Unrestricted research on marine biology, plankton and ecology; occasional undergraduate instruction.

SEASON OF OPERATION: All year.

PHYSICAL ENVIRONMENT ACCESSIBLE: Red Sea; sandy and silty beaches, rocky and gravelly shores and coral reefs.

PROVISIONS FOR VISITING SCIENTISTS: Research and living space for 4 visitors; fees charged for research space.

MAJOR RESEARCH AND TEACHING FACILITIES: Moderately complete library; running sea water, large outdoor ponds and tanks, small aquarium tanks; research and identified reference collections of algae, fishes, Crustacea, Mollusca, Echinodermata, Annelida, Alcyonaria, Madreporaria, etc.; machine and wood shop; small boats with outboard motors or sails.

INSTRUCTIONAL PROGRAM: General oceanography, marine ecology, general invertebrate zoology, embryology of marine invertebrates, coral reef problems and biology, fishes, marine mammals, plankton, physiology, algae and marine phanerogams.

SIZE OF STAFF: Eight at professional level; 3 technicians.

IMPORTANT SPECIES AVAILABLE FOR LABORATORY STUDIES:

Most species typical of Indo-Pacific coral reefs are present.

MAJOR CURRENT RESEARCH PROJECTS AND SCIENTIFIC LEADERS:

Mammals, fishes, Crustacea, Mollusca, and Coelentrata (Hamed A. F. Gohar)
Plankton (Fathi M. Ghazzawi and A. A. Al-Kholy)
Crustacea (A. A. Al-Kholy)
Physical oceanography (El-Sayed M. Hassan)

PUBLICATIONS ISSUED: *Publications Marine Biological Station, Al-Ghardaqa, Red Sea* (occasionally published journal)

UNITED KINGDOM, ENGLAND

British Ministry of Agriculture, Fisheries and Food Laboratories:

1. Fisheries Laboratory, Burnham-on-Crouch
2. Fisheries Laboratory, Lowestoft
3. Radiological Laboratory
4. Salmon and Fresh-Water Fisheries Laboratory

(Descriptions follow.)

Fisheries Laboratory, Burnham-on-Crouch

POSTAL ADDRESS: Remembrance Avenue, Burnham-on-Crouch, Essex County, England.

LOCATION: Near Southend-on-Sea, England.

EXECUTIVE OFFICER: A. C. Simpson, Director.

YEAR FOUNDED: 1947.

SCOPE OF ACTIVITIES: Officially restricted research on the biology and bionomics of shellfisheries of England and Wales.

SEASON OF OPERATION: All year.

PHYSICAL ENVIRONMENT ACCESSIBLE: Rivers Crouch, Roach and Blackwater, southern North Sea; sandy and silty beaches, estuarine conditions.

PROVISIONS FOR VISITING SCIENTISTS: None at present.

MAJOR RESEARCH FACILITIES: Moderately complete library; running sea and fresh-water, small aquarium tanks; extensive living research collection of marine flagellates; limited identified reference collections of fauna and flora from local estuaries; small boats and outboard motors; one 48 ft LOA powered oyster dredger, *Wystrys,* and 35 ft LOA dredger, *Jassa.*

SIZE OF STAFF: Seven at professional level; 6 technicians.

FISHERIES LABORATORY, BURNHAM-ON-CROUCH

IMPORTANT SPECIES AVAILABLE FOR LABORATORY STUDIES:

Flagellata: Various species

Mollusca: *Ostrea edulis, Cardium edule, Crepidula fornicata, Urosalpinx cinerea*

MAJOR CURRENT RESEARCH PROJECTS AND SCIENTIFIC LEADERS:

Oyster cultivation (G. D. Waugh)

Cockle and whelk bionomics (D. A. Hancock)

Crab biology (M. N. Mistakidis)

Shellfish sanitation (P. C. Wood)

Taxonomy of marine flagellates (R. W. Butcher)

Biochemistry of marine flagellates (D. M. Collyer)

PUBLICATIONS ISSUED: *Fisheries Investigations Series II, H.M.S.O.* (occasionally published)

Fisheries Laboratory, Lowestoft

POSTAL ADDRESS: Lowestoft, Suffolk, England.

LOCATION: Near Norwich, England.

EXECUTIVE OFFICER: Dr. H. A. Cole, Director, Fishery Research.

YEAR FOUNDED: 1920.

SCOPE OF ACTIVITIES: Officially restricted marine fisheries research with special reference to the stocks of fish and shellfish of importance to the United Kingdom; fisheries training.

SEASON OF OPERATION: All year.

PHYSICAL ENVIRONMENT ACCESSIBLE: North Sea, English Channel, Irish Sea; sandy and silty beaches, rocky and gravelly shores, estuarine conditions, brackish, shallow bays.

PROVISIONS FOR VISITING SCIENTISTS: Research space for up to 6 visitors; no fees charged; living quarters available nearby.

MAJOR RESEARCH FACILITIES: Very extensive library; large and small aquarium tanks; limited research collections of Arctic invertebrates; identified reference collections of local flora and fauna available at British Museum (Natural History), London; machine and wood shop, electrical and electronic shop, skilled shop workmen available; vessels: 194 ft LOA, *Ernest Holt,* 155 ft LOA, *Clione,* 90 ft LOA, *Platessa,* and 55 ft LOA, *Tellina.*

INSTRUCTIONAL PROGRAM: A few university students receive full-time training in fishery biology while employed at the Laboratory. No formal course work is offered.

SIZE OF STAFF: Twenty-eight at professional level; 42 technicians.

IMPORTANT SPECIES AVAILABLE FOR LABORATORY STUDIES:

Pisces: *Squalus acanthias, Raia clavata, Clupea harengus, C. sprattus, Gadus callarias, G. merlangus, G. virens, Pleuronectes platessa, Solea solea*

Mollusca: *Mactra corallina*

FISHERIES LABORATORY, LOWESTOFT

MAJOR CURRENT RESEARCH PROJECTS AND SCIENTIFIC LEADERS:
- *Population Section* (R. J. H. Beverton, Section Head)
  - Population and catch prediction studies of plaice, sole, haddock, hake and cod (J. A. Gulland)
  - Studies on distribution of fish populations using underwater photographic techniques (R. W. Blacker)
  - Studies on behavior of trawls under water, and tagging studies of sole populations (A. R. Margetts)
  - Studies on cod and redfish populations (G. C. Trout)
  - Age determination studies of fishes, and tagging studies on elasmobranchs (M. J. Holden)
  - Population studies on coalfish (B. Jones)
- *Biology Section* (H. A. Cole, Section Head)
  - Studies on the culture of plaice (J. E. Shelbourne and J. D. Riley)
  - Studies on ACTH in the cod pituitary, and other hormonal studies relating to fish behavior (P. M. J. Woodhead)
  - Plankton studies in northern seas (J. Corlett)
  - Plankton studies in near waters (J. Caltley)
  - Dynamics of the benthonic bivalve *Mactra stultorum* (L. Birkett)
- *Pelagic Section* (D. H. Cushing, Section Head)
  - Biological production studies at various trophic levels (D. H. Cushing)
  - Herring population studies (D. H. Cushing, A. C. Burd and T. D. Iles)
  - Studies on mackerel populations around the British Isles (C. C. Bolster)
  - Studies on the sprat fishery (P. O. Johnson)
  - Behavior of pelagic fish (F. R. Harden Jones)

PUBLICATIONS ISSUED: Fishery Investigations (occasionally published)

Radiobiological Laboratory

POSTAL ADDRESS: Hamilton Dock, Lowestoft, England.
LOCATION: Near Norwich, England.
EXECUTIVE OFFICER: F. Morgan, Physicist-in-Charge.
YEAR FOUNDED: 1948.
SCOPE OF ACTIVITIES: Research on the controlled disposal of radioactive waste into waters; monitoring of radioactive discharges into rivers and the sea.
SEASON OF OPERATION: All year.
PHYSICAL ENVIRONMENT ACCESSIBLE: All United Kingdom coastline, including river estuaries and inland waters.
PROVISIONS FOR VISITING SCIENTISTS: Limited.
MAJOR RESEARCH FACILITIES: Facilities of Fisheries Laboratory, Lowestoft, are available.
SIZE OF STAFF: Four at professional level; 24 technicians.
PUBLICATIONS ISSUED: *Fishery Investigations* (occasionally published)

Salmon and Fresh-Water Fisheries Laboratory

POSTAL ADDRESS: Whitehall Place (East Block), London, England.
EXECUTIVE OFFICERS: Mr. F. T. K. Pentelow, Chief Officer. Mr. I. R. H. Allan, Deputy Chief Officer.
YEAR FOUNDED: 1958.
SCOPE OF ACTIVITIES: Officially sponsored research on fresh-water fisheries; emphasis on migratory fish stocks, protection of fresh-water fishes from industrial pollution, and hazards to migration (fish screens, fish ladders, etc.)
SEASON OF OPERATION: All year.
PHYSICAL ENVIRONMENT ACCESSIBLE: Rivers.
PROVISIONS FOR VISITING SCIENTISTS: None.
MAJOR RESEARCH FACILITIES: Small aquarium tanks, large indoor tank; machine and wood shop, electrical and electronic shop; small boats and outboard motors.
SIZE OF STAFF: Ten at professional level; 8 technicians.
MAJOR CURRENT RESEARCH PROJECTS AND SCIENTIFIC LEADERS:
- Salmon population studies (I. R. H. Allan)
- Sea trout population studies (A. Swain)
- Fish detection and protection (W. G. Hartley)
- Effects of pollution (including heat) (J. S. Alabaster)
- Fish behavior and movement (B. Stott)

PUBLICATIONS ISSUED: *Fishery Investigations Series I* (occasionally published)

University of Durham, King's College, Dove Marine Laboratory

POSTAL ADDRESS: Cullercoats (Northumberland), England.
LOCATION: Near Newcastle-upon-Tyne, England.
EXECUTIVE OFFICER: Dr. H. O. Bull, Deputy Director and Reader in Marine Biology.
YEAR FOUNDED: 1897.
SCOPE OF ACTIVITIES: Unrestricted research on general marine biology; graduate and undergraduate instruction.
SEASON OF OPERATION: All year.
PHYSICAL ENVIRONMENT ACCESSIBLE: North Sea;

DOVE MARINE LABORATORY, CULLERCOATS

sandy beaches, rocky and gravelly shores, estuarine conditions.

PROVISIONS FOR VISITING SCIENTISTS: Research space for 6 visitors; fees charged; living quarters available nearby.

MAJOR RESEARCH AND TEACHING FACILITIES: Very extensive library; small aquarium tanks, large, private aquarium for research; identified reference collection of local marine fauna; machine and wood shop, skilled shop workman available; one 53 ft vessel, *R. V. Alexander Meek.*

INSTRUCTIONAL PROGRAM: General marine biology; post graduate research leading to M.Sc. or Ph.D. degrees from the University of Durham.

SIZE OF STAFF: Five at professional level; 5 technicians.

IMPORTANT SPECIES AVAILABLE FOR LABORATORY STUDIES:

Foraminifera: *Astrorhiza limicola*
Anthozoa: *Metridium senile*
Turbellaria: *Procerodes ulva*
Polychaeta: *Nereis* sp.
Diptera: *Coelopa* sp.
Lamellibranchia: *Mya arenaria*
Crustacea: *Carcinus maenas, Homarus vulgaris*
Selachii: *Raia radiata*
Teleostei: *Gadus morhua*

MAJOR CURRENT RESEARCH PROJECTS AND SCIENTIFIC LEADERS:

Ethology of the lobster, other crustaceans and fish (H. O. Bull)
Benthonic communities in relation to sediments, currents, and feeding (J. B. Buchanan)
Biology of *Crangon allmani*; the ligament of Lucinacea; development of *Pandora* (J. A. Allen)
Plankton distribution in relation to water movements; inshore current systems (F. Evans)

National Institute of Oceanography

POSTAL ADDRESS: Wormley, Godalming, Surrey, England.

LOCATION: Near London, England.

EXECUTIVE OFFICERS: Dr. G. E. R. Deacon, Director of Institute. Mr. R. I. Currie, Head of Marine Biological Program.

SPONSORING AGENCY: National Oceanographic Council (Governmental).

YEAR FOUNDED: 1949.

SCOPE OF ACTIVITIES: Unrestricted research in general oceanography, including marine biology.

SEASON OF OPERATION: All year.

PHYSICAL ENVIRONMENT ACCESSIBLE: North Sea, English Channel, Irish Sea, Atlantic Ocean.

PROVISIONS FOR VISITING SCIENTISTS: Research space for 3-4 postgraduate workers only; no fees charged; living quarters available nearby.

MAJOR RESEARCH FACILITIES: Very extensive library; research collections of the *Discovery,* mainly Southern Ocean plankton; machine and wood shop, electrical and electronic shop, skilled shop workman available; 261 ft LOA, R.R.S. *Discovery II.*

SIZE OF STAFF OF THE INSTITUTE: Fifty at professional level; 25 technicians.

MAJOR CURRENT BIOLOGICAL RESEARCH PROJECTS AND SCIENTIFIC LEADERS:

Bionomics of whales (N. A. Mackintosh, R. M. Laws and S. G. Brown)
Productivity of oceanic waters (R. I. Currie and P. Foxton)
Taxonomy and distribution of Southern Ocean Chaetagnatha (P. M. David)
Biological and ecological studies on *Euphausia superba* (J. W. S. Marr)
Ecological and productivity studies of the Southern Ocean (T. J. Hart)
Studies on sperm whales (R. H. Clarke)

PUBLICATIONS ISSUED: *Discovery Reports* (published regularly)

NATIONAL INSTITUTE OF OCEANOGRAPHY, WORMLEY

The Plymouth Laboratory of the Marine Biological Association of the United Kingdom

POSTAL ADDRESS: Citadel Hill, Plymouth, England.
EXECUTIVE OFFICER: Dr. F. S. Russell, Director.
YEAR FOUNDED: 1888.
SCOPE OF ACTIVITIES: Unrestricted marine research; undergraduate instruction.
SEASON OF OPERATION: All year.
PHYSICAL ENVIRONMENT ACCESSIBLE: Plymouth Sound, English Channel; sandy and silty beaches, rocky and gravelly shores, estuarine conditions, brackish, shallow bays.
PROVISIONS FOR VISITING SCIENTISTS: Research space for 40 visitors; fees charged; living quarters nearby.
MAJOR RESEARCH AND TEACHING FACILITIES: Very extensive library; running sea and fresh-water, large and small aquarium tanks; partially complete identified reference collection of local fauna and flora; machine and wood shop, electrical and electronic shop,

THE PLYMOUTH LABORATORY, PLYMOUTH

skilled shop workman available; small boat and outboard motor; vessels: 128 ft LOA *R.V. Sarsia* (research ship), 61 ft LOA, *Sula* (motor fishing type), 25 ft LOA, *Gammarus*.
INSTRUCTIONAL PROGRAM: Short vacation courses in marine biology and physiology for British University undergraduates only.
SIZE OF STAFF: Eighteen at professional level; 16 technicians.
IMPORTANT SPECIES AVAILABLE FOR LABORATORY STUDIES: Very great variety of invertebrates and fishes available for experimental studies.
MAJOR CURRENT RESEARCH PROJECTS OF THE PERMANENT STAFF AND SCIENTIFIC LEADERS (as of 1958):
Effects of deep oceanic circulation on biological production of shallow seas (L. H. N. Cooper)
Studies on the state of iodine in sea water (T. I. Shaw and L. H. N. Cooper)
Studies on ammonia, total inorganic nitrogen and other rarer constituents in deep sea water (F. A. Armstrong and E. I. Butler)
Studies on nannoplankton and maintenance of unialgal cultures (Mary Parke and I. M. Adams)
Biology of deep sea Scyphomedusae (F. S. Russell)
Biology of hyperiid amphipods and population studies on the microspecies of the isopod *Jaera albifrons* (G. M. Spooner)
Planktonic studies (A. J. Southward and P. G. Corbin)
Development of polychaetes and studies on the breeding behavior of the Black Sea-bream and the male Cuckoo Wrasse (D. P. Wilson)
Taxonomic studies on fishes and crustaceans (P. G. Corbin)
Studies on benthonic invertebrate populations by the use of grab samples (N. A. Holme)
Studies on underwater rock fauna in the vicinity of Plymouth (G. R. Forster)
Distribution and abundance of barnacles and other shore animals (A. J. Southward)
Distribution and systematics of Pogonophora of the Atlantic (A. J. Southward and Eve Southward)
Studies on the uptake of I^{131} by the sea weed *Laminaria digitata* (T. I. Shaw)
Studies on bioluminescence (J. A. C. Nicol)
Studies on vision of fishes (E. J. Denton)
Studies on buoyancy of deep sea fishes and squids (E. J. Denton)
Studies on crustacean hormones (D. B. Carlisle)
Studies on the toxicity of heavy metals to marine organisms (E. D. S. Corner)
Note: Many additional research projects, too numerous to mention, are carried out both by regular staff members and by visiting scientists.
PUBLICATIONS ISSUED: *Journal of the Marine Biological Association of the United Kingdom* (published regularly)

United Kingdom Atomic Energy Authority, Radiobiology Group, Health and Safety Branch

POSTAL ADDRESS: Production Group, Windscale and Calder Works, Sellafield, Seascale, Cumberland, England.
LOCATION: Near Carlisle, England.
EXECUTIVE OFFICER: W. L. Templeton, Senior Officer.
YEAR FOUNDED: 1949.
SCOPE OF ACTIVITIES: Officially restricted research on the effect of discharge of radioactive isotopes to the aquatic environment.
SEASON OF OPERATION: All year.
PHYSICAL ENVIRONMENT ACCESSIBLE: North Irish Sea; oligotrophic lakes, rivers and streams.

PROVISIONS FOR VISITING SCIENTISTS: None.

MAJOR RESEARCH FACILITIES: Small library; large outdoor ponds and tanks, small aquarium tanks; machine and wood shop, electrical and electronic shop; skilled shop workman available; one 45 ft LOA vessel.

SIZE OF STAFF: Six at professional level; 8 technicians.

MAJOR CURRENT RESEARCH PROJECTS AND SCIENTIFIC LEADERS:

The distribution and accumulation of fission product wastes by marine organisms in the North Irish Sea (J. Mauchline)

The study of the effect of fission product wastes discharged into fresh-water (V. M. Brown)

University of Liverpool, Marine Biological Station

POSTAL ADDRESS: Port Erin, Isle of Man, England.

EXECUTIVE OFFICER: John S. Colman, Director.

YEAR FOUNDED: 1885.

SCOPE OF ACTIVITIES: Unrestricted research on general marine biology; undergraduate and graduate instruction.

SEASON OF OPERATION: All year.

PHYSICAL ENVIRONMENT ACCESSIBLE: Irish Sea; sandy and silty beaches, rocky and gravelly shores, estuarine conditions, shallow bays, streams, wide variety of sea bottoms.

PROVISIONS FOR VISITING SCIENTISTS: Research space for 8 visitors; fees charged; living quarters available nearby.

MAJOR RESEARCH AND TEACHING FACILITIES: Moderately complete library; large outdoor ponds and tanks, small aquarium tanks, public aquarium, seafish hatchery; identified reference collections of many marine fish, invertebrates and algae; machine and wood shop, skilled shop workman available; small boats and outboard motors, diesel vessels; 60 ft LOA, *William Herdman,* and 29 ft LOA, *Cypris.*

INSTRUCTIONAL PROGRAM: General marine biology.

SIZE OF STAFF: Eight at professional level; 5 technicians.

IMPORTANT SPECIES AVAILABLE FOR LABORATORY STUDIES:

Algae: *Laminaria hyperborea*

Pisces: *Pleuronectes platessa*

MAJOR CURRENT RESEARCH PROJECTS AND SCIENTIFIC LEADERS:

Bottom fauna; taxonomy of Cumacea (N. S. Jones)

Herring and scallop fisheries (A. B. Bowers)

Zooplankton; decapod larvae (D. I. Williamson)

Submarine algae (Joanna Kain)

Chaetognatha (J. S. Colman)

PUBLICATIONS ISSUED: L. M. B. C. Memoirs (on typical marine plants and animals) (published occasionally)

University of London, Queen Mary College, Marine Biological Laboratory

POSTAL ADDRESS: Sea Wall, Whitstable, England.

LOCATION: Near Canterbury, England.

EXECUTIVE OFFICER: G. E. Newell, Professor of Zoology, Queen Mary College, Mile End Road, London E. 1, England.

YEAR FOUNDED: 1952.

SCOPE OF ACTIVITIES: Unrestricted research on general biology, behavior and physiology of shore fauna; graduate and undergraduate instruction.

SEASON OF OPERATION: Mainly March to November.

PHYSICAL ENVIRONMENT ACCESSIBLE: Thames Estuary and English Channel; sandy and silty beaches, estuarine conditions, brackish, shallow bays.

PROVISIONS FOR VISITING SCIENTISTS: Space for 5 visitors; no fees charged; living quarters available nearby.

MAJOR RESEARCH AND TEACHING FACILITIES: Small library; running sea water, small aquarium tanks; identified reference collection of local fauna and flora available at Laboratory and at Queen Mary College, London; vessels may be hired from local inshore fishermen.

INSTRUCTIONAL PROGRAM: Short courses in marine biology are given usually during vacation periods; in alternate years a 1 week course in comparative physiology is offered.

SIZE OF STAFF: One technician.

IMPORTANT SPECIES AVAILABLE FOR LABORATORY STUDIES: All common species of the English coast are available. A fauna list has been published in the Annals and Magazine of Natural History.

MAJOR CURRENT RESEARCH PROJECTS AND SCIENTIFIC LEADERS:

Physiology and behavior of intertidal mollusks (G. E. Newell)

Behavior of small intertidal Crustacea (J. D. Carthy)

Physiology of trematodes (R. F. H. Freeman)

Chemical and physical properties of sands in variation to respiration of burrowing animals (H. M. Fox)

Water Pollution Research Laboratory

POSTAL ADDRESS: Elder Way, Stevenage, Herts, England.

LOCATION: Near London.

EXECUTIVE OFFICER: Dr. B. A. Southgate, Director.

SPONSORING AGENCY: Department of Scientific and Industrial Research.

YEAR FOUNDED: 1927.

SCOPE OF ACTIVITIES: Officially restricted research on the prevention of the pollution of rivers and other sources of water supply.

SEASON OF OPERATION: All year.

WATER POLLUTION RESEARCH LABORATORY, STEVENAGE

PROVISIONS FOR VISITING SCIENTISTS: None.

MAJOR RESEARCH FACILITIES: Moderately complete library; small aquarium tanks, supply of unchlorinated well water; machine and wood shop, electrical and electronic shop, skilled shop workmen available; small boats and ou board motors.

SIZE OF STAFF: Ninety at professional level; 50 technicians.

MAJOR CURRENT RESEARCH PROJECTS:
- Biochemistry and bacteriology of treating liquids containing organic matter
- Flocculation and sedimentation of suspended matter
- Factors affecting aeration of liquids
- Factors affecting drying of organic sludges
- Digestion of sewage sludge and industrial wastes
- Comparison of the efficiency of different types of filtering material
- Study of oxygen balance of fresh-water streams
- Effects of polluting substances on fish
- Study of coastal pollution

PUBLICATIONS ISSUED:
- *Water Pollution Abstracts* (published monthly)
- *Notes on Water Pollution* (published quarterly)
- Technical Papers (published occasionally)

The Fresh-Water Biological Association, Windermere Laboratory

POSTAL ADDRESS: The Ferry House, Far Sawrey, Ambleside, Westmorland, England.

LOCATION: Near Kendal, England.

EXECUTIVE OFFICER: Mr. H. C. Gilson, Director and Secretary.

SPONSORING AGENCY: The Fresh-water Biological Association.

YEAR FOUNDED: 1931.

SCOPE OF ACTIVITIES: Unrestricted research on fresh-water biology; undergraduate instruction.

SEASON OF OPERATION: All year.

PHYSICAL ENVIRONMENT ACCESSIBLE: Windermere and other local eutrophic and oligotrophic lakes, mountain streams.

PROVISIONS FOR VISITING SCIENTISTS: Research and living space for up to 5-6 visitors; fees charged for research space unless visitors' organization maintains a table at the laboratory.

MAJOR RESEARCH AND TEACHING FACILITIES: Very extensive library; usual variety of small aquarium tanks; research and identified reference collections of Mollusca, Plecoptera, Hemiptera, Heteroptera, Ephemeroptera (including nymphs), Trichoptera, Coleoptera, Chironomidae, Calcidae, Bryozoa, Crustacea and Pisces; machine and wood shop, electrical and electronic shop, skilled shop workman available; small boats and outboard motors; one 30 ft LOA motor launch *Velia.*

INSTRUCTIONAL PROGRAM: Annual 14-day course on fresh-water biology.

SIZE OF STAFF: Fifteen at professional level; 24 technicians.

IMPORTANT SPECIES AVAILABLE FOR LABORATORY STUDIES: A wide variety of fresh-water species is readily available for experimental work. A catalog of specimens offered for sale is available from the Director.

MAJOR CURRENT RESEARCH PROJECTS AND SCIENTIFIC LEADERS:
- Taxonomy and ecology of fresh-water algae (J. W. G. Lund)
- Biology of invertebrates (T. T. Macan)
- Biology of pike (*Esox*) and char (*Salvelinus*) (Winifred E. Frost)
- Population dynamics of perch and trout (E. D. Le Cren)
- Bacteriology of fresh-waters (V. G. Collins)
- Mycology of fresh-waters (L. G. Willoughby)
- Primary production in lakes (J. F. Talling)

WINDERMERE LABORATORY, AMBLESIDE

UNITED KINGDOM, SCOTLAND

Gatty Marine Laboratory and Wellcome Laboratory of Comparative Pharmacology

POSTAL ADDRESS: The University of St. Andrews, Fife, Scotland.

EXECUTIVE OFFICER: Dr. G. Adrian Horridge, Director.

SPONSORING AGENCY: University of St. Andrews and the Wellcome Foundation.

YEAR FOUNDED: 1883.

SCOPE OF ACTIVITIES: Unrestricted research on the biology of marine vertebrates, invertebrates, and algae; emphasis on comparative physiology, comparative pharmacology, structure and physiology of invertebrate nervous systems, algal physiology; graduate and undergraduate instruction.

GATTY MARINE LABORATORY, FIFE

SEASON OF OPERATION: All year.

PHYSICAL ENVIRONMENT ACCESSIBLE: North Sea; sandy and silty beaches, rocky and gravelly shores, estuarine conditions, and rivers and streams.

PROVISIONS FOR VISITING SCIENTISTS: Research space for 4 visitors; living quarters available nearby.

MAJOR RESEARCH AND TEACHING FACILITIES: Very extensive library; running sea and fresh-water, small aquarium tanks, 800 gallon indoor tanks; research collection of local algae; machine and wood shop; small boats and outboard motors; electronic gear.

INSTRUCTIONAL PROGRAM: Comparative physiology (2 weeks each Easter vacation), marine biology, and comparative endocrinology to undergraduate students of St. Andrews University.

SIZE OF STAFF: Seven at professional level; 5 technicians.

IMPORTANT SPECIES AVAILABLE FOR LABORATORY STUDIES:
- Typical North Sea fauna and flora
- Fauna and flora list in press

MAJOR CURRENT RESEARCH PROJECTS AND SCIENTIFIC LEADERS:
- Structure and physiology of invertebrate nervous systems (G. A. Horridge)
- Thyroid physiology in fish (A. J. Matty)
- Algal taxonomy and ecology (H. C. Blackler)
- Algal physiology (D. C. Weeks)

Institute of Seaweed Research

POSTAL ADDRESS: Inveresk, Midlothian, Scotland.

LOCATION: Near Edinburgh.

EXECUTIVE OFFICER: E. Booth, Principal Scientific Officer.

SPONSORING AGENCY: Development Commission (semi-governmental).

YEAR FOUNDED: 1944.

SCOPE OF ACTIVITIES: Officially restricted research on the chemistry and biochemistry of algae; information and technical assistance service.

SEASON OF OPERATION: All year.

PHYSICAL ENVIRONMENT ACCESSIBLE: Firth of Forth, North Sea; sandy and silty beaches, rocky and gravelly shores, estuarine conditions, and brackish, shallow bays.

PROVISIONS FOR VISITING SCIENTISTS: None.

MAJOR RESEARCH FACILITIES: Small library; 30 ft LOA vessel, M. V. *Jean*.

SIZE OF STAFF: Four at professional level.

MAJOR CURRENT RESEARCH PROJECTS AND SCIENTIFIC LEADERS:
- Note: All research is done by contract with various universities.
- Chemistry of algal enzymes (E. L. Hirst and S. Peat)
- Chemical composition of marine algae (G. E. Fogg)
- Algal proteins (G. T. Young)
- Algal antibiotics (C. G. C. Chesters)

INSTITUTE OF SEAWEED RESEARCH, INVERESK

Department of Agriculture and Fisheries for Scotland

LABORATORIES:

1. Freshwater Fisheries Laboratory
2. The Marine Laboratory, Aberdeen

(Descriptions follow.)

Freshwater Fisheries Laboratory

POSTAL ADDRESS: Faskally, Pitlochry, Perthshire, Scotland.

LOCATION: Near Perth.

EXECUTIVE OFFICER: Mr. K. A. Pyefinch, Officer-in-Charge.

YEAR FOUNDED: 1948.

SCOPE OF ACTIVITIES: Officially restricted research on fresh-water fish, especially salmonids and on other parts of the fresh-water community.

SEASON OF OPERATION: All year.

PHYSICAL ENVIRONMENT ACCESSIBLE: Lochs Faskally and Tummel (oligotrophic lakes) ; rivers and streams.

PROVISIONS FOR VISITING SCIENTISTS: Research space for 1-2 visitors; no fees charged.

MAJOR RESEARCH FACILITIES: Small library; large outdoor ponds and tanks, small aquarium tanks; limited reference collections of invertebrate fresh-water fauna, especially insects; machine and wood shop, small boats and outboard motors.

SIZE OF STAFF: Thirteen at professional level; 6 technicians.

IMPORTANT SPECIES AVAILABLE FOR LABORATORY STUDIES:

Pisces: *Salmo trutta, S. salar*

MAJOR CURRENT RESEARCH PROJECTS AND SCIENTIFIC LEADERS:

Investigations of the behavior of salmonids (T. A. Stuart and D. H. A. Marr)

Biology of salmon and sea trout (K. A. Pyefinch, T. A. Stuart and W. R. Munro)

Effects of hydro-electric developments on salmon rivers and their stocks (K. A. Pyefinch, T. A. Stuart and D. H. Mills)

Invertebrate fauna of streams (H. J. Egglishaw)

Physical and chemical characteristics of streams (A. V. Holden)

Pollution problems, especially those involving insecticides (A. V. Holden)

PUBLICATIONS ISSUED: *Freshwater and Salmon Fisheries Research, Department of Agriculture and Fisheries* (occasionally published journal)

The Marine Laboratory, Aberdeen

POSTAL ADDRESS: P. O. Box 101, Victoria Road, Aberdeen, Scotland.

EXECUTIVE OFFICER: Dr. C. E. Lucas, Director of Fisheries Research.

YEAR FOUNDED: 1882.

SCOPE OF ACTIVITIES: Investigation of marine fish, including shellfish, and fishing processes with related environmental studies.

SEASON OF OPERATION: All year.

PHYSICAL ENVIRONMENTT ACCESSIBLE: North Sea; cruises made to Faroe-Shetland waters, Iceland, and Greenland; high seas.

PROVISIONS FOR VISITING SCIENTISTS: Very limited space for visitors; living quarters available nearby.

MAJOR RESEARCH FACILITIES: Very extensive library; running sea and fresh-water, large outdoor ponds and tanks, small aquarium tanks, fairly large indoor tanks; extensive research collections of marine plankton and bottom fauna; identified reference collections of chaetognaths and Thaliacea of N. E. Atlantic area, specimens of many other planktonic groups, bottom fauna, parasitic copepods, fish, etc.; machine and wood shop, electrical and electronic shop, skilled shop workman available; vessels, 183 ft LOA B P *Explorer II,* 164 ft LOA B P *Scotia,* 73 ft LOA *Mara,* 75 ft LOA B P *Clupea,* and one small motorboat.

SIZE OF STAFF: Forty-three at professional level; 34 technicians.

IMPORTANT SPECIES AVAILABLE FOR LABORATORY STUDIES:

Pisces: *Gadus aeglefinus, G. callarias, G. merlangus,*

FRESHWATER FISHERIES LABORATORY, PITLOCHRY

THE MARINE LABORATORY, ABERDEEN

G. virens, Pleuronectes platessa, Clupea harengus, Salmo salar, S. trutta
Crustacea: *Homarus homarus, Nephrops norvegicus, Cancer pagurus*

MAJOR CURRENT RESEARCH PROJECTS AND SCIENTIFIC LEADERS:
Plankton and botttom fauna (J. H. Fraser)
Pelagic and demersal roundfish and related international conservation matters (B. B. Parrish)
Flatfish and national regulations (B. B. Rae)
Shellfish (H. J. Thomas)
Many other biological studies, too numerous to mention, are also being conducted at this station.

PUBLICATIONS ISSUED:
Marine Research Series, Scotland (occasionally published journal)
Annual Report of the Fisheries of Scotland.

Scottish Marine Biological Association

LABORATORIES:
1. Marine Station, Millport
2. The Oceanographic Laboratory, Edinburgh

(Descriptions follow.)

Marine Station, Millport

POSTAL ADDRESS: Millport, Isle of Cumbrae, Scotland.

LOCATION: Near Glasgow.

EXECUTIVE OFFICER: Dr. C. H. Mortimer, Director and Secretary.

YEAR FOUNDED: 1884.

SCOPE OF ACTIVITIES: Unrestricted research on general marine biology; graduate and undergraduate instructions.

SEASON OF OPERATION: All year.

PHYSICAL ENVIRONMENT ACCESSIBLE: Firth of Clyde and Scottish west coast, northern Irish Sea; sandy and silty beaches, rocky and gravelly shores.

PROVISIONS FOR VISITING SCIENTISTS: Research space for 6 visitors; fees charged; living quarters available nearby.

MAJOR RESEARCH AND TEACHING FACILITIES: Moderately complete library; running sea and fresh-water, a 70,000 gallon tank normally used for oyster culture, small aquarium tanks, raft for suspension of experimental panels; working reference collection of main phyla in the animal kingdom available for research, small reference collection of phytoplankton cultures; Robertson mollusk collection; machine and wood shop, electrical and electronic shop, skilled shop workman available; vessels, 70 ft LOA, R. V. *Calanus,* 40 ft LOA, R. V. *Mizpah,* and smaller boats for shore collecting.

INSTRUCTIONAL PROGRAM: General marine zoology courses in spring and fall for university graduates.

SIZE OF STAFF: Fifteen at professional level; 12 technicians.

SCOTTISH MARINE BIOLOGICAL ASSOCIATION, MARINE STATION, MILLPORT

IMPORTANT SPECIES AVAILABLE FOR LABORATORY STUDIES (wide variety including):
Mollusca: *Patella vulgata, P. aspersa*
Crustacea: *Balanus* spp., *Chthamalus* sp., *Calanus finmarchicus, Megarycriphanes novegicus, Marinogammarus* sp., *Ligia oceanica, Carcinus maenas, Sacculina carcina*
Echinodermata: *Echinus esculentus, Psammechinus miliaris*
Tunicata: *Ciona intestinalis*
Pisces: *Squalus acanthias, Raia batis*

MAJOR CURRENT RESEARCH PROJECTS AND SCIENTIFIC LEADERS:
Plankton and copepod biology (S. M. Marshall)
Barnacle biology and marine chemistry (H. Barnes)
Decapod taxonomy and life histories (R. B. Pike)
Ascidiacea and oyster culture (R. H. Millar)
Phytoplankton nutrition (M. R. Droop)
Seaweeds and shore ecology (H. T. Powell)
Biology of fishes (T. B. Bagenal)
Phytoplankton, particularly Hydromedusae (C. Edwards)
Bottom fauna (P. R. O. Barnett)
Water movements (C. H. Mortimer)

PUBLICATIONS ISSUED: *The Fauna of the Clyde Sea Area* (published in occasional parts)

The Oceanographic Laboratory

POSTAL ADDRESS: 78 Craighall Road, Edinburgh 6, Scotland.

EXECUTIVE OFFICER: R. S. Glover, Officer-in-Charge.

YEAR FOUNDED: 1931.

SCOPE OF ACTIVITIES: Unrestricted research on the ecology of plankton of the North Sea and north Atlantic Ocean with emphasis on sampling with Continuous Plankton Recorders and Plankton Indicators. Plankton studies are related to problems of fluctuations in commercial fisheries, especially herring.

SEASON OF OPERATION: All year.

PHYSICAL ENVIRONMENT ACCESSIBLE: Firth of Forth, North Sea; north Atlantic Ocean, Irminger Sea, Norwegian Sea, and Arctic Ocean.

SCOTTISH MARINE BIOLOGICAL ASSOCIATION, THE OCEANOGRAPHIC LABORATORY

PROVISIONS FOR VISITING SCIENTISTS: Research space for 3 visitors; fees charged.
MAJOR RESEARCH FACILITIES: Moderately complete library; research collections of plankton; machine and wood shop, skilled shop workman available; vessels of the Scottish Marine Biological Association available at Millport; plankton collections are normally from merchant vessels and ocean weather ships.
SIZE OF STAFF: Sixteen at professional level; 5 technicians.
MAJOR CURRENT RESEARCH PROJECTS AND SCIENTIFIC LEADERS:
The continuous plankton recorder survey of the North Sea and the north Atlantic Ocean (R. S. Glover)
An ecological survey of the drift-net herring fishery off the north-east coast of Scotland
PUBLICATIONS ISSUED: *Bulletins of Marine Ecology* (occasionally published journal)

UNITED KINGDOM, WALES

British Ministry of Agriculture, Fisheries and Food, Fisheries Experiment Station

POSTAL ADDRESS: Castle Bank, Conway, Caernarvonshire, Wales.
LOCATION: Near Llandudno.
EXECUTIVE OFFICER: Dr. N. Reynolds, Officer-in-Charge.
YEAR FOUNDED: 1918.
SCOPE OF ACTIVITIES: Officially restricted research on development of commercial molluscan and crustacean shellfish and fisheries.

BRITISH MINISTRY OF AGRICULTURE, FISHERIES AND FOOD, FISHERIES EXPERIMENT STATION

SEASON OF OPERATION: All year.
PHYSICAL ENVIRONMENT ACCESSIBLE: Conway River, Conway Bay, Irish Sea; sandy and silty beaches, rocky and gravelly shores, estuarine conditions.
PROVISIONS FOR VISITING SCIENTISTS: Research space for 2 visitors; no fees charged; living quarters available nearby.
MAJOR RESEARCH FACILITIES: Small library; large outdoor ponds and tanks, small aquarium tanks; machine and wood shop; small boats and outboard motors; one 24 ft LOA general purpose fishing boat; other vessels of the Ministry of Agriculture, Fisheries and Food are also available nearby.
SIZE OF STAFF: Five at professional level; 4 technicians.
IMPORTANT SPECIES AVAILABLE FOR LABORATORY STUDIES:
Mollusca: *Mytilus edulis, Ostrea edulis, Pecten maximus*
Crustacea: *Homarus vulgaris, Leander serratus, Crangon vulgaris*
MAJOR CURRENT RESEARCH PROJECTS AND SCIENTIFIC LEADERS:
Mussel purification and cultivation (N. Reynolds)
Artificial rearing of oysters (P. R. Walne)
Lobster bionomics (B. T. Hepper)
PUBLICATIONS ISSUED: *Fisheries Investigation,* Series II (occasionally published journal)

Federated University of Wales, Marine Biology Station

POSTAL ADDRESS: Menai Bridge, Anglesey, North Wales.
LOCATION: Near Bangor (Chester).
EXECUTIVE OFFICER: Professor D. J. Crisp, Director.
YEAR FOUNDED: 1949.
SCOPE OF ACTIVITIES: Unrestricted research on sessile organisms, especially cirripedes; animal behavior, bio-

chemical studies of marine organisms; graduate and undergraduate instruction.

SEASON OF OPERATION: All year.

PHYSICAL ENVIRONMENT ACCESSIBLE: Menai Strait, Caernarvon Bay, St. George's Channel, Conway Bay, Irish Sea; sandy and silty beaches, rocky and gravelly shores, estuarine conditions, and brackish, shallow bays.

PROVISIONS FOR VISITING SCIENTISTS: Research space for visitors is available by special arrangement only; fees charged; living quarters available nearby.

MAJOR RESEARCH AND TEACHING FACILITIES: Running sea and fresh-water, small aquarium tanks; type specimen collection of local animals and algae; fauna and flora lists with card index available for reference; shop facilities available elsewhere in the college; vessels, 40 ft LOA trawler, 20 ft LOA cabin cruiser, raft for experiments in sea, dinghy and outboard motor.

INSTRUCTIONAL PROGRAM: Subsidiary course in oceanography; vacation courses (10-14 days) in marine biology.

SIZE OF STAFF: Six at professional level.

IMPORTANT SPECIES AVAILABLE FOR LABORATORY STUDIES:

Echinodermata: *Psammechinus miliaris*

Crustacea: *Carcinus maenas, Elminius modestus, Balanus* sp., *Palaemonetes* sp.

Mollusca: *Littorina littorea, L. obtusata, L. saxatilis, Spisula solida, Mytilus edulis*

Polychaeta: *Arenicola marina, Pomatoceros triqueter*

Algae: *Phaeodactylum tricornutum*

MAJOR CURRENT RESEARCH PROJECTS AND SCIENTIFIC LEADERS:

Biology of cirripedes and other sessile organisms (D. J. Crisp)

Fouling in British ports (D. J. Crisp and A. P. Austin)

Biology of Enteropneusta (C. Burdon-Jones)

Hatching factor of cirripedes (D. J. Crisp and C. P. Spencer)

Growth of *Phaeodactylum* (C. P. Spencer)

Effect of exposure on algae (W. E. Jones)

Effect of toxic substances on enzymes (A. O. Christie)

FEDERATED UNIVERSITY OF WALES, MARINE BIOLOGY STATION

UNITED STATES OF AMERICA

The Academy of Natural Sciences of Philadelphia, Department of Limnology

POSTAL ADDRESS: Nineteenth and the Parkway, Philadelphia 3, Pennsylvania, USA.

EXECUTIVE OFFICER: Dr. Ruth Patrick, Curator of Limnology.

SPONSORING AGENCY: Department of Academy of Natural Science, a privately endowed institution.

YEAR FOUNDED: 1947.

SCOPE OF ACTIVITIES: Unrestricted research on systematics and ecology of plankton and bottom living plants and animals found in fresh-water and estuaries; chemical and bacteriological analyses of waters and sediments in rivers and estuaries.

SEASON OF OPERATION: All year.

PHYSICAL ENVIRONMENT ACCESSIBLE: Fresh-water, estuarine and marine.

PROVISIONS FOR VISITING SCIENTISTS: Space for 3-6 visitors; living quarters available nearby.

MAJOR RESEARCH AND TEACHING FACILITIES: Very extensive library; running sea, brackish and fresh-water; small aquarium tanks; research and identified reference collections of fish, mollusks, crustaceans and lower invertebrates, fresh-water aquatic insects, diatoms and algae, both fresh-water and marine (these collections have both local and world-wide representation); machine and wood shop; small boats and outboard motors.

INSTRUCTIONAL PROGRAM: Direction of graduate thesis work in limnology and systematics of diatoms.

SIZE OF STAFF: Fourteen at professional level; 9 technicians.

IMPORTANT SPECIES AVAILABLE FOR LABORATORY STUDIES:

Pisces: *Lepomis macrochirus*

Diatoms: *Nitzschia linearis, Navicula seminulum* var. *hustedti*

Blue-green algae: Various species of *Oscillatoria*

MAJOR CURRENT RESEARCH PROJECTS AND SCIENTIFIC LEADERS:

Diatoms of continental United States (book in preparation) (Ruth Patrick, Charles Reimer)

Systematic study on the Tendipedidae (Selwyn S. Roback)

The fauna and flora of the Peruvian headwaters of the Amazon Basin (John Cairns, S. S. Roback, Frederich Aldrich, Ruth Patrick)

The establishment of the fauna and flora in a new stream (Ruth Patrick, J. Cairns, S. S. Roback, C. Reimer)

Chemicals commonly found in industrial wastes (Ruth Patrick, John Cairns)

PUBLICATIONS ISSUED: *Proceedings* and *Memoirs* (regularly published scientific journals).

Agricultural and Mechanical College of Texas Laboratories

POSTAL ADDRESS:

Headquarters: Department of Oceanography and Meteorology, A. & M. College of Texas, College Station, Texas, USA.

Marine Laboratory: A. & M. Marine Laboratory, Building 311, Fort Crockett, Galveston, Texas.

EXECUTIVE OFFICER: Dr. Dale F. Leipper, Head of Department of Oceanography and Meteorology.

SEASON OF OPERATION: All year.

YEAR FOUNDED: Department of Oceanography and Meteorology, 1949; A. & M. Marine Laboratory, 1953.

GALVESTON MARINE LABORATORY

SCOPE OF ACTIVITIES: Unrestricted oceanographic research; graduate instruction.

PHYSICAL ENVIRONMENT ACCESSIBLE: Gulf of Mexico; open ocean, sandy beach, estuarine conditions, and brackish, shallow bays.

PROVISIONS FOR VISITING SCIENTISTS: At the Department, space for 5 visitors; living quarters available nearby. At the Galveston Laboratory, research and living space for 5 visitors.

MAJOR FACILITIES: Laboratory; 60,000 square ft, partly air conditioned, basic research facilities. Research vessel, *Alaminos,* 180 feet, 770 gross tons, 6,000 mile range, air conditioned, bow propulsion unit, thermal tow, gravity meter, two 30,000 foot hydrographic winches, dredging winch, other standard equipment; ready July 1963. Instrumented offshore platforms, Panama City, Florida, 3 and 11 miles from shore in 60 and 100 feet of water respectively, unmanned observations, 40 sensor channels. Two buildings on campus with offices, classrooms, and fully equipped laboratories for oceanography and meteorology; 10 cm and 3 cm weather radars; laboratories for biological, geological, and chemical oceanography; library; also 2 mobile instrumented trailers for micrometeorological research. Campus Data Processing Center (IBM 650 and 709 available) and Nuclear Science Center.

INSTRUCTIONAL PROGRAM: All aspects of oceanography and meteorology including physical, chemical, biological, geological, and engineering. B.S. in meteorology, and M.S. and Ph.D. programs in both oceanography and meteorology.

SIZE OF STAFF: Thirty-two in research and instruction; 69 other full-time; 70 part time, including research assistants.

IMPORTANT SPECIES AVAILABLE FOR LABORATORY STUDIES:

Crustacea: *Penaeus setiferus, Palaemonetes pugio*
Mollusca: *Ostrea virginica, Modiolus modiolus*
Pisces: *Galeichthys* spp., *Fundulus* spp.

MAJOR CURRENT RESEARCH PROJECTS AND SCIENTIFIC LEADERS:

Organic materials and trace elements in sea water (D. W. Hood)
Marine fatty acids (D. W. Hood)
$CaCO_3$ saturation level (D. W. Hood)
Reef environments (Louis Kornicker)
Primary productivity in the southern ocean (Sayed Z. El-Sayed)
Effects of antibiotics on fungus parasites in oysters (Sammy Ray)

Alabama Marine Laboratory

POSTAL ADDRESS: Bayou LaBatre, Alabama, USA.

LOCATION: Near Mobile.

EXECUTIVE OFFICER: George W. Allen, Chief, Alabama Division of Seafood.

SPONSORING AGENCIES: Alabama State Department of Conservation and University of Alabama.

YEAR FOUNDED: 1950.

SCOPE OF ACTIVITIES: Restricted and unrestricted research directed towards management of seafood resources.

SEASON OF OPERATION: All year.

PHYSICAL ENVIRONMENT ACCESSIBLE: Gulf of Mexico, Mobile Bay, Mississippi Sound; open ocean, estuarine conditions and brackish, shallow bays.

PROVISIONS FOR VISITING SCIENTISTS: Research and living space for 3 visitors; no fees charged for research space.

MAJOR RESEARCH FACILITIES: Small library; running sea and fresh-water; machine and wood shop; small boats and outboard motors; vessels, 32 ft and 38 ft LOA.

SIZE OF STAFF: Three at professional level; 2 technicians.

Alaska Department of Fish and Game, Kitoi Bay Research Station

POSTAL ADDRESS: Kodiak, Alaska, USA.
EXECUTIVE OFFICER: William L. Sheridan, Research Biologist.
YEAR FOUNDED: 1954.
SCOPE OF ACTIVITIES: Restricted basic research on life history and population dynamics of salmon and trout.
SEASON OF OPERATION: All year.
PHYSICAL ENVIRONMENT ACCESSIBLE: Kitoi Bay, Ishut Bay on Afognak Island; open ocean, sandy beaches, rocky and gravelly shores, estuarine conditions, brackish, shallow bays, oligotrophic lakes, rivers and streams.
PROVISIONS FOR VISITING SCIENTISTS: Research and living space available for visitors; fees charged for research space.
MAJOR RESEARCH FACILITIES: Small library; large outdoor ponds and tanks, small aquarium tanks; limited research and reference collections of fauna and flora; machine and wood shop, skilled shop workman available; small boats and outboard motors.
SIZE OF STAFF: Three at professional level; 3 technicians.
IMPORTANT SPECIES AVAILABLE FOR LABORATORY STUDIES:
Salmonidae: *Oncorhynchus nerka, O. gorbuscha, O. kisutch, Salvelinus malma*
Cottidae: *Cottus aleuticus*
Gasterosteidae: *Gasterosteus aculeatus*
MAJOR CURRENT RESEARCH PROJECTS AND SCIENTIFIC LEADERS:
Sockeye salmon studies (Robert R. Parker)
Pink salmon studies (William L. Sheridan)
Watershed nutrient dynamics (Richard Dugdale)

The Allan Hancock Foundation for Scientific Research

POSTAL ADDRESS: University of Southern California, Los Angeles 7, California, USA.
EXECUTIVE OFFICER: Dr. Leslie A. Chambers, Scientific Director.
SPONSORING AGENCY: Privately financed laboratory.
YEAR FOUNDED: 1940.
SCOPE OF ACTIVITIES: Research fields restricted to fundamental studies on marine biology, geology and oceanography; graduate instruction.
SEASON OF OPERATION: All year.
PHYSICAL ENVIRONMENT ACCESSIBLE: Pacific Oceean.
PROVISIONS FOR VISITING SCIENTISTS: Space available for visitors.
MAJOR RESEARCH AND TEACHING FACILITIES: Large research and identified reference collections of algae, marine invertebrates, especially crustaceans, mollusks, polychaetes, and echinoderms; machine and wood shop; 110 ft LOA oceanographic vessel, *Velero IV*.
INSTRUCTIONAL PROGRAM: Biological oceanography, parasitology, general invertebrate zoology, aquatic invertebrate and vertebrate systematics, submarine geology.
SIZE OF STAFF: Seven at professional level.
IMPORTANT SPECIES AVAILABLE FOR LABORATORY STUDIES: All species found along the coast of southern California.
MAJOR CURRENT RESEARCH PROJECTS AND SCIENTIFIC LEADERS:
Oceanic survey of the southern California shelf (R. E. Stevenson)
Benthonic Foraminifera as indictators of pollution (R. E. Stevenson)
Sulfur isotopes in sediments (S. C. Rittenberg and K. O. Emery)
Benthos of submarine canyons (Olga Hartman and K. O. Emery)
Oxygen in basin waters (K. O. Emery)

THE ALLAN HANCOCK FOUNDATION FOR SCIENTIFIC RESEARCH

Ecological survey of mid-water fishes and crustaceans (J. S. Garth and J. M. Savage)
Monograph of Pacific American Cancroidea (J. S. Garth)

Auburn University, Farm Ponds Laboratory

POSTAL ADDRESS: Fisheries Building, Auburn University, Auburn, Alabama, USA.
EXECUTIVE OFFICER: H. S. Swingle, Fish Culturist.
SPONSORING AGENCY: Alabama Agricultural Experiment Station of Auburn University.
YEAR FOUNDED: 1934.
SCOPE OF ACTIVITIES: Extensive research on fresh-water pond management and river and impoundment surveys; graduate and undergraduate instruction.
SEASON OF OPERATION: All year.
PHYSICAL ENVIRONMENT ACCESSIBLE: Streams, ponds and large impoundments.

FISHERIES BUILDING, FARM PONDS LABORATORY, AUBURN UNIVERSITY

PROVISIONS FOR VISITING SCIENTISTS: None.

MAJOR RESEARCH AND TEACHING FACILITIES: Very extensive library; 154 experimental ponds, small aquarium tanks, feeding troughs; machine and wood shop, skilled shop workman available; small boats and outboard motors.

INSTRUCTIONAL PROGRAM: Limnology, plankton, ecology, general and comparative physiology, biochemistry, embryology, parasitology, phycology, general invertebrate zoology, ichthyology, aquatic entomology, fishery biology, biometry, population dynamics, fisheries and hatchery management and pond construction.

SIZE OF STAFF: Six at professional level; 6-10 technicians.

IMPORTANT SPECIES AVAILABLE FOR LABORATORY STUDIES:

Aquatic plants: *Pithophora, Anacharis* spp., *Potamogeton* spp., *Microcystis, Heteranthera dubia, Alternanthera philoxeroides.*

Trematoda: *Gyrodactylus* sp., *Dactylogyrus.*

Gastropoda: *Physa* sp.

Insecta: Chironomidae.

Pisces: 35 species of fresh-water fishes in ponds including *Tilapia nilotica* and *T. mossambica.* Other local species available include *Lepomis macrochirus, Micropterus salmoides, Pimephales promelas, Ictalurus punctatus* and *I. catus.*

AERIAL VIEW OF 48 OF THE 164 EXPERIMENTAL FRESH-WATER PONDS OPERATED BY THE AGRICULTURAL EXPERIMENTAL STATION, AUBURN UNIVERSITY

MAJOR CURRENT RESEARCH PROJECTS AND SCIENTIFIC LEADERS:

Parasites of fish (Ray Allison)
Fish food organisms (J. S. Dendy)
Chemical control of pond weeds (J. M. Lawrence)
Sport fish management (H. S. Swingle and E. E. Prather)
Minnow production (E. E. Prather)
Commercial fish production (H. S. Swingle)
Screening aquatic herbicides (J. M. Lawrence, Don Davis and R. Blackburn)
Toxicity of rotenone formulations to fish (F. E. Hester)
Biological weed control (E. W. Shell)
Surveys of Alabama rivers (Staff)
Biological control of snails (Ray Allison)

Battelle Memorial Institute, North Florida Research Station

POSTAL ADDRESS: 5222 South Peninsula Drive, Daytona Beach, Florida, USA.

EXECUTIVE OFFICER: B. J. Merrell, Operator.

SPONSORING AGENCY: Battelle Memorial Institute, Columbus, Ohio. (Industrial research organization which contracts individual research programs for industrial firms, governmental agencies, etc.)

YEAR FOUNDED: 1948.

SCOPE OF ACTIVITIES: Research on the protection of materials from deterioration in marine environments.

SEASON OF OPERATION: All year.

PHYSICAL ENVIRONMENT ACCESSIBLE: Atlantic Ocean; sandy and silty beaches, and estuarine conditions.

PROVISIONS FOR VISITING SCIENTISTS: None.

MAJOR RESEARCH FACILITIES: No library; marine dock designed for exposure of specimens to sea water; small reference collection of principal fouling and wood-destroying organisms; small machine and wood shop, skilled shop workman available; small boats and outboard motors.

SIZE OF STAFF: One at professional level; 1 technician.

IMPORTANT SPECIES AVAILABLE FOR LABORATORY STUDIES:

Crustacea: *Balanus eburneus, B. improvisus* and other species of barnacles; *Limnoria tripunctata*

Pelecypoda: *Anomia simplex, Crassostrea virginica, Mytilus* sp., *Teredo* sp., *Bankia* sp., *Martesia* sp.

Polychaeta: *Hydroides* sp.

Hydrozoa: *Bugula* sp.

MAJOR CURRENT RESEARCH PROJECTS:

Corrosion of metals
Durability and effectiveness of protective coatings
Wood preservatives
Anti-fouling coatings

Bears Bluff Laboratories

POSTAL ADDRESS: Wadmalaw Island, South Carolina,, USA.

LOCATION: Near Charleston.

EXECUTIVE OFFICER: G. Robert Lunz, Jr., Director.

SPONSORING AGENCY: South Carolina Wildlife Resources Commission.

YEAR FOUNDED: 1946.

SCOPE OF ACTIVITIES: Unrestricted research in marine and fresh-water biology.

SEASON OF OPERATION: All year.

PHYSICAL ENVIRONMENT ACCESSIBLE: Atlantic Ocean, Wadmalaw and North Edisto Rivers.

PROVISIONS FOR VISITING SCIENTISTS: Research and living space for 6 visitors; no fees charged for research space.

MAJOR RESEARCH FACILITIES: Small library; running sea water, large outdoor ponds, small aquarium tanks;

BEARS BLUFF LABORATORIES

identified natural history collection at Charleston Museum; machine and wood shop; vessels, 65 ft, 40 ft, and 26 ft LOA.

SIZE OF STAFF: Three at professional level; 2 technicians.

IMPORTANT SPECIES AVAILABLE FOR LABORATORY STUDIES:

- Crustacea: *Penaeus* spp., *Callinectes sapidus*
- Mollusca: *Crassostrea virginica*
- Pisces: various species

MAJOR CURRENT RESEARCH PROJECTS AND SCIENTIFIC LEADERS:

- General survey of shrimp industry: determiniation of abundance of shrimp, crabs, and fin fish normally taken in otter trawls (C. M. Bearden and G. Robert Lunz)
- Pond cultivation of shrimp (G. Robert Lunz)
- General survey of oyster beds, their productiveness and oyster pest study (Henry W. Hodges)

Beaudette Foundation, Institute of Marine Bioresearch

POSTAL ADDRESS: 1597 Calzada Rd., Santa Ynez, California, USA.

EXECUTIVE OFFICERS: Palmer T. Beaudette, President, Beaudette Foundation.

SPONSORING AGENCY: Privately financed laboratory.

YEAR FOUNDED: 1958.

SCOPE OF ACTIVITIES: Restricted research on the taxonomy and ecology of fauna and flora of Pacific Latin America.

SEASON OF OPERATION: All year.

PHYSICAL ENVIRONMENT ACCESSIBLE: Pacific Ocean; sandy and silty beaches, rocky and gravelly shores.

PROVISIONS FOR VISITING SCIENTISTS: Research and living space for 2 visitors; no fees charged for research space.

MAJOR RESEARCH FACILITIES: Small library; small aquarium tanks; extensive research collections of algae of eastern Pacific, California to Panama, Mexican invertebrates; identified reference collections of Mexican Amphipoda and eastern Pacific algae; machine and wood shop; small boats and outboard motors; 103 ft LOA power vessel under construction.

SIZE OF STAFF: Two at professional level; 2 technicians.

MAJOR CURRENT RESEARCH PROJECTS AND SCIENTIFIC LEADERS:

- Red algae of Mexico (E. Yale Dawson)
- Marine flora of El Salvador (E. Yale Dawson)
- Amphipoda of eastern Pacific Ocean (J. L. Barnard)
- Hydrobiology of San Quentin Bay, B. California (J. L. Barnard and staff)
- Abyssal Amphipoda of *Galathea* and *Vema* collections (J. L. Barnard)
- Atoll marine Amphipoda of Micronesia (J. L. Barnard)

PUBLICATIONS ISSUED: *Pacific Naturalist* (occasionally published journal)

INSTITUTE OF MARINE BIORESEARCH, CALIFORNIA

BENNER SPRING FISH RESEARCH STATION

Benner Spring Fish Research Station

POSTAL ADDRESS: P. O. Box 200C., R. D. No. 1, Bellefonte, Pennsylvania, USA.

EXECUTIVE OFFICER: Mr. Gordon L. Trembley, Chief Aquatic Biologist.

SPONSORING AGENCY: Pennsylvania Fish Commission.

YEAR FOUNDED: 1955.

SCOPE OF ACTIVITIES: Research on fishery management and fish culture.

SEASON OF OPERATION: All year.

PHYSICAL ENVIRONMENT ACCESSIBLE: Fresh-water streams and lakes (eutrophic and oligotrophic) of Pennsylvania.

PROVISIONS FOR VISITING SCIENTISTS: Space for 3 visitors; no fees charged; living quarters available nearby.

MAJOR RESEARCH FACILITIES: 25 acres; one two-story building, 100 ft by 40 ft; small library; three laboratories; research collection of fresh-water fish; hatching facilities; small aquaria; 150 experimental concrete ponds, raceways and earthen ponds for trout; numerous large ponds for warm water fish species; machine and wood shop, skilled shop workmen available; small boats and outboard motors.

SIZE OF STAFF: Five at professional level; 13 technicians.

MAJOR CURRENT RESEARCH PROJECTS AND SCIENTIFIC LEADERS:

- Blood group studies and immuno-genetics in trout (James E. Wright, Jr.)
- Selective breeding, nutrition and improved mechanical techniques for trout culture; refinements in esocid culture (Keen Buss)
- Diseases of fishes, and immunological studies (Arthur D. Bradford)
- Experimental electro-fishing gear (Jack G. Miller)

Bingham Oceanographic Laboratory

POSTAL ADDRESS: P. O. Box 2025, Yale Station, New Haven, Connecticut, USA.

EXECUTIVE OFFICER: Dr. Daniel Merriman, Director.

SPONSORING AGENCY: Yale University.

YEAR FOUNDED: 1930.

SCOPE OF ACTIVITIES: Unrestricted research on biological and physical oceanography and general marine biology; graduate and undergraduate instruction.

SEASON OF OPERATION: All year.

PHYSICAL ENVIRONMENT ACCESSIBLE: Atlantic Ocean, Long Island and Block Island Sounds; sandy and silty beaches, rocky and gravelly shores, estuarine conditions and brackish, shallow bays.

PROVISIONS FOR VISITING SCIENTISTS: Space for 3 visitors; no fees charged; living quarters available nearby.

MAJOR RESEARCH AND TEACHING FACILITIES: Very extensive library; running sea and fresh-water, small aquarium tanks; laboratory for handling radioactive materials; good research and reference collections of invertebrates and fishes; machine and wood shop; vessels, 30-60 ft LOA available by charter.

INSTRUCTIONAL PROGRAM: Plankton, biological, chemical and physical oceanography, ichthyology, and fishery biology.

SIZE OF STAFF: Nine at professional level; 3 technicians.

IMPORTANT SPECIES AVAILABLE FOR LABORATORY STUDIES:

Pisces: *Fundulus heteroclitus*

MAJOR CURRENT RESEARCH PROJECTS AND SCIENTIFIC LEADERS:

- Teleost eggs, larvae and juveniles (S. W. Richards)
- Oceanography of Long Island Sound (Gordon A. Riley)
- Fish taxonomy (Alfred W. Ebeling)
- Plankton: seasonal cycles and abundance (G. B. Deavey)
- Physical oceanography (Alyn C. Duxbury)
- Fish endocrinology (G. E. Pickford)
- Elasmobranch life history (Daniel Merriman)

PUBLICATIONS ISSUED: *Journal of Marine Research* (regularly published journal)

BINGHAM OCEANOGRAPHIC LABORATORY

California Academy of Sciences

POSTAL ADDRESS: Golden Gate Park, San Francisco 18, California, USA.

EXECUTIVE OFFICER: Dr. Robert C. Miller, Director.

SPONSORING AGENCY: Privately financed laboratory.

YEAR FOUNDED: 1853.

SCOPE OF ACTIVITIES: Unrestricted research in general marine and fresh-water biology; graduate instruction.

SEASON OF OPERATION: All year.

PHYSICAL ENVIRONMENT ACCESSIBLE: Pacific Ocean, San Francisco Bay and tributaries, Tomales and Bolinas bays, Lake Merced (oligotrophic lake); several small fresh-water lakes and ponds, sandy and silty beaches, rocky and gravelly shores, estuarine conditions and brackish, shallow bays.

PROVISIONS FOR VISITING SCIENTISTS: Space for visitors; no fees charged; living quarters available nearby.

MAJOR RESEARCH AND TEACHING FACILITIES: Very extensive library; running sea and fresh-water, small aquarium tanks; considerable research collection of marine invertebrates, much of it from deep water; large identified reference collections of named aquatic insects, Crustacea, Mollusca, Bryozoa, Brachiopoda, Echinodermata, etc.

INSTRUCTIONAL PROGRAM: Limnology, fishery biology, population dynamics, general marine biology and invertebrate paleontology. Graduate credit to be obtained from neighboring universities.

SIZE OF STAFF: Thirty at professional level; 20 technicians.

IMPORTANT SPECIES AVAILABLE FOR LABORATORY STUDIES:

Polychaeta: *Nereis limnicola*
Mysidacea: *Neomysis mercedis*
Echinodermata: *Pisaster ochraceus, Strongylocentrotus* (3 sp.)
Elasmobranchii: *Squalus suckleyi, Notorynchus maculatus*

MAJOR CURRENT RESEARCH PROJECTS AND SCIENTIFIC LEADERS:

Distribution and biology of marine mammals (Robert T. Orr)
Taxonomy and distribution of California fishes (W. I. Follett)
Aquatic resources of San Francisco Bay (Earl S. Herald)
Fish diseases (Robert P. Dempster)
Biology of marine boring organisms (Robert C. Miller)
Behavior of clupeoid fishes (Anatole S. Loukashkin)
Aquatic Coleoptera (Hugh B. Leech)
Mollusca of Point Barrow (G. Dallas Hanna)
Amphineura of the world (Allyn G. Smith)

PUBLICATIONS ISSUED:

Proceedings (occasionally published contributions)
Pacific Discovery (bi-monthly)
Annual report for general distribution

STEINHART AQUARIUM OF THE CALIFORNIA ACADEMY OF SCIENCES

California State Department of Fish and Game

LABORATORIES:

1. Marine Resources Branch
   a. Marine Resources Operation
2. Inland Fisheries Branch (Field Station)

PUBLICATIONS ISSUED:

California Fish and Game (quarterly journal)
Biennial Reports, California Fish and Game

Marine Resources Branch (Administrative Headquarters)

POSTAL ADDRESS: 822 Capitol Avenue, Sacramento, California, USA.

EXECUTIVE OFFICER: William Ellis Ripley, Acting Chief.

SCOPE OF ACTIVITIES: Restricted and unrestricted research related to the development of the marine fisheries of California.

SIZE OF STAFF: Eleven at professional level; about 10 technicians.

Marine Resources Operation

POSTAL ADDRESS:

Operational Headquarters: State Fisheries Laboratory, 511 Tuna Street, Terminal Island, California.

Branches:

1. Hopkins Marine Station, Pacific Grove, California.
2. Stanford Laboratory, North Rotunda, Museum Building, Stanford, California.
3. Eureka Laboratory, 127 G Street, Eureka, California.

LOCATION: Headquarters is near Los Angeles.

EXECUTIVE OFFICER: Phil M. Roedel, Manager.

CALIFORNIA STATE FISHERIES LABORATORY, TERMINAL ISLAND

YEAR FOUNDED:
State Fisheries Laboratory, 1917.
Hopkins Marine Station Branch, 1920.
Stanford Laboratory Branch, 1930.
Eureka Laboratory Branch, 1935.

SCOPE OF ACTIVITIES: Restricted research on the sport and commercial marine fishes of California, with associated statistical and management functions.

SEASON OF OPERATION: All year.

PHYSICAL ENVIRONMENT ACCESSIBLE: Pacific Ocean.

PROVISIONS FOR VISITING SCIENTISTS: None.

MAJOR RESEARCH FACILITIES: Very extensive library; running sea and fresh-water; small boats and outboard motors; vessels, 100 ft LOA, *N. B. Scofield,* 100 ft LOA, *Alaska,* 50 ft LOA, *Nautilus,* and 28 ft LOA, *Mollusc.*

SIZE OF STAFF: Thirty eight at professional level; 10 sub-professional; 70 clerical, vessel crew, etc.

MAJOR CURRENT RESEARCH PROJECTS AND SCIENTIFIC LEADERS:
Southern California Investigations (J. E. Fitch, in charge):
- Tuna (H. B. Clemens)
- Barracuda-Seabass (L. Pinkas)
- Sportfish (P. H. Young)
- Special studies (J. L. Baxter)
- Habitat development (J. G. Carlisle)
- Sardine and mackerel (J. Radovich)

Northern California Investigations (H. Orcutt, in charge):
- Trawl fisheries (E. Best)
- Shell fisheries (J. A. Aplin)
- Rockfish (J. B. Phillips)
- Sportfish (D. Miller)

Inland Fisheries Branch (Field Station)

POSTAL ADDRESS: 987 Jedsmith Drive, Sacramento 19, California, USA.

EXECUTIVE OFFICER: Dr. Alex Calhoun, Chief, Inland Fisheries Branch.

YEAR FOUNDED: 1959.

SCOPE OF ACTIVITIES: Restricted and unrestricted research directed towards the management and development of the inland fisheries of California, including research on diseases and parasites of fresh-water and anadromous fishes.

SEASON OF OPERATION: All year.

PHYSICAL ENVIRONMENT ACCESSIBLE: Sacramento-San Joaquin River system; estuarine conditions, brackish, shallow bays, eutrophic and oligotrophic lakes, and fresh-water impoundments.

PROVISIONS FOR VISITING SCIENTISTS: None.

MAJOR RESEARCH FACILITIES: Very extensive library in State Office Building in Sacramento; running fresh-water, small aquarium tanks; identified reference collection of California fresh-water and anadromous fishes; machine and wood shop; small boats and outboard motors.

SIZE OF STAFF: Twelve at professional level.

MAJOR CURRENT RESEARCH PROJECTS AND SCIENTIFIC LEADERS:
Projects on trout, warm water game fishes, striped bass, sturgeon, reservoirs, and fish diseases and parasites (Alex Calhoun)

CALIFORNIA DEPARTMENT OF FISH AND GAME, FIELD STATION

The Cape Haze Marine Laboratory

POSTAL ADDRESS: 9501 Blind Pass Road, Sarasota, Florida, USA.

EXECUTIVE OFFICER: Dr. Eugenie Clark, Director.

YEAR FOUNDED: 1955.

SCOPE OF ACTIVITIES: Unrestricted research on general marine biology.

SEASON OF OPERATION: All year.

PHYSICAL ENVIRONMENT ACCESSIBLE: Sarasota Bay, Gulf of Mexico; open ocean, sandy and silty beaches, estuarine conditions, brackish, shallow bays, rivers and streams, mud flats, and shallow bays with sand bars.

PROVISIONS FOR VISITING SCIENTISTS: Space for 6 visitors; no fees charged; living quarters available nearby.

MAJOR RESEARCH FACILITIES: Running sea and fresh-water, four shark pens, small aquarium tanks; research

THE CAPE HAZE MARINE LABORATORY

collections of local fishes, invertebrates and marine plants; identified reference collections of local fishes, birds, algae and some invertebrates; scientific library; machine and wood shop, skilled shop workman available; one 33 ft LOA power vessel.

SIZE OF STAFF: Three at professional level; 3 technicians.

IMPORTANT SPECIES AVAILABLE FOR LABORATORY STUDIES: Several species of sharks, gobies, blennies and groupers.

MAJOR CURRENT RESEARCH PROJECTS AND SCIENTIFIC LEADERS:

A study of the abdominal pores and associated structures in elasmobranch fishes (Eugenie Clark)
Studies on the reproductive behavior and embryology of a hermaphroditic serranid fish (Eugenie Clark)
Instrumental conditioning of sharks (Eugenie Clark)
Study of elasmobranch liver lipids (John H. Heller)
Oxytocic fractions in elasmobranch pituitary (Anthony Perks)

Chesapeake Bay Institute

POSTAL ADDRESS:

Permanent address: The Johns Hopkins University, Baltimore 18, Maryland, USA.
Field Laboratory: Box 32A, Route 3, Annapolis, Maryland.

EXECUTIVE OFFICER: Dr. Donald W. Pritchard, Director.

SPONSORING AGENCY: The Johns Hopkins University.

YEAR FOUNDED: 1948.

SCOPE OF ACTIVITIES: Restricted and unrestricted research in physical, chemical and biological oceanography with emphasis on estuaries and coastal waters; graduate instruction.

SEASON OF OPERATION: All year.

PHYSICAL ENVIRONMENT ACCESSIBLE: Chesapeake Bay; estuarine conditions.

PROVISIONS FOR VISITING SCIENTISTS: Space for 3 visitors; no fees charged; living quarters available nearby.

MAJOR RESEARCH AND TEACHING FACILITIES: Very extensive library at Johns Hopkins, small library at Field Laboratory; machine and wood shop, electrical and electronic shop, skilled shop workman available; small boats and outboard motors; 63 ft LOA, M/V *Maury,* 38 ft LOA, M/V *Lydia Louise II.*

INSTRUCTIONAL PROGRAM: Biological, chemical and physical oceanography.

SIZE OF STAFF: Twenty-one at professional level; 16 technicians.

IMPORTANT SPECIES AVAILABLE FOR LABORATORY STUDIES:

Brachyura: *Neopanope texana, Callinectes sapidus*
Mollusca: *Crassostrea virginica*
Copepoda: *Acartia clausii*

MAJOR CURRENT RESEARCH PROJECTS AND SCIENTIFIC LEADERS:

Chemostat studies of limiting factors for phytoplankton (W. R. Taylor)
Studies of uptake of radioactive isotopes by marine organisms (W. R. Taylor)
Studies of basic productivity in Chesapeake Bay (W. R. Taylor)
Larval development of crabs in estuaries (W. R. Taylor)

Chesapeake Biological Laboratory

POSTAL ADDRESS: P. O. Box 38, Solomons, Maryland, USA.

LOCATION: Near Washington, D. C.

EXECUTIVE OFFICER: Dr. L. Eugene Cronin, Director.

SPONSORING AGENCY: Natural Resources Institute of the University of Maryland.

YEAR FOUNDED: 1925.

SCOPE OF ACTIVITIES: Unrestricted research on basic and applied estuarine biology.

SEASON OF OPERATION: All year.

PHYSICAL ENVIRONMENT ACCESSIBLE: Chesapeake Bay; estuarine conditions.

PROVISIONS FOR VISITING SCIENTISTS: Research and living space for 5 visitors; no fees charged for research space.

MAJOR RESEARCH FACILITIES: Small library; running fresh- and brackish water, large outdoor ponds and tanks, small aquarium tanks, aquatic cages; research and identified reference collections of local fauna and flora planned for future; machine and wood shop, skilled shop workman available; small boats and outboard motors; 42 ft LOA, *Cobia* equipped for dredging and trawling, 40 ft LOA, *John A. Ryder* equipped for hydraulic dredging and 34 ft LOA, *Anomia* used for general collecting.

SIZE OF STAFF: Twenty-six at professional level; 7 technicians.

ESTUARINE RESEARCH LABORATORY, CHESAPEAKE BIOLOGICAL LABORATORY

IMPORTANT SPECIES AVAILABLE FOR LABORATORY STUDIES:
- Ctenophora: *Mnemiopsis leidyi*
- Scyphozoa: *Dactylometra quinquecirrha*
- Pelecypoda: *Crassostrea virginica, Mya arenaria, Mercenaria (Venus) mercenaria*
- Crustacea: *Callinectes sapidus*
- Polychaeta: *Glycera dibranchiata, Neanthes succinea*
- Pisces: *Roccus saxatilis, Morone americana, Opsanus tau, Alosa sapidissima, Perca flavescens*

MAJOR CURRENT RESEARCH PROJECTS AND SCIENTIFIC LEADERS:
- Causes of oyster mortalities (G. Francis Beaven)
- Eggs and larvae of estuarine fishes (Romeo J. Mansueti)
- Effects of hydraulic dredging on estuarine benthos (Hayes T. Pfitzenmeyer)
- Microbiology of *Mya* and its habitat (Donald W. Lear)
- Biology of *Callinectes* (David G. Cargo)
- Factors affecting abundance of striped bass (Romeo J. Mansueti)
- Ecology and biology of a shallow coastal bay (Fred W. Sieling)
- Faunal survey of Chesapeake Bay (Frank J. Schwartz)
- Factors affecting oyster recruitment (G. Francis Beaven)
- Evaluation of passing migratory fish over dams of the lower Susquehanna River (Richard R. Whitney)

PUBLICATIONS ISSUED: *Chesapeake Science* (regularly published journal)

William F. Clapp Laboratories, Inc.

POSTAL ADDRESS: Washington Street, Duxbury, Massachusetts, USA.
EXECUTIVE OFFICER: Albert P. Richards, Director.
SPONSORING AGENCY: Private, non-profit laboratory.
YEAR FOUNDED: 1934.
SCOPE OF ACTIVITIES: Restricted research on taxonomy and biology of marine borers and fouling organisms.
SEASON OF OPERATION: All year.
PHYSICAL ENVIRONMENT ACCESSIBLE: Atlantic Ocean, Massachusetts Bay.
PROVISIONS FOR VISITING SCIENTISTS: Space for 3 visitors, living quarters available nearby.
MAJOR RESEARCH FACILITIES: Small library; running sea water; machine and wood shop; small boats and outboard motors, larger vessels.
SIZE OF STAFF: Two at professional level; 3 technicians.
PUBLICATIONS ISSUED: *Annual Report of Test Boards Operated During the Year.*

Colorado Cooperative Fishery Research Unit

POSTAL ADDRESS: Colorado State University, Fort Collins, Colorado, USA.
EXECUTIVE OFFICER: Dr. Howard A. Tanner, Leader.
SPONSORING AGENCIES: Colorado State University and Colorado Game and Fish Department.
YEAR FOUNDED: 1949.
SCOPE OF ACTIVITIES: Unrestricted research on improvement of fisheries in warm water irrigation reservoirs; graduate instruction.
SEASON OF OPERATION: All year.
PHYSICAL ENVIRONMENT ACCESSIBLE: Horsetooth Reservoir, Cache La Poudre River; warm water irrigation reservoirs and streams; high mountain lakes and streams.
PROVISIONS FOR VISITING SCIENTISTS: None.
MAJOR RESEARCH AND TEACHING FACILITIES: Small library; small lake on campus; machine and wood shop, skilled shop workman available; small boats and outboard motors.
INSTRUCTIONAL PROGRAM: Limnology, ecology, parasitology, general invertebrate zoology, ichthyology, aquatic entomology, fishery biology and fisheries management.
SIZE OF STAFF: Two at professional level.

Colorado State Game and Fish Department Research Center

POSTAL ADDRESS: 317 West Prospect Street, Fort Collins, Colorado, USA.
EXECUTIVE OFFICER: Dr. Howard A. Tanner.
YEAR FOUNDED: 1960.
SCOPE OF ACTIVITIES: Restricted fresh-water fishery research applied towards management information; fresh-water ecology; physiology of game fish species, water analysis pollution; graduate instruction.
SEASON OF OPERATION: All year.
PHYSICAL ENVIRONMENT ACCESSIBLE: Eutrophic and oligotrophic lakes, Cache la Poudre and Red Feather Rivers, Horsetooth Reservoir (a fluctuating power and irrigation reservoir.)
PROVISIONS FOR VISITING SCIENTISTS: None.

MAJOR RESEARCH FACILITIES: Small library; small aquarium tanks, research collection of Colorado fish; small boats and outboard motors.

IMPORTANT SPECIES AVAILABLE FOR LABORATORY STUDIES:

Pisces: *Salvelinus fontinalis, S. namaycush; Salmo gairdneri, S. trutta, S. clarki.*

MAJOR CURRENT RESEARCH PROJECTS AND SCIENTIFIC LEADERS: Laboratory is not yet completed. Research program will be initiated upon completion of facilities.

Comision Interamericana del Atun Tropical

INTER-AMERICAN TROPICAL TUNA COMMISSION

POSTAL ADDRESS:

Headquarters: Scripps Institution of Oceanography, La Jolla, California, USA.

Branch laboratories: Puntarenas, Costa Rica; Balboa, Canal Zone, P. O. Box 3665; Guayaquil, Ecuador, P. O. Box 5951.

EXECUTIVE OFFICER: Dr. Milner B. Schaefer, Director.

SPONSORING AGENCIES: Governments of Costa Rica, Ecuador, Panama and the United States.

SEASON OF OPERATION: All year.

YEAR FOUNDED: 1951.

SCOPE OF ACTIVITIES: Restricted research on the biology, ecology and population dynamics of tropical tuna and of baitfishes.

PHYSICAL ENVIRONMENT ACCESSIBLE: Pacific Ocean; estuarine conditions.

PROVISIONS FOR VISITING SCIENTISTS: None.

MAJOR RESEARCH FACILITIES: Small library; small boats and outboard motors, 30 ft LOA launches at Ecuador, research vessels of Scripps Institution of Oceanography used on cooperative basis.

SIZE OF STAFF: Twenty at professional level; 21 technicians.

MAJOR CURRENT RESEARCH PROJECTS AND SCIENTIFIC LEADERS:

Physical and chemical oceanography of the Eastern tropical Pacific (E. Bennett)

Tuna biology and life history (G. Broadhead)

Biology and ecology of baitfishes (C. L. Peterson)

Compilation and analysis of catch statistics (F. G. Alverson)

Biological oceanography (M. B. Schaefer)

PUBLICATIONS ISSUED: *Bulletin of the Inter-American Tropical Tuna Commission* (occasionally published journal)

David Worth Dennis Biological Station

POSTAL ADDRESS: Syracuse, Indiana, USA.

LOCATION: Near North Webster.

EXECUTIVE OFFICER: Dr. Murvel R. Garner, Director of Station, Department of Zoology, Earlham College, Richmond, Indiana.

SPONSORING AGENCY: Earlham College.

YEAR FOUNDED: 1946.

SCOPE OF ACTIVITIES: Unrestricted research; graduate and undergraduate instruction.

SEASON OF OPERATION: Late June to early August.

PHYSICAL ENVIRONMENT ACCESSIBLE: Dewart Lake (eutrophic lake).

PROVISION FOR VISITING SCIENTISTS: Space for 3 visitors; living quarters available nearby.

MAJOR RESEARCH AND TEACHING FACILITIES: Small library; small aquarium tanks; machine and wood shop; small boats and outboard motors.

INSTRUCTIONAL PROGRAM: Limnology, plankton, ecology, and aquatic invertebrate systematics.

Duke University Marine Laboratory

POSTAL ADDRESS: Beaufort, North Carolina, USA.

LOCATION: Piver's Island.

EXECUTIVE OFFICER: Dr. Cazlyn G. Bookhout, Director.

YEAR FOUNDED: 1937.

SCOPE OF ACTIVITIES: Unrestricted research in all phases of marine biology; graduate and undergraduate instruction.

SEASON OF OPERATION: All year. Summer instructional session: June 10 to August 20.

PHYSICAL ENVIRONMENT ACCESSIBLE: Atlantic Ocean; sandy and silty beaches and estuarine conditions.

PROVISIONS FOR VISITING SCIENTISTS: Research and living space for 30 visitors; fees charged for research space.

MAJOR RESEARCH AND TEACHING FACILITIES: Small library; running sea and fresh-water, large outdoor ponds and tanks, small aquarium tanks, wooden tanks 48″ x 30″; research collection of marine algae of North Carolina; on main Duke Campus, research and named reference collections of algae and aquatic plants

DUKE UNIVERSITY MARINE LABORATORY

of the United States and surrounding territories; machine and wood shop, electrical and electronic shop (1/4 mile from laboratory), skilled shop workman available; small boats and outboard motors, vessels; 27 ft LOA, M/V *Veliger,* and 40 ft LOA, M/V *Venus;* 118 ft LOA research vessel planned.

INSTRUCTIONAL PROGRAM: Ecology, embryology, phycology, general invertebrate zoology, fishery biology, mycology, physiological ecology, radiation biology, parasitology, and oceanography.

SIZE OF STAFF: Ten at professional level; 6 technicians.

IMPORTANT SPECIES AVAILABLE FOR LABORATORY STUDIES:
- Hydrozoa: *Pennaria tiarella, Tubularia crocea*
- Polychaeta: *Amphitrite ornata, Sabellaria vulgaris, Chaetopterus variopedatus*
- Mollusca: *Busycon* (3 species)
- Decapoda: *Uca* (3 species)
- Echinoidea: *Arbacia punctulata, Lytechinus variegatus, Mellita quinquiesperforata*
- Pisces: *Fundulus* (3 species)
- Algae: *Dictyota, Padina vickersiae*

MAJOR CURRENT RESEARCH PROJECTS AND SCIENTIFIC LEADERS:
- Distribution of marine fungi and their role in the decomposition of wood (Terry Johnson)
- The larval development of barnacles and crabs in relation to physical factors (C. G. Bookhout)
- The effects of environmental factors on larvae of the blue crab (John D. Costlow)
- Determination of oxygen consumption of trematodes (Wanda S. Hunter and Winona Vernberg)
- Studies in the physiological mechanism for climatic adaptation (F. John Vernberg)
- Metabolism of shell-forming tissue in mollusks (Karl Wilbur)
- Ecological survey of the fauna of the Cape Hatteras region (Irving E. Gray)
- Deep sea biology (Robert J. Menzies)

Flathead Lake Biological Laboratory

POSTAL ADDRESS: Flathead Lake, Bigfork, Montana, USA.

EXECUTIVE OFFICER: Dr. Richard A. Solberg, Biological Station Director, Montana State University, Missoula, Montana.

SPONSORING AGENCY: Montana State University.

YEAR FOUNDED: 1898.

SCOPE OF ACTIVITIES: Unrestricted research; graduate and undergraduate instruction.

SEASON OF OPERATION: Middle of June to middle of August.

PHYSICAL ENVIRONMENT ACCESSIBLE: Flathead Lake; eutrophic and oligotrophic lakes, rivers and streams and kettle ponds.

PROVISIONS FOR VISITING SCIENTISTS: Research and living space for visitors; fees charged.

MAJOR RESEARCH AND TEACHING FACILITIES: Small library; large outdoor ponds and tanks, small aquarium tanks; identified reference collections of invertebrates; machine and wood shop; small boats and outboard motors; one 25 ft LOA vessel.

INSTRUCTIONAL PROGRAM: Limnology, plankton, aquatic invertebrate systematics, aquatic entomology, fishery biology, acquatic plants and algology.

SIZE OF STAFF: Three at professional level; 4 technicians.

IMPORTANT SPECIES AVAILABLE FOR LABORATORY STUDIES:
- Pelecypoda: *Sphaerium* and *Musculium*
- Pisces: *Ptychocheilus oregonensis, Mylocheilus caurinum, Salvelinus malma*

MAJOR CURRENT RESEARCH PROJECTS AND SCIENTIFIC LEADERS:
- Limnological study of lakes of the area (R. B. Brunson)
- Ecology, taxonomy and zoogeography of invertebrates of the area (R. B. Brunson)

Florida Game and Fresh-Water Fish Commission, Fish Management Division

POSTAL ADDRESS:
- *Headquarters:* Tallahassee, Florida, USA.
- *Branch Office:* Lake Fisheries Experiment Station, Leesburg, Florida.

EXECUTIVE OFFICER: Edward T. Heinen, Chief Fisheries Biologist.

YEAR FOUNDED: 1943.

SCOPE OF ACTIVITIES: Restricted research on management of game and commercial fish; summer instruction.

SEASON OF OPERATION: All year.

PHYSICAL ENVIRONMENT ACCESSIBLE: Rivers, streams and lakes.

PROVISIONS FOR VISITING SCIENTISTS: Space for visitors; living quarters available nearby.

MAJOR RESEARCH AND TEACHING FACILITIES: Small library; small aquarium tanks; limited identified reference collections of local fauna and flora; machine and wood shop; small boats and outboard motors.

INSTRUCTIONAL PROGRAM: Limited instruction during the summer in fishery biology, population dynamics and fisheries management.

SIZE OF STAFF: Eighteen at professional level; 4 aides.

IMPORTANT SPECIES AVAILABLE FOR LABORATORY STUDIES: Florida fresh-water fishes.

MAJOR CURRENT RESEARCH PROJECTS AND SCIENTIFIC LEADERS:
- Management of fresh-water lakes and streams for maximum production of game and commercial fish in specified lakes. (Melvin T. Huish)

PUBLICATIONS ISSUED: *Special Technical Bulletins* (occasionally published contributions).

MARINE LABORATORY, FLORIDA STATE BOARD OF CONSERVATION

Florida State Board of Conservation, Marine Laboratory

POSTAL ADDRESS: Maritime Base, Building 4, Bayboro Harbor, St. Petersburg, Florida, USA.

EXECUTIVE OFFICER: Dr. Robert M. Ingle, Director of Research.

YEAR FOUNDED: 1955.

SCOPE OF ACTIVITIES: Restricted research on general marine biology for purpose of wise utilization of biological resources.

SEASON OF OPERATION: All year.

PHYSICAL ENVIRONMENT ACCESSIBLE: Gulf of Mexico, Tampa Bay; open ocean, sandy and silty beaches, estuarine conditions and brackish, shallow bays.

PROVISIONS FOR VISITING SCIENTISTS: Space for 3-4 visitors; no fees charged; living quarters available nearby.

MAJOR RESEARCH FACILITIES: Small library; small aquarium tanks; research and identified reference collections of fishes, shrimps, parasites, algae and seagrasses; machine and wood shop, skilled shop workman available; vessels, 25 ft LOA, *Kingfish,* and 34 ft LOA, *Gator.*

SIZE OF STAFF: Ten at professional level; 3 technicians.

IMPORTANT SPECIES AVAILABLE FOR LABORATORY STUDIES:

Protozoa: *Gymnodinium breve*
Trematoda: *Mesostephanus appendiculatoides*
Crustacea: *Penaeus duorarum*
Pisces: *Branchiostoma caribaeum, Gobiosoma robustum, Mollienesia latipinna, Lagodon rhomboides*
Seagrasses: *Thalassia testudinum, Diplanthera wrightii*
Algae: *Gracilaria verrucosa, Hypnea musciformis*

MAJOR CURRENT RESEARCH PROJECTS AND SCIENTIFIC LEADERS:

Shrimp biology (Bonnie Eldred)
Fish biology (Martin A. Moe, Jr.)
Coastal and estuarine ecology (Kenneth D. Woodburn)
Marine botany
Red tide (Lula P. Bravos)
Parasites of marine and coastal animals (Robert F. Hutton)

Florida State University, Oceanographic Institute

POSTAL ADDRESSES:

Oceanographic Institute: Florida State University, Tallahassee, Florida, USA.
Florida State University Marine Laboratory: Route 1, Alligator Point, Crawfordville, Florida.

EXECUTIVE OFFICER: Dr. Albert Collier, Director, Oceanographic Institute.

YEAR FOUNDED: 1949.

SCOPE OF ACTIVITIES: Unrestricted research on developmental and cellular physiology of invertebrates, marine ecology, mariculture, oceanography of Gulf of Mexico, sedimentation and other basic marine studies; graduate research.

SEASON OF OPERATION: All year.

PHYSICAL ENVIRONMENT ACCESSIBLE: Atlantic Ocean, Apalachee Bay, eastern Gulf of Mexico; sandy and silty beaches, estuarine conditions, coral reefs and oligotrophic lakes.

PROVISIONS FOR VISITING SCIENTISTS: Research and living space for 2-6 visitors; no fees charged for research space.

MAJOR RESEARCH AND TEACHING FACILITIES: Very extensive library on Tallahassee campus; running sea and fresh-water, large outdoor ponds and tanks, small aquarium tanks; identified reference collections of invertebrates and vertebrates (check list available on request); machine and wood shop, electrical and electronic shop, skilled shop workman available; small boats and outboard motors; one 34 ft LOA vessel.

OCEANOGRAPHIC INSTITUTE, FLORIDA STATE UNIVERSITY

INSTRUCTIONAL PROGRAM: Courses offered at the University: marine bacteriology, survey of marine science, problems in marine biology, bioecology, algae, mycology, geography of the oceans, micropaleontology, sedimentation, marine geology, physical oceanography, comparative physiology of marine animals, biology of invertebrates, ichthyology, and fishery biology. Some classes offered at the Alligator Harbor Marine Laboratory.

SIZE OF STAFF: Seven faculty; 17 graduate assistants and fellows; 2 research associates; 4 technicians.

IMPORTANT SPECIES AVAILABLE FOR LABORATORY STUDIES:

Chordata: *Amphioxus, Styela*
Echinodermata: *Arbacia punctulata, Lytechinus variegatus*
Mollusca: *Crassostrea virginica, Venus campechiensis, Musculus lateralis*
Arthropoda: *Callinectes sapidus, Limulus*
Brachiopoda: *Glottidea pyramidata*

MAJOR CURRENT RESEARCH PROJECTS AND SCIENTIFIC LEADERS:

Genetic studies on bivalves; mariculture of *Venus* (R. W. Menzel)
Physiological aspects of mitosis in sea urchin eggs (R. C. Rustad)
Physiology of fertilization in sea urchins and other invertebrates (C. B. Metz)
Biochemical studies on sea urchin egg particulates (J. R. Fisher)
Conditioned responses in *Limulus* (H. D. Baker)
Hydrography and geology of the Florida Shelf (D. S. Gorsline)
Dynamics of circulation in near shore and open ocean (T. Ichiye)
Polychaete taxonomy; special distribution of benthonic animals (M. L. Jones)
Chemical model of life's origin (S. W. Fox)

Foresta Institute for Ocean and Mountain Studies

POSTAL ADDRESS: 621 Franktown Road, Washoe Valley, Carson City, Nevada, USA.

EXECUTIVE OFFICER: Richard Gordon Miller, Director.

SPONSORING AGENCY: Privately financed institute.

YEAR FOUNDED: 1960.

SCOPE OF ACTIVITIES: Unrestricted research on high altitude lake fauna and flora with special emphasis on ecology and life histories.

SEASON OF OPERATION: All year.

PHYSICAL ENVIRONMENT ACCESSIBLE: Lakes Tahoe, Washoe, Pyramid and "Sierra"; eutrophic and oligotrophic as well as lakes above 1800 m, desert lakes, hot springs, rivers and streams.

PROVISIONS FOR VISITING SCIENTISTS: Space for 2-3 visitors; research costs only charged; living quarters available nearby.

FORESTA INSTITUTE FOR OCEAN AND MOUNTAIN STUDIES

MAJOR RESEARCH FACILITIES: Small library; large outdoor ponds and tanks; research and identified reference collections of invertebrates and fishes of the Sierra Nevada and Great Basin; loan collection of Antarctic fishes; machine and wood shop; electrical and electronic shop available; small boats and outboard motors.

SIZE OF STAFF: One-two at professional level.

IMPORTANT SPECIES AVAILABLE FOR LABORATORY STUDIES:

Pisces: *Cottus beldingi, Richardsonius egregius, Siphateles bicolor*

MAJOR CURRENT RESEARCH PROJECTS AND SCIENTIFIC LEADERS:

Food sources and distribution of Antarctic fishes (Richard G. Miller)
Natural history studies of Lake Tahoe fishes (Richard G. Miller)

Fort Johnson Marine Biological Laboratory

POSTAL ADDRESS: Route 1, Charleston, South Carolina, USA.

LOCATION: Eleven miles from Charleston.

EXECUTIVE OFFICER: Dr. Joseph R. Merkel, Director.

SPONSORING AGENCY: College of Charleston.

YEAR FOUNDED: 1955.

SCOPE OF ACTIVITIES: Unrestricted research on marine microbiology, chemistry and biology; undergraduate instruction.

SEASON OF OPERATION: All year.

PHYSICAL ENVIRONMENT ACCESSIBLE: Atlantic Ocean; sandy and silty beaches, estuarine conditions, and brackish, shallow bays.

PROVISIONS FOR VISITING SCIENTISTS: Research and living space for 6-8 visitors, particularly those whose work has a bearing on the role of marine bacteria in the sea; fees charged for research space.

MAJOR RESEARCH AND TEACHING FACILITIES: Small library at the Laboratory, library facilities of Medical College of South Carolina available; research collections of marine bacteria; large, catalogued shell collection on display; machine and wood shop; small boats and outboard motors.

INSTRUCTIONAL PROGRAM: At the Laboratory: Introductory microbiology, microbial physiology, and undergraduate research problems in marine microbiology. At the College of Charleston: Invertebrate zoology and general ecology.

SIZE OF STAFF: Two at professional level; 4 technicians.

IMPORTANT SPECIES AVAILABLE FOR LABORATORY STUDIES:

Algae: *Porphyra leucosticta, Enteromorpha* (various species), *Ulva*

Crustacea: *Limnoria tripunctata*

The above species are being cultivated in the Laboratory. Wide variety of intertidal species available to the Laboratory.

MAJOR CURRENT RESEARCH PROJECTS AND SCIENTIFIC LEADERS:

Transformation of carotenoids by marine bacteria (J. R. Merkel and G. D. Braithwaite)

Bacteria-Limnoria relationships (J. R. Merkel)

Proteolytic activity of marine bacteria (J. R. Merkel and G. D. Braithwaite)

FORT JOHNSON MARINE BIOLOGICAL LABORATORY

Franz Theodore Stone Laboratory

POSTAL ADDRESS:

In summer: Put-In-Bay, Ohio, USA.

September-June: Department of Zoology and Entomology, Ohio State University, Columbus 10, Ohio.

LOCATION: South Bass Island, Lake Erie.

EXECUTIVE OFFICER: Dr. Loren S. Putnam, Director of Summer Program, Department of Zoology and Entomology, Ohio State University, Columbus 10, Ohio.

FRANZ THEODORE STONE LABORATORY

SPONSORING AGENCY: Ohio State University.

YEAR FOUNDED: 1896.

SCOPE OF ACTIVITIES: Unrestricted research on factors influencing productivity of Lake Erie, with emphasis on fisheries and limnology; graduate and undergraduate instruction.

SEASON OF OPERATION: June 10 to August 30; other periods by arrangement.

PHYSICAL ENVIRONMENT ACCESSIBLE: Lake Erie (eutrophic lake); rocky and gravelly shores.

PROVISIONS FOR VISITING SCIENTISTS: Research and living space for visitors; fees charged for research space.

MAJOR RESEARCH AND TEACHING FACILITIES: Small library; small aquarium tanks; avian, entomological, botanical, ichthyological and herpetological research collections; machine and wood shop, skilled shop workman available; small boats and outboard motors, vessels, 37 ft, 42 ft and 25 ft LOA.

INSTRUCTIONAL PROGRAM: Limnology, ecology, comparative physiology, parasitology, phycology, general invertebrate zoology, ichthyology, aquatic invertebrate and vertebrate systematics, aquatic entomology, general physiology, fishery biology, fisheries management, climatology, ornithology and mycology.

SIZE OF STAFF: Seven at professional level; 4 technicians.

IMPORTANT SPECIES AVAILABLE FOR LABORATORY STUDIES: Most mid-continental aquatic plants and animals are available.

Friday Harbor Laboratories

POSTAL ADDRESS: Friday Harbor, Washington, USA.

LOCATION: Near Seattle.

EXECUTIVE OFFICER: Dr. Robert L. Fernald, Director and Associate Professor in Zoology, 212 Johnson Hall, University of Washington, Seattle, Washington.

SPONSORING AGENCY: University of Washington.

YEAR FOUNDED: 1904.

FRIDAY HARBOR LABORATORIES

SCOPE OF ACTIVITIES: Unrestricted research in marine sciences; graduate instruction.

SEASON OF OPERATION: All year, but emphasis placed on summer program.

PHYSICAL ENVIRONMENT ACCESSIBLE: Washington and Puget Sounds, Straits of Georgia and Juan de Fuca; sandy and silty beaches, rocky and gravelly shores, protected marine waters.

PROVISIONS FOR VISITING SCIENTISTS: Research and living space available for 35 visitors; fees charged for research space.

MAJOR RESEARCH AND TEACHING FACILITIES: Moderately complete library; running sea and fresh-water, small aquarium tanks, aquatic cages; machine and wood shop; small boats and outboard motors; one 55 ft LOA vessel.

INSTRUCTIONAL PROGRAM: Biological oceanography, ecology, comparative invertebrate physiology, invertebrate embryology, phycology, general invertebrate zoology, fishery biology, and marine meteorology.

SIZE OF STAFF: One at professional level.

IMPORTANT SPECIES AVAILABLE FOR LABORATORY STUDIES:

- Hydrozoa: *Halistaura cellularia*
- Polychaeta: *Arctonoe fragilis*
- Amphineura: *Cryptochiton stelleri*
- Cephalopoda: *Octopus dofleini*
- Echinoidea: *Strongylocentrotus* spp.
- Crustacea: *Cancer magister, Limnoria lignorum*
- Ascidiacea: *Chelyosoma productum*
- Chondrichthyes: *Hydrolagus colliei, Squalus suckleyi*
- Algae: wealth of species
- Very numerous other species of both invertebrates and vertebrates.

MAJOR CURRENT RESEARCH PROJECTS AND SCIENTIFIC LEADERS:

- Electrical, chemical and mechanical aspects of neuromuscular inhibition in decapod Crustacea (Ernst Florey)
- Systematics of Copepoda (Paul L. Illg)
- Nutritional physiology of *Limnoria* (Dixy Lee Ray)
- Comparative histology of the male gonad in invertebrates (Edward Roosen-Runge)
- Study of the mechanism of uptake of radioactive phosphate from sea water by embryos of sea urchins (Arthur H. Whiteley)
- Distribution of formate-activating enzyme in marine invertebrates (Helen R. Whiteley)
- Reproduction in the Phaeophyta (Michael Neusul)
- Comparative physiology of reproduction (Frederick L. Hisaw, Sr.)

Gulf Coast Research Laboratory

POSTAL ADDRESS: Ocean Springs, Mississippi, USA.

LOCATION: Near Biloxi, Mississippi.

EXECUTIVE OFFICER: Dr. Gordon Gunter, Director.

SPONSORING AGENCY: Board of Trustees of Institutions of Higher Learning of the State of Mississippi.

YEAR FOUNDED: 1947.

SCOPE OF ACTIVITIES: Unrestricted research on all phases of marine science, particularly biological; graduate and undergraduate instruction.

SEASON OF OPERATION: All year; instruction in summer only.

PHYSICAL ENVIRONMENT ACCESSIBLE: Mississippi Sound, Gulf of Mexico, Biloxi Bay; open ocean, sandy and silty beaches and brackish, shallow bays.

PROVISIONS FOR VISITING SCIENTISTS: Research and living space for 12 visitors; no fees charged.

MAJOR RESEARCH AND TEACHING FACILITIES: Moderately complete library; running sea and fresh-water, small aquarium tanks; relatively complete collection of marine flora and fauna of the region; machine and wood shop; small boats and outboard motors, one 40 ft LOA power vessel, one 65 ft vessel, and several 17 ft outboards.

INSTRUCTIONAL PROGRAM: Marine invertebrate zoology, marine vertebrate zoology and ichthyology, marine zoology for teachers, marine geology, problems in

TEACHING LABORATORY, GULF COAST RESEARCH LABORATORY

sedimentation and marine botany.

SIZE OF STAFF: Seven at professional level; 1 technician; 7 summer teachers.

IMPORTANT SPECIES AVAILABLE FOR LABORATORY STUDIES:

- Acrania: *Branchiostoma*
- Polychaeta: *Arenicola, Chaetopterus*
- Pelecypoda: *Crassostrea*
- Crustacea: *Penaeus*
- Pisces: *Mugil, Fundulus*

MAJOR CURRENT RESEARCH PROJECTS AND SCIENTIFIC LEADERS:

- Racial studies of menhaden (Gordon Gunter)
- Faunistic survey of Louisiana offshore waters (Gordon Gunter)

Hanford Atomic Products Operation, Biology Operation, Sub Sections: Aquatic Biology and Radioecology

POSTAL ADDRESS: Richland, Washington, USA.

LOCATION: Near Yakima.

EXECUTIVE OFFICERS: Dr. H. A. Kornberg, Manager, Biology Operation. Dr. R. E. Nakatani, Manager, Aquatic Biology. Mr. J. J. Davis, Manager, Radioecology.

SPONSORING AGENCIES: U. S. Atomic Energy Commission and General Electric Company.

YEAR FOUNDED: 1945.

SCOPE OF ACTIVITIES: Restricted radiobiological research related to physiology, toxicology and ecology of aquatic forms.

SEASON OF OPERATION: All year.

PHYSICAL ENVIRONMENT ACCESSIBLE: Columbia River.

PROVISIONS FOR VISITING SCIENTISTS: Space available for 1-2 visitors; no fees charged; living quarters nearby.

MAJOR RESEARCH AND TEACHING FACILITIES: Very extensive library; large outdoor ponds and tanks, small aquarium tanks; identified reference collection of most common forms of the fauna and flora of the Columbia River; machine and wood shop, electrical and electronic shop, skilled shop workmen available; small boats and outboard motors.

INSTRUCTIONAL PROGRAM: A course in radiation biology is occasionally offered through the Graduate School Branch of the University of Washington.

SIZE OF STAFF: At professional level, 3 in aquatic biology, 7 in radioecology; at technician level, 4 in aquatic biology and 7 in radioecology.

IMPORTANT SPECIES AVAILABLE FOR LABORATORY STUDIES:

- Salmonidae: *Oncorhynchus tschawytscha, Salmo gairdnerii*
- Catostomidae: *Catostomus macrocheilus*
- Coregonidae: *Prosopium williamsoni*
- Various Crustacea, Mollusca, Insecta, algae and vascular plants.

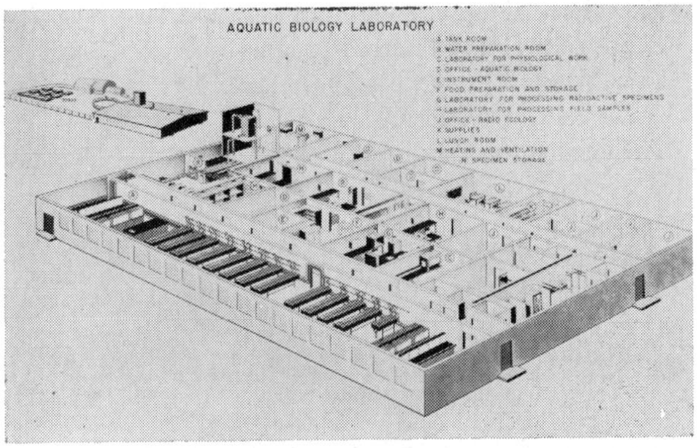

AQUATIC BIOLOGY LABORATORY, HANFORD

MAJOR CURRENT RESEARCH PROJECTS AND SCIENTIFIC LEADERS:

- Absorption and metabolism of radioisotopes by aquatic organisms (R. E. Nakatani)
- Toxicity of radioelements to aquatic organisms (R. E. Nakatani)
- Accumulation and transfer of radioisotopes by ecological systems (Jared J. Davis)
- Effects of radioactive materials upon ecological systems (Jared J. Davis)

Hawaii Department of Land and Natural Resources, Division of Fish and Game

POSTAL ADDRESS: 400 South Beretania Street, Honolulu, Hawaii, USA.

EXECUTIVE OFFICER: Mr. Michio Takata, Director.

YEAR FOUNDED: Reorganized in 1958.

SCOPE OF ACTIVITIES: Restricted research on fisheries development and management, both sport and commercial.

SEASON OF OPERATION: All year.

PHYSICAL ENVIRONMENT ACCESSIBLE: Pacific Ocean; sandy beaches and coral reefs.

PROVISIONS FOR VISITING SCIENTISTS: None.

MAJOR RESEARCH FACILITIES: Small library; large outdoor ponds and tanks, small aquarium tanks; 65 ft LOA, M/V, *Makua*.

SIZE OF STAFF: Eight at professional level; 4 technicians.

IMPORTANT SPECIES AVAILABLE FOR LABORATORY STUDIES:

- Teleostei: *Trachurops crumenophthalmus, Polydactylus sexfilis* and various species of pomacentrids, holocentrids, labrids, chaetodontids, acanthurids, etc.
- Elasmobranchii: *Eulamia menisorra, Galeocerdo cuvier, Carcharhinus limbatus*
- Crustacea: *Panulirus japonicus, P. penicillatus*

MAJOR CURRENT RESEARCH PROJECTS AND SCIENTIFIC LEADERS:

- Survey of fishermen and creel census (Donald Morris)
- Introduction of exotic marine fish (Donald Morris)

Experimental tagging program (Donald Morris)
Shark control and research program (Donald Morris)
Life history of bigeye scad (*Trachurops crumenophthalmus* (Donald Morris)
Artificial marine shoals and fish shelters (Donald Morris)
Life history of moi (*Polydactylus sexfilis*) (Donald Morris)
Life history of spiny lobster (*Panulirus japonicus* and *P. penicillatus*) (Donald Morris)

Hawaii Marine Laboratory

POSTAL ADDRESS: University of Hawaii, Honolulu 14, Hawaii, USA.
LOCATIONS:
Coconut Island Branch: Kaneohe Bay, Oahu, Hawaii.
Waikiki Branch: Honolulu, Oahu, Hawaii.
EXECUTIVE OFFICER: Vernon E. Brock, Director.
SPONSORING AGENCY: University of Hawaii.
YEAR FOUNDED: 1951.
SCOPE OF ACTIVITIES: Unrestricted research in general marine biology; graduate and undergraduate instruction in cooperation with the Departments of Zoology and Botany.
SEASON OF OPERATION: All year.
PHYSICAL ENVIRONMENT ACCESSIBLE: Pacific Ocean; estuarine conditions and coral reefs.
PROVISIONS FOR VISITING SCIENTISTS: Space for 6-12 visitors; fees charged; living quarters available nearby.
MAJOR RESEARCH AND TEACHING FACILITIES: Extensive library; running sea and fresh-water, large outdoor ponds and tanks, small aquarium tanks; identified general invertebrate and marine fish collections; machine and wood shop; 46 ft LOA, M/V *Salpa*.
INSTRUCTIONAL PROGRAM: Courses at the University, but offered in part at the Waikiki Branch of the Hawaii Marine Laboratory: plankton, biological oceanography, general and physiological ecology, embryology, parasitology, phycology, general invertebrate zoology, ichthyology, aquatic invertebrate and vertebrate systematics, general and comparative physiology, fishery biology, fisheries management, biometry, population dynamics, algology, marine productivity, experimental marine biology, oceanographic chemistry, and marine geology.
SIZE OF STAFF: Seven at professional level.
IMPORTANT SPECIES AVAILABLE FOR LABORATORY STUDIES:
Anthozoan corals: *Porites, Fungia, Montipora,* etc.
Crustacea: Alpheid and palaemonid shrimp, portunid, xanthid and grapsoid crabs
Pelecypoda: *Pinctada, Isognomon, Ostrea,* etc.
Gastropoda: *Conus, Cypraea, Tethys,* etc.
Echinodermata: *Echinometra, Tripneustes, Diadema, Holothuria, Stichopus, Opheodesoma,* etc.
Enteropneusta: *Ptychodera*
Urochordata: *Ascidia, Styela,* etc.
Pisces: *Tilapia, Chaetodon, Acanthurus* and many other common reef and pelagic fishes.
MAJOR CURRENT RESEARCH PROJECTS AND SCIENTIFIC LEADERS:
Biological origin of toxins in poisonous fishes (Albert H. Banner, Philip Helfrich and S. Sasaki)
Chemistry and pharmacology of toxins in poisonous fishes (Albert H. Banner, Paul Scheuer, Philip Helfrich and S. Sasaki)
Zoogeography of snapping shrimp (Albert H. Banner)
Susceptibility of birds to the Hawaiian Schistosome (George Chu)
Isotope techniques for the determination of algal productivity (Maxwell S. Doty)
Taxonomic studies on central Pacific fishes (William A. Gosline)
Uptake of radioisotopes and their transfer through food chains in marine organisms (Sidney J. Townsley and Della Reid)
Calcium uptake in sea urchin eggs (Sidney C. Hsiao)
Factors affecting shark behavior (Albert L. Tester)

SITE OF HAWAII MARINE LABORATORY, COCONUT ISLAND

Hopkins Marine Station

POSTAL ADDRESS: Pacific Grove, California, USA.
EXECUTIVE OFFICER: Dr. Lawrence R. Blinks, Director.
SPONSORING AGENCY: Hopkins Trust (Stanford University).
YEAR FOUNDED: 1892.
SCOPE OF ACTIVITIES: Unrestricted research in general marine biology; year around graduate instruction; summer undergraduate instruction.
SEASON OF OPERATION: All year.
PHYSICAL ENVIRONMENT ACCESSIBLE: Monterey Bay, Elkhorn Slough, Salinas and Carmel Rivers, Pacific Ocean; sandy and silty beaches, rocky and gravelly shores, estuarine conditions, brackish, shallow bays, oligotrophic lakes, rivers and streams, natural and artificial saturated brine pools.
PROVISIONS FOR VISITING SCIENTISTS: Space for 10-12 visitors in winter and 4-5 in summer; fees charged; living quarters available nearby.

HOPKINS MARINE STATION

MAJOR RESEARCH AND TEACHING FACILITIES: Extensive library; running sea and fresh-water, large outdoor ponds and tanks, small aquarium tanks, "Marinostat" (light and temperature controlled sea water); reasonably complete identified reference collections of algae and fish; good local manuals of invertebrates and algae; machine and wood shop, shop workman available; small boats and outboard motors; one 40 ft LOA diesel powered vessel.

INSTRUCTIONAL PROGRAM: Summer session: ecology, biochemistry, phycology, invertebrate zoology, ichthyology, ecological physiology, physiology of algae, and embryology. Academic year: research courses for graduate students.

SIZE OF STAFF: Five at professorial level; 5 technicians.

IMPORTANT SPECIES AVAILABLE FOR LABORATORY STUDIES:

- Echinodermata: *Strongylocentrotus purpuratus, S. franciscanus*
- Mollusca: *Haliotis* (3 species), *Cryptochiton stelleri, Mytilus californianus*
- Cephalopoda: *Loligo opalescens*
- Asteroidea: *Pisaster ochracea*
- Arthropoda: *Artemia salina, Cancer magister*
- Echiuroidea: *Urechis caupo*
- Pisces: *Porichthys notatus*
- Chlorophyceae: *Halicystis ovalis, Bryopsis corticulans*
- Bangiales: *Smithora naiadum*
- Phaeophyceae: *Nereocystis luetkeana*

MAJOR CURRENT RESEARCH PROJECTS AND SCIENTIFIC LEADERS:

- Invertebrate zoology, ecology, development (Donald P. Abbott)
- Biochemical microbiology (Cornelis B. van Niel)
- Taxonomy of various fishes, especially deep sea (Rolf L. Bolin)
- Physiology of algae, especially photosynthesis (Lawrence R. Blinks)
- Invertebrate physiology (Arthur C. Giese)
- Comparative biochemistry (John H. Phillips)

Illinois Department of Conservation, Division of Fisheries, Central Area Fisheries Headquarters

POSTAL ADDRESS:

Central Administrative office: Room 102, State Office Building, 400 South Spring Street, Springfield, Illinois, USA.

Field laboratory headquarters: Havana Field Headquarters, Havana, Illinois.

Field laboratories: The Division of Fisheries cooperates with the Natural History Survey in the use of its field laboratories.

EXECUTIVE OFFICER: William J. Harth, Superintendent, Division of Fisheries.

YEAR FOUNDED: 1952.

SCOPE OF ACTIVITIES: Restricted research on fishery management.

SEASON OF OPERATION: All year.

PHYSICAL ENVIRONMENT ACCESSIBLE: Lakes Anderson, Rice and Chautauqua; rivers and streams.

PROVISIONS FOR VISITING SCIENTISTS: Space for 3 visitors; living quarters available nearby.

MAJOR RESEARCH FACILITIES: No library; large tanks (used as a fish distribution point); machine and wood shop; small boats and outboard motors.

SIZE OF STAFF: Three at professional level.

Illinois Natural History Survey Division, Aquatic Biology Section

POSTAL ADDRESS:

Central Laboratory: Urbana, Illinois, USA.

Branch laboratories:

Havana Laboratory, RFD, Havana, Illinois.

Ridge Lake Laboratory, Fox Ridge State Park, Charleston, Illinois.

McGraw Hydrobiological Laboratory, 602 Higgins Road, Dundee, Illinois.

EXECUTIVE OFFICER: Dr. George W. Bennett, Head of Section.

RIDGE LAKE FIELD LABORATORY

SPONSORING AGENCY: Illinois Department of Registration and Education.

YEAR FOUNDED: Central Lab., 1858; Havana Lab., 1940; Ridge Lake Lab., 1941; McGraw Hydrobiological Lab., 1956.

SCOPE OF ACTIVITIES: Restricted and unrestricted research on general aquatic biology with emphasis on fishery biology.

SEASON OF OPERATION: All year at Havana, Urbana and Dundee; June 1 to September 1 at Ridge Lake.

PHYSICAL ENVIRONMENT ACCESSIBLE: Eutrophic and oligotrophic lakes, rivers and streams.

PROVISIONS FOR VISITING SCIENTISTS: Space for visitors; living quarters available nearby.

MAJOR RESEARCH FACILITIES: Very extensive library in Urbana; large outdoor ponds and tanks, small aquarium tanks; very complete research collections of aquatic insects; identified reference collections of aquatic vertebrates and invertebrates; machine and wood shop at Urbana and Havana, skilled shop workmen at Urbana and Havana; small boats and outboard motors; larger vessels.

SIZE OF STAFF: Seven at professional level; 7 technicians.

IMPORTANT SPECIES AVAILABLE FOR LABORATORY STUDIES:

Pisces: *Lepomis macrochirus, Micropterus salmoides*

MAJOR CURRENT RESEARCH PROJECTS AND SCIENTIFIC LEADERS:

Lake management investigations (George W. Bennett)

Stream management investigations (R. Weldon Larimore)

Commercial fisheries operations on large rivers (William C. Starrett)

Studies of carrying capacity and standing crops of fishes (D. Homer Buck)

Pond fertilization (Donald F. Hansen)

Biochemistry of fishes (Robert C. Hiltibran)

Institute of Oceanography and Marine Biology

POSTAL ADDRESS: P. O. Box 432, Oyster Bay, New York, USA.

LOCATION: Near New York City.

EXECUTIVE OFFICER: Walter E. Tolles, Director.

SPONSORING AGENCY: Privately financed laboratory.

YEAR FOUNDED: 1959.

SCOPE OF ACTIVITIES: Unrestricted research in general oceanography and marine biology with special emphasis on physical techniques and methods.

SEASON OF OPERATION: All year.

PHYSICAL ENVIRONMENT ACCESSIBLE: Oyster Bay, Long Island Sound; rocky and gravelly shores and brackish, shallow bays.

PROVISIONS FOR VISITING SCIENTISTS: None.

MAJOR RESEARCH AND TEACHING FACILITIES: Small library; large outdoor ponds and tanks, small aquarium tanks; machine and wood shop, electrical and electronic shop, skilled shop workman available; small boats and outboard motors. Laboratory quarters are temporary.

International Pacific Halibut Commission

POSTAL ADDRESS: Fisheries Hall No. 2, University of Washington, Seattle 5, Washington, USA.

EXECUTIVE OFFICER: Henry A. Dunlop, Director of Investigations.

SPONSORING AGENCIES: U. S. and Canadian governments.

YEAR FOUNDED: 1925.

SCOPE OF ACTIVITIES: Restricted research on effective management of the Pacific halibut fishery.

SEASON OF OPERATION: All year.

PHYSICAL ENVIRONMENT ACCESSIBLE: Pacific Ocean; shallow coastal seas off Canada and Alaska.

PROVISIONS FOR VISITING SCIENTISTS: None.

MAJOR RESEARCH FACILITIES: All facilities of the College of Fisheries, University of Washington, available; moderately complete library; research collection of plankton materials collected incidentally during investigations of the planktonic life of the halibut; research and fishing vessels chartered as needed.

SIZE OF STAFF: Ten at professional level; 3 technicians.

MAJOR CURRENT RESEARCH PROJECTS AND SCIENTIFIC LEADERS:

Biological statistics (F. Howard Bell)

Age composition and associated studies (William H. Hardman)

Tagging and associated studies (Richard J. Myhre)

Growth and associated studies (G. Morris Southward)

Pre-commercial life of halibut (Richard A. Kautz)

Iowa Cooperative Fisheries Research Unit

POSTAL ADDRESS: Department of Zoology and Entomology, Science Building, Iowa State University, Ames, Iowa, USA.

EXECUTIVE OFFICER: Dr. K. D. Carlander, Professor of Zoology and Director.

SPONSORING AGENCIES: Iowa State University and Iowa State Conservation Commission.

YEAR FOUNDED: 1941.

SCOPE OF ACTIVITIES: Unrestricted research on fishery biology; graduate and undergraduate instruction.

SEASON OF OPERATION: All year.

PHYSICAL ENVIRONMENT ACCESSIBLE: Clear Lake (eutrophic lake), Des Moines River.

PROVISIONS FOR VISITING SCIENTISTS: Space for 3 visitors; living quarters available nearby.

MAJOR RESEARCH AND TEACHING FACILITIES: Moderately complete library in the aquatic field at the University library; small aquarium tanks; identified reference collections of fishes and aquatic plants; machine and wood shop, electrical and electronic shop, skilled

SCIENCE BUILDING, IOWA STATE UNIVERSITY

IOWA LAKESIDE LABORATORY

shop workmen available; small boats and outboard motors.

INSTRUCTIONAL PROGRAM: Limnology, ecology, comparative and general physiology, biochemistry, embryology, microbiology, parasitology, phycology, general invertebrate zoology, ichthyology, aquatic entomology, fishery biology, fisheries management, biometry and population dynamics.

SIZE OF STAFF: Two at professional level in fisheries work and 15-20 in allied fields such as biometry, entomology, etc.; 5-10 graduate assistants in fisheries research.

MAJOR CURRENT RESEARCH PROJECTS AND SCIENTIFIC LEADERS:

Dynamics of fish populations in Clear Lake (K. D. Carlander)

Primary production studies using C-14 and studies on utilization by organisms (K. D. Carlander and John S. Dodd)

River biology with particular reference to water level (K. D. Carlander)

Farm fish pond investigations (K. D. Carlander and Robert Moorman)

Ephemeroptera and Trichoptera populations of the Mississippi River (K. D. Carlander)

Iowa Lakeside Laboratory

POSTAL ADDRESS: Milford, Iowa, USA.

LOCATION: Near Spencer.

EXECUTIVE OFFICER: Robert L. King, Director of Laboratory, Department of Zoology, State University of Iowa, Iowa City, Iowa.

SPONSORING AGENCY: State University of Iowa.

YEAR FOUNDED: 1909.

SCOPE OF ACTIVITIES: Unrestricted research on general limnology, bottom ecology, distribution and dispersal; graduate and undergraduate instruction. Facilities oriented toward field studies rather than experimental laboratory studies.

SEASON OF OPERATION: June to September.

PHYSICAL ENVIRONMENT ACCESSIBLE: Lakes Okoboji and Spirit (eutrophic lakes); glacial moraines and contained ponds.

PROVISION FOR VISITING SCIENTISTS: Research and living space for 6 visitors; no fees charged for research space.

MAJOR RESEARCH AND TEACHING FACILITIES: Small library; small aquarium tanks, large indoor tanks with running lake water, aquatic cages; complete herbarium of local seed plants; machine and wood shop, skilled shop workman available; small boats and outboard motors, one 30 ft LOA power vessel.

INSTRUCTIONAL PROGRAM: Limnology, microbiology, parasitology, general invertebrate zoology, ichthyology, aquatic entomology, and fishery biology.

SIZE OF STAFF: Seven at professional level; 2 technicians.

IMPORTANT SPECIES AVAILABLE FOR LABORATORY STUDIES: Diverse flora and fauna from habitats ranging from deep lakes to temporary ponds; vascular plants, algae and plankton outstanding.

MAJOR CURRENT RESEARCH PROJECTS AND SCIENTIFIC LEADERS:

Helminth life cycles and intermediate hosts (M. J. Ulmer)

Comprehensive studies of local algae (John Dodd)

Bottom fauna, dispersal studies (R. V. Bovbjerg)

Jackson Hole Biological Research Station

POSTAL ADDRESS: Moran, Wyoming, USA.

LOCATION: Teton National Park.

EXECUTIVE OFFICER: Dr. L. Floyd Clarke, Director of Station, Department of Zoology, University of Wyoming, Laramie, Wyoming.

SPONSORING AGENCIES: University of Wyoming and New York Zoological Society.

YEAR FOUNDED: 1948.

SCOPE OF ACTIVITIES: Unrestricted research on any of

JACKSON HOLE BIOLOGICAL RESEARCH STATION

the local flora and fauna; graduate students at the University can register for research problems under supervision.

SEASON OF OPERATION: June 1 to September 10.

PHYSICAL ENVIRONMENT ACCESSIBLE: Lakes Jackson, Two Ocean, Emma Matilda and Yellowstone (eutrophic and oligotrophic lakes), and Snake River; variety of ponds and alpine streams.

PROVISIONS FOR VISITING SCIENTISTS: Research and living space for 20 visitors; nominal fee charged for research space.

MAJOR RESEARCH FACILITIES: Small library; aquaria; herbarium of major types of flora; small collection of animals available for taxonomic study, etc.; machine and wood shop; small boats and outboard motors.

SIZE OF STAFF: Three at professional level; 1 technician.

IMPORTANT SPECIES AVAILABLE FOR LABORATORY STUDIES:

Amphibia: *Amblystoma trigrinum melanosticum*
Pisces: *Leuciscus cephalus*
Many species typical of high mountain lakes, rivers and streams.

MAJOR CURRENT RESEARCH PROJECTS AND SCIENTIFIC LEADERS:

Aquatic fungi of the area (John W. Baxter)
Effects of sewage effluent on ecology of Swan Lake (L. Floyd Clarke)
Regeneration of Amphibia (Charles S. Thornton)
Fish populations in Two Ocean Lake (Kenneth L. John)
Inheritance factors in the crooked back and the Utah chub (Kenneth L. John)

Kansas State Forestry, Fish and Game Commission

POSTAL ADDRESS: Pratt, Kansas, USA.

EXECUTIVE OFFICER: Roy Schnoonover, Fisheries Biologist.

SPONSORING AGENCIES: State of Kansas in cooperation with the Kansas State Teachers College.

YEAR FOUNDED: 1948.

SCOPE OF ACTIVITIES: Restricted research on physical, chemical and biological studies of strip-mine lakes, including warm water fishery management.

SEASON OF OPERATION: All year.

PHYSICAL ENVIRONMENT ACCESSIBLE: Coal-mine strip-pit lakes.

PROVISIONS FOR VISITING SCIENTISTS: None.

MAJOR RESEARCH FACILITIES: Small library; small aquarium tanks; small boats and outboard motors.

The W. K. Kellogg Gull Lake Biological Station

POSTAL ADDRESS: Route 1, Hickory Corners, Michigan, USA.

LOCATION: Near Battle Creek.

EXECUTIVE OFFICER: Dr. Walter F. Morofsky, Director.

SPONSORING AGENCY: Michigan State University.

YEAR FOUNDED: 1954.

SCOPE OF ACTIVITIES: Unrestricted research on aquatic and terrestrial ecology, taxonomy, limnology and fresh-water biology; graduate and undergraduate instruction.

SEASON OF OPERATION: All year for research; June 20 to August 12 for instruction.

PHYSICAL ENVIRONMENT ACCESSIBLE: Lakes Gull, Wintergreen, Stony, Gun, Crooked, Purdy, Wall and Michigan, Augusta Creek, Kalamazoo River; eutrophic and oligotrophic lakes.

PROVISIONS FOR VISITING SCIENTISTS: Research and living space for 8-12 visitors; no fees charged for research space.

MAJOR RESEARCH AND TEACHING FACILITIES: Small library; small aquarium tanks; small research and identified reference collections of local fauna and

JOSEPH STACK RESEARCH BUILDING, GULL LAKE BIOLOGICAL STATION

flora; machine and wood shop; small boats and outboard motors.

INSTRUCTIONAL PROGRAM: Fresh-water algae, aquatic plants, aquatic insects, limnology, ichthyology and other courses in botany and zoology.

SIZE OF STAFF: Eleven at professional level in summer, 2 remainder of the year; 1 technician.

IMPORTANT SPECIES AVAILABLE FOR LABORATORY STUDIES: All organisms found in north central United States.

MAJOR CURRENT RESEARCH PROJECTS AND SCIENTIFIC LEADERS:

Nasal mites of vertebrates (K. E. Hyland)
Diseases caused by protozoa, bacteria, viruses, and helminths (David T. Clark)
Distribution of algae by waterfowl (Harold Schlicting)
Seasonal studies on the algae flora of an acid and alkaline bog (J. C. Elliott)
Research on ecology of shore-line vegetation (W. E. Wade and Adrienne Mandossian)
The ecology, age and growth rate of the Central Johnny Darter, *Boleosoma nigrum nigrum* (Rafinesque) (Peter I Tack and Edward Speare)
Preliminary survey of the parasites of crayfish (T. W. Porter and Donald Blake)
An ecological and taxonomic study of the Bryozoa of Michigan (T. W. Porter and John Bushnell)
A survey of the benthonic fauna of Wintergreen Lake (T. W. Porter and Thomas Mitchell)
A survey of the parasites found in the fishes of Wintergreen Lake (T. W. Porter and Reginald Nash)

Kentucky State Department of Fish and Wildlife Resources, Biological Laboratory

POSTAL ADDRESS: Frankfort, Kentucky, USA.

EXECUTIVE OFFICER: Minor E. Clark, Commissioner.

YEAR FOUNDED: 1946.

SCOPE OF ACTIVITIES: Restricted research for the development and management of Kentucky's fishery resources.

SEASON OF OPERATION: All year.

PHYSICAL ENVIRONMENT ACCESSIBLE: Kentucky and Rough Rivers, Lakes Kentucky, Cumberland, Herrington and Dewey.

PROVISIONS FOR VISITING SCIENTISTS: Space for visitors; no fees charged; living quarters available nearby.

MAJOR RESEARCH FACILITIES: Small library; large outdoor ponds and tanks, small aquarium tanks; small research collection of fishes, but most of the fish collected are sent to the University of Louisville; machine and wood shop; small boats and outboard motors.

SIZE OF STAFF: Ten at professional level; 6 technicians.

IMPORTANT SPECIES AVAILABLE FOR LABORATORY STUDIES:

Pisces: *Micropterous salmoides, Lepomis macrochinus*

MAJOR CURRENT RESEARCH PROJECTS AND SCIENTIFIC LEADERS:

State-owned lakes investigations (John F. Hall)
Investigations and management of the Herrington and Dewey Lake fishery (William A. Smith, Jr.)
Investigations of the Ohio River fishery (James R. Charles)
Pre- and post-impoundment surveys (William R. Turner)
Investigations of walleye and white bass fishery (James P. Henley)
Small stream investigations (James P. Carter)

Kerckhoff Marine Laboratory

POSTAL ADDRESS: 101 Dahlia Street, Corona Del Mar, California, USA.

EXECUTIVE OFFICER: Chairman, Division of Biology, California Institute of Technology, Pasadena, California.

SPONSORING AGENCY: California Institute of Technology.

YEAR FOUNDED: 1930.

SCOPE OF ACTIVITIES: Unrestricted research.

SEASON OF OPERATION: All year.

PHYSICAL ENVIRONMENT ACCESSIBLE: Newport Bay; open ocean, sandy and silty beaches, rocky and gravelly shores, and mud flats.

PROVISIONS FOR VISITING SCIENTISTS: Space for 12-15 visitors; living quarters available nearby.

MAJOR RESEARCH FACILITIES: Small library; running sea water, small aquarium tanks, aquatic cages; small identified reference collection of local fauna; machine and wood shop, skilled shop workman available; small boats and outboard motors; one 24 ft LOA power vessel.

SIZE OF STAFF: Used primarily by members of the Division of Biology, California Institute of Technology.

KERCKHOFF MARINE LABORATORY

IMPORTANT SPECIES AVAILABLE FOR LABORATORY STUDIES:
Echinodermata: *Strongylocentrotus purpuratus, S. franciscanus, Lytechinus pictus, Dendraster excentricus*
Gephyrea: *Urechis caupo*
Polychaeta: *Chaetopterus variopedatus*
Gastropoda: *Megathura crenulata*
Urochorda: *Ciona intestinalis, Styela barnharti*
Acrania: *Branchistoma californiense*

MAJOR CURRENT RESEARCH PROJECTS AND SCIENTIFIC LEADERS:
Immunochemical problems of fertilization and early development (Albert Tyler)
Neurophysiology of crustaceans (C. A. G. Wiersma)
Correlative biological and paleontological investigations on marine mollusks (H. Lowenstam)
Nerve regeneration and behavior in fishes (R. W. Sperry and H. Arora)

Laboratory of Radiation Biology

POSTAL ADDRESS: Fisheries Center, University of Washington, Seattle 5, Washington, USA.
EXECUTIVE OFFICER: Dr. Lauren R. Donaldson, Director and Professor of Fisheries.
SPONSORING AGENCIES: Division of Biology and Medicine, U. S. Atomic Energy Commission; University of Washington.
SCOPE OF ACTIVITIES: Research on radiation biology, with emphasis upon the ecological aspects; graduate instruction.
SEASON OF OPERATION: All year.
PROVISION FOR VISITING SCIENTISTS: Accommodations for 4 visitors, no fees charged; living quarters available nearby.
PHYSICAL ENVIRONMENT ACCESSIBLE: Pacific Ocean, Lakes Washington and Fern (oligotrophic lakes), estuarine conditions, rivers, and streams. The laboratory frequently engages in research in the Marshall Islands where coral reefs are abundant.
MAJOR RESEARCH AND TEACHING FACILITIES: Very extensive library; running sea and fresh-water, large outdoor ponds and tanks, small aquarium tanks; research collections of fish, invertebrates, algae, and flora from the Marshall Islands as well as marine forms from the Chukchi Sea; identified reference collections of fishes from the North Pacific and from local fresh-water areas; machine and wood shop, electrical and electronic shop, skilled shop workmen available; small boats and outboard motors; larger vessels for marine work are chartered.
INSTRUCTIONAL PROGRAM: Pre- and postdoctoral training in radiation biology.
SIZE OF STAFF: Ten at professional level; 10 technicians.

IMPORTANT SPECIES AVAILABLE FOR LABORATORY STUDIES:
Coelenterata: *Hydra oligactis, Metridium*
Mollusca: *Modiolus modiolus, Mytilus edulus, Crassostrea gigas, Ostrea lurida, Ocinebra japonica, Thais lamellosa, Helisoma*
Crustacea: *Calliopius, Allorchestes, Pandalus borealis, Pandalopsis, Astacus, Balanus*
Echinodermata: *Strongylocentrotus*
Pisces: *Salmo gairdnerii, S. lewisii, Oncorhynchus tshawytscha, O. keta, O. gorbuscha, O. nerka, O. kisutch, Ictalurus nebulosus, Sebastodes, Hippoglossus hippoglossus, Parophrys vetulus.*

MAJOR CURRENT RESEARCH PROJECTS AND SCIENTIFIC LEADERS:
Aquatic resources (trace-mineral metabolism) (L. R. Donaldson)
X-radiation studies (K. Bonham)
Natural history studies (A. D. Welander)
High intensity radiation studies, Bikini-Eniwetok (R. F. Palumbo)
Marine surveys (measurement of radiation and its movement in the sea. Waste disposal effects—in sea) (A. H. Seymour)
Rongelap ecology studies (E. E. Held)

Lake Itasca Forestry and Biological Station

POSTAL ADDRESS: Lake Itasca P. O., Minnesota, USA.
LOCATION: Near Bemidji.
EXECUTIVE OFFICER: Dr. William H. Marshall, Director of the Lake Itasca Biology Session, 300 Coffey Hall, University of Minnesota, St. Paul 14, Minnesota.
SPONSORING AGENCY: University of Minnesota.
YEAR FOUNDED: 1934.
SCOPE OF ACTIVITIES: Unrestricted research on general fresh-water biology; graduate and undergraduate instruction.
SEASON OF OPERATION: June to September.
PHYSICAL ENVIRONMENT ACCESSIBLE: Lake Itasca; eutrophic and oligotrophic lakes, rivers and streams.

LAKESIDE LABORATORY, ITASCA

PROVISIONS FOR VISITING SCIENTISTS: Research and living space for 15 visitors; fees charged for research space.

MAJOR RESEARCH AND TEACHING FACILITIES: Small library; large outdoor ponds and tanks, small aquarium tanks; research and identified reference collections of common fresh-water vertebrates, mosses and aquatic flowering plants; machine and wood shop; small boats and outboard motors.

INSTRUCTIONAL PROGRAM: Summer courses in aquatic flowering plants, fresh-water algae, natural history of invertebrates and fishes, limnology, biology of immature insects and a variety of terrestrial courses.

SIZE OF STAFF: Seven to ten at professional level; 1 technician.

IMPORTANT SPECIES AVAILABLE FOR LABORATORY STUDIES:

Amphibia: *Rana pipiens, R. septentrionalis*
Pisces: *Micropterus salmonoides*
Crustacea: *Orconectes virilis*
Neuroptera: *Corydalus cornuta*
Diptera: *Wyeomyia smithii, Simulium* spp.
Coleoptera: *Dystiscus fasciventris*
Hydrocharitaceae: *Elodea canadensis*
Sarraceniaceae: *Sarracenia purpurea*

MAJOR CURRENT RESEARCH PROJECTS AND SCIENTIFIC LEADERS:

Fresh-water Chrysophyceae (R. E. Norris)
Revision of the genus *Ochromonas* (R. E. Norris)
Cytotaxonomy of the genus *Potamogeton* (K. R. Stern)
Comparative plant ecology of prairie and forest ponds (J. R. Tester)
Ecology of amphibians (W. H. Marshall)

Lamont Geological Observatory

LAMONT GEOLOGICAL OBSERVATORY

POSTAL ADDRESS: Palisades, New York, USA.

LOCATION: Near New York City.

EXECUTIVE OFFICER: Maurice Ewing, Director.

SPONSORING AGENCY: Columbia University.

YEAR FOUNDED: 1949.

SCOPE OF ACTIVITIES: Unrestricted research on geophysics, geochemistry, marine geology and biology as applied to the geology and structure of the earth; graduate instruction.

SEASON OF OPERATION: All year.

PHYSICAL ENVIRONMENT ACCESSIBLE: Atlantic Ocean and Hudson River.

PROVISION FOR VISITING SCIENTISTS: Accommodations can be made by arrangement; living space available nearby.

MAJOR RESEARCH AND TEACHING FACILITIES: Very extensive library at the New York City campus and moderately complete at the Palisades campus; excellent apparatus; identified reference collections of planktonic and benthonic Foraminifera, Pteropoda and Isopoda; machine and wood shop, electrical and electronic shop, skilled shop workmen available; small boats; vessels, 202 ft LOA, R/V *Vema,* 72 ft LOA, R/V *Goldberger,* and 136 ft LOA, R/V *Sir Horace Lamb,* 210 ft LOA, R/V *Conrad.*

INSTRUCTIONAL PROGRAM: In the Zoology Department of Columbia University: general zoology, biometrics, embryology, genetics, cellular physiology. In the Geology Department: geophysics, geochemistry, seismology, submarine topography and oceanography.

SIZE OF STAFF: Fifty at professional level; 150 technicians and others.

MAJOR CURRENT BIOLOGICAL RESEARCH PROJECTS AND SCIENTIFIC LEADERS:

Ecology of living planktonic Foraminifera (Allan W. H. Be)
Marine microbiology (P. R. Burkholder)
Research expeditions of R/V *Vema* (Maurice Ewing)
Biological studies from Arctic drifting stations and from ice islands (Jack Oliver)

Maine State Department of Inland Fisheries and Game, Fishery Research and Management Division

POSTAL ADDRESS: Department of Zoology, University of Maine, Orono, Maine, USA.

EXECUTIVE OFFICER: Dr. W. Harry Everhart, Head of Division and Professor of Zoology, University of Maine.

SPONSORING AGENCIES: State of Maine and University of Maine.

YEAR FOUNDED: 1950.

SCOPE OF ACTIVITIES: Restricted research on the management of the inland fisheries.

SEASON OF OPERATION: All year.

PHYSICAL ENVIRONMENT ACCESSIBLE: Estuarine conditions, eutrophic and oligotrophic lakes, rivers and streams; all inland waters of Maine.

MAINE DEPARTMENT OF INLAND FISHERIES AND GAME

MARINE BIOLOGICAL LABORATORY, WOODS HOLE

PROVISIONS FOR VISITING SCIENTISTS: None.

MAJOR RESEARCH AND TEACHING FACILITIES: Very extensive library at University of Maine; small aquarium tanks; two hatcheries, at East Orland and Enfield; teaching collections of fish fauna; machine and wood shop; small boats and outboard motors.

INSTRUCTIONAL PROGRAM: Ecology, embryology, parasitology, general invertebrate zoology, ichthyology, general physiology, fishery biology, biometry, fisheries management, general zoology and wildlife management.

SIZE OF STAFF: Seventeen at professional level (12 stationed in regional offices); 1 technician.

MAJOR CURRENT RESEARCH PROJECTS AND SCIENTIFIC LEADERS:

Atlantic salmon restoration (Richard E. Cutting)

Study of the American smelt utilizing serological techniques (Robert S. Rupp)

Life history and management of the landlocked salmon, *Salmo salar* (Kendall Warner, Keith Havey and Charles Ritzi)

Smallmouth and largemouth bass (Robert E. Foye and John Kelley)

Migrations of eastern brook trout and their biology in Moosehead Lake (Roger P. AuClair)

Lake trout, *Cristivomer namaycush* (Stuart E. DeRoche)

Marine Biological Laboratory

POSTAL ADDRESS: Woods Hole, Massachusetts, USA.

EXECUTIVE OFFICER: Dr. Philip B. Armstrong, Director.

SPONSORING AGENCY: Privately financed laboratory.

YEAR FOUNDED: 1888.

SCOPE OF ACTIVITIES: Unrestricted research in general biology; graduate and undergraduate instruction.

SEASON OF OPERATION: All year, although most of the activity is from June to August.

PHYSICAL ENVIRONMENT ACCESSIBLE: Atlantic Ocean, Martha's Vineyard Sound, Cape Cod and Buzzards Bays; sandy and silty beaches, rocky and gravelly shores, estuarine conditions and brackish, shallow bays.

PROVISIONS FOR VISITING SCIENTISTS: Research and living space for 175 visitors; fees charged for research space.

MAJOR RESEARCH AND TEACHING FACILITIES: Very extensive library (about 45,000 volumes and 250,000 catalogued reprints); running sea and brackish water, large outdoor ponds and tanks, small aquarium tanks, aquatic cages; machine and wood shop, electrical and electronic shop, skilled shop workmen available; small boats and outboard motors; powered vessels, two 26 ft, one 32 ft, two 40 ft and one 55 ft LOA.

INSTRUCTIONAL PROGRAM: Summer instruction: ecology, embryology, physiology, general invertebrate zoology, phycology and marine botany.

SIZE OF STAFF: None permanently employed at professional level; 10 technicians.

IMPORTANT SPECIES AVAILABLE FOR LABORATORY STUDIES: About 200 species are collected and distributed for research.

MAJOR CURRENT RESEARCH PROJECTS AND SCIENTIFIC LEADERS: All research projects are done by visitors.

The Marine Laboratory

POSTAL ADDRESS: Department of Biological Sciences, University of California, Santa Barbara, Goleta, California, USA.

LOCATION: On University campus.

EXECUTIVE OFFICER: Chairman, Committee on Marine Biology, Department of Biological Sciences, University of California, Santa Barbara.

SPONSORING AGENCY: University of California, Santa Barbara.

YEAR FOUNDED: 1954.

SCOPE OF ACTIVITIES: Unrestricted research in general

marine biology; graduate and undergraduate instruction.

SEASON OF OPERATION: All year.

PHYSICAL ENVIRONMENT ACCESSIBLE: Santa Barbara Channel; open ocean, sandy and silty beaches, rocky and gravelly shores and estuarine conditions.

PROVISIONS FOR VISITING SCIENTISTS: Research space all year; space (spring semester only), for 2-3 visitors at the laboratory; no fees charged for research space; living quarters on campus available nearby all year round.

MAJOR RESEARCH AND TEACHING FACILITIES: Extensive library; running sea and fresh-water, small aquarium tanks; identified reference collection of local marine algae; machine and wood shop, electrical and electronic shop, skilled shop workman available; small boats and outboard motors.

INSTRUCTIONAL PROGRAM: General invertebrate zoology and ecology.

SIZE OF STAFF: Six at professional level.

IMPORTANT SPECIES AVAILABLE FOR LABORATORY STUDIES:

Echinoidea: *Strongylocentrotus purpuratus, S. franciscanus*

Asteroidea: *Pisaster ochraceus, Patiria miniata*

Gastropoda: *Haliotis,* 2 sp., *Tethys* sp.

Lamellibranchia: *Tivela, Protothaca, Mytilus,* etc.

Cephalopoda: *Octopus* sp.

Amphineura: *Lepidochitoxia,* etc.

Crustacea: *Balanus, Mitella, Panulirus, Cancer, Emerita, Orchestia,* etc.

MAJOR CURRENT RESEARCH PROJECTS AND SCIENTIFIC LEADERS:

Comparative serology of marine organisms (John Cushing)

Behavior and specificity in marine symbioses (Demorest Davenport)

Study of protozoan parasites of marine fishes (Elmer Noble)

Development of embiotocid fishes (Edward Triplett)

Life cycles of marine algae of Rhodymeniaceae (Shirley Sparling)

Population dynamics of barnacles (Joseph Connell)

Marineland of the Pacific Biological Laboratory

POSTAL ADDRESS: Palos Verdes Estates, California, USA.

LOCATION: Near Los Angeles.

EXECUTIVE OFFICER: Mr. John H. Prescott, Curator.

SPONSORING AGENCY: Privately financed laboratory.

YEAR FOUNDED: 1954.

SCOPE OF ACTIVITIES: Biological research in which the oceanarium facilities are pertinent.

SEASON OF OPERATION: All year.

PHYSICAL ENVIRONMENT ACCESSIBLE: Pacific Ocean, San Pedro Channel; sandy and silty beaches, rocky and gravelly shores.

PROVISIONS FOR VISITING SCIENTISTS: Space for 2-3 visitors; no fees charged; living quarters available nearby.

MAJOR RESEARCH FACILITIES: Small library; running sea and fresh-water, small aquarium tanks; living collections of local fish and marine mammal fauna; machine and wood shop, skilled shop workman available; various skiffs and outboards; one 37 ft LOA gill net boat equipped with salt water tank.

SIZE OF STAFF: Two at professional level; 2 technicians; 2 marine collectors.

IMPORTANT SPECIES AVAILABLE FOR LABORATORY STUDIES: Cetaceans, numerous species of fish and miscellaneous marine invertebrates.

MAJOR CURRENT RESEARCH PROJECTS AND SCIENTIFIC LEADERS:

Porpoise locomotion and sonar studies (K. S. Norris and staff)

Marineland Research Laboratory

POSTAL ADDRESS: Marineland, St. Augustine, Florida, USA.

LOCATION: Near St. Augustine.

EXECUTIVE OFFICER: F. G. Wood, Jr., Curator.

SPONSORING AGENCY: Laboratory of Marine Studios, Inc.

YEAR FOUNDED: 1951.

SCOPE OF ACTIVITIES: Restricted research on general marine biology.

SEASON OF OPERATION: All year.

PHYSICAL ENVIRONMENT ACCESSIBLE: Atlantic Ocean, Intracoastal Waterway; coquina sand beach, rocky shore, estuarine conditions, brackish, shallow bays, tidal pools and flats, mangrove swamps, inlets and ponds.

PROVISIONS FOR VISITING SCIENTISTS: Space for 4-6 visitors; no fees charged; living quarters available nearby.

MAJOR RESEARCH FACILITIES: Small library; running sea and fresh-water, large outdoor tanks, small aquarium tanks; machine and wood shop; 46 ft LOA

MARINELAND RESEARCH LABORATORY, FLORIDA

collecting boat (trawler type), *Porpoise III.*
SIZE OF STAFF: Two at professional level; 1 technician; collecting crew of the studios usually available.
IMPORTANT SPECIES AVAILABLE FOR LABORATORY STUDIES:
Cetacea: *Tursiops truncatus, Stenella plagiodon*
Elasmobranchii: *Narcine brasiliensis*
Cephalopoda: *Octopus vulgaris*
Reptilia: *Caretta c. caretta, Chelonia m. mydas*
Crustacea: *Hippa*
Mollusca: *Donax variabilis, Venus, Pinna*
MAJOR CURRENT RESEARCH PROJECTS AND SCIENTIFIC LEADERS: All research work is done by visiting scientists whose interests vary from person to person.

Massachusetts Division of Fisheries and Game Field Headquarters

POSTAL ADDRESS: Westboro, Massachusetts, USA.
EXECUTIVE OFFICER: William A. Tompkins, Chief Aquatic Biologist.
YEAR FOUNDED: 1957.
SCOPE OF ACTIVITIES: Restricted research on fisheries management, fresh-water and marine biology.
SEASON OF OPERATION: All year.
PHYSICAL ENVIRONMENT ACCESSIBLE: Atlantic Ocean; sandy and silty beaches, rocky and gravelly shores, estuarine conditions, brackish, shallow bays, eutrophic and oligotrophic lakes, rivers and streams.
PROVISIONS FOR VISITING SCIENTISTS: Space for visitors; no fees charged; living quarters available nearby.
MAJOR RESEARCH FACILITIES: Moderately complete library; running sea and fresh-water, large outdoor ponds and tanks, small aquarium tanks; machine and wood shop, skilled shop workman available; small boats and outboard motors.
SIZE OF STAFF: Ten at professional level; 14 technicians.
MAJOR CURRENT RESEARCH PROJECTS AND SCIENTIFIC LEADERS:
Quabbin Reservoir investigations (Robert McCaig)
Trout pond reclamations (James Mullan)
Warm water reclamations (Frank Grice)
Harvest studies on managed ponds (Robert McCaig)
Sterilization and sex reversal studies (William A. Tompkins)
Reclamation of the Deerfield River for trout and evaluation of techniques applied (James Mullan)
Marine sport fisheries inventory (William A. Tompkins)
Connecticut River survey (James Mullan)

Mendocino Biological Field Station

POSTAL ADDRESS: Pacific Union College, Angwin, California, USA.
EXECUTIVE OFFICER: D. V. Hemphill, Director.
SPONSORING AGENCY: Pacific Union College.
YEAR FOUNDED: 1947.
SCOPE OF ACTIVITIES: Unrestricted research on marine ecology; graduate and undergraduate instruction.
SEASON OF OPERATION: June to August.
PHYSICAL ENVIRONMENT ACCESSIBLE: Pacific Ocean, Albion, Little and Navarro Rivers; sandy and silty beaches, rocky and gravelly shores and estuarine conditions.
PROVISIONS FOR VISITING SCIENTISTS: Space for 3 visitors; living quarters available nearby.
MAJOR RESEARCH AND TEACHING FACILITIES: Small library; running sea and fresh-water, small aquarium tanks; small boats and outboard motors.
INSTRUCTIONAL PROGRAM: Ecology, general invertebrate zoology, ichthyology, and aquatic invertebrate systematics.
SIZE OF STAFF: Two-three at professional level.

Michigan Department of Conservation, Institute for Fisheries Research

POSTAL ADDRESS:
Headquarters: The University of Michigan Museums Annex, Ann Arbor, Michigan, USA.
Branch laboratories:
Fish Pathology Laboratory, Grayling, Michigan. Dr. Leonard Allison, Supervisor.
Hunt Creek Trout Research Station, Star Route 1, Lewiston, Michigan. Dr. David S. Shetter, Supervisor.
Marquette Fisheries Research Station, State Fish Hatchery, Marquette, Michigan. Merle Galbraith, Acting Supervisor.
Pigeon River Trout Research Station, Vanderbilt, Michigan. Dr. William C. Latta, Supervisor.
Rifle River Fisheries Research Station, Lupton, Michigan. Mercer H. Patriarche, Supervisor.
Hastings Fisheries Research Station, Hastings, Michigan. Dr. John E. Williams, Supervisor.
EXECUTIVE OFFICER: Dr. Gerald P. Cooper, Director.
SPONSORING AGENCY: Michigan Department of Conservation, Division of Fisheries, in cooperation with the University of Michigan.
YEAR FOUNDED: 1930.
SCOPE OF ACTIVITIES: Restricted and unrestricted research in sport fisheries.
SEASON OF OPERATION: All year.
PHYSICAL ENVIRONMENT ACCESSIBLE: Huron River; eutrophic and oligotrophic lakes.
PROVISIONS FOR VISITING SCIENTISTS: Space for visitors at Lewiston and Vanderbilt; living quarters available nearby.
MAJOR RESEARCH FACILITIES: Small library at Ann Arbor and Lewiston; large outdoor ponds and tanks near Ann Arbor and at the Hastings Station, small aquarium tanks at Ann Arbor and Hastings; machine and wood shop, skilled shop workmen available at Ann Arbor; small boats and outboard motors.
SIZE OF STAFF: Twenty-three at professional level; 40 technicians.

MAJOR CURRENT RESEARCH PROJECTS AND SCIENTIFIC LEADERS:

Limnological investigations and surveys (Frank F. Hooper)
Warm water fisheries research (John E. Williams)
Fish pathology (Leonard N. Allison)
Stream trout research (David S. Shetter)
Sea lamprey research (Thomas M. Stauffer)
Experimental fish management (Walter R. Crowe)

Michigan State University, Department of Fisheries and Wildlife

POSTAL ADDRESS: East Lansing, Michigan, USA.
EXECUTIVE OFFICER: Dr. Peter I. Tack, Head.
YEAR FOUNDED: 1940.
SCOPE OF ACTIVITIES: Unrestricted research on fundamentals of aquatic productivity; graduate and undergraduate instruction.
SEASON OF OPERATION: All year.
PHYSICAL ENVIRONMENT ACCESSIBLE: Lake Lansing (eutrophic lake), Red Cedar and Grand Rivers.
PROVISIONS FOR VISITING SCIENTISTS: None.
MAJOR RESEARCH AND TEACHING FACILITIES: Moderately complete library; large outdoor ponds and tanks, small aquarium tanks; limited research collections of vertebrates and Great Lakes area flora; identified reference collections of most local vertebrates as well as nearly all local plants; small boats and outboard motors.
INSTRUCTIONAL PROGRAM: Limnology, plankton, ecology, parasitology, general invertebrate zoology, ichthyology, aquatic entomology, general physiology, fishery biology, biometry, population dynamics and fisheries management.
SIZE OF STAFF: Ten at professional level; 2 technicians.
MAJOR CURRENT RESEARCH PROJECTS:

Study of primary productivity in a warm water stream and estimation of total community metabolism
Study of productivity in a trout stream ecosystem
Tracing of nutrients through the food complex (radioactive isotope tracer study)
Relationships of food production to predation in a fish population
A study of the ecological importance of stream drift
Study of methods of estimation of primary production in a stream ecosystem

Minnesota State Department of Conservation, Division of Game and Fish, Fisheries Research Unit

POSTAL ADDRESS:

Headquarters: 390 Centennial Building, St. Paul 1, Minnesota, USA.
Branch Laboratories:

1. Brainerd District Headquarters, 315 Charles Street, N.W., Brainerd, Minnesota; John E. Maloney, Aquatic Biologist.
2. Detroit Lakes District Headquarters, Detroit Lakes, Minnesota; D. E. Olson, Aquatic Biologist.
3. Glenwood District Headquarters, Glenwood, Minnesota; Dennis Schupp, Aquatic Biologist.
4. Grand Rapids District Headquarters, Grand Rapids, Minnesota; Fritz Johnson, Aquatic Biologist.
5. St. Peter District Headquarters, St. Peter, Minnesota; Donald E. Woods, Aquatic Biologist.

EXECUTIVE OFFICER: Dr. John Moyle, Research Supervisor.
YEAR FOUNDED: Central laboratory in 1941; Brainerd laboratory, 1949, Glenwood and St. Peter laboratories, 1950.
SCOPE OF ACTIVITIES: Restricted research on applied aquatic and fisheries biology.
SEASON OF OPERATION: All year.
PHYSICAL ENVIRONMENT ACCESSIBLE: Eutrophic and oligotrophic lakes, rivers and streams.
PROVISIONS FOR VISITING SCIENTISTS: None.
MAJOR RESEARCH FACILITIES: Small library; large outdoor ponds and tanks, small aquarium tanks; machine and wood shop, skilled shop workman available at central laboratory.
SIZE OF STAFF: Ten at professional level; 5 technicians.

Missouri Cooperative Fishery Unit

POSTAL ADDRESS: Department of Zoology, University of Missouri, Columbia, Missouri, USA.
EXECUTIVE OFFICER: Dr. Robert S. Campbell, Chairman, Department of Zoology.
SPONSORING AGENCIES: University of Missouri; Missouri Conservation Commission; U. S. Fish and Wildlife Service; industrial direct support; private support.
YEAR FOUNDED: 1937.
SCOPE OF ACTIVITIES: Unrestricted research on limnology and fishery biology; graduate and undergradute instruction.
SEASON OF OPERATION: All year.
PHYSICAL ENVIRONMENT ACCESSIBLE: Rivers, streams, farm ponds and reservoirs.
PROVISIONS FOR VISITING SCIENTISTS: None.
MAJOR RESEARCH AND TEACHING FACILITIES: Moderately complete library; large outdoor ponds; machine and wood shop; skilled shop workmen on University-wide basis available; identified reference and research collections of Missouri fishes; small boats and outboard motors.
INSTRUCTIONAL PROGRAM: Limnology, ecology, general and comparative physiology, biochemistry, embryology, phycology, general invertebrate zoology, ichthyology, fisheries biology, biometry, population dynamics, fisheries management and methods in hydrobiology.

E. SYDNEY STEPHENS HALL, HOUSING THE MISSOURI COOPERATIVE FISHERY UNIT

SIZE OF STAFF: Five at professional level in limnology and fisheries.

IMPORTANT SPECIES AVAILABLE FOR LABORATORY STUDIES:

Pisces: *Aplodinotus grunniens, Micropterus salmoides, M. dolomieu, Pomoxis annularis, Lepomis cyanellus, L. macrochirus, Fundulus catenatus, F. kansae, Lepisosteus osseus, Ictalurus lacustris.*

MAJOR CURRENT RESEARCH PROJECTS AND SCIENTIFIC LEADERS:

The white crappie in the Niangua Arm, Lake of the Ozarks (Arthur Witt, Jr.)

Length frequency distributions of ancient and recent fresh-water drum (Arthur Witt, Jr.)

The limnology of Lake Taneycomo, Missouri (Robert S. Campbell)

Distribution of fishes in the Platte River, Nebraska (Arthur Witt, Jr.)

Growth of channel catfish in the Platte River, Nebraska (Arthur Witt, Jr.)

Life history of the longnose gar (Arthur Witt, Jr.)

Montana State Department of Fish and Game, State Fisheries Laboratory

POSTAL ADDRESS: Department of Zoology and Entomology, Montana State College, Bozeman, Montana, USA.

EXECUTIVE OFFICERS: John R. Heaton, Department of Fish and Game. Dr. C. J. D. Brown, Professor of Limnology.

SPONSORING AGENCIES: Montana Department of Fish and Game and the Montana State College Agricultural Experiment Station.

YEAR FOUNDED: 1948.

SCOPE OF ACTIVITIES: Restricted and unrestricted research on applied limnology and fisheries of fresh-waters; graduate and undergraduate instruction.

SEASON OF OPERATION: All year.

PHYSICAL ENVIRONMENT ACCESSIBLE: Headwaters of Missouri River and reservoirs on cold water streams and mountain lakes.

PROVISIONS FOR VISITING SCIENTISTS: Research and living space available for 2-3 visitors; no fees charged for research space.

MAJOR RESEARCH AND TEACHING FACILITIES: Moderately complete library; small aquarium tanks, use of fish hatchery facilities in the State; research collections of aquatic plants, fish and aquatic invertebrates; identified reference collections of fish and plants; machine and wood shop at the College; small boats and outboard motors.

INSTRUCTIONAL PROGRAM: The following courses are offered by the Department of Zoology and Entomology, Montana State College: limnology, ecology, biochemistry, embryology, microbiology, parasitology, ichthyology, fisheries management, aquatic plants, advanced aquatic ecology, aquatic insects and fish culture.

SIZE OF STAFF: Two full-time and 4 part-time scientists at professional level (6 additional professional staff on the College faculty).

IMPORTANT SPECIES AVAILABLE FOR LABORATORY STUDIES:

Pisces: *Salmo gairdneri, S. clarki, S. trutta, Salvelinus fontinalis, S. malma, Prosopium williamsoni, Noturus flavus, Catostomus* and several species of Cyprindae.

Insecta: Many species of stoneflies, Caddis, mayflies, etc.

MAJOR CURRENT RESEARCH PROJECTS AND SCIENTIFIC LEADERS:

Trout test stream studies (Jack E. Bailey)

Montana fishes (C. J. D. Brown)

Age and growth of Montana fishes (John Heaton)

Phytoplankton production in reservoirs (John C. Wright)

Reservoir influences on cold water streams (John Heaton and J. Stober)

Lake population studies (J. Posewitz and R. Johnson)

DDT effects on fish and fish foods (N. Schoenthal)

Life history of cutthroat trout (H. Johnson)

Trout parasites (A. Fox)

Winter movements of trout (S. Logan)

Effects of Toxaphene on fish-food organisms (R. Needham)

Mount Desert Island Biological Laboratory

POSTAL ADDRESS: Salsbury Cove, Maine, USA.

LOCATION: Near Bar Harbor.

EXECUTIVE OFFICER: Dr. Alvin F. Rieck, Director of Laboratory, Department of Physiology, Marquette University School of Medicine, 561 North Fifteenth Street, Milwaukee 3, Wisconsin.

SPONSORING AGENCY: Privately financed laboratory.

YEAR FOUNDED: 1898-1921 known as Harpswell Laboratory; relocated and renamed in 1921.

SCOPE OF ACTIVITIES: Restricted research in cardiovascular-renal physiology and development; training research workers.

SEASON OF OPERATION: June 15 to September 15.

PHYSICAL ENVIRONMENT ACCESSIBLE: Atlantic Ocean; estuarine conditions.

PROVISIONS FOR VISITING SCIENTISTS: Space for visitors; fees charged; living quarters available nearby.

MAJOR RESEARCH FACILITIES: Small library; running sea and fresh-water, large outdoor tanks, small aquarium tanks, aquatic cages; machine and wood shop; vessels.

SIZE OF STAFF: No permanent staff.

IMPORTANT SPECIES AVAILABLE FOR LABORATORY STUDIES:

Coelenterata: *Aurelia aurita*

Mollusca: *Littorina littorea, Thais lapillus, Mytilus edulis*

Crustacea: *Gammarus locusta*

Echinodermata: *Echinoarachnius parma, Cucumaria frondosa*

Pisces: *Squalus acanthias, Myxocephalus scorpius, M. octodecimspinosus Pseudopleuronectes americanus, Lophius piscatorius*

MAJOR CURRENT RESEARCH PROJECTS AND SCIENTIFIC LEADERS:

Transport in renal tubules (Roy Forster)
Differentiation (C. E. Wilde)
Active transport (A. Hogben)

Mountain Lake Biological Station

POSTAL ADDRESS: University of Virginia, Charlottesville, Virginia, USA.

LOCATION: Route 1, Pembroke, Virginia.

EXECUTIVE OFFICER: Dr. James L. Riopel, Director.

SPONSORING AGENCY: University of Virginia.

YEAR FOUNDED: 1930.

SCOPE OF ACTIVITIES: Unrestricted research on fresh-water and terrestrial ecology; graduate and undergraduate instruction.

MOUNTAIN LAKE BIOLOGICAL STATION, UNIVERSITY OF VIRGINIA

SEASON OF OPERATION: June 15 to August 23.

PHYSICAL ENVIRONMENT ACCESSIBLE: Mountain Lake (oligotrophic lake), James and New Rivers.

PROVISIONS FOR VISITING SCIENTISTS: Research and living space for 6 visitors; fees charged for research space.

MAJOR RESEARCH AND TEACHING FACILITIES: Small library; small aquarium tanks; identified reference collections of birds and mammals, archegoniate and seed-plants; small boats.

INSTRUCTIONAL PROGRAM: Limnology, physiology, paleontology, cyto- and histo-chemistry, cell morphology, radiation biology, ecology, plant anatomy, algology, bacteriology, plant morphology, spermatophytes, archegoniates, mycology, plant ecology, paleobotany, acoelomate invertebrates, coelomate invertebrates, entomology, protozoology, helminthology, arthropods, ornithology, animal ecology, and experimental embryology.

SIZE OF STAFF: Nine at professional level.

IMPORTANT SPECIES AVAILABLE FOR LABORATORY STUDIES:

Turbellaria: *Planaria dactylingera*

Crustacea: *Cambarus sciotensis, C. longulus*

Gastropoda: *Tridopsis albolabris*

Amphibia: *Plethodon cinereus, Rana clamitans, Triturus v. viridescens*

Narragansett Marine Laboratory

POSTAL ADDRESS: Kingston, Rhode Island, USA.

EXECUTIVE OFFICER: Dr. John A. Knauss, Director.

SPONSORING AGENCY: University of Rhode Island.

YEAR FOUNDED: 1937.

SCOPE OF ACTIVITIES: Restricted research on marine resources of Rhode Island; coastal and high seas oceanography; unrestricted research on oceanography with special emphasis on biological aspects; graduate instruction.

SEASON OF OPERATION: All year.

PHYSICAL ENVIRONMENT ACCESSIBLE: Narragansett Bay, Rhode Island Sound; open ocean, sandy and silty beaches, rocky and gravelly shores, estuarine conditions, brackish, shallow bays, rivers and streams.

PROVISIONS FOR VISITING SCIENTISTS: Space by invitation for three visitors; living quarters available nearby.

MAJOR RESEARCH AND TEACHING FACILITIES: Very extensive library at the University, small one at the Laboratory; running sea and fresh-water, small aquarium tanks; machine and wood shop; small boats and outboard motors; vessels, 30 ft and 46 ft LOA.

INSTRUCTIONAL PROGRAM: Plankton, biological and physical oceanography, fishery biology, population dynamics, geological oceanography, nekton and benthos.

NARRAGANSETT MARINE LABORATORY

SIZE OF STAFF: Fifteen at professional level; 7 technicians.

MAJOR CURRENT RESEARCH PROJECTS AND SCIENTIFIC LEADERS:

Biological oceanography (open ocean plankton and bioacoustics) (Charles J. Fish and Marie P. Fish)

Estuarine productivity (phytoplankton production, regeneration of nutrients by bacteria, epibenthos and vertical migration) (David M. Pratt and John McN. Sieburth)

Salt ponds (productivity of brackish waters) (Charles J. Fish and Harry P. Jeffries)

Underwater acoustics (Ambient noise studies) (Frank T. Dietz)

National Oceanographic Data Center

POSTAL ADDRESS: Building 160, Naval Yard Annex, Washington 25, D.C., USA.

EXECUTIVE OFFICER: Woodrow C. Jacobs, Director.

YEAR FOUNDED: 1960.

SCOPE OF ACTIVITIES: All aspects (including physics, chemistry, biology, geology, geophysics, dynamics, etc.) of marine environment from air-sea interface through surface waters and underlying waters to the ocean bottom. Principal mission is to acquire, process, and disseminate all oceanographic data and information (and correlative data and information) for the purposes of oceanographic research and the support of all types of maritime activities. A real interest includes all the oceans of the world, including nearshore areas, and will eventually encompass estuarine waters.

SEASON OF OPERATION: All year.

PROVISIONS FOR VISITING SCIENTISTS: Study rooms available, for any length of time, for visiting scientists wishing to use the collection archived at the Center or collections in various facilities in Washington, D.C., area. Advance notice for reservation of a study room is desirable.

MAJOR RESEARCH FACILITIES: Largest collection of physical and chemical oceanographic data in the United States; machine processing equipment for special handling of data available on cost basis for special research projects. Center is near all major libraries in Washington, D.C., and convenient to all specialized collections of oceanographic data, such as those of U.S. National Museum (Smithsonian), U.S. Coast and Geodetic Survey, U.S. Bureau of Commercial Fisheries, U.S. Naval Oceanographic Office, etc.

SIZE OF STAFF: Approximately 70; including oceanographers, mathematician-programmers, physical science technicians, cartographers, illustrators, and clerical personnel.

MAJOR CURRENT RESEARCH PROJECTS:

Continuing research problems in regard to processing and quality control of oceanographic data.

Specialists perform many and varied analyses of oceanographic data in response to specific requests.

New Hampshire Fish and Game Department, Management and Research Division

POSTAL ADDRESS:

Headquarters: Concord, New Hampshire, USA.

Branch Laboratory: Pathology Laboratory, Powder Mill Fish Hatchery, New Durham, New Hampshire.

EXECUTIVE OFFICER: Hilbert R. Siegler, Chief.

SPONSORING AGENCIES: U. S. Government and the State of New Hampshire.

YEAR FOUNDED: 1931.

SCOPE OF ACTIVITIES: Restricted research on lake ecology and fisheries management studies.

SEASON OF OPERATION: All year.

PHYSICAL ENVIRONMENT ACCESSIBLE: Eutrophic and oligotrophic lakes, rivers and streams.

PROVISIONS FOR VISITING SCIENTISTS: None.

MAJOR RESEARCH FACILITIES: Small library; large outdoor ponds and tanks, aquatic cages; machine and wood shop; small boats and outboard motors.

SIZE OF STAFF: Eighteen at professional level; 3 technicians.

IMPORTANT SPECIES AVAILABLE FOR LABORATORY STUDIES:

Pisces: *Esox niger, Salmo salar, Salvelinus f. fontinalis, Micropterus d. dolomieu.*

MAJOR CURRENT RESEARCH PROJECTS AND SCIENTIFIC LEADERS:

Bass management investigations (Arthur D. Riel)

Evaluation of Bow Lake fishery (George R. Morrison)

Trout stream investigations (Howard C. Nowell)

Land-locked salmon management investigation (Richard G. Seamans, Jr.)

Life history and ecology of the chain pickerel (William C. Jerome)

Chlorine as a fish toxicant (C. F. Jackson)

New Jersey Division of Fish and Game, Fisheries Laboratories

POSTAL ADDRESS:
New Jersey Fisheries Laboratory (fresh-water unit), Lebanon, New Jersey, USA.
New Jersey Marine Fisheries Laboratory, Box 92, Seaside Park, New Jersey.
EXECUTIVE OFFICER: Roland F. Smith, Principal Fisheries Biologist, New Jersey Fisheries Laboratory, Lebanon, New Jersey.
SPONSORING AGENCY: New Jersey, Department of Conservation and Economic Development.
YEAR FOUNDED: 1951 and 1956.
SCOPE OF ACTIVITIES: Restricted research in marine and fresh-water fisheries management.
SEASON OF OPERATION: All year.
PHYSICAL ENVIRONMENT ACCESSIBLE: Atlantic Ocean; many bays, rivers, eutrophic and oligotrophic lakes, rocky and gravelly shores (fresh-water), estuarine conditions, brackish, shallow bays, acidotrophic waters, and polluted waters.
PROVISIONS FOR VISITING SCIENTISTS: Space for 1-2 visitors at each laboratory; no fees charged; living quarters available nearby.
MAJOR RESEARCH FACILITIES: Very extensive libraries at nearby universities, small library at laboratories; running sea and fresh-water planned, large outdoor ponds and tanks, small aquarium tanks; identified reference collections of fish; machine and wood shop, skilled shop workmen available; small boats and outboard motors; larger vessels available on charter basis.
SIZE OF STAFF: Nine at professional level; 3-6 technicians.
MAJOR CURRENT RESEARCH PROJECTS AND SCIENTIFIC LEADERS:
Establishing parameters of Porgy populations, *Stenotomus chrysops,* from New Jersey to Massachusetts (Paul Hamer)
Trout and shad studies in coastal rivers (Bruce Pyle)
Evaluation of trout stocking programs (Richard Gross)
Introduction of new species (Walter Murowski)
PUBLICATIONS ISSUED:
New Jersey Fisheries Survey Reports (occasionally published contributions)
Progress or Administrative Reports
Miscellaneous reports (processed)

New Jersey Oyster Research Laboratory

POSTAL ADDRESS:
Headquarters: Department of Zoology, Rutgers University, New Brunswick, New Jersey, USA.
Field Stations:
Oyster Research Laboratory, Bivalve, New Jersey.
Oyster Research Laboratory, R.F.D. 2, Cape May Court House, New Jersey. (Summer only)
EXECUTIVE OFFICER: Dr. Harold H. Haskin, Professor of Zoology and Biologist in charge.
SPONSORING AGENCIES: Rutgers University Agricultural Experiment Station. Substantial support from New Jersey State Division of Shell Fisheries, Department of Conservation and Economic Development.
YEAR FOUNDED: 1888.
SCOPE OF ACTIVITIES: Unrestricted research on the biology of shell fisheries; graduate instruction.
SEASON OF OPERATION: All year at Cape May Court House and at Bivalve; June 15-August 31, laboratory houseboat in New Jersey coastal estuaries.
PHYSICAL ENVIRONMENT ACCESSIBLE: Delaware Bay and coastal estuaries, Raritan and Barnegat Bays; sandy and silty beaches, estuarine conditions and brackish, shallow bays.
PROVISIONS FOR VISITING SCIENTISTS: Limited research and living space for visitors; no fees charged for research space.
MAJOR RESEARCH AND TEACHING FACILITIES: Very extensive library at Rutgers, Oyster reprint library in Cape May Court House; running sea and fresh-water, small aquarium tanks, extensive tidal flats in front of laboratory, bare at low tide, provide large area for experimentation; identified reference collection of shells of various species of oysters; machine and wood shop; small boats and outboard motors, one 48 ft LOA diesel vessel.
INSTRUCTIONAL PROGRAM: Oyster Research Laboratory is closely affiliated with the Department of Zoology of Rutgers University which offers work leading to the Ph.D. in marine biology. Special courses available include coastal oceanography, estuarine ecology, malacology, and limnology.
SIZE OF STAFF: Five at professional level; 3 technicians.
IMPORTANT SPECIES AVAILABLE FOR LABORATORY STUDIES:
Pelecypoda: *Crassostrea virginica, Mercenaria mercenaria, Mytilus edulis, Tagelus divisus*
Gastropoda: *Urosalpinx cinerea, Polynices duplicata*

CAPE MAY COURT HOUSE FIELD STATION, NEW JERSEY OYSTER RESEARCH LABORATORY

Crustacea: *Pinnotheres ostreum,* various xanthid crabs
Arachnoidea: *Limulus polyphemus*
Various plankton, algae and bottom diatoms.

MAJOR CURRENT RESEARCH PROJECTS AND SCIENTIFIC LEADERS:
Mortality of oysters (Harold H. Haskin)
Cytology of oyster disease now rampant (Walter Canzonier and John Meyhre)
Host parasite relationships (Sung Yen Feng)
Abundance and distribution of oyster larvae (Harold H. Haskin and Donald Kunkle)

New York Aquarium

LABORATORIES:
1. Department of Marine Biochemistry and Ecology
2. Genetics Laboratory
(Descriptions follow.)

Department of Marine Biochemistry and Ecology

POSTAL ADDRESS: New York Aquarium, Brooklyn 24, New York, USA.
EXECUTIVE OFFICER: Ross F. Nigrelli, Chairman.
SPONSORING AGENCY: New York Zoological Society.
YEAR FOUNDED: 1957.
SCOPE OF ACTIVITIES: Unrestricted research on general aquatic biology with special emphasis on the biochemical ecology of the sea; graduate instruction.
SEASON OF OPERATION: All year.
PHYSICAL ENVIRONMENT ACCESSIBLE: New York Bight, Long Island Sound, Hudson and Raritan estuaries, Atlantic Ocean; sandy and silty beaches, rocky and gravelly shores, estuarine conditions and brackish, shallow bays.
PROVISIONS FOR VISITING SCIENTISTS: Space for 2 visitors; no fees charged; living quarters available nearby.
MAJOR RESEARCH AND TEACHING FACILITIES: Very extensive library in New York; running sea water, large outdoor ponds and tanks, small aquarium tanks.
INSTRUCTIONAL PROGRAM: Fish diseases, ichthyology and fisheries biology.
SIZE OF STAFF: Three at professional level; 1 technician.
IMPORTANT SPECIES AVAILABLE FOR LABORATORY STUDIES:
Pisces: *Fundulus, Opsanus* and others
Echinodermata: *Arbacia, Asterias* and others
Porifera: *Microciona* and others
Protochordata: *Mogula* and others

MAJOR CURRENT RESEARCH PROJECTS AND SCIENTIFIC LEADERS:
Toxic metabolites from marine invertebrates (Ross F. Nigrelli)
Antibacterial agents from marine invertebrates (Ross F. Nigrelli)
Metabolism of copper in marine organisms (Ross F. Nigrelli)

NEW YORK AQUARIUM

Nucleic acids of marine invertebrates (Martin F. Stempien, Jr.)
Physiology of coral animals and coral reef formation (Thomas Goreau)
Biochemistry of holothurin, steriod saponin from a sea cucumber (Harry F. Sobotka)
Hepatoma in trout (Ross F. Nigrelli)
Microsporidiosis in the angler fish (Sophie Jakowska)

PUBLICATIONS ISSUED: *Zoologica* (New York) (regularly published journal)

Genetics Laboratory

POSTAL ADDRESS: New York Aquarium, Brooklyn 24, New York, USA.
STAFF OFFICER: Klaus D. Kallman, Research Associate in Genetics.
SPONSORING AGENCY: New York Zoological Society.
YEAR FOUNDED: 1939.
SCOPE OF ACTIVITIES: Unrestricted research on genetics and correlated studies of small, warm fresh-water fishes; graduate instruction.
SEASON OF OPERATION: All year.
PROVISIONS FOR VISITING SCIENTISTS: Space for 1 visitor; no fees charged; living quarters available nearby.
MAJOR RESEARCH AND TEACHING FACILITIES: Very extensive library at American Museum of Natural History; small aquarium tanks; histological equipment.
INSTRUCTIONAL PROGRAM: Fish genetics.
SIZE OF STAFF: Three at professional level; 2 technicians.
IMPORTANT SPECIES AVAILABLE FOR LABORATORY STUDIES: The following genetic strains are available for research:
Inbred strains of *Xiphophorus maculatus* and *X. hellerii.*
Special color strains of the same two species.
Tumorous strains of the same two species and their hybrids.

Xiphophorus couchianus, X. montezumae cortezi, X. variatus xiphidium, Mollienesia formosa, M. sphenops, and *Limia vittata.*

MAJOR CURRENT RESEARCH PROJECTS AND SCIENTIFIC LEADERS:

Correlated studies of pigment cell growth (Sylvia S. Greenberg)

Tissue transplantation, population genetics and endocrinology of fishes (Klaus D. Kallman)

Genetic studies in thyroid tumor susceptibility (Klaus D. Kallman)

Genetic studies in sex inheritance and reversal (Klaus D. Kallman)

Oklahoma Fishery Research Laboratory

POSTAL ADDRESS: North Campus, Box 14, University of Oklahoma, Norman, Oklahoma, USA.

EXECUTIVE OFFICER: Alfred Houser, Director.

SPONSORING AGENCIES: Oklahoma Department of Wildlife Conservation and the University of Oklahoma.

YEAR FOUNDED: 1947.

SCOPE OF ACTIVITIES: Unrestricted research on the ecology and management of fresh-water fish in Oklahoma; graduate and undergraduate instruction.

SEASON OF OPERATION: All year.

PHYSICAL ENVIRONMENT ACCESSIBLE: Hydroelectric power and flood control reservoirs.

PROVISION FOR VISITING SCIENTISTS: Space for 3 visitors; no fees charged; living quarters available nearby.

MAJOR RESEARCH FACILITIES: Small library; small aquarium tanks; identified reference collection of fresh-water fish of Oklahoma; machine and wood shop; small boats and outboard motors.

SIZE OF STAFF: Two at professional level; 1 technician.

MAJOR CURRENT RESEARCH PROJECTS AND SCIENTIFIC LEADERS:

Statewide growth-rate of drum, bullhead catfish and gizzard shad (Alfred Houser and O'Reilly Sandoz)

Fish population estimate on Fort Gibson Reservoir (Alfred Houser)

Fish population sampling by rotenone on Texoma, Grand, Tenkiller and Murray Lakes (Alfred Houser and O'Reilly Sandoz)

Pre-impoundment survey on Rock Creek, Murray County (O'Reilly Sandoz)

Fish population studies on Lake Lawtonka (Alfred Houser)

Catch statistics (Leonard Jones)

Oregon Fish Commission Research Laboratories

POSTAL ADDRESS:

Headquarters: Route 1, Box 31-A Clackamas, Oregon, USA.

Branch laboratories:

859 Olney Avenue, Astoria, Oregon.

220 S. W. Bay Boulevard, Newport, Oregon.

P. O. Box 529, Charleston, Oregon.

P. O. Box 392, Oakridge, Oregon.

Route 1, Box 590, Sandy, Oregon.

LOCATION: Headquarters near Portland.

EXECUTIVE OFFICER: Jack M. Van Hyning, Director of Research.

YEAR FOUNDED: Astoria, 1938; Clackamas and Newport, 1947; Charleston, 1949; Oakridge, 1953; Sandy, 1957.

SCOPE OF ACTIVITIES: Restricted research on general fisheries biology and commercial fisheries management.

SEASON OF OPERATION: All year.

PHYSICAL ENVIRONMENT ACCESSIBLE: Pacific Ocean, Columbia River and tributaries, Yaquina and Coos Bays; sandy and silty beaches, rocky and gravelly shores, estuarine conditions, continental shelf, and brackish, shallow bays.

PROVISIONS FOR VISITING SCIENTISTS: None.

MAJOR RESEARCH FACILITIES: Library; aquarium tanks at Newport, experimental hatchery; machine and wood shop; small boats and outboard motors; fisheries pathology laboratory.

SIZE OF STAFF: Fifty-six at professional level; 14 technicians.

IMPORTANT SPECIES AVAILABLE FOR LABORATORY STUDIES:

Pisces: *Eopsetta zordeni, Acipenser medirostris, Sebastodes* sp., *Oncorhynchus tshawytscha, Thunnus germo, Thalichthys pacificus*

Pelecypoda: *Siliqua patula, Ostrea gigas*

Crustacea: *Cancer magister, Pandalus jordani*

MAJOR CURRENT RESEARCH PROJECTS AND SCIENTIFIC LEADERS:

Ocean troll salmon studies (Robert E. Loeffel)

Otter trawl investigations (Alfred R. Morgan)

Albacore investigations

Columbia River investigations (Robert Thompson)

Coastal River investigations (Thomas Kruse)

Shellfish investigations (C. Dale Snow)

Hatching biology (Wallace Hublou)

Columbia River development (Raymond Willis)

Mark analysis investigation (Earl Pulford)

Oregon Institute of Marine Biology

POSTAL ADDRESS: Charleston, Oregon, USA.

LOCATION: Near Coos Bay.

EXECUTIVE OFFICER: Chairman, Department of Biology, University of Oregon, Eugene, Oregon.

SPONSORING AGENCY: Oregon State System of Higher Education.

YEAR FOUNDED: 1937.

SCOPE OF ACTIVITIES: Unrestricted research on physiological ecology and general marine biology; graduate and undergraduate instruction.

SEASON OF OPERATION: June to September with limited

facilities available at any time.

PHYSICAL ENVIRONMENT ACCESSIBLE: Coos Bay, Pacific Ocean; sandy and silty beaches, rocky and gravelly shores, estuarine conditions and brackish, shallow bays.

PROVISIONS FOR VISITING SCIENTISTS: Space for 2-6 visitors; nominal fees charged; living quarters available nearby.

MAJOR RESEARCH AND TEACHING FACILITIES: Small library; running sea (summer only) and fresh-water, small aquarium tanks; herbarium of marine algae; machine and wood shop, skilled shop workman available; one 36 ft LOA vessel.

INSTRUCTIONAL PROGRAM: General invertebrate zoology, marine algae, invertebrate embryology, marine ecology and parasitology.

SIZE OF STAFF: Seven at professional level; 6 technicians.

IMPORTANT SPECIES AVAILABLE FOR LABORATORY STUDIES:

Echinodermata: *Strongylocentrotus purpuratus*
Gastropoda: *Acmaea,* various other species
Sipunculida: *Phascolosoma*
Amphineura: *Ischnochiton* and other genera
Crustacea: *Hemigrapsus, Pachygrapsus, Cancer*
Nemertea: *Lineus*
Anthozoa: *Tealia, Metridium, Anthopleura*
Pisces: Cottidae (*Oligocottus,* etc.)

MAJOR CURRENT RESEARCH PROJECTS AND SCIENTIFIC LEADERS:

Productivity of sessile diatoms (R. W. Castenholz)
Regeneration in nemerteans (Marie Tucker)
Antigen-antibody relations in Amphineura (B. McConnaughey)
Recruitment, death and growth rates in *Acmaea digitalis* (P. Frank)
Taxonomy of apostomatous ciliates (E. Kozloff)

Pacific Marine Station

POSTAL ADDRESS: Dillon Beach, Marin County, California, USA.

LOCATION: About 50 miles north of San Francisco.

EXECUTIVE OFFICER: Dr. Joel W. Hedgpeth, Director.

SPONSORING AGENCY: University of the Pacific.

YEAR FOUNDED: 1948.

SCOPE OF ACTIVITIES: Research on marine ecology, especially bottom organisms of Tomales Bay, plankton of nearby ocean and general systematic study of local fauna; graduate and undergraduate instruction.

SEASON OF OPERATION: All year.

PHYSICAL ENVIRONMENT ACCESSIBLE: Pacific Ocean; Tomales and Bodega Bays; sandy and silty beaches, rocky and gravelly shores, estuarine conditions (marine bay), small streams, ponds, and mud flats.

PROVISIONS FOR VISITING SCIENTISTS: Research and living space for 3-6 visitors; fees charged for research space.

MAJOR RESEARCH AND TEACHING FACILITIES: Small library; running sea water (under reconstruction); small aquarium tanks; research collections of invertebrates, especially crustaceans and mollusks of California coast; many other groups well represented but unstudied; identified reference collections of common local invertebrates and algae; machine and wood shop, skilled shop workman available; small boats and outboard motors; 36 ft LOA power vessel with deck winch and gear, 26 ft whale boat, ocean going fishing boat available on charter.

INSTRUCTIONAL PROGRAM: Intensive summer courses in invertebrate zoology, comparative physiology and marine ecology; also geology, oceanography, or botany as visiting staff permits. Year round instruction in invertebrate zoology, systematics and ecology on tutorial basis.

SIZE OF STAFF: Four at professional level (2 part-time), also several research associates affiliated with local institutions; 3 technicians.

MAJOR CURRENT RESEARCH PROJECTS AND SCIENTIFIC LEADERS:

Long term ecological-paleoecological study of Tomales Bay (R. G. Johnson and J. W. Hedgpeth)
Environmental physiology (John S. Tucker)
Monthly plankton and hydrographic sampling (J. W. Hedgpeth)

Potamological Institute

POSTAL ADDRESS: 3005 Upper River Road, Louisville 7, Kentucky, USA.

EXECUTIVE OFFICER: Dr. William M. Clay, Executive Director.

SPONSORING AGENCY: University of Louisville.

YEAR FOUNDED: 1960.

SCOPE OF ACTIVITIES: Unrestricted research on potamology (biology and ecology of flowing streams); graduate and undergraduate instruction.

SEASON OF OPERATION: All year.

PHYSICAL ENVIRONMENT ACCESSIBLE: Ohio River.

PROVISIONS FOR VISITING SCIENTISTS: Space for 3-6 visitors; no fees charged; living quarters available nearby.

MAJOR RESEARCH AND TEACHING FACILITIES: Small library; small aquarium tanks, direct pipeline to Ohio River for raw river water; research and identified reference collection of fishes of the Ohio River drainage system, limited herpetological collection, herbarium of the seed plants of Kentucky; small boats and outboard motors; 23 ft LOA inboard cruiser.

INSTRUCTIONAL PROGRAM: Conservation of aquatic resources, fresh-water biology, ecology and economics of flowing waters, ichthyology, limnology, and invertebrate zoology.

SIZE OF STAFF: Four at professional level; 3 technicians.

POTAMOLOGICAL INSTITUTE, UNIVERSITY OF LOUISVILLE

IMPORTANT SPECIES AVAILABLE FOR LABORATORY STUDIES:
Large population of cave fauna, including *Chologaster agassizi*.

MAJOR CURRENT RESEARCH PROJECTS AND SCIENTIFIC LEADERS:
- Surveillance of aquatic life resources of the Ohio River (William M. Clay)
- Phytoplankton ecology in the Ohio River (D. F. Jackson)
- Radiation ecology of the Ohio River (A. T. Krebs)
- Taxonomy and distribution of the fishes of Kentucky (William M. Clay)
- Ecology of phytoplankton blooms (D. F. Jackson)

Pymatuning Laboratory of Field Biology

POSTAL ADDRESS: Linesville, Pennsylvania, USA.

EXECUTIVE OFFICER: Dr. C. A. Tryon, Jr., Professor of Zoology, University of Pittsburgh, Pittsburgh 13, Pennsylvania.

SPONSORING AGENCY: University of Pittsburgh.

YEAR FOUNDED: 1949 (continuation of Lake Laboratory founded 1926.)

SCOPE OF ACTIVITIES: Unrestricted research on aquatic and terrestrial ecology with emphasis on algae, physical and chemical limnology, aquatic insects, and vertebrate ecology; graduate and undergraduate instruction.

SEASON OF OPERATION: All year for research; May 1 to September 1 for instruction.

PHYSICAL ENVIRONMENT ACCESSIBLE: Pymatuning Reservoir (eutrophic lake), Ohio River; swamps, marshes, small ponds, and lakes.

PROVISIONS FOR VISITING SCIENTISTS: Research and living space for 5 visitors; variable fees charged for research space.

MAJOR RESEARCH AND TEACHING FACILITIES: Small library; small aquarium tanks; limited research collection of local fish; machine and wood shop; small boats and outboard motors; 28 ft LOA vessel on Ohio River.

INSTRUCTIONAL PROGRAM: Limnology, aquatic plant ecology, vertebrate ecology, and invertebrate ecology. Students specialize within these topics.

SIZE OF STAFF: Four at professional level; 1 technician.

MAJOR CURRENT RESEARCH PROJECTS AND SCIENTIFIC LEADERS:
- Primary nitrogen fixation in natural waters (R. C. Dugdale)
- Ecologic potential of the Ohio River (C. A. Tryon)
- Invertebrate succession in streams and pools (E. J. Kormondy)
- Ecology of algae (R. T. Hartman)

PYMATUNING LABORATORY OF FIELD BIOLOGY (LOCATED ON WOODED POINT IN LEFT MIDDLEGROUND)

Quetico-Superior Wilderness Research Center

POSTAL ADDRESS: Box 479, Ely, Minnesota, USA.
Winter address: 215 West Oxford Street Duluth 3, Minnesota.

LOCATION: Near Duluth.

EXECUTIVE OFFICER: Clifford E. Ahlgren, Director.

SPONSORING AGENCY: Wilderness Research Foundation.

YEAR FOUNDED: 1948.

SCOPE OF ACTIVITIES: Unrestricted research on ecology of Quetico-Superior-Wilderness area, including freshwater biology.

SEASON OF OPERATION: May 15 through September 15.

PHYSICAL ENVIRONMENT ACCESSIBLE: Eutrophic and oligotrophic lakes, rivers and streams. Station located on Basswood Lake.

PROVISIONS FOR VISITING SCIENTISTS: Research and liv-

QUETICO-SUPERIOR WILDERNESS RESEARCH CENTER

ing space for 6 visitors; no fees charged for research space.

MAJOR RESEARCH FACILITIES: Small library; entomological research collection; herbarium which includes local aquatic mosses and vascular plants; machine and wood shop, skilled shop workman available; small boats and outboard motors.

SIZE OF STAFF: Two at professional level; 4 technicians. (summer only).

MAJOR CURRENT RESEARCH PROJECTS: While space is available for scientists interested in the hydrobiology of the area, no work is being done in this field now.

Reelfoot Lake Biological Station

POSTAL ADDRESS: Route 2, Hickman, Kentucky, USA.

LOCATION: Near Union City, Tennessee.

EXECUTIVE OFFICER: Dr. C. L. Baker, Director, of Station, c/o Southwestern College, Memphis, Tennessee.

REELFOOT LAKE BIOLOGICAL STATION

SPONSORING AGENCY: Tennessee Academy of Sciences.

YEAR FOUNDED: 1935.

SCOPE OF ACTIVITIES: Unrestricted biological studies on lakes, swamps and forests.

SEASON OF OPERATION: June, July and August.

PHYSICAL ENVIRONMENT ACCESSIBLE: Reelfoot Lake (oligotrophic lake).

PROVISIONS FOR VISITING SCIENTISTS: Research and living space for 4 visitors; no fees charged for research space.

MAJOR RESEARCH FACILITIES: Small library; small aquarium tanks; small boats and outboard motors.

SIZE OF STAFF: Two at professional level.

IMPORTANT SPECIES AVAILABLE FOR LABORATORY STUDIES:

Insecta: *Anopheles walkeri*
Amphibia: *Amphiuma tridactylum*

MAJOR CURRENT RESEARCH PROJECTS AND SCIENTIFIC LEADERS:

Fishes of Reelfoot Lake (C. L. Baker)
Growth rate of fishes (R. J. Schoffman)

Sagehen Creek Experimental Wildlife and Fisheries Station

POSTAL ADDRESS: P. O. Box 447, Truckee, California, USA.

LOCATION: Tahoe National Forest.

EXECUTIVE OFFICER: Dr. Paul R. Needham, Professor of Zoology, University of California, Berkeley 4, California.

SPONSORING AGENCY: University of California.

YEAR FOUNDED: 1951.

SCOPE OF ACTIVITIES: Unrestricted research on population structures of both fish and game species; cooperative research with State agencies; graduate and undergraduate instruction.

SEASON OF OPERATION: All year.

PHYSICAL ENVIRONMENT ACCESSIBLE: Sagehen Creek, Truckee River, Lakes Tahoe, Independence and Webber and many other high lakes and streams.

PROVISION FOR VISITING SCIENTISTS: Space for 3 visitors; no fees charged; living quarters available nearby.

MAJOR RESEARCH AND TEACHING FACILITIES: Small library; small aquarium tanks; two underwater observation tanks in Sagehen Creek; research collections of local fish; list of local plant species available; machine and wood shop, skilled shop workman available; small boats and outboard motors.

INSTRUCTIONAL PROGRAM: On Berkeley campus: limnology, ecology, plankton, ichthyology, aquatic entomology, fishery biology, population dynamics, fisheries, and game management. Summer instruction at Sagehen Creek Project: plant geography, plant taxonomy, and fish and game management.

SIZE OF STAFF: Two at professional level; 1 technician.

UNDERWATER OBSERVATION TANK, SAGEHEN CREEK EXPERIMENTAL WILDLIFE AND FISHERIES STATION

IMPORTANT SPECIES AVAILABLE FOR LABORATORY STUDIES:

Pisces: *Salmo gairdneri, S. trutta, Salvelinus fontinalis*

Diptera: *Chironomus* spp.

Ephemeroptera: *Ephemerella* spp.

MAJOR CURRENT RESEARCH PROJECTS AND SCIENTIFIC LEADERS:

Population fluctuations coupled with exploitation rates derived from creel census (P. R. Needham and Richard Gard)

Fluctuations in abundance of the macrofauna of Sagehen Creek (P. R. Needham)

Research on a hanging bog (H. L. Mason)

Experimental improvements of tributaries of Sagehen Creek at high elevations (Richard Gard)

Scripps Institution of Oceanography

POSTAL ADDRESS: P. O. Box 109, La Jolla, California, USA.

LOCATION: Northwestern San Diego.

EXECUTIVE OFFICER: Dr. Roger Revelle, Director.

SPONSORING AGENCY: University of California, San Diego.

YEAR FOUNDED: 1903.

SCOPE OF ACTIVITIES: Restricted and unrestricted research in general oceanography; graduate instruction.

SEASON OF OPERATION: All year.

PHYSICAL ENVIRONMENT ACCESSIBLE: Pacific Ocean; sandy and silty beaches, rocky and gravelly shores.

PROVISIONS FOR VISITING SCIENTISTS: Space for visitors; living quarters available nearby.

MAJOR RESEARCH AND TEACHING FACILITIES: Extensive library; running sea and fresh-water; large research collections especially of marine fishes and zooplankton; living culture collections of phytoplankton and bacteria; a good many identified reference collections of local fauna and flora; machine and wood shops, electrical and electronic shop, skilled shop workmen available; small boats inboard and outboard; larger vessels with shipboard laboratories: 215 ft LOA, *Argo,* 180 ft LOA, *Alexander Agassiz,* 143 ft LOA, *Spencer F. Baird*, 143 ft LOA, *Horizon,* 128 ft LOA, *Hugh M. Smith,* 100 ft LOA, *Oconostota,* 134 ft LOA, *Stranger,* 80 ft LOA, *Paolina-T,* 65 ft LOA, *T-441.*

INSTRUCTIONAL PROGRAM: Plankton, biological, chemical and physical oceanography, biochemistry, physiology, microbiology, and marine vertebrates.

SIZE OF STAFF: Very large.

IMPORTANT SPECIES AVAILABLE FOR LABORATORY STUDIES:

Marine culture collections include various marine dinoflagellates, diatoms and bacteria.

Various invertebrate species of the major marine phyla and classes.

MAJOR CURRENT RESEARCH PROJECTS AND SCIENTIFIC LEADERS:

Ecology of benthic invertebrates (E. W. Fager)

Physiology of diving animals (P. F. Scholander)

Dynamic analysis of zoogeography (Carl L. Hubbs)

Effects of increased pressure on microorganisms (Claude E. ZoBell)

Nature, distribution and function of algal pigments (Francis T. Haxo)

Biology of marine zooplankton (Martin W. Johnson)

Marine life research program (John D. Isaacs)

Biochemistry of animal pigments (D. L. Fox)

Biochemistry of skeleton formation by diatoms (B. E. Volcani)

Factors affecting movements of flagellates (Ralph A. Lewin)

Biochemistry of lipids (A. A. Benson)

PUBLICATIONS ISSUED: *Bulletin of the Scripps Institution of Oceanography* (occasionally published)

SCRIPPS INSTITUTION OF OCEANOGRAPHY

South Dakota State Department of Game, Fish and Parks, Fisheries Division

POSTAL ADDRESS: Woonsocket, South Dakota, USA.

EXECUTIVE OFFICER: James T. Shields, Superintendent of Fisheries, Department of Game, Fish and Parks, Pierre, South Dakota.

SPONSORING AGENCIES: U. S. Government and State of South Dakota.

YEAR FOUNDED: 1949.

SCOPE OF ACTIVITIES: Restricted research concerned with statewide fisheries investigations.

SEASON OF OPERATION: All year.

PHYSICAL ENVIRONMENT ACCESSIBLE: Fresh-water rivers, streams, lakes and reservoirs.

PROVISIONS FOR VISITING SCIENTISTS: None.

MAJOR RESEARCH FACILITIES: Small library; large outdoor ponds and tanks, small aquarium tanks; limited collections of fish; machine and wood shop; small boats and outboard motors.

SIZE OF STAFF: Six at professional level.

MAJOR CURRENT RESEARCH PROJECTS AND SCIENTIFIC LEADERS:

Large impoundment studies (Ned E. Fogle and James W. Sprague)

Small lakes studies (Marvin F. Boussu and Don T. Weber)

Trout water studies (R. Keith Stewart)

Texas State Game and Fish Commission Laboratories

POSTAL ADDRESS:

Marine Laboratory, P. O. Box 1117, Rockport, Texas, USA.

Field Laboratory: Seabrook, Texas.

Fish Hatchery Laboratory: San Marcos, Texas.

EXECUTIVE OFFICERS: Terrance R. Leary, Coordinator, Coastal Fisheries. Marion Toole, Coordinator, Inland Fisheries.

YEAR FOUNDED: Marine Laboratory, 1946; Fish Hatchery Laboratory, 1948.

TEXAS STATE GAME AND FISH COMMISSION LABORATORIES

SCOPE OF ACTIVITIES: Laboratories function primarily for research on fishery resources and their management, but unrestricted research on general marine and fresh-water biology is encouraged.

SEASON OF OPERATION: All year.

PHYSICAL ENVIRONMENT ACCESSIBLE: Gulf of Mexico and coastal embayments; sandy and silty beaches and brackish, shallow bays; oligothrophic lakes, rivers and streams.

PROVISIONS FOR VISITING SCIENTISTS: None. Living quarters available nearby.

MAJOR RESEARCH FACILITIES: Small library; running brackish water at Rockport, large outdoor ponds and tanks and small aquarium tanks at San Marcos; machine and wood shop at San Marcos and Rockport; skiffs and outboards; 12 cabin cruisers 21 ft to 36 ft LOA, and a 39 ft LOA bay shrimp trawler.

SIZE OF STAFF: Forty at professional level; 23 technicians.

MAJOR CURRENT RESEARCH PROJECTS:

Fisheries, shrimp, crab, and oyster investigations of all bays

Limnological studies and management of lakes and streams

Pollution abatement and control

PUBLICATIONS ISSUED: *Bulletins of Texas Game and Fish Commission, Marine Laboratory Series*

United States Department of the Interior, Fish and Wildlife Service, Bureau of Commercial Fisheries

POSTAL ADDRESS:

Headquarters: Washington 25, D.C., USA.

Branch laboratories:

1. Biological Laboratory, Ann Arbor, Michigan
2. Biological Laboratory, Auke Bay, Alaska
3. Biological Laboratory, Beaufort, North Carolina
4. Biological Laboratory, Boothbay Harbor, Maine
5. Biological Laboratory, Brunswick, Georgia
6. Biological Laboratory, Galveston, Texas
7. Biological Laboratory, Gulf Breeze, Florida
8. Biological Laboratory, Honolulu, Hawaii
9. Biological Laboratory, La Jolla, California
10. Biological Laboratory, Milford, Connecticut
11. Biological Laboratory, Oxford, Maryland
12. Biological Laboratory, San Diego, California
13. Biological Laboratory, Seattle, Washington
14. Biological Laboratory (Fish Passage Research), Seattle, Washington (Not described in the *Directory.*)
15. Biological Laboratory (Marine Mammal Research, Seattle, Washington (Not described in the *Directory.*)
16. Biological Laboratory, Stanford, California
17. Biological Laboratory, Washington, D. C.

18. Biological Laboratory, Woods Hole, Massachusetts
19. Ichthyological Laboratory
(Descriptions follow.)

EXECUTIVE OFFICER: Donald L. McKernan, Director.

PUBLICATIONS:
Fishery Bulletins (regularly published journal)
Commercial Fisheries Review (processed, monthly)
Special Scientific Reports: Fisheries (Series) (processed)
Progressive Fish-Culturist (published quarterly)

Biological Laboratory, Ann Arbor, Michigan

POSTAL ADDRESS:
Headquarters: 1220 East Washington Street, P. O. Box 640, Ann Arbor, Michigan, USA.
Seven field stations are associated with this administrative unit.

EXECUTIVE OFFICER: Dr. James W. Moffett, Laboratory Director.

YEAR FOUNDED: Headquarters, 1927.

SCOPE OF ACTIVITIES: Restricted and unrestricted research on general fishery biology with emphasis on limnology and sea lamprey control in the Great Lakes.

SEASON OF OPERATION: All year.

PHYSICAL ENVIRONMENT ACCESSIBLE: Great Lakes; sandy and silty beaches, rocky and gravelly shores, estuarine conditions, eutrophic and oligotrophic lakes, rivers and streams.

PROVISIONS FOR VISITING SCIENTISTS: Space for 3 visitors at Ann Arbor; no fees charged; living quarters available nearby.

MAJOR RESEARCH FACILITIES: Very extensive library; small aquarium tanks; at branch laboratories, facilities for aquatic research are extensive; research collections of fauna and flora available at the University of Michigan Museum of Zoology; identified reference collections of fishes and invertebrates; machine and wood shop, electrical and electronic shop; small boats and outboard motors; vessels, 60.5 ft LOA, M/V *Cisco,* 52.8 ft LOA, M/V *Siscowet,* and 42 ft LOA, M/V *Musky.*

SIZE OF STAFF: Fifty-one at professional level; 40 technicians.

IMPORTANT SPECIES AVAILABLE FOR LABORATORY STUDIES: The flora and fauna of the Great Lakes.

MAJOR CURRENT RESEARCH PROJECTS AND SCIENTIFIC LEADERS:
Evaluation of chemical control (Alberton L. McLain)
Experimental sea lamprey control—chemical (Bernard R. Smith)
Research in sea lamprey life history and ecology (John C. Howell)
Fishery investigations—Lake Erie (Vernon C. Applegate)
Fishery investigations—Lake Michigan (William Dryer)
Fishery investigations—Lake Michigan (Stanford H. Smith)
Limnology of the Great Lakes (Alfred M. Beeton)

Biological Laboratory, Auke Bay, Alaska

POSTAL ADDRESS:
Headquarters: P. O. Box 1155, Auke Bay, Alaska, USA.
Field Stations:
Little Port Walter, Baranof Island
Karluk Lake, Kodiak Island
Brooks Lake
Kasitsna Bay on Cook Inlet
Traitors Cove, near Ketchikan
Olsen Bay, Prince William Sound

LOCATION: Headquarters at Auke Bay, 12 miles from Juneau.

EXECUTIVE OFFICER: Dr. George Y. Harry, Laboratory Director.

YEAR FOUNDED: 1956.

SCOPE OF ACTIVITIES: Restricted research concerning the biology and ecology of marine fish, shellfish and anadromous species of commercial importance; oceanographic research.

SEASON OF OPERATION: All year, although field work is concentrated during the spring, summer and fall.

PHYSICAL ENVIRONMENT ACCESSIBLE: Stephens Passage, Chatham Straits, Cook Inlet, Karluk and Brooks Lakes (oligotrophic lakes), waters of Southeastern Alaska; rocky and gravelly shores, estuarine conditions, rivers and streams.

PROVISIONS FOR VISITING SCIENTISTS: Space at headquarters and occasionally at field stations for visitors; no fees charged; living quarters available nearby.

MAJOR RESEARCH FACILITIES: Small library; running sea and fresh-water (available 1963), small aquarium tanks; small research collection of Alaska fish; machine and wood shop (available 1963); small boats and outboard motors; vessels, 38 ft LOA, M/V *Sablefish,* 58 ft LOA, M/V *Heron,* 88 ft power barge, *Murre II.*

SIZE OF STAFF: Twenty-five at professional level; 5 technicians.

IMPORTANT SPECIES AVAILABLE FOR LABORATORY STUDIES:
Salmonidae: *Oncorhynchus nerka, O. gorbuscha, O. keta, O kisutch, O. tshawytscha*
Crustacea: *Paralithodes camtschatica*
Mollusca: *Saxidomus giganteus*
Clupeidae: *Clupea harengus pallasii*
Shrimp: *Pandalus borealis*

MAJOR CURRENT RESEARCH PROJECTS AND SCIENTIFIC LEADERS:
Red salmon studies (C. J. DiCostanzo)
Pink and chum salmon studies (T. R. Merrell, Jr.)
Marine fisheries studies (R. H. Hatch)
Oceanography (H. E. Bruce)
Shell fish investigation (R. M. Yancey)

Biological Laboratory, Beaufort, North Carolina

POSTAL ADDRESS: Beaufort, North Carolina, USA.
LOCATION: Near Morehead City.
EXECUTIVE OFFICER: G. B. Talbot, Laboratory Director.
YEAR FOUNDED: 1901.
SCOPE OF ACTIVITIES: Restricted and unrestricted research on marine fishes; radiobiological and radiochemical studies relating to the accumulation of fission products and other radionuclides by marine organisms.
SEASON OF OPERATION: All year.
PHYSICAL ENVIRONMENT ACCESSIBLE: Atlantic Ocean, Onslow Bay, Bogue, Core and Pamlico Sounds, and Neuse River; sandy and silty beaches, estuarine conditions, brackish, shallow bays, and bird rookeries.
PROVISIONS FOR VISITING SCIENTISTS: Research and living space for 1-3 visitors; no fees charged for research space.
MAJOR RESEARCH FACILITIES: Moderately complete library; running sea and fresh-water, large outdoor ponds and tanks, small aquarium tanks; research collection of fish maintained in cooperation with North Carolina Fisheries Institute; machine and wood shop, skilled shop workmen available; small boats, outboard motors and trailers; vessels, 40 ft LOA cruiser and 26 ft LOA launch.

BIOLOGICAL LABORATORY, BEAUFORT

SIZE OF STAFF: Twenty-six at professional level; 19 technicians.
IMPORTANT SPECIES AVAILABLE FOR LABORATORY STUDIES: Most Atlantic coast fishes, shellfish, crustaceans and plants found in this locality.
MAJOR CURRENT RESEARCH PROJECTS AND SCIENTIFIC LEADERS:
- Radiobiological investigations (Walter A. Chipman)
- Menhaden investigations (Fred C. June)
- Striped bass investigations (James E. Sykes)
- Shad investigations (Charles H. Walburg)
- Blue crab investigations (Charles H. Walburg)

Biological Laboratory, Boothbay Harbor, Maine

POSTAL ADDRESS: McKown Point, Boothbay Harbor, Maine, USA.
LOCATION: Near Portland.
EXECUTIVE OFFICER: Bernard E. Skud, Laboratory Director.
YEAR FOUNDED: 1949.
SCOPE OF ACTIVITIES: Restricted and unrestricted research in fishery biology.
SEASON OF OPERATION: All year.
PHYSICAL ENVIRONMENT ACCESSIBLE: Gulf of Maine; open ocean, rocky and gravelly shores.
PROVISIONS FOR VISITING SCIENTISTS: Space for 2 visitors; no fees charged; living quarters available nearby.
MAJOR RESEARCH FACILITIES: Small library; running sea and fresh-water, small aquarium tanks, outdoor live-cars, large indoor tanks; limited identified reference collection of invertebrates; machine and wood shop; small boats and outboard motors; vessels, 41 ft.
SIZE OF STAFF: Fifteen biologists; 10 technicians and fishery aides.
IMPORTANT SPECIES AVAILABLE FOR LABORATORY STUDIES:
- Echinodermata: *Asterias forbesi, Strongylocentrotus droebbachiensis, Echinarachnius parma*
- Crustacea: *Homarus americanus, Carcinides maenas*
- Annelida: *Glycera dibranchiata, Nereis virens*
- Mollusca: *Mytilus edulis*

MAJOR CURRENT RESEARCH PROJECTS AND SCIENTIFIC LEADERS:
- Clam investigations (Walter R. Welch)
- Clam physiology (Alden P. Stickney)
- Herring investigations (Carl J. Sindermann)
- Herring migration studies (John E. Watson)
- Plankton studies (John B. Colton, Jr.)
- Herring ecology (Joseph J. Graham)
- Herring biology (Harold C. Boyar)

BIOLOGICAL LABORATORY, BOOTHBAY HARBOR

Biological Laboratory, Brunswick, Georgia

POSTAL ADDRESS: P. O. Box 280, Federal Building, Brunswick, Georgia, USA.

EXECUTIVE OFFICER: William W. Anderson, Laboratory Director.

YEAR FOUNDED: 1952.

SCOPE OF ACTIVITIES: Restricted research with emphasis on the biochemical characteristics of sea water, currents of the Atlantic coast of southern United States and studies on fishes of the area.

SEASON OF OPERATION: All year.

PHYSICAL ENVIRONMENT ACCESSIBLE: Atlantic Ocean; sandy and silty beaches, estuarine conditions, brackish, shallow bays, rivers and streams.

PROVISIONS FOR VISITING SCIENTISTS: Research space for short periods.

MAJOR RESEARCH FACILITIES: Small library; good research collections of larval, juvenile and adult fish of the area; extensive research collections of plankton of the area; identified reference collections of local fish.

SIZE OF STAFF: Nine at professional level; 7 technicians and other help.

IMPORTANT SPECIES AVAILABLE FOR LABORATORY STUDIES: Wide variety of fish and crustaceans.

MAJOR CURRENT RESEARCH PROJECTS AND SCIENTIFIC LEADERS:

Biochemistry and physical characteristics of sea water off south Atlantic Coast (W. W. Anderson)

Identification, abundance and distribution of fish larvae (J. W. Gehringer and W. D. Anderson, Jr.)

Life history series of various fishes (J. W. Gehringer and staff)

Identification of juvenile and adult fish (J. W. Gehringer and G. C. Miller)

Biological Laboratory, Galveston, Texas

POSTAL ADDRESS: Fort Crockett, Galveston, Texas, USA.

Field Stations:

Pascagula, Florida

Miami, Florida

EXECUTIVE OFFICER: Dr. George A. Rounsefell, Director.

YEAR FOUNDED: 1950.

SCOPE OF ACTIVITIES: Restricted and unrestricted basic research on marine biology, fisheries and biological oceanography.

SEASON OF OPERATION: All year.

PHYSICAL ENVIRONMENT ACCESSIBLE: Gulf of Mexico and continuous inshore areas of protected bays and marshes; open ocean, sandy and silty beaches, estuarine conditions and brackish, shallow bays.

PROVISIONS FOR VISITING SCIENTISTS: Space for visitors; living quarters available nearby.

MAJOR RESEARCH FACILITIES: Moderately complete library; circulating and raw sea water systems with many

BIOLOGICAL LABORATORY, GALVESTON

tanks, small aquarium tanks; very small research collection of fauna and flora; machine and wood shop; small boats and outboard motors; larger vessels are chartered, although station has 43 ft research vessel.

SIZE OF STAFF: Twenty-six at professional level; 24 technicians.

IMPORTANT SPECIES AVAILABLE FOR LABORATORY STUDIES: Various species common along the coast of the Gulf of Mexico.

MAJOR CURRENT RESEARCH PROJECTS AND SCIENTIFIC LEADERS:

Shrimp fishery (J. B. Kinsey)

Physiology and behavior (Dr. D. V. Aldrich)

Estuarine (Charles M. Chapman)

Industrial fishes

Biological Laboratory, Gulf Breeze, Florida

POSTAL ADDRESS: Sabine Island, Gulf Breeze, Florida, USA.

LOCATION: Near Pensacola.

EXECUTIVE OFFICER: Dr. Philip A. Butler, Laboratory Director.

YEAR FOUNDED: 1938.

SCOPE OF ACTIVITIES: Restricted research on the ecology of commercial shellfish.

SEASON OF OPERATION: All year.

PHYSICAL ENVIRONMENT ACCESSIBLE: Gulf of Mexico, Santa Rosa Sound and Pensacola Bay; sandy and silty beaches, estuarine conditions, and brackish, shallow bays.

PROVISIONS FOR VISITING SCIENTISTS: Research and living space for 2-3 visitors; no fees charged for research space.

MAJOR RESEARCH FACILITIES: Small library; running brackish water (15-31 parts per thousand), large outdoor ponds and tanks, small aquarium tanks and aquatic cages; identified reference collections of fauna —invertebrate and fish; machine and wood shop, skilled shop workman available; small boats and out-

BIOLOGICAL LABORATORY, GULF BREEZE

board motors; one 36 ft LOA power vessel.

SIZE OF STAFF: Six at professional level; 6 technicians.

IMPORTANT SPECIES AVAILABLE FOR LABORATORY STUDIES:

Pelecypoda: *Crassostrea virginica*

Gastropoda: *Thais haemastoma; Polynices duplicata*

Crustacea: *Callinectes sapidus*

Typical estuarine invertebrate fauna.

MAJOR CURRENT RESEARCH PROJECTS AND SCIENTIFIC LEADERS:

Environmental factors affecting oysters (Philip A. Butler)

Factors affecting estuarine productivity (Nelson R. Cooley)

Effects of insecticides on marine shellfish (Alfred J. Wilson, Jr.)

Biological Laboratory, Honolulu

POSTAL ADDRESS: P. O. Box 3830, Honolulu 12, Hawaii, USA.

EXECUTIVE OFFICER: John C. Marr, Director.

YEAR FOUNDED: 1949.

SCOPE OF ACTIVITIES: Restricted research on fishery resources of the tropical and subtropical Pacific (including oceanography, ecology, behavior, genetics, etc.)

BIOLOGICAL LABORATORY, HONOLULU

SEASON OF OPERATION: All year.

PHYSICAL ENVIRONMENT ACCESSIBLE: Pacific Ocean; sandy and silty beaches, rocky and gravelly shores, estuarine conditions, brackish, shallow bays, and coral reefs.

PROVISIONS FOR VISITING SCIENTISTS: Space for visitors; no fees charged; living quarters available nearby.

MAJOR RESEARCH FACILITIES: Small library at laboratory, but extensive library of University of Hawaii available; running sea and fresh-water, large outdoor ponds and tanks, small aquarium tanks (sea water facilities all at Kewalo Basin); research and identified reference collections of pelagic fishes and zooplankton; machine and wood shop; 117 ft LOA, M/V *Charles H. Gilbert,* equipped with bow and stern underwater viewing ports, as well as oceanographic, biological and fishing gear.

SIZE OF STAFF: Twenty-five at professional level; 50 technicians and other personnel.

IMPORTANT SPECIES AVAILABLE FOR LABORATORY STUDIES:

Pisces: *Katsuwonus pelamis* and other tropical Pacific tunas

MAJOR CURRENT RESEARCH PROJECTS AND SCIENTIFIC LEADERS:

Fishery potentials (Richard S. Shomura)

Skipjack ecology (Brian J. Rothschild)

Albacore ecology (Tamio Otsu)

Behavior (John J. Magnuson)

Subpopulations (Lucian Sprague)

Oceanography (Richard A. Barkley)

Biological Laboratory, La Jolla, California

POSTAL ADDRESS: P. O. Box 271, La Jolla, California, USA.

LOCATION: Near San Diego.

EXECUTIVE OFFICER: Dr. Elbert H. Ahlstrom, Laboratory Director.

YEAR FOUNDED: 1937.

SCOPE OF ACTIVITIES: Restricted research on the description and understanding of the variations in distribution and abundance of the Pacific sardine and associated species.

SEASON OF OPERATION: All year.

PHYSICAL ENVIRONMENT ACCESSIBLE: Pacific Ocean; sandy and silty beaches.

PROVISIONS FOR VISITING SCIENTISTS: Space for 2 visitors; living quarters available nearby.

MAJOR RESEARCH FACILITIES: Very extensive library available at Scripps Institution of Oceanography; running sea water at Scripps, small aquarium tanks at Scripps; extensive collection of fishes from eastern Pacific; one 152 ft LOA vessel.

SIZE OF STAFF: Fifteen at professional level; 15 technicians.

BIOLOGICAL LABORATORY, LA JOLLA

IMPORTANT SPECIES AVAILABLE FOR LABORATORY STUDIES:

Pisces: *Sardinops caerulea, Engraulis mordax, Pneumatophorus diego, Trachurus symmetricus*

MAJOR CURRENT RESEARCH PROJECTS AND SCIENTIFIC LEADERS:

Population size investigation (Elbert H. Ahlstrom)
Age and growth investigation (Robert S. Wolf)
Fecundity investigation (John S. MacGregor)
Year-class size investigation (David Kramer)
Physiology investigation (Reuben Lasker)
Sardine population dynamics investigation (Clyde C. Taylor)
Availability investigation (Charles P. O'Connell)
Plankton investigation (James R. Thrailkill)
Ecologically associated fishes (Frederick H. Berry)

Biological Laboratory, Milford, Connecticut

POSTAL ADDRESS: Cottage Street, Milford, Connecticut, USA.

LOCATION: Near New Haven.

EXECUTIVE OFFICER: Dr. James E. Hanks, Laboratory Director.

YEAR FOUNDED: 1935.

SCOPE OF ACTIVITIES: Restricted research on marine biology, particularly on commercial mollusks, including studies of their physiology, ecology and control of competitors and enemies.

SEASON OF OPERATION: All year.

PHYSICAL ENVIRONMENT ACCESSIBLE: Long Island Sound; estuarine conditions.

PROVISIONS FOR VISITING SCIENTISTS: Space for 1-2 visitors; no fees charged; living quarters available nearby.

MAJOR RESEARCH FACILITIES: Small library but libraries of Bingham Oceanographic Laboratory and Yale University are accessible; running sea and fresh-water, large outdoor ponds and tanks, small aquarium tanks, special lead-lined large troughs with continuously circulating sea water; research collections of fauna and flora of Bingham Oceanographic Laboratory and Yale University are accessible; machine and wood shop, electrical and electronic shop, skilled shop workmen available; small boats and outboard motors; vessels, 50 ft LOA, M/V *Shang Wheeler,* and the 65 ft State of Connecticut Shellfish Commission boat is available when needed.

INSTRUCTIONAL PROGRAM: No special instructional programs are offered; however, graduate students of Yale and other nearby universities, majoring in oceanography or marine biology, frequently work on thesis problems at this laboratory. Laboratory facilities, including the research vessel, are also used by faculty members and graduate students of Bingham Oceanographic Laboratory for studies of physical, chemical and biological oceanography.

SIZE OF STAFF: Ten at professional level; 5 technicians.

IMPORTANT SPECIES AVAILABLE FOR LABORATORY STUDIES:

Pelecypoda: *Crassostrea virginica, Venus mercenaria, Mya arenaria, Mytilus edulis, Pecten irradians*
Echinodermata: *Asterias forbesi*
Gastropoda: *Urosalpinx cinerea, Eupleura caudata*
Crustacea: *Cancer irroratus, Carcinides maenas*

MAJOR CURRENT RESEARCH PROJECTS AND SCIENTIFIC LEADERS:

Ecological factors affecting existence of certain lamellibranchs (J. E. Hanks)
Physiological and ecological requirements of bivalve larvae (H. C. Davis)
Utilization of salt water ponds for cultivation of lamellibranchs (W. S. Landers)
Microbiota affecting growth and survival of bivalves (R. Ukeles)
Hatchery techniques for producing commercial mollusks (W. S. Landers and Henry Cook)
Control of enemies of commercial mollusks (J. E. Hanks and C. L. MacKenzie, Jr.)

BIOLOGICAL LABORATORY, MILFORD

Biological Laboratory, Oxford, Maryland

POSTAL ADDRESS: P. O. Box 278, Oxford, Maryland, USA.

LOCATION: Near Easton.

EXECUTIVE OFFICER: James B. Engle, Laboratory Director.

YEAR FOUNDED: 1944.

SCOPE OF ACTIVITIES: Restricted research on invertebrate marine biology and ecology.

SEASON OF OPERATION: All year.

PHYSICAL ENVIRONMENT ACCESSIBLE: Chesapeake and Chincoteague Bays; seaside bay of high salinity, estuarine conditions, and brackish, shallow bays.

PROVISIONS FOR VISITING SCIENTISTS: Limited space for several visitors; no fees charged; living quarters available nearby.

MAJOR RESEARCH FACILITIES: Small library; running sea water, large outdoor ponds and tanks, small aquarium tanks; limited research and reference collections of marine and brackish invertebrate fauna; machine and wood shop, skilled shop workman available; small boats and outboard motors; one 50 ft LOA converted shrimp trawler.

SIZE OF STAFF: Eight at professional level; 8 technicians.

IMPORTANT SPECIES AVAILABLE FOR LABORATORY STUDIES:

Mollusca: *Crassostrea virginica, Mercenaria mercenaria, Mya arenaria, Brachidontes recurvus, Spisula solidissina, Urosalpinx cinerea, Eupleura caudata*

Crustacea: *Balanus* spp., *Callinectes sapidus,* Xanthidae

Vertebrate: many kinds of fish.

MAJOR CURRENT RESEARCH PROJECTS AND SCIENTIFIC LEADERS:

Physiology and ecology of mollusks (James E. Hanks)

Economic invertebrates (James B. Engle)

Shellfish pathology and mortality (Richard Burton)

Ecology of shellfish predation (George Griffith)

Culture of mollusks of economic importance (John R. Webster)

Control of predators on mollusks of economic importance (Michael Castagna)

Bottom soils in marine environments (Thomas Carver)

Biological Laboratory, San Diego, California

POSTAL ADDRESS: P. O. Box 6317, Pt. Loma Station, San Diego, California, USA.

EXECUTIVE OFFICER: Mr. Gerald V. Howard, Laboratory Director.

YEAR FOUNDED: 1959.

SCOPE OF ACTIVITIES: Restricted research on oceanography, tuna behavior and fishing strategy in the eastern Pacific for the specific purpose of contributing to the fishing efficiency of United States tuna vessels.

SEASON OF OPERATION: All year.

PHYSICAL ENVIRONMENT ACCESSIBLE: Eastern Pacific Ocean.

PROVISIONS FOR VISITING SCIENTISTS: Space for 2 visitors; no fees charged; living quarters available nearby.

MAJOR RESEARCH FACILITIES: No water supply at present; library, shop facilities and vessels available at Scripps Institution of Oceanography.

SIZE OF STAFF: Twelve at professional level; 5 technicians.

MAJOR CURRENT RESEARCH PROJECTS AND SCIENTIFIC LEADERS:

Forecasting tuna availability through oceanographic studies (James H. Johnson)

Tuna behavior studies (Arthur R. Marshall and Dr. Richard R. Whitney)

Operations research to develop an optimum fishing strategy (Dr. Richard R. Whitney)

Biological Laboratory, Seattle, Washington

POSTAL ADDRESS: 2725 Montlake Boulevard, Seattle 2, Washington, USA.

EXECUTIVE OFFICER: Clinton E. Atkinson, Laboratory Director. Clifford J. Burner, Assistant Laboratory Director.

YEAR FOUNDED: 1930.

SCOPE OF ACTIVITIES: Primary research agency for the American Section of the International North Pacific Fisheries Commission on salmon and king crab; freshwater environment of salmon and other anadromous fish; specialized studies in immunology, behavior, geochemistry, radioisotopes and ecology of both marine and anadromous fish.

SEASON OF OPERATION: All year.

PHYSICAL ENVIRONMENT ACCESSIBLE: Pacific Ocean, Lake Washington, Puget Sound, Straits of Juan de Fuca; sandy and silty beaches, rocky and gravelly shores, estuarine conditions, brackish, shallow bays, eutrophic and oligotrophic lakes, rivers and streams.

PROVISIONS FOR VISITING SCIENTISTS: None.

MAJOR RESEARCH FACILITIES: Moderately complete li-

BIOLOGICAL LABORATORY, SEATTLE

brary; outdoor ponds and tanks and aquaria; 177 ft research vessel; small boats and outboard motors.

SIZE OF STAFF: Seventy-six at professional level; 15 technicians.

IMPORTANT SPECIES AVAILABLE FOR LABORATORY STUDIES:

Pisces: *Oncorhynchus kisutch, O. tshawytscha, O. nerka, Salmo gairdnerii gairdnerii, Gasterosteus aculeatus, Cyprinus carpio;* other marine and freshwater species available locally.

MAJOR CURRENT RESEARCH PROJECTS AND SCIENTIFIC LEADERS:

Marine Research Investigations (North Pacific Program) (Fred C. Cleaver)
- Oceanography (Felix Favorite)
- Serology (George J. Ridgway)
- Morphology (Francis M. Fukuhara)
- Scale studies (Kenneth H. Mosher)
- High seas distribution (Robert R. French)
- King crab (Takashi Miyahara)
- Ocean growth (Alvin E. Peterson)

Freshwater Research Program (Kingsley G. Weber)
- Sockeye salmon biology (Donovan R. Craddock)
- Chinook and silver salmon biology (Richard L. Major)
- Salmon nursery research (Harold A. Gangmark)
- Salmon predators and competitors (Richard B. Thompson)
- Trace element studies (Dr. Timothy Joyner)
- Non-radioactive isotope fish marks (Anthony Novotny)
- Salmon transition and estuarine studies (Murray H. Amos)
- Salmon compendium (Galen H. Maxfield)
- Serological studies on chinook salmon (Dr. George J. Ridgway)
- Fish sound discrimination and response (Duane T. Rodman)
- Biometrics unit (Reynold A. Fredin)
- Fishery translation coordination center (Paul T. Macy)

Biological Laboratory, Stanford, California

POSTAL ADDRESS: 450-B Jordan Hall, Stanford, California, USA.

EXECUTIVE OFFICER: Dr. Oscar E. Sette, Laboratory Director.

YEAR FOUNDED: 1955.

SCOPE OF ACTIVITIES: Restricted research on interrelations of fluctuation in atmospheric and oceanic conditions on an ocean-wide basis in relation to their influence on the abundance and distribution of marine fish populations.

SEASON OF OPERATION: All year.

PROVISIONS FOR VISITING SCIENTISTS: Space for 1-2 visitors; no fees charged; living quarters available nearby.

MAJOR RESEARCH FACILITIES: Access to very extensive libraries of Stanford University.

SIZE OF STAFF: Four at professional level.

MAJOR CURRENT RESEARCH PROJECTS AND SCIENTIFIC LEADERS:

- Case studies of environment and fluctuations in Pacific commercial fisheries (O. E. Sette)
- Variation in North Pacific atmospheric circulation and its effect on surface oceanographic conditions (L. E. Eber)
- Changes in monthly mean sea surface temperature and sea levels, North Pacific (J. F. T. Saur)

Biological Laboratory, Washington, D. C.

POSTAL ADDRESS: Building 74, Naval Yard Annex, Washington 25, D.C., USA.

EXECUTIVE OFFICER: Vernon E. Brock, Laboratory Director.

YEAR FOUNDED: 1958.

SCOPE OF ACTIVITIES: Relation of the physical and chemical oceanographic factors, including those related to the air-sea interaction processes, and the character, distribution and abundance of the marine biota; oceanographic, marine biological and fishery studies in the tropical Atlantic, with particular emphasis on the tuna resources in the Gulf of Guinea; broad geographical study of the benthic marine organisms, portraying distribution of individual species and environmental factors controlling their distribution and abundance; development and testing of oceanographic instruments of particular interest to Bureau of Commercial Fisheries, and coordination of the Bureau's oceanographic instrumentation programs.

SEASON OF OPERATION: All year.

PROVISIONS FOR VISITING SCIENTISTS: Laboratory and office space and facilities in shore laboratory and aboard research vessels.

PHYSICAL ENVIRONMENT ACCESSIBLE: Tropical and temperate Atlantic Ocean.

MAJOR RESEARCH AND TEACHING FACILITIES: Laboratory in Washington, D. C., 25,000 square feet of laboratory and office space; two research vessels (converted ATA's, first scheduled for operation in January 1963, second in January 1964) with space for 10 scientists, 400 square feet of laboratory space, oceanographic and trawling winches, 9,000 mile cruising range; research efforts conducted in cooperation with U. S. National Museum, National Oceanographic Data Center, U. S. Navy Oceanographic Office and other Government supported and University activities.

SIZE OF STAFF: Nine at professional level; 2 technicians; plus administrative, vessel supervisory and vessel crew.

MAJOR CURRENT RESEARCH PROJECTS AND SCIENTIFIC LEADERS:

- Assistant Laboratory Director and Oceanographer (Thomas S. Austin)
- Tropical Atlantic fishery-oceanography program (Robert C. Wilson)
- Environmental oceanographic research program (J. Lockwood Chamberlin)
- Oceanographic instrumentation program (Julius Rockwell, Jr.)

Biological Laboratory, Woods Hole, Massachusetts

POSTAL ADDRESS: Woods Hole, Massachusetts, USA.

EXECUTIVE OFFICER: Dr. Herbert W. Graham, Laboratory Director.

YEAR FOUNDED: 1885.

SCOPE OF ACTIVITIES: Restricted fishery and oceanographic research with emphasis on groundfish.

SEASON OF OPERATION: All year.

PHYSICAL ENVIRONMENT ACCESSIBLE: Gulf of Maine, Georges Bank, New York Bight, and Atlantic Ocean.

PROVISIONS FOR VISITING SCIENTISTS: Space for visitors; no fees charged; living quarters available nearby.

MAJOR RESEARCH FACILITIES: Very extensive library at adjacent institution, small library at Laboratory; running sea and fresh-water, small aquarium tanks; research collections of bottom invertebrates; small boats and outboard motors; one 180 ft LOA trawler-oceanographic ship.

SIZE OF STAFF: Twenty at professional level; 20 technicians.

IMPORTANT SPECIES AVAILABLE FOR LABORATORY STUDIES: See Marine Biological Laboratory, Woods Hole, page 224.

MAJOR CURRENT RESEARCH PROJECTS AND SCIENTIFIC LEADERS:

- Cod investigation (A. C. Jensen)
- Flounder investigation (F. E. Lux)
- Haddock investigation (M. D. Grosslein)
- Hake investigation (R. E. Fritz)
- Industrial fishery investigation (R. L. Edwards)
- Redfish investigation (G. F. Kelly)
- Sea scallop investigation (J. A. Posgay)
- Bottom ecology investigations (R. L. Wigley)
- Plankton ecology (J. B. Colton)
- Fish behavior investigation (R. Livingstone, Jr.)
- Population dynamics investigation (R. C. Hennemuth)
- Oyster biology (P. S. Galtsoff)

BIOLOGICAL LABORATORY, WOODS HOLE

Ichthyological Laboratory

POSTAL ADDRESS: Room 71, U. S. National Museum, Washington, D.C., USA.

EXECUTIVE OFFICER: Dr. Daniel M. Cohen, Director.

SCOPE OF ACTIVITIES: Research on taxonomy of fishes and mollusks; effects of environment on distribution of marine fishes.

SEASON OF OPERATION: All year.

PHYSICAL ENVIRONMENT ACCESSIBLE: Field work on vessels of Fish and Wildlife Service and cooperating agencies.

PROVISIONS FOR VISITING SCIENTISTS: Space for 2 visitors.

MAJOR RESEARCH FACILITIES: Very extensive library; research collections of fauna and flora of the Smithsonian Institution are available; machine and wood shop, electrical and electronic shop, skilled shop workmen available.

SIZE OF STAFF: Three at professional level; 3 technicians.

MAJOR CURRENT RESEARCH PROJECTS AND SCIENTIFIC LEADERS:

- Studies on abyssal fishes of the family Brotulidae (D. M. Cohen)
- Taxonomy and distributional problems in midwater argentinoid fishes (D. M. Cohen)
- Studies on gadoid fishes (D. M. Cohen)
- Studies on tunas and related fishes (B. B. Collette)
- Studies on hemirhamphid fishes (B. B. Collette)
- Studies on bivalve mollusks of the family *Tellinidae* (K. J. Boss)

United States Department of the Interior, Fish and Wildlife Service, Bureau of Sport Fisheries and Wildlife, Branch of Fishery Research

POSTAL ADDRESS:

Headquarters: Washington 25, D.C., USA.

Branch laboratories:

1. Convict Creek Experiment Station
2. Eastern Fish Disease Laboratory
3. Eastern Fish Nutrition Laboratory
4. Fish Control Laboratory
5. Fish-Pesticide Research Laboratory
6. North Central Reservoir Investigations
7. Salmon-Cultural Laboratory

8. Sandy Hook Marine Laboratory
9. Southeastern Fish-Cultural Laboratory
10. Western Fish Disease Laboratory
11. Western Fish Nutrition Laboratory

(Descriptions follow.)

EXECUTIVE OFFICER: Paul E. Thompson, Chief.

PUBLICATIONS: See Bureau of Commercial Fisheries, page 238.

California-Nevada Sport Fishery Investigations, Convict Creek Experiment Station

POSTAL ADDRESS: Route 3, Box 198, Bishop, California, USA.

LOCATION: East Central California.

EXECUTIVE OFFICER: Reed S. Nielson, Fishery Research Biologist.

YEAR FOUNDED: 1936.

SCOPE OF ACTIVITIES: Restricted research on trout management in alpine lakes and streams.

SEASON OF OPERATION: All year.

PHYSICAL ENVIRONMENT ACCESSIBLE: Lakes and streams; Central Sierra Nevada Range.

PROVISIONS FOR VISITING SCIENTISTS: Limited to 2.

MAJOR RESEARCH FACILITIES: Small library; biology-limnology laboratory; one mile of experimental stream divided into four sections; machine and wood shop; small boats and outboard motors.

SIZE OF STAFF: Four at professional level; 1 technician.

Eastern Fish Disease Laboratory

POSTAL ADDRESS: Leetown, P. O., Kearneysville, West Virginia, USA.

LOCATION: 75 miles north-west of Washington, D. C.

EXECUTIVE OFFICER: Dr. Stanislas F. Snieszko, Chief.

YEAR FOUNDED: 1947.

SCOPE OF ACTIVITIES: Restricted and unrstricted research on the nature, treatment and prevention of fish disease; special training courses in fish pathology for federal and state fishery workers.

SEASON OF OPERATION: All year.

PHYSICAL ENVIRONMENT ACCESSIBLE: Potomac and Shenandoah Rivers; ponds.

PROVISIONS FOR VISITING SCIENTISTS: No space available except under special arrangements.

MAJOR RESEARCH AND TEACHING FACILITIES: Small library; large outdoor ponds and tanks, small aquarium tanks; machine and wood shop.

INSTRUCTIONAL PROGRAM: Fish diseases and parasites (for personnel of Fish and Wildlife Service).

SIZE OF STAFF: Six at professional level; 3-4 technicians while in training.

IMPORTANT SPECIES AVAILABLE FOR LABORATORY STUDIES:

Pisces: Fresh water salmonids and centrarchids.

EASTERN FISH DISEASE LABORATORY, WEST VIRGINIA

MAJOR CURRENT RESEARCH PROJECTS AND SCIENTIFIC LEADERS:

- Bacterial diseases of fishes (S. F. Snieszko)
- Virus diseases of fishes (Kenneth E. Wolf)
- Fish parasitology (Glenn L. Hoffman)
- Fish hematology (S. F. Snieszko)
- Histopathology (C. E. Dunbar)
- Diagnosis, treatments (L. L. Pettijohn)

Eastern Fish Nutrition Laboratory

POSTAL ADDRESS: RFD, Cortland, New York, USA.

EXECUTIVE OFFICER: Dr. Arthur M. Phillips, Jr., Director.

SPONSORING AGENCIES: U.S. Department of the Interior; State of New York Conservation Department; Cornell University.

YEAR FOUNDED: 1932.

SCOPE OF ACTIVITIES: Restricted research on the physiology and nutrition of trout.

SEASON OF OPERATION: All year.

PROVISIONS FOR VISITING SCIENTISTS: None.

MAJOR RESEARCH FACILITIES: Small library.

EASTERN FISH NUTRITION LABORATORY, NEW YORK

SIZE OF STAFF: Five at professional level; 2 technicians.

IMPORTANT SPECIES AVAILABLE FOR LABORATORY STUDIES:

Pisces: *Salvelinus fontinalis, S. namaycush, Salmo trutta, S. gairdnerii irideus.* (These species are all reared at the Laboratory).

MAJOR CURRENT RESEARCH PROJECTS AND SCIENTIFIC LEADERS:

Radio-isotope tracer studies (Henry A. Podoliak)
Nutrition and physiology (Arthur M. Phillips, Jr.)
The chemical composition of trout blood (Henry A. Booke)
The metabolism of trout (Hugh A. Poston)
The effect of size on the growth rate of trout (Earl Pyle)

Fish Control Laboratory

POSTAL ADDRESS: P. O. Box 862, Riverside Park, LaCrosse, Wisconsin, USA.

EXECUTIVE OFFICER: Dr. Robert E. Lennon, Director.

YEAR FOUNDED: 1959.

SCOPE OF ACTIVITIES: Restricted research on chemical, biological and electrical agents and methods for the control of undersirable fishes in fresh-waters.

SEASON OF OPERATION: All year.

PHYSICAL ENVIRONMENT ACCESSIBLE: Mississippi River and nearby sloughs and impoundments; eutrophic lake.

PROVISIONS FOR VISITING SCIENTISTS: Space for four visitors; living quarters nearby; no fees charged for research space.

MAJOR RESEARCH FACILITIES: Small library; large outdoor ponds and tanks, small aquarium tanks, concrete holding tanks, fiber glass troughs; small private research collections of local fishes; machine and wood shop, skilled shop workman available; small boats and outboard motors.

SIZE OF STAFF: Five at professional level; 4-5 technicians.

FISH CONTROL LABORATORY, LACROSSE

IMPORTANT SPECIES AVAILABLE FOR LABORATORY STUDIES: There is an abundance of both warm-water and cold-water fauna and flora in the Upper Mississippi River area. Through the cooperation of the States of Iowa, Wisconsin and Minnesota, a great variety of plants and animals is available for experimental studies.

Fish-Pesticide Research Laboratory

POSTAL ADDRESS: Building 45, Denver Federal Center, Denver 25, Colorado, USA.

EXECUTIVE OFFICER: Dr. Oliver B. Cope, Chief.

YEAR FOUNDED: 1959.

SCOPE OF ACTIVITIES: Restricted research on investigations of effects of economic poisons on fish.

SEASON OF OPERATION: All year.

PHYSICAL ENVIRONMENT ACCESSIBLE: Mountain streams and lakes (both eutrophic and oligotrophic) of Colorado.

PROVISIONS FOR VISITING SCIENTISTS: Space for 2 visitors; no fees charged; living quarters available nearby.

MAJOR RESEARCH FACILITIES: Small library; large outdoor ponds and tanks, small aquarium tanks; research and identified reference collection of Colorado aquatic invertebrates; machine and wood shop; small boats and outboard motors.

SIZE OF STAFF: Six at professional level; 2 technicians.

IMPORTANT SPECIES AVAILABLE FOR LABORATORY STUDIES:

Pisces: Salmo gairdneri

MAJOR CURRENT RESEARCH PROJECTS AND SCIENTIFIC LEADERS:

Acute toxicities of pesticides to fish (Walter R. Bridges)
Pest control operations (Walter R. Bridges)
Physiology and pesticides (Burton Kallman)

North Central Reservoir Investigations

POSTAL ADDRESS: P. O. Box 139, Yankton, South Dakota, USA.

LOCATION: Near Sioux City, Iowa.

EXECUTIVE OFFICER: Norman G. Benson, Chief.

YEAR FOUNDED: 1961.

SCOPE OF ACTIVITIES: Research on relationships of population dynamics of fish and limnology of large reservoirs to water fluctuations and exchange rate.

SEASON OF OPERATION: All year.

PHYSICAL ENVIRONMENT ACCESSIBLE: Large mainstem reservoirs at Missouri River.

PROVISIONS FOR VISITING SCIENTISTS: Office space, field equipment and limited laboratory space.

MAJOR RESEARCH FACILITIES: Library; laboratory and shop; boats; fish and limnological collecting gear; ponds.

SIZE OF STAFF: Five at professional level.

IMPORTANT SPECIES AVAILABLE FOR LABORATORY STUDIES: Warm water plankton and fishes.
MAJOR CURRENT RESEARCH PROJECTS AND SCIENTIFIC LEADERS:
Projects:
Fish and sampling and measurement of statistics of fish stock
Determination of relationship of reservoir limnology of water management
Development of methods for monitoring reservoir ecology and fish populations
Leaders: Norman G. Benson, Charles H. Walburg, William Nelson, George Swanson

Salmon-Cultural Laboratory

POSTAL ADDRESS: Entiat, Washington, USA.
LOCATION: Abernathy Creek, 15 miles from Longview, Washington.
EXECUTIVE OFFICER: Roger E. Burrows, Fishery Research Biologist.
YEAR FOUNDED: 1951.
SCOPE OF ACTIVITIES: Unrestricted research on artificial propagation, nutrition and physiology of salmon and trout; restricted research on improved methods of artificial propagation of salmon and trout.
SEASON OF OPERATION: All year.
PHYSICAL ENVIRONMENT ACCESSIBLE: Columbia River.
PROVISIONS FOR VISITING SCIENTISTS: None.
MAJOR RESEARCH FACILITIES: Small library; large outdoor ponds and tanks, small aquarium tanks; machine and wood shop, skilled shop workman available.
SIZE OF STAFF: Seven at professional level; 4 technicians.
IMPORTANT SPECIES AVAILABLE FOR LABORATORY STUDIES: Several species of salmon and trout.
MAJOR CURRENT RESEARCH PROJECTS AND SCIENTIFIC LEADERS:
Diet formulation for salmon (B. D. Combs)
Effect of rearing pond environment of fingerling salmon (R. E. Burrows)
Characteristics of fingerling salmon necessary for maximum adult survival (R. E. Burrows)
Temperature thresholds for development of salmon and trout eggs (B. D. Combs)

Sandy Hook Marine Laboratory

POSTAL ADDRESS: P. O. Box 428, Highlands, New Jersey, USA.
LOCATION: Near New York City.
EXECUTIVE OFFICER: Lionel A. Walford, Laboratory Director.
YEAR FOUNDED: 1960.
SCOPE OF ACTIVITIES: Restricted research on general biology (including systematics, life history, ecology and ethology) of migratory marine game fishes.
SEASON OF OPERATION: All year.

SANDY HOOK MARINE LABORATORY

PHYSICAL ENVIRONMENT ACCESSIBLE: Atlantic Ocean, Sandy Hook Bay; sandy and silty beaches, rocky and gravelly shores, estuarine conditions, brackish, shallow bays, rivers and streams.
PROVISIONS FOR VISITING SCIENTISTS: Research and living space for 10-15 visitors; no fees charged for research space.
MAJOR RESEARCH FACILITIES: Small library; running sea and fresh-water, small aquarium tanks, large indoor tanks; research collections of fauna and flora available from nearby institutions in New York, Philadelphia and New Haven; machine and wood shop; small boats and outboard motors; larger vessels available by arrangement.
SIZE OF STAFF: Ten at professional level; 5 technicians.

Southeastern Fish-Cultural Laboratory

POSTAL ADDRESS: Marion, Alabama, USA.
EXECUTIVE OFFICER: Kermit E. Sneed, Chief.
YEAR FOUNDED: 1959.
SCOPE OF ACTIVITIES: Restricted research on fish culture, fish hormones, etc.
SEASON OF OPERATION: All year.
PHYSICAL ENVIRONMENT ACCESSIBLE: Fish cultural ponds.
MAJOR RESEARCH FACILITIES: Small library; large outdoor ponds and tanks, small aquarium tanks; machine and wood shop; small boats and outboard motors.
SIZE OF STAFF: Three at professional level.
IMPORTANT SPECIES AVAILABLE FOR LABORATORY STUDIES: Warm-water, fresh-water fishes only.
MAJOR CURRENT RESEARCH PROJECTS:
Propagation requirements of channel catfish and flathead catfish.
Artificial spawning of largemouth bass with gonadotropic hormones.
Inhibition of reproduction in fishes.

SOUTHEASTERN FISH-CULTURAL LABORATORY, MARION

Western Fish Disease Laboratory

POSTAL ADDRESS: Building #204, Sand Point Naval Air Station, Seattle 15, Washington, USA.
EXECUTIVE OFFICER: Dr. Robert R. Rucker, Chief and Fishery Research Biologist.
YEAR FOUNDED: 1936.
SCOPE OF ACTIVITIES: Restricted and unrestricted research on the etiology, etiologic agents and therapeutic agents of fish diseases; extension information to fish hatcheries.
SEASON OF OPERATION: All year.
PROVISIONS FOR VISITING SCIENTISTS: None.
MAJOR RESEARCH FACILITIES: (Facilities of the University of Washington School of Fisheries as well as Air Station facilities are used). Very extensive library.
SIZE OF STAFF: Five at professional level; 5 technicians.
IMPORTANT SPECIES AVAILABLE FOR LABORATORY STUDIES: Several species of salmon and trout.
MAJOR CURRENT RESEARCH PROJECTS AND SCIENTIFIC LEADERS:

Redmouth disease of rainbow trout (R. R. Rucker)
Mycobacterial survey and taxonomy (A. J. Ross)
Virus disease of chinook salmon (T. J. Parisot)
Hexamitiasis in fish (J. R. Uzmann)
Pathology of fish diseases (W. T. Yasutake)

WESTERN FISH DISEASE LABORATORY, SEATTLE

Western Fish Nutrition Laboratory

POSTAL ADDRESS: Cook, Washington, USA.
LOCATION: Near Portland, Oregon.
EXECUTIVE OFFICER: John E. Halver, Chief, Western Fish Nutrition Investigations.
YEAR FOUNDED: 1953.
SCOPE OF ACTIVITIES: Restricted research on determination of nutritional requirements of salmon.
SEASON OF OPERATION: All year.
PHYSICAL ENVIRONMENT ACCESSIBLE: Columbia River.
PROVISIONS FOR VISITING SCIENTISTS: Research and living space available for visitors; no fees charged for research space.
MAJOR RESEARCH FACILITIES: Small library; large outdoor ponds and tanks, small aquarium tanks; identified reference collection of normal and abnormal salmonid tissues; machine and wood shop.
SIZE OF STAFF: Six at professional level; 8 technicians.
MAJOR CURRENT RESEARCH PROJECTS AND SCIENTIFIC LEADERS:

WESTERN FISH NUTRITION LABORATORY, NR. PORTLAND

Vitamin requirements of salmon (John E. Halver)
Amino acid requirements of salmon (John E. Halver)
Mineral requirements of salmon (A. N. Woodall)
Digestive enzymes of salmonids (C. B. Croston)
Biological availability studies (W. E. Shanks)
Hematology of salmonids (E. F. Hesser)
Histology studies in salmonids (E. F. Hesser)

United States Navy Electronics Laboratory

POSTAL ADDRESS: San Diego 52, California, USA.
EXECUTIVE OFFICER: Harry C. Mason, Captain, USN, Commanding Officer and Director.
YEAR FOUNDED: 1940.
SCOPE OF ACTIVITIES: Restricted research in oceanography and acoustics, electronics and systems.
SEASON OF OPERATION: All year.
PHYSICAL ENVIRONMENT ACCESSIBLE: San Diego and Mission Bays, and the Pacific Ocean.

U.S. NAVY ELECTRONICS LABORATORY, SAN DIEGO

PROVISIONS FOR VISITING SCIENTISTS: Space by special arrangement for 1-3 visitors; fees charged depending upon individual circumstances; living quarters available nearby.

MAJOR RESEARCH FACILITIES: Very extensive library; running sea and fresh-water, small aquarium tanks; machine and wood shop, electrical and electronic shop, skilled shop workmen available; one 85 ft LOA sailing vessel, USS *Saluda,* and two power vessels, USS *Marysville* and USS *Reaburg,* and one submarine, USS *Baya.*

SIZE OF STAFF: One professional biologist; 1 visiting (part time) biologist.

MAJOR CURRENT BIOLOGICAL RESEARCH PROJECTS AND SCIENTIFIC LEADERS:

Effects of biological activity and organisms on other physical properties of sea water and on various equipment (Eric G. Barham and Palle G. Hansen)

United States Naval Oceanographic Office, Marine Sciences Department

POSTAL ADDRESS: Washington 25, D. C., USA.

EXECUTIVE OFFICERS: Boyd E. Olson, Acting Director. A. R. Gordon, Jr., Director, Oceanographic Division. Kenneth W. Kaye, Head, Biological Section.

YEAR FOUNDED: 1946.

U.S. NAVAL OCEANOGRAPHIC OFFICE, WASHINGTON, D.C.

SCOPE OF BIOLOGICAL ACTIVITIES: Restricted research on marine fouling and borers, sonic and dangerous animals, vegetation, bioluminescence, and DSL phenomena as a part of the overall oceanography program.

SEASON OF OPERATION: All year.

PHYSICAL ENVIRONMENT ACCESSIBLE: Survey vessels have operated in all major oceans and seas including Arctic and Antarctic.

PROVISIONS FOR VISITING SCIENTISTS: Space available for visitors by prearrangement.

MAJOR RESEARCH AND TEACHING FACILITIES: Very extensive library (60,000 oceanographic volumes and journals); small, partially identified collection of plankton and fouling organisms; machine and wood shop, electrical and electronic shop, skilled shop workmen available; vessels, 310 ft LOA, USS *San Pablo,* 310 ft LOA, USS *Rehoboth,* 132 ft LOA, USS *Littlehales,* part time oceanographic work on other survey ships and icebreakers, 8 shipboard laboratories.

INSTRUCTIONAL PROGRAM: Basic oceanography (6 weeks) for college students, trainees, reservists, foreign civilians and officers. U. S. Department of Agriculture Graduate School, with the Oceanographic Office, offers various courses in oceanography including biological oceanography.

SIZE OF STAFF: Ten full time and 5 part time biological oceanographers; 1 part time technician on marine biological work.

MAJOR CURRENT BIOLOGICAL RESEARCH PROJECTS AND SCIENTIFIC LEADERS:

Investigation of biological fouling (W. E. Maloney, S. A. Arny and F. M. Daugherty, Jr.)

Antarctic biota (J. Q. Tierney)

Deep scattering layer (K. W. Kaye)

Geographic distribution and prediction of bioluminescence (W. S. Glidden and R. F. Staples)

Geographic distribution of sonic marine animals (F. M. Daugherty, Jr. and W. T. Leapley)

PUBLICATIONS ISSUED: *Technical Report Series; Special Publications Series* (both occasionally published)

United States Navy Mine Defense Laboratory

POSTAL ADDRESS: Panama City, Florida, USA.

EXECUTIVE OFFICER: Captain R. K. Anderson, USN, Commanding Officer and Director.

YEAR FOUNDED: 1946.

SCOPE OF ACTIVITIES: Restricted research on general oceanography as related to over-all missions—mine countermeasures.

SEASON OF OPERATION: All year.

PHYSICAL ENVIRONMENT ACCESSIBLE: Gulf of Mexico.

PROVISIONS FOR VISITING SCIENTISTS: Space is available for visitors but security classification restricts visits; no fees charged for research space; living quarters available nearby.

MAJOR RESEARCH FACILITIES: Very extensive library; running sea and fresh-water, large outdoor ponds and

U.S. NAVY MINE DEFENSE LABORATORY, PANAMA CITY

tanks, small aquarium tanks, indoor test tank; machine and wood shop, electrical and electronic shop, skilled shop workmen available; all sizes of boats from small up to 191 ft LOA.

SIZE OF STAFF: About 200 at professional level.

MAJOR CURRENT RESEARCH PROJECTS AND SCIENTIFIC LEADERS:

Marine environment vs. echo variability (G. B. Austin)
Arctic oceanography (G. B. Dowling)
Porpoise noise vs. shark behavior (F. C. W. Olson)

United States Naval Radiological Defense Laboratory

POSTAL ADDRESS: San Francisco 24, California, USA.

EXECUTIVE OFFICER: Captain J. H. McQuilkin, Commanding Officer and Director.

YEAR FOUNDED: 1946.

SCOPE OF ACTIVITIES: Restricted research on the physical and biological effects of hazardous nuclear and thermal radiations; undergraduate instruction under a cooperative educational program, and graduate instruction for employees.

U.S. NAVAL RADIOLOGICAL DEFENSE LABORATORY, SAN FRANCISCO

SEASON OF OPERATION: All year.

PHYSICAL ENVIRONMENT ACCESSIBLE: Pacific Ocean, San Francisco Bay System; sandy and silty beaches, rocky and gravelly shores, estuarine conditions, brackish shallow bays, rivers and streams.

PROVISIONS FOR VISITING SCIENTISTS: Space available for a few visitors at a time on a case basis; a scientist-in-residence program is being developed; no fees normally charged for research space; living quarters available nearby.

MAJOR RESEARCH AND TEACHING FACILITIES: Very extensvie library; small explosives test pond under construction; research and identified reference collections of the University of California and the California Academy of Sciences are accessible; machine and wood shop, electrical and electronic shop, skilled shop workmen available; surface craft requirements must be justified and requested through Navy channels on a case basis.

SIZE OF STAFF: Two hundred and forty-six at professional level, 87 technicians.

United States Public Health Service

LABORATORIES:

1. Arctic Health Research Center
2. Communicable Disease Center, Puerto Rico Field Station
3. National Water Quality Network Laboratory
4. Robert A. Taft Sanitary Engineering Center, Aquatic Biology Section
5. Robert A. Taft Sanitary Engineering Center, Shellfish Sanitation Laboratory

(Descriptions follow.)

Arctic Health Research Center

POSTAL ADDRESS: Box 960, Anchorage, Alaska, USA.

EXECUTIVE OFFICER: Dr. A. B. Colyar, Medical Officer in Charge.

YEAR FOUNDED: 1948.

SCOPE OF ACTIVITIES: Restricted research on fresh-water organisms, particularly zoo- and phytoplankton in relation to environmental conditions in low temperature areas.

SEASON OF OPERATION: All year.

PHYSICAL ENVIRONMENT ACCESSIBLE: Dystrophic lakes of central Alaska and of Kenai peninsula.

PROVISIONS FOR VISITING SCIENTISTS: Space for three visitors; no fees charged; living quarters available nearby.

MAJOR RESEARCH FACILITIES: Very extensive library; small aquarium tanks; identified herbarium at University of Alaska, Fairbanks; machine and wood shop, skilled shop workman available; boats obtained by rental as needed.

SIZE OF STAFF: One at professional level.

IMPORTANT SPECIES AVAILABLE FOR LABORATORY STUDIES:

Chrysomonadales: *Mallomonas, Synura, Dinobryon, Hyalobryon, Kephyrion, Pseudokephyrion, Stenokalyx* and *Chrysococcus.*

MAJOR CURRENT RESEARCH PROJECTS AND SCIENTIFIC LEADERS:

Periodicity, ecology and systematics of the Chrysomonadales of some Alaska lakes and ponds (Douglas K. Hilliard)

Electron microscope observation on *Mallomonas* and *Synura* in Alaskan ponds (Douglas K. Hilliard)

Observations on the algae of an oxidation pond (Douglas K. Hilliard)

Taxonomic significance of eggs and coracidia of diphyllobothriid cestodes (Douglas K. Hilliard)

Phycological studies of Cape Thompson and environs (Douglas K. Hilliard)

ARCTIC HEALTH RESEARCH CENTER, ANCHORAGE

Communicable Disease Center, Puerto Rico Field Station

POSTAL ADDRESS: P. O. Box 52, San Juan, Puerto Rico.

EXECUTIVE OFFICER: Dr. F. F. Ferguson Chief, Puerto Rico Field Station.

YEAR FOUNDED: 1952.

SCOPE OF ACTIVITIES: Restricted research on the control of schistosomiasis.

SEASON OF OPERATION: All year.

PHYSICAL ENVIRONMENT ACCESSIBLE: Brackish, shallow bays, eutrophic and oligotrophic lakes, rivers and streams, and irrigation systems.

PROVISIONS FOR VISITING SCIENTISTS: Available.

MAJOR RESEARCH FACILITIES: Small library; large outdoor ponds and tanks, small aquarium tanks, irrigation systems; research and identified reference collections of various planorbid snails; machine and wood shop, electrical and electronic shop, skilled shop workman available.

SIZE OF STAFF: Four at professional level; 5 technicians.

MAJOR CURRENT RESEARCH PROJECTS AND SCIENTIFIC LEADERS:

Investigation on the biology and control of schistomomiasis (F. F. Ferguson, W. B. Rowan, H. Negron, and W. R. Jobin)

National Water Quality Network Laboratory

POSTAL ADDRESS: 1014 Broadway, Cincinnati 2, Ohio, USA.

EXECUTIVE OFFICER: Leo Weaver, Chief, Water Quality Section.

SPONSORING AGENCY: Basic Data Branch, Division of Water Supply and Pollution Control.

YEAR OF FOUNDING: 1957.

SCOPE OF ACTIVITIES: Collect, interpret, and disseminate basic data on water quality of the Nation's waters as related to water supply and pollution control. Samples for analysis are collected from 125 locations located throughout the Nation on major streams.

RESEARCH: Restricted.

SEASON OF OPERATION: All year.

PHYSICAL ENVIRONMENT ACCESSIBLE: The 125 existing stations are sampled with cooperation by local, state, and federal agencies. Analysis of unstable characteristics are performed locally and other analyses performed in the laboratories of the National Water Quality Network at Cincinnati, Ohio. Laboratories include facilities for analysis of: inorganic chemicals, trace elements, organic extracts from carbon adsorption units, bacteria, radioactivity, plankton, benthos, and fish populations. Equipment development for sampling and electronic detection of water quality is also carried on. Annual compilations of data published as Public Health Service Publication No. 663, 3 volumes and 2 supplements.

PROVISION FOR VISITING SCIENTISTS: Visits arranged for laboratory tours or for instruction on methods.

MAJOR RESEARCH AND TEACHING FACILITIES: Laboratories and library available for research; short courses conducted cooperatively with the Robert A. Taft Sanitary Engineering Center.

SIZE OF STAFF: 54 employees.

IMPORTANT SPECIES AVAILABLE FOR LABORATORY STUDIES: Permanent diatom slides, semi-monthly preserved plankton samples from nationwide collections, bottom fauna, and fish collections.

MAJOR CURRENT RESEARCH PROJECTS AND SCIENTIFIC LEADERS:

Projects:

Plankton laboratory

Benthos field and laboratory

Fish census field studies

Inorganic water analyses

Organic analyses from carbon adsorption unit
Bacterial analysis of water
Radioactivity analyses of suspended and dissolved matter

Leaders:

J. B. Anderson (Aquatic biology)
Dr. L. G. Williams (Plankton)
L. B. Tebo (Fish Studies)
Dr. E. B. Henson (Benthos)
Dr. A. W. Breidenbach (Organic chemistry)
R. C. Kroner (Inorganic Chemistry)
S. L. Baker (Radioactivity)
C. G. Shower (Bacteriology)
H. Stierli (Equipment development)

Robert A. Taft Sanitary Engineering Center, Aquatic Biology Section

POSTAL ADDRESS:
Headquarters: Robert A. Taft Sanitary Engineering Center 4676 Columbia Parkway, Cincinnati 26, Ohio, USA.
Branch Laboratory: Pacific Cooperative Water Pollution and Fisheries Research Laboratory, Oregon State College, Corvallis, Oregon.

EXECUTIVE OFFICERS: Harry G. Hanson, Director, R. A. Taft Sanitary Engineering Center. Clarence M. Tarzwell, Chief, Aquatic Biology Section.

YEAR FOUNDED: 1915; Corvallis Branch, 1953.

SCOPE OF ACTIVITIES: Restricted research on biological problems of water supply and water pollution.

SEASON OF OPERATION: All year.

PHYSICAL ENVIRONMENT ACCESSIBLE: Rivers and streams, reservoirs and lakes.

PROVISIONS FOR VISITING SCIENTISTS: None.

MAJOR RESEARCH FACILITIES: Moderately complete library; outdoor ponds and tanks, small aquarium tanks, constant flow apparatus for bioassays; small reference collections of local fish and aquatic insects; machine and wood shops, electrical and electronic shops, skilled shop workmen available; small boats and outboard motors.

SIZE OF STAFF: Fifteen at professional level; 3 technicians.

IMPORTANT SPECIES AVAILABLE FOR LABORATORY STUDIES:

Chlorophyceae: *Chlorococcum macrostigmatum, Chlorella variegata, Scenedesmus obliquus, S. vasilensis, Chlorella pyrenoidosa.*

Cyanophyceae: *Anacystis nidulans, Plectonema boryanum.*

Pisces: *Pimephales promelas, Lepomis macrochirus, Carassius auratus, Lebistes reticulatus, Micropterus salmoides, Oncorhynchus tsawytscha, O. kisutch, Salmo gairdnerii, Gasterosteus aculeutus.*

MAJOR CURRENT RESEARCH PROJECTS AND SCIENTIFIC LEADERS:

Determination of water quality requirements for protection of aquatic life; basic studies in fish toxicology, physiology, and ecology (Peter Doudoroff)
Practical methods for application of bioassays (Jerry Hubschman, Donald I. Mount, Quentin H. Pickering, and Eugene W. Surber)
Role of algae in environmental sanitation; algae in waste treatment (Thomas E. Maloney, C. M. Palmer and R. Safferman)
Role of algae in environmental sanitation; algal growths in surface waters (Thomas E. Maloney, C. M. Palmer and R. Safferman)
Role of algae in environmental sanitation; algae and other interference organisms in water supplies (C. M. Palmer).

ROBERT A. TAFT SANITARY ENGINEERING CENTER

Robert A. Taft Sanitary Engineering Center, Shellfish Sanitation Laboratory

POSTAL ADDRESS: Star Route, Box 576, Gig Harbor, Washington, USA.

LOCATION: Near Tacoma.

EXECUTIVE OFFICER: Cornelius B. Kelly, Chief.

YEAR FOUNDED: 1948.

SCOPE OF ACTIVITIES: Research restricted to problems in sanitary control of shellfish, harvesting, processing and marketing.

SEASON OF OPERATION: All year.

PHYSICAL ENVIRONMENT ACCESSIBLE: Lower Puget Sound; sandy and silty beaches, rocky and gravelly shores, estuarine conditions, rivers and streams.

PROVISIONS FOR VISITING SCIENTISTS: None.

MAJOR RESEARCH FACILITIES: Small library; running sea water, small aquarium tanks; skilled shop workman available; small boats and outboard motors.

MAJOR CURRENT RESEARCH PROJECTS:

Evaluation of the sanitary significance of "fecal coliform organisms" in shellfish and shellfish waters.
Development and evaluation of methods for the exam-

ination of sea water and shellfish.
Accumulation and elimination of bacteria by shellfish.
Survival of enteric organisms in sea water and shellfish.
Investigations of commercial practices of harvesting, packing, and marketing of shellfish.

University of Connecticut, Marine Research Laboratory

POSTAL ADDRESS: Noank, Connecticut, USA.
LOCATION: Near New London.
EXECUTIVE OFFICER: Dr. John S. Rankin, Jr., Director.
YEAR FOUNDED: 1955.
SCOPE OF ACTIVITIES: Unrestricted research in general marine biology; graduate and undergraduate instruction.
SEASON OF OPERATION: All year.
PHYSICAL ENVIRONMENT ACCESSIBLE: Block Island, Fishers Island and Long Island Sounds; sandy and silty beaches, rocky and gravelly shores, rivers and streams, estuarine conditions, and brackish, shallow bays.
PROVISIONS FOR VISITING SCIENTISTS: Space for 3 visitors; no fees charged; living quarters available nearby.
MAJOR RESEARCH AND TEACHING FACILITIES: Small library; running sea water, small aquarium tanks; float with live cars; research and identified reference collection of marine and estuarine organisms; machine and wood shop, skilled shop workman available; small boats and outboard motors.
INSTRUCTIONAL PROGRAM: Ecology, chemistry, biochemistry, parasitology, invertebrate zoology, algology, bacteriology, ichthyology, fishery biology and management and physiology.
SIZE OF STAFF: Two at professional level; 2 technicians.
IMPORTANT SPECIES AVAILABLE FOR LABORATORY STUDIES:
Clorophyceae: *Ulva, Enteromorpha*
Phaeophyceae: *Laminaria*

UNIVERSITY OF CONNECTICUT MARINE RESEARCH LABORATORY

Echinoidea: *Arbacia punctulata*
Asteroidea: *Asterias forbesi*
Hydrozoa: *Tubularia crocea, Campanularia flexuosa*
Scyphozoa: *Aurelia aurita*
Sipunculida: *Phascolosoma gouldii*
Tunicata: *Molgula manhattensis*
MAJOR CURRENT RESEARCH PROJECTS AND SCIENTIFIC LEADERS:
Estuarine micropopulation distribution (John S. Rankin, Jr.)
Estuarine macrobenthos ecology (David Dean)
Radioactivity in organisms and environment (Donald M. Skauen)
Ecology of estuarine fishes (Ralph Wetzel and Russell Hunter)
Growth and development of marine algae (Francis R. Trainor)
Coastal climatology (George R. Rumney)

University of Delaware Marine Laboratories

POSTAL ADDRESS:
Campus unit: Department of Biological Sciences, University of Delaware, Newark, Delaware, USA.
Field Station: Bayside Laboratory, P. O. Box 514, Lewes, Delaware.
EXECUTIVE OFFICER: Dr. Carl N. Shuster, Jr., Director, Marine Laboratories, Department of Biological Sciences, University of Delaware, Newark, Delaware.
SPONSORING AGENCY: State of Delaware.
YEAR FOUNDED: 1951.
SCOPE OF ACTIVITIES: Unrestricted research on estuarine ecology and productivity; graduate and undergraduate instruction.
SEASON OF OPERATION: All year at both laboratories.
PHYSICAL ENVIRONMENT ACCESSIBLE: Atlantic Ocean, Delaware River and Bay; sandy and silty beaches, estuarine conditions, brackish, shallow bays, rivers and streams, and tidal marshes.
PROVISIONS FOR VISITING SCIENTISTS: None.
MAJOR RESEARCH AND TEACHING FACILITIES: Small library; small aquarium tanks; extensive research collections of zooplankton; identified reference collections of benthonic invertebrates and fishes of Delaware Bay and adjoining waters; machine and wood shop, electrical and electronic shop, skilled shop workman, all on campus; small boats and outboard motors.
INSTRUCTIONAL PROGRAM: Introduction to biological oceanography, estuarine ecology, marine invertebrate zoology, ichthyology, and fisheries biology.
SIZE OF STAFF: Six at professional level; 1 technician.
IMPORTANT SPECIES AVAILABLE FOR LABORATORY STUDIES:
Xiphosura: *Limulus polyphemus*
Crustacea: *Callinectes sapidus*
Cephalopoda: *Loligo pealii*
Mollusca: *Crassostrea virginica, Mercenaria mercenaria, Bucycon* sp.

UNIVERSITY OF DELAWARE MARINE LABORATORY, BAYSIDE LABORATORY

Elasmobranchii: *Raja eglanteria*

MAJOR CURRENT RESEARCH PROJECTS AND SCIENTIFIC LEADERS:

Tidal marsh ecology (Franklin C. Daiber)
Physiology of digestion in skates (Franklin C. Daiber)
Reproduction in elasmobranchs (Franklin C. Daiber)
Ichthyoplankton in Delaware Bay (Donald P. deSylva)
Fisheries biology (Donald P. deSylva)
Ecology, morphology and physiology of mollusks and arthropods (Carl N. Shuster, Jr.)
Shellfish pathology and immunology (Marenes R. Tripp)
Shellfisheries biology (Carl N. Shuster, Jr.)
Benthonic invertebrate survey (William H. Amos)
Hydrography of estuarine waters (Staff)

PUBLICATIONS ISSUED: *Estuarine Bulletin* (regularly published journal)

University of Florida Marine Laboratory

POSTAL ADDRESS: Cedar Key, Florida, USA.
LOCATION: On Seahorse Key.
EXECUTIVE OFFICER: E. Lowe Pierce, Supervisor of the Laboratory, Department of Biology, University of Florida, Gainesville, Florida.
YEAR FOUNDED: 1952.
SCOPE OF ACTIVITIES: Unrestricted research on marine ecology, systematics of marine animals, and life histories of marine animals.
SEASON OF OPERATION: All year.
PHYSICAL ENVIRONMENT ACCESSIBLE: Gulf of Mexico; open ocean, sandy and silty beaches, estuarine conditions, rivers and streams.
PROVISION FOR VISITING SCIENTISTS: Research and living space for several visitors; fees charged for research space.
MAJOR RESEARCH FACILITIES: No library; running sea water, small aquarium tanks; small synoptic collection of common marine animals; small boats and outboard motors; 25 ft LOA motor launch.
SIZE OF STAFF: One at professional level; 1 technician.

IMPORTANT SPECIES AVAILABLE FOR LABORATORY STUDIES:

Echinodermata: *Lytechninus variegatus*
Crustacea: *Callinectes sapidus, Uca pugilator*
Mollusca: *Crassostrea virginica*
Arthropoda: *Limulus polyphemus*
Hydrozoa: *Hydractinia* sp.
Polychaeta: *Diopatra cuprea, Chaetopterus pergamentaceus*
Brachiopoda: *Glottidia audebarti*
Elasmobranchii: *Dasyatis say*

MAJOR CURRENT RESEARCH PROJECTS AND SCIENTIFIC LEADERS:

Abundance and distribution of Amphioxus (E. Lowe Pierce)
Systematics of Bryozoa (Frank Maturo)
Systematics and occurance of Hydrozoa (E. Lowe Pierce)
Ecological studies of Polychaeta (E. Lowe Pierce)

University of Georgia Marine Institute

POSTAL ADDRESS: Sapelo Island, Georgia, USA.
LOCATION: Near Brunswick.
EXECUTIVE OFFICER: George H. Lauff, Director.
SPONSORING AGENCIES: Sapelo Island Research Foundation and University of Georgia.
YEAR FOUNDED: Foundation, 1949. Marine Institute, 1953.
SCOPE OF ACTIVITIES: Unrestricted basic research with emphasis on marine biology and geology, primarily with ecology of estuaries and coastal waters and related habitats; graduate instruction.
SEASON OF OPERATION: All year.
PHYSICAL ENVIRONMENT ACCESSIBLE: Atlantic Ocean,

UNIVERSITY OF FLORIDA MARINE LABORATORY

UNIVERSITY OF GEORGIA MARINE INSTITUTE

Doboy Sound; sandy and silty beaches, estuarine conditions, brackish, shallow bays, rivers and streams, salt marshes, fresh-water ponds, and cypress swamps.

PROVISIONS FOR VISITING SCIENTISTS: Research and living space for 3 visitors; a modest charge is made for use of facilities.

MAJOR RESEARCH AND TEACHING FACILITIES: Small library; running sea water, small aquarium tanks; research and identified reference collections of local invertebrate animals; machine and wood shop; small boats and outboard motors; 65 ft LOA, M/V *Kit Jones*.

INSTRUCTIONAL PROGRAM: Courses offered at University of Georgia with field work at Sapelo Island: invertebrate zoology, marine biology, ecology, fisheries biology, and ichthyology. Facilities are also available to other visiting class groups.

SIZE OF STAFF: Seven at professional level; 4 technicians.

IMPORTANT SPECIES AVAILABLE FOR LABORATORY STUDIES:

Anthozoa: *Renilla reniformis*
Crustacea: *Uca pugnax, U. pugiliator, U. minax*
Gastropoda: *Littorina irrorata*
Pelecypoda: *Modiolous demissus*
Asteroidea: *Luidia clathrata*

MAJOR CURRENT RESEARCH PROJECTS AND SCIENTIFIC LEADERS:

The cycle of phosphorus in natural waters (Lawrence R. Pomeroy)
Energy flow in the salt marsh ecasystem (Eugene P. Odum)
Near-shore sediments, ecology, and environments (John H. Hoyt)
Macrobenthos-sediment relationships (Dirk Frankenberg)
Coastal processes; marsh and lagoonal sediments (Vernon J. Henry)
Sediment geochemistry and diagensis (Orrin H. Pilkey)
Physiology of salt marsh holophytes (Kenneth L. Webb)

University of Miami Marine Laboratory

POSTAL ADDRESS: 1, Rickenbacker Causeway, Virginia Key, Miami 49, Florida, USA.

EXECUTIVE OFFICER: Dr. F. G. Walton Smith, Director.

YEAR FOUNDED: 1943.

SCOPE OF ACTIVITIES: Restricted and unrestricted research in all fields of marine science including meteorology; graduate and undergraduate instruction.

SEASON OF OPERATION: All year.

PHYSICAL ENVIRONMENT ACCESSIBLE: Straits of Florida, Gulf of Mexico, Caribbean Sea; open ocean, coral reef, and tropical Atlantic.

PROVISIONS FOR VISITING SCIENTISTS: Space for 25 visitors; fees charged; living quarters available at the laboratory and nearby.

MAJOR RESEARCH AND TEACHING FACILITIES: Very extensive library, running sea and fresh-water, small aquarium tanks; research and identified reference collections of tropical Atlantic fauna and flora; machine and wood shop, electrical and electronic shop, skilled shop workmen available; small boats and outboard motors; vessels, 80 ft, 75 ft, 60 ft and 45 ft LOA; two shipboard laboratories.

INSTRUCTIONAL PROGRAM: Year-round instruction in cooperation with Department of Zoology, University of Miami; plankton, biological, chemical and physical oceanography, ecology, general and comparative physiology, biochemistry, embryology, microbiology, phycology, general invertebrate zoology, ichthyology, marine

UNIVERSITY OF MIAMI MARINE LABORATORY

invertebrate and vertebrate systematics, fishery biology, biometry, population dynamics, fisheries management, submarine geology, chemistry, physics and meteorology.

SIZE OF STAFF: One hundred twenty at professional level; 20 technicians.

PUBLICATIONS ISSUED: *Bulletin of Marine Science of the Gulf-Caribbean* (issued quarterly)

University of Michigan Biological Station

POSTAL ADDRESS: Pellston, Michigan, USA.

LOCATION: Near Cheboygan, between Douglas and Burt Lakes.

EXECUTIVE OFFICER: Alfred H. Stockard, Director. Postal address: June 15-September 1, University of Michigan Biological Station, Pellston, Michigan; September 1-June 15, 2129 Natural Science Building, University of Michigan, Ann Arbor, Michigan.

YEAR FOUNDED: 1909.

SCOPE OF ACTIVITIES: Unrestricted research in general field biology, including aquatic biology and limnology; graduate and undergraduate instruction.

SEASON OF OPERATION: June 20-August 20, but Station open throughout the year on arrangement by individuals or small groups.

PHYSICAL ENVIRONMENT ACCESSIBLE: Lakes Douglas, Mullet, and Burt, Great Lakes and connecting waters; sandy and silty beaches, rocky and gravelly shores, eutrophic and oligotrophic lakes, streams, swamps and bogs.

PROVISIONS FOR VISITING SCIENTISTS: Research and living space for 25 visitors; fees charged for research space.

MAJOR RESEARCH AND TEACHING FACILITIES: Moderately complete library; large outdoor ponds and tanks, small aquarium tanks; research and identified reference collections of Insecta, parasitic Trematoda and Cestoda; identified reference collections of other invertebrates, fishes, amphibians, reptiles, etc.; machine and wood shop, skilled shop workman available; three 22 ft LOA vessels.

INSTRUCTIONAL PROGRAM: Taxonomy of the flowering plants, fresh-water algae, plant ecology, bryophytes, lower fungi, higher fungi, pteridophytes and gymnosperms, aquatic flowering plants, lichens, ornithology, biology of fishes, entomology, natural history of invertebrates, biology of terrestrial vertebrates, limnology, introduction to parasites, biology of the protozoa, and helminthology.

SIZE OF SUMMER STAFF: Fifteen at professional level; 15 technicians.

IMPORTANT SPECIES AVAILABLE FOR LABORATORY STUDIES: To be representative, this list would include hundreds of species from many phyla of plants and animals.

MAJOR CURRENT RESEARCH PROJECTS AND SCIENTIFIC LEADERS:

- Algae and aquatic fungi (F. K. Sparrow, Jr.)
- Lichens and bryophytes (A. J. Sharp)
- Higher fungi (A. H. Smith)
- Taxonomy of higher plants (E. U. Clover)
- Ecology of plants (John E. Cantlon)
- Forest ecology (Robert Zahner)
- Aquatic bacteria (George W. Saunders)
- Parasitic protozoa (James H. Barrow)
- Parasitic helminths (James R. Hendricks and D. M. Wootton)
- Insects and mites (Robert E. Beer)
- General invertebrates (Frank E. Eggleton)
- Ichthyology (Charles W. Creaser and R. O. Legault)
- Terrestrial vertebrate ecology (Frederick H. Test)
- Ornithology (Olin S. Pettingill, Jr.)
- Limnology (David C. Chandler)

University of Michigan, Department of Fisheries

POSTAL ADDRESS: Ann Arbor, Michigan, USA.

EXECUTIVE OFFICER: Dr. K. F. Lagler, Chairman.

YEAR FOUNDED: 1950.

SCOPE OF ACTIVITIES: Unrestricted research; graduate and undergraduate instruction.

SEASON OF OPERATION: All year.

PHYSICAL ENVIRONMENT ACCESSIBLE: The Great Lakes and tributary and connecting waters; sandy and silty beaches, rocky and gravelly shores, eutrophic and oligotrophic lakes; polluted and unpolluted waters.

PROVISIONS FOR VISITING SCIENTISTS: Space for 4 visitors; no fees charged; living quarters available nearby.

MAJOR RESEARCH AND TEACHING FACILITIES: Very extensive library; large outdoor ponds and tanks, small aquarium tanks; research and identified reference collections of fauna and flora available at University Museum; machine and wood shop, electrical and electronic shop, skilled shop workman available; small boats and outboard motors, large vessels available.

INSTRUCTIONAL PROGRAM: Fish physiology and behavior, ichthyology, aquiculture, fishery biology, and commercial fisheries.

SIZE OF STAFF: Two at professorial level; 7 research associates; 6 technicians.

IMPORTANT SPECIES AVAILABLE FOR LABORATORY STUDIES: Two-hundred species of indigenous fresh-water fishes including families such as Petromyzontidae, Amiidae, Lepisosteidae, Clupeidae, Salmonidae, Cyprinidae, Catostomidae, Esocidae, Cyprinodontidae, Percidae, and Centrarchidae.

MAJOR CURRENT RESEARCH PROJECTS AND SCIENTIFIC LEADERS:

- Rhythmic activity of fishes (John E. Bardach)
- Skin senses of fishes (John E. Bardach)
- Textbook of Ichthyology (Karl F. Lagler *et al.*)
- Monograph of Great Lakes fishes (Karl F. Lagler)
- Distribution of Michigan fishes (Carl L. Hubbs)

Day-night shifts in shore fishes (Karl F. Lagler)
Fish toxicology (Karl F. Lagler and John E. Bardach)
Book: Continental Fisheries (Karl F. Lagler and Richard Vibert)

University of Michigan, Great Lakes Research Division, Institute of Science and Technology

POSTAL ADDRESS: Ann Arbor, Michigan, USA.
EXECUTIVE OFFICER: David C. Chandler, Director.
YEAR FOUNDED: 1945.
SCOPE OF ACTIVITIES: Unrestricted physical, chemical and biological research on the waters of the Great Lakes and their drainage basin; graduate research.
SEASON OF OPERATION: All year, with field program April–October.
PROVISIONS FOR VISITING SCIENTISTS: Space for 4 visitors; no fees charged for research space; living quarters available nearby.
PHYSICAL ENVIRONMENT ACCESSIBLE: Lakes Erie, Huron, Michigan, Ontario and Superior; sandy and silty beaches, rocky and gravelly shores, eutrophic and oligotrophic lakes, rivers and streams.
MAJOR RESEARCH FACILITIES: Very extensive library; small aquarium tanks; research and identified reference collections of fauna and flora available at the University Museum; machines and wood shop, skilled shop workman available; 35 ft LOA motor launch, 114 ft and 50 ft diesel powered vessels.
SIZE OF INSTITUTE STAFF: Eleven at professional level (5 in aquatic biology); 3 technicians.
MAJOR CURRENT RESEARCH PROJECTS AND SCIENTIFIC LEADERS:

Circulation and dilution in Little Traverse Bay (John C. Ayers)
Aging phenomena in lakes (John C. Ayers)
The sediments of the Straits of Mackinac (John C. Ayers)
Coring in bottom of Lake Superior (James H. Zumberge)
Turbulent transfer processes over the Great Lakes (Donald J. Portman)
Evaluation of quantitative methods for measuring biological productivity in the Great Lakes (George H. Lauff)
The Stanley low-water stage of Lake Huron (Jack L. Hough)
Benthos of the Straits of Mackinac (E. Bennette Henson and David C. Chandler)
Distribution of bacteria and their metabolism in natural waters (George W. Saunders)
Submarine geology in Little Traverse Bay (Wm. E. French)
Physical coefficients of mixing processes, and development of new instrumentation for Great Lakes physical studies (Vincent E. Noble)
Relationship of winds to Great Lakes currents (Charles F. Powers)
Assessment of water plant hydrographic data (Charles F. Powers)
Oceanography of Little Port Walter, Alaska (Charles F. Powers)
Atmospheric diffusion in transitional states (E. Wendell Hewson)
Analysis and evaluation of the factors influencing the determination of recent rates of crustal movement in the Great Lakes region (W. F. MacLean)

University of Minnesota, Department of Entomology, Fisheries, and Wildlife, Fishery Research Laboratory

POSTAL ADDRESS: Institute of Agriculture, University Farm, St. Paul 1, Minnesota, USA.
EXECUTIVE OFFICER: Dr. Lloyd L. Smith, Jr., Professor.
YEAR FOUNDED: 1946.
SCOPE OF ACTIVITIES: Unrestricted research on fish population dynamics and basic productivity; graduate instruction.
SEASON OF OPERATION: All year.
PHYSICAL ENVIRONMENT ACCESSIBLE: Mississippi River, Lakes Minnetonka and Red (eutrophic lakes).
PROVISIONS FOR VISITING SCIENTISTS: Space for 3 visitors; living quarters available nearby.
MAJOR RESEARCH AND TEACHING FACILITIES: Very extensive library; small aquarium tanks; research collections of Minnesota fishes and aquatic insects; machine and wood shop, electric and electronic shop, skilled shop workmen available; small boats and outboard motors.
INSTRUCTIONAL PROGRAM: Ecology, comparative physiology, ichthyology, fishery biology, biometry, fisheries management and basic productivity.
SIZE OF STAFF: Three at professional level; 5-6 student technicians.
MAJOR CURRENT RESEARCH PROJECTS AND SCIENTIFIC LEADERS:

Causes of fluctuation in commercial fish (L. L. Smith, Jr.)
Year class formation in large mouth bass (Robert Kramer)
Shore fish ecology Red Lakes (L. L. Smith, Jr.)
Basic production of benthos in streams (T. F. Waters)
Plankton production Red Lake (Robert Knapp)
Food conversion in streams (T. F. Waters)

University of North Carolina, Institute of Fisheries Research

POSTAL ADDRESS: P. O. Box 629, Morehead City, North Carolina, USA.
EXECUTIVE OFFICER: Dr. A. F. Chestnut, Director.
YEAR FOUNDED: 1947.
SCOPE OF ACTIVITIES: Restricted and unrestricted research on general marine biology.
SEASON OF OPERATION: All year.

INSTITUTE OF FISHERIES RESEARCH, UNIVERSITY OF NORTH CAROLINA

PHYSICAL ENVIRONMENT ACCESSIBLE: Atlantic Ocean, Bogue and Pamlico Sounds; sandy and silty beaches, estuarine conditions, and brackish, shallow bays.

PROVISIONS FOR VISITING SCIENTISTS: Space for 5 visitors; no fees charged; living quarters available nearby.

MAJOR RESEARCH FACILITIES: Small library; running sea and fresh-water, large outdoor ponds and tanks, small aquarium tanks; 2500 identified and catalogued fish, 950 Crustacea and 705 Mollusca; machine and wood shop, skilled shop workman available; skiffs with outboard motors; 47 ft LOA power vessel with trawling and dredging gear and deck laboratory.

SIZE OF STAFF: Six at professional level; 4 technicians.

IMPORTANT SPECIES AVAILABLE FOR LABORATORY STUDIES:

Crustacea: *Penaeus* (3 spp.), *Callinectes sapidus, Uca* (3 spp.), *Balanus* spp.

Pelecypoda: *Crassostrea virginica, Venus mercenaria, V. campechiensis*

Gastropoda: *Urosalpinx cinerea, Nassa obsoleta*

Pisces: *Paralichthys* (3 spp.), *Cynoscion* (2 spp.)

MAJOR CURRENT RESEARCH PROJECTS AND SCIENTIFIC LEADERS:

Plankton ecology of a positive bar-built estuary (Gerald S. Posner)

Biology and ecology of *Paralichthys lethostigma* (Earl E. Deubler, Jr.)

Experiments on meristic structures in fishes (William E. Fahy)

Decapod crustaceans of southeastern United States (Austin B. Williams)

Influence of temperature on osmoregulation in *Penaeus* (Austin B. Williams)

Biology and ecology of *Venus mercenaria* and *V. campechiensis* (Hugh J. Porter)

Setting behavior of oyster larvae (A. F. Chestnut)

University of Oklahoma Biological Station

POSTAL ADDRESS: Lake Texoma, Willis, Oklahoma, USA.

LOCATION: Near Madill.

EXECUTIVE OFFICER: Dr. Carl D. Riggs, Director of Station, University of Oklahoma, Norman, Oklahoma.

YEAR FOUNDED: 1950.

SCOPE OF ACTIVITIES: Unrestricted research on ecology, taxonomy and biology of impoundments; graduate and undergraduate instruction.

SEASON OF OPERATION: All year for research; June to August for instruction.

PHYSICAL ENVIRONMENT ACCESSIBLE: Lake Texoma, a 95,000 acre impoundment; rivers and streams.

PROVISIONS FOR VISITING SCIENTISTS: Research and living space for 15 visitors; fees charged for research space.

MAJOR RESEARCH AND TEACHING FACILITIES: Small library; large indoor and outdoor concrete tanks, small aquarium tanks, cages in lake; large research collections of local flora and fauna; identified reference collections of fishes, amphibians, and reptiles; machine and wood shop; small boats and outboard motors; one 36 ft LOA vessel.

INSTRUCTIONAL PROGRAM: Summer courses in algology, ecology of aquatic plants, herpetology, natural history of invertebrates, natural history of vertebrates, ichthyology, limnology, biology of fishes, and other courses in biology; 5 research courses.

SIZE OF STAFF: Ten at professional level, 6 graduate assistants; 2 technicians.

IMPORTANT SPECIES AVAILABLE FOR LABORATORY STUDIES: Typical mid-continental lake fauna and flora.

MAJOR CURRENT RESEARCH PROJECTS AND SCIENTIFIC LEADERS:

Effect of lake level fluctuations upon marginal plants (Wm. T. Penfound)

Parasites of the fishes of Lake Texoma (J. Teague Self)

Osteology and the lateral line-system of centrarchid fishes (George A. Moore)

Life histories of local fishes (Carl D. Riggs)

UNIVERSITY OF OKLAHOMA BIOLOGICAL STATION

University of Puerto Rico, Institute of Marine Biology

POSTAL ADDRESS: Mayaguez, Puerto Rico.

LOCATION: On island near La Parguera.

EXECUTIVE OFFICERS: Dr. Juan A. Rivero, Director. Dr. John E. Randall, Director of Research.

YEAR FOUNDED: 1954.

SCOPE OF ACTIVITIES: Unrestricted in general marine biology, systematics, plankton and ecology; graduate and undergraduate instruction.

SEASON OF OPERATION: All year.

PHYSICAL ENVIRONMENT ACCESSIBLE: Caribbean Sea, Bahia Fosforecente (Phosphorescent Bay), Bahia Boqueron, Laguna Joyuda; estuarine conditions, coral reefs, and mangrove swamps.

PROVISIONS FOR VISITING SCIENTISTS: Research and living space for 2-4 visitors; no fees charged for research space; dormitory rooms, $2 per day.

MAJOR RESEARCH AND TEACHING FACILITIES: Small library; running sea and fresh-water, small aquarium tanks, large aquatic pens; identified reference collections of echinoderms, sponges, gastropods, pelecypods, horny corals, stony corals and other coelenterata, fishes, some annelids, and crustaceans (copepods); machine and wood shop, electrical and electronic shop (at University Campus); small boats and outboard motors; vessels, 65 ft LOA, *Carite,* 27 ft LOA, *Pelicano,* 18 ft LOA, *Physalia.*

INSTRUCTIONAL PROGRAM: Marine ecology (summer).

SIZE OF STAFF: Seven at professional level.

IMPORTANT SPECIES AVAILABLE FOR LABORATORY STUDIES:

Coelenterata: *Cassiopeia xamachana, Aurelia aurita*
Tunicata: *Ascidia nigra, Ecteinascidia turbinata*
Echinodermata: *Oreaster reticulatus, Ophiocoma echinata, Diadema antillarum, Tripneustes esculentus*

MAJOR CURRENT RESEARCH PROJECTS AND SCIENTIFIC LEADERS:

Copepods of Puerto Rico (Juan G. Gonzalez and Thomas E. Bowman)
Coral reef and mangrove algae of southwestern Puerto Rico (Luis R. Almodovar)
Antibiotics of algae (Paul Burkholder)
Comparative study of voices of the Antillean frogs of genus *Eleutherodactylus* (Juan A. Rivero)
Sponges of La Parguera (Willard Hartman)
Productivity of Puerto Rican seas (Juan G. Gonzalez)
Classification and biology of West Indian fishes (John E. Randall)
Coral reef ecology (Peter Glynn)
Ecology of agar-producing red algae and their epiphytes (Manuel Diaz Piferrer)
Biology of West Indian topshell (*Cittarium pica*) (Helen A. Randall)
Classification of Caribbean mollusks (Germaine L. Warmke)

INSTITUTE OF MARINE BIOLOGY, MAYAGUEZ

University of Texas, Institute of Marine Science

POSTAL ADDRESS: Pork Aransas, Texas, USA.

EXECUTIVE OFFICER: Dr. Howard T. Odum, Director.

YEAR FOUNDED: 1941.

SCOPE OF ACTIVITIES: Unrestricted basic marine research; graduate instruction.

SEASON OF OPERATION: All year.

PHYSICAL ENVIRONMENT ACCESSIBLE: Gulf of Mexico, Laguna Madre, Bays Corpus Christi, Aransas, and Redfish; sandy beaches, estuarine conditions, brackish, shallow bays, grass flats, rock jetties, hypersaline bays, and oyster reefs.

PROVISIONS FOR VISITING SCIENTISTS: Research and living space for those interested in functional processes of environments or those with local residences; no fees charged for research space.

MAJOR RESEARCH AND TEACHING FACILITIES: Moderately complete library; running sea and fresh-water, large outdoor ponds and tanks under construction, small aquarium tanks; identified reference collections of fishes, invertebrates and small herbarium; machine and wood shop, skilled shop workman available; small boats and outboard motors; vessels, two 18 ft LOA cruisers and trailers, 42 ft LOA, M/V *Ciencia.*

INSTRUCTIONAL PROGRAM: Biological oceanography, advanced invertebrate zoology, marine chemistry, marine geology, marine bacteriology, general marine science, and marine botany.

SIZE OF STAFF: Six at professional level; 22 predoctoral and employed graduate students.

IMPORTANT SPECIES AVAILABLE FOR LABORATORY STUDIES: Stress is placed on understanding functional processes in environmental sciences and not with emphasis on individual organisms.

MAJOR CURRENT RESEARCH PROJECTS AND SCIENTIFIC LEADERS:

Metabolism of ecological microcosms (H. T. Odum and Robert J. Beyers)
Metabolism of marine bays of Texas (H. T. Odum)
Study of marine blue green algae (C. Van Baalen)
Distribution of marine fishes (J. C. Briggs)

UNIVERSITY OF TEXAS, INSTITUTE OF MARINE SCIENCE

Quantitative measurements of stocks of fish and shrimp in Texas waters (H. T. Odum)
Three dimensional studies of post Pleistocene sedimentation in the Texas bays with sub-bottom echo sounder (sonoprobe) (E. W. Behrens)
Origin of carbonate banks on the continental shelf off the Texas coast (E. W. Behrens)

PUBLICATIONS ISSUED: *Publications of the Institute of Marine Science* (regularly published journal)

University of Washington, College of Fisheries and Fisheries Research Institute

POSTAL ADDRESS: Fisheries Center, University of Washington, Seattle 5, Washington, USA.
EXECUTIVE OFFICER: Dr. Richard Van Cleve, Dean.
YEAR FOUNDED: 1919.
SCOPE OF ACTIVITIES: Unrestricted research on marine and fresh-water biology, especially as it applies to fish and fisheries; graduate and undergraduate instruction.
SEASON OF OPERATION: All year for research; October to June for instruction.
PHYSICAL ENVIRONMENT ACCESSIBLE: Pacific Ocean, Puget Sound and Lake Washington; sandy and silty beaches, rocky and gravelly shores, estuarine conditions, brackish, shallow bays, eutrophic and oligotrophic lakes, rivers and streams.
PROVISIONS FOR VISITING SCIENTISTS: Space for 3 visitors during academic year and 3-6 in summer; living quarters available nearby.
MAJOR RESEARCH AND TEACHING FACILITIES: Very extensive library; recirculated sea and running freshwater, large outdoor ponds and tanks, small aquarium tanks, and hatchery troughs; extensive research collections of fish and invertebrates; identified reference collections of fresh-water and marine fishes and invertebrates from the waters of Washington, Chukchi Sea, Alaska, mid-Pacific and Marshall Islands; shop facilities available at the University; small boats and outboard motors; vessels, 67 ft LOA diesel powered, *Commando,* one 16 ft, two 12 ft, two 8 ft and one 19 ft LOA.
INSTRUCTIONAL PROGRAM: Ecology, parasitology and fish diseases, ichthyology, aquatic invertebrate systematics, fishery biology, biometry, population dynamics, fisheries management, and fish nutrition.
SIZE OF STAFF: Twenty-seven at professional level; 41 technicians.
IMPORTANT SPECIES AVAILABLE FOR LABORATORY STUDIES: All species of marine invertebrates and fishes of the Washington coast of the Pacific Ocean, together with all anadromous fishes of the region.
MAJOR CURRENT RESEARCH PROJECTS AND SCIENTIFIC LEADERS:

Japanese oyster studies (Albert K. Sparks)
Fish tissue studies (Alexander Dollar)
Sealed aquatic systems (Albert K. Sparks and John Liston)
Fish populations (R. Van Cleve)
Frozen sea food studies (John Liston)
Bacterial taxonomy (John Liston)
Puget Sound rockfish (A. DeLacy)
Research on Bristol Bay and Chignik Lakes (Ole A. Mathisen)
Kvichak salmon studies V (Ole A. Mathisen)
Wood River studies I (Ole A. Mathisen)
Kodiak Island research (Donald E. Bevan)
Effects of logging IV (Robert L. Burgner)
Prince of Wales tagging III (Robert L. Burgner)
Cook-Inlet—Prince William Sound tagging III (Robert L. Burgner)
High Seas tagging VI (Allan C. Hartt)
Spring Creek I
Fern Lake trace mineral metabolism study (Lauren Donaldson)
Rainbow trout study (Lauren Donaldson)

COLLEGE OF FISHERIES AND FISHERIES RESEARCH INSTITUTE, UNIVERSITY OF WASHINGTON, SEATTLE

UNIVERSITY OF WASHINGTON, DEPARTMENT OF OCEANOGRAPHY, SEATTLE

University of Washington, Department of Oceanography

POSTAL ADDRESS: Seattle 5, Washington, USA.

EXECUTIVE OFFICER: Richard H. Fleming, Professor and Executive Officer.

YEAR FOUNDED: 1951.

SCOPE OF ACTIVITIES: Unrestricted research in general oceanography; graduate and undergraduate instruction.

SEASON OF OPERATION: All year.

PHYSICAL ENVIRONMENT ACCESSIBLE: Puget Sound, Strait of Juan de Fuca, northeast Pacific Ocean, Lakes Washington and Union; sandy and silty beaches, rocky and gravelly shores, estuarine conditions, brackish, shallow bays.

PROVISIONS FOR VISITING SCIENTISTS: Space for a few visitors; no fees charged for research space; living quarters available nearby.

MAJOR RESEARCH AND TEACHING FACILITIES: Very extensive library; running sea and fresh-water, closed sea water system; research collections of plankton, polychaetes, and barnacles; machine shop, electrical and electronic shop, skilled shop workman available; small boats and outboard motors; 114 ft LOA vessel, *Brown Bear,* and 65 ft ex-tug, *Hoh.*

INSTRUCTIONAL PROGRAM: Survey of oceanography, introduction to oceanography, methods and instruments in oceanography, field experience in oceanography, general oceanography, biological oceanography, benthos ecology, nekton ecology, advanced plankton ecology, seminar in biological oceanography, and marine microbiology.

SIZE OF STAFF: Twenty-four at professional level; 30 technicians.

MAJOR CURRENT RESEARCH PROJECTS AND SCIENTIFIC LEADERS:

- Oceanographic studies in Puget Sound and northeast Pacific (R. H. Fleming and staff)
- Plankton ecology of the Chukchi Sea (K. Banse, W. Dawson, and T. S. English)
- Productivity studies in Puget Sound (G. C. Anderson)
- Zooplankton production (G. C. Anderson, K. Banse, and Y. Komaki)
- Nekton studies (I. S. English)
- Studies of level bottom infauna in Puget Sound (K. Banse and U. Lie)
- Ecological studies of barnacles of eastern Pacific Ocean (D. P. Henry)
- Foraminifera from northeastern Pacific cores (J. S. Creager and B. J. Enbysk)
- Recent sediments in northeastern Pacific (J. S. Creager and Y. R. Nayudu)

University of Wisconsin Hydrobiological Laboratory

POSTAL ADDRESS: Hydrobiology Laboratory, University of Wisconsin, Madison 6, Wisconsin, USA.

EXECUTIVE OFFICER: Dr. Arthur D. Hasler, Professor of Zoology.

YEAR FOUNDED: 1896.

SCOPE OF ACTIVITIES: Unrestricted basic limnological research; graduate and undergraduate instruction.

SEASON OF OPERATION: All year.

PHYSICAL ENVIRONMENT ACCESSIBLE: Lakes Mendota, Trout, Superior, and Michigan; eutrophic and oligotrophic lakes, rivers and streams, bog lakes, and marshes.

PROVISIONS FOR VISITING SCIENTISTS: Space for 3 visitors; living quarters available nearby.

MAJOR RESEARCH AND TEACHING FACILITIES: Very extensive library; large outdoor ponds, small aquarium tanks and aquatic cages; machine and wood shop, electrical and electronic shop, skilled shop workmen available; small boats and outboard motors; vessels, 40 ft

UNIVERSITY OF WISCONSIN CAMPUS, WITH HYDROBIOLOGICAL LABORATORY IN THE LOWER RIGHT HAND CORNER

LOA diesel powered launch and a barge 8 ft by 24 ft with submersible observation chamber. New Hydrobiology Building, 18,000 sq ft on Lake Mendota.

INSTRUCTIONAL PROGRAM: Limnology, physical and biological oceanography, plant and animal ecology, general and comparative physiology, biochemistry, embryology, microbiology, parasitology, invertebrate zoology, aquatic invertebrate and vertebrate systematics, fishery biology, biometry and population dynamics, ecology of fishes, genetics, biophysics, cytology, algae and bacteriology.

SIZE OF STAFF: Fifteen at professorial level; 3 technicians and 15 research assistants.

IMPORTANT SPECIES AVAILABLE FOR LABORATORY STUDIES:

Pisces: *Roccus chrysops, Perca flavescens*
Crustacea: *Daphnia pulex*
Insecta: *Chironomus*
Normal plant and animal communities of temperature zone, soft and hard water lakes, ponds and streams.

MAJOR CURRENT RESEARCH PROJECTS AND SCIENTIFIC LEADERS:

Mechanisms of orientation in migratory fishes (A. Hasler)
General limnology (A. Hasler)
Nitrogen fixation (J. Neess)
Circulation dynamics (R. Bryson)
Heat budgets (R. Ragotzkie)
Chemical budget and pollution abatement (G. Rohlich and Fred Lee)
Physiology of algae (O. Holm-Hansen)
Bacteriological ecology (W. Sarles)
Limnological instrumentation (L. Whitney and D. Livermore)
Dynamics and ecology of fish populations (G. Schumann)
Sedimentation (R. Batten)
Marine geology (L. Cline)
Radio-limnology (J. Anderegg)
Marine geophysics (G. Woollard)

Virginia Institute of Marine Science

POSTAL ADDRESS: Glouchester Point, Virginia, USA.

LOCATION: Near Williamsburg.

EXECUTIVE OFFICER: Dr. William J. Hargis, Jr., Institute Director and Dean, School of Marine Science.

YEAR FOUNDED: 1940.

SCOPE OF ACTIVITIES: Restricted and unrestricted research on basic and applied marine biology; physical, chemical and geological oceanography; and fisheries. Graduate and undergraduate instruction.

SEASON OF OPERATION: All year.

PHYSICAL ENVIRONMENT ACCESSIBLE: Atlantic Ocean, Chesapeake Bay and tributaries; sandy and silty beaches, estuarine conditions and brackish, shallow bays.

PROVISIONS FOR VISITING SCIENTISTS: Research space available for 10-16 visitors.

MAJOR RESEARCH AND TEACHING FACILITIES: Moderately complete library; radiobiology laboratory; running sea and fresh-water, large outdoor ponds and tanks, small aquarium tanks; research collection of monogenetic trematodes, benthos and phyto- and zooplankton; identified reference collection of fishes, mollusks and crustaceans; machine and wood shop; small boats and outboard motors; two vessels, 55 ft, R/V *Pathfinder,* and 80 ft LOA, R/V *Langley.*

INSTRUCTIONAL PROGRAM: Courses offered in the School of Marine Science of the College of William and Mary: limnology, biological, chemical and physical oceanography, ecology, general invertebrate zoology, ichthyology, fishery biology, biometry and fisheries management, cybernetics, microbiology, marine pollution, radiobiology, taxonomy and phylogeny, marine biology, and others.

SIZE OF STAFF: Thirty-four full-time and 1 part-time at professional level; 24 full-time and 16 part-time technicians.

IMPORTANT SPECIES AVAILABLE FOR LABORATORY STUDIES:

Spermatophyta: *Zostera marina* (eel grass)
Mollusca: *Crassostrea virginica, Mya arenaria, Mercenaria mercenaria, Urosalpinx cinerea*
Crustacea: *Callinectes sapidus,* Xanthid crabs
Pisces: *Micropogon undulatus, Brevoortia tyrannus, Opsanus tau*
An annotated check-list of organisms is available from the Director).

MAJOR CURRENT RESEARCH PROJECTS AND SCIENTIFIC LEADERS:

Epidemiology of oyster diseases (J. D. Andrews)
Study of disease-producing microorganisms affecting shellfish (J. L. Wood)
Productivity and phytoplankton (B. C. Patten)
Pollution problems in estuaries (M. L. Brehmer)
Study of offshore spawning grounds of several commercially important finfishes (Edwin B. Joseph)
Host-specificity and zoogeography of monogenetic tre-

VIRGINIA INSTITUTE OF MARINE SCIENCE

matodes of fishes of the world (W. J. Hargis, Jr.)
Physiology of oysters and other mollusks (D. S. Haven)
Biology of *Callinectes sapidus* (W. A. VanEngel)
Parasites of Antarctic vertebrates (W. J. Hargis, Jr.)
Studies of respiration and respiratory enzymes metabolism in marine embryos (R. E. L. Black)
Ecology of *Foraminifera,* properties of marine sediments (M. M. Nichols)
Littoral processes of Virginia coast (P. W. Harrison)
Survey of Chesapeake Bay benthic fauna (M. L. Wass)
Physiology of predatory gastropods (L. Wood)
Uses of fluorescent antibody techniques in marine microbiology (G. Moskovits)

Walla Walla College Biological Station

POSTAL ADDRESS: Anacortes, Washington, USA.
EXECUTIVE OFFICER: Harold G. Coffin, Professor of Zoology, Walla Walla College, College Place, Washington.
YEAR FOUNDED: 1947.
SCOPE OF ACTIVITIES: Research in general marine biology and vertebrate natural history; graduate and undergraduate instruction.
SEASON OF OPERATION: June 10 to August 25.
PHYSICAL ENVIRONMENT ACCESSIBLE: Puget Sound; sandy and silty beaches, rocky and gravelly shores, and eutrophic lakes.
PROVISIONS FOR VISITING SCIENTISTS: Research and living space for 2 visitors; fees charged.
MAJOR RESEARCH AND TEACHING FACILITIES: Small library; running sea and fresh-water, large outdoor ponds and tanks, small aquarium tanks; fair research and identified reference collections of fish, invertebrates and algae; skilled shop workman available; small boats and outboard motors; vessels, 26 ft and 38 ft LOA.
INSTRUCTIONAL PROGRAM: Some of the following courses are offered each summer: limnology, ecology, parasitology, phycology, general invertebrate zoology, ichthyology, aquatic invertebrate and vertebrate systematics, fishery biology, ornithology, oceanography, biochemistry, and comparative physiology.
SIZE OF STAFF: Five at professional level; 2 technicians.
IMPORTANT SPECIES AVAILABLE FOR LABORATORY STUDIES:
Pisces: *Squalus suckleyi, Raja binoculata, Onchorhynchus* spp., *Sebastodes melanops*
Coelenterata: *Gonionemus, Metridium*
Echinodermata: *Pisaster, Strongylocentrotus* spp.
Mollusca: *Cryptochiton stelleri, Octopus*
MAJOR CURRENT RESEARCH PROJECTS AND SCIENTIFIC LEADERS:
Life cycles of Crustacea (Harold G. Coffin)
Natural history and breeding habits of local waterbirds (Ernest S. Booth)
Parasites of local sharks (Donald W. Rigby)

WALLA WALLA COLLEGE BIOLOGICAL STATION

Washington State Department of Fisheries, Biological Division

POSTAL ADDRESS:
Headquarters: Biological Division Laboratory, Fisheries Center, University of Washington, Seattle, Washington, USA.
Field Station: State Shellfish Laboratory, Quilcene, Washington. Cedric E. Lindsay, Supervisor.
EXECUTIVE OFFICER: Richard T. Pressey, Supervisor of Research.
YEAR FOUNDED: Headquarters, 1932; Shellfish Laboratory, 1939.
SCOPE OF ACTIVITIES: Restricted and unrestricted research as well as industrial advice on shellfish, including effects of pollution.
SEASON OF OPERATION: All year.
PHYSICAL ENVIRONMENT ACCESSIBLE: Hood Canal (Quilcene and Dabob Bays); rocky and gravelly shores, and brackish, shallow bays.
PROVISIONS FOR VISITING SCIENTISTS: None.
MAJOR RESEARCH FACILITIES: Small library at both laboratories; running sea water at Quilcene, running brackish water at Seattle and Quilcene, large outdoor ponds and tanks, small aquarium tanks; identified reference collection of miscellaneous shellfish; machine and wood shop; small boats and outboard motors.
SIZE OF STAFF: Thirty-seven at professional level; 6 technicians.
IMPORTANT SPECIES AVAILABLE FOR LABORATORY STUDIES:
Pelecypoda: *Ostrea lurida, Crassostrea gigas, Panope generosa, Saxidomus nuttallii, Paphia staminea*
Crustacea: *Cancer magister, C. productus, Pandalus borealis, P. platyceros*
MAJOR CURRENT RESEARCH PROJECTS AND SCIENTIFIC LEADERS:
Effects of pulp mill wastes on shellfish (Cedric E. Lindsay)

WASHINGTON STATE DEPARTMENT OF FISHERIES

Artificial culture of clams and oysters (Charles E. Woelke)
Hydrographic studies in Puget Sound (Ronald E. Westley)

Winona Lake Biological Station

POSTAL ADDRESS: Winona Lake, Indiana, USA.
EXECUTIVE OFFICER: Dr. Shelby D. Gerking, Director of Station, Department of Zoology, Indiana University, Bloomington, Indiana.
SPONSORING AGENCY: Indiana University.
YEAR FOUNDED: 1895.
SCOPE OF ACTIVITIES: Unrestricted research on general limnology and ecology of fishes.
SEASON OF OPERATION: June 1 to September 1.
PHYSICAL ENVIRONMENT ACCESSIBLE: Winona Lake (eutrophic lake), rivers and streams.
PROVISIONS FOR VISITING SCIENTISTS: Research and living space available for visitors.

WINONA LAKE BIOLOGICAL STATION

MAJOR RESEARCH FACILITIES: No library; large outdoor ponds and tanks, small aquarium tanks; herbarium and fish collection for research purposes on Bloomington campus; machine and wood shop; small boats and outboard motors.
SIZE OF STAFF: Two at professional level.
IMPORTANT SPECIES AVAILABLE FOR LABORATORY STUDIES: Plants and animals common to the north central United States.
MAJOR CURRENT RESEARCH PROJECTS AND SCIENTIFIC LEADERS:
Efficiency of food utilization by a fish population (Shelby D. Gerking)
PUBLICATIONS ISSUED: *Investigations of Indiana Lakes and Streams* (occasionally published bulletin)

Wisconsin State Conservation Department, Research and Planning Division

POSTAL ADDRESS:
Headquarters: Nevin Fish Hatchery, Route No. 2, Madison 11, Wisconsin, USA.
Field Stations:
Warm water Research Group
1. Spooner, Wisconsin
2. Woodruff, Wisconsin
3. Oshkosh, Wisconsin
4. Delafield, Wisconsin

Cold water Research Group
1. Madison, Wisconsin
2. Westfield, Wisconsin

Pathology and Nutrition Group
1. Madison, Wisconsin
2. Westfield, Wisconsin

EXECUTIVE OFFICER: Lyle M. Christenson, Chief Fishery Biologist.
YEAR FOUNDED: Madison laboratory, 1936; Spooner and Woodruff, 1939; Oshkosh, 1952; Delafield, 1953; Westfield (cold water station), 1955; Westfield (Pathology and Nutrition station), 1959.
SCOPE OF ACTIVITIES: Research on restricted and unrestricted angling regulations, evaluation of current fish management practices, trout diseases and nutrition, fish population dynamics, and life histories of fish.
PHYSICAL ENVIRONMENT ACCESSIBLE: Lawrence Creek, Murphy Flowage, Lakes Escanaba, Pallette, Nebish, Winnebago, LaBelle, Spruce, Mystery (eutrophic and dystrophic lakes) and Wolf River.
PROVISIONS FOR VISITING SCIENTISTS: Space for 2 visitors at Spooner, Woodruff and Madison; living quarters available nearby.
MAJOR RESEARCH FACILITIES: Very extensive library at University of Wisconsin; large outdoor ponds and tanks, small aquarium tanks; no research or identified reference collections, but contribute to and utilize fish collections at University of Wisconsin; machine and wood shop, skilled shop workmen available; small boats and outboard motors; one 35 ft LOA vessel.

WISCONSIN CONSERVATION DEPARTMENT, FISHERY RESEARCH STATION

SIZE OF STAFF: Twelve at professional level; 10 technicians.

IMPORTANT SPECIES AVAILABLE FOR LABORATORY STUDIES: Pisces: Brook, brown and rainbow trout, walleye, muskellunge, northern pike, lake sturgeon, fresh-water drum, bluegill, largemouth and smallmouth bass.

MAJOR CURRENT RESEARCH PROJECTS AND SCIENTIFIC LEADERS:

Evaluation of muskellunge stocking (Leon Johnson)
Evaluation of liberalized angling regulations (warm water species) (Warren Churchill and Howard Snow)
Effects of various angling regulations on a wild brook trout population (Robert Hunt)
Life history and management of lake sturgeon (Thomas Wirth and Gordon Priegel)
Evaluation of walleye stocking (Warren Churchill and Donald Mraz)
Evaluation of habitat development practices (Ray White)
Survival and growth of stocked trout (Oscar Brynildson and Ray White)

Woods Hole Oceanographic Institution

POSTAL ADDRESS: Woods Hole, Massachusetts, USA.

EXECUTIVE OFFICER: Dr. Paul M. Fye, Director.

SPONSORING AGENCY: Privately endowed corporation.

YEAR FOUNDED: 1930.

SCOPE OF ACTIVITIES: Restricted and unrestricted research in general oceanography.

SEASON OF OPERATION: All year.

PHYSICAL ENVIRONMENT ACCESSIBLE: Atlantic Ocean, Vineyard Sound, Buzzards Bay, Mediterranean Sea, Indian Ocean; estuarine conditions.

PROVISIONS FOR VISITING SCIENTISTS: Space for a variable number of visitors; no fees charged; living quarters available nearby.

MAJOR RESEARCH AND TEACHING FACILITIES: Very extensive library at the Marine Biological Laboratory, small one at the Oceanographic Institution; large outdoor tanks, small aquarium tanks; machine and wood shop, electrical and electronic shop, skilled shop workmen available; small boats, 142 ft LOA diesel powered ketch, *Atlantis,* 125 ft LOA cutter, *Crawford,* 210 ft LOA, twin screw oceanographic research vessel, *Atlantis II,* 215 ft LOA ARS type ship, *Chain,* 110 ft LOA diesel, *Bear,* 40 ft LOA flounder dragger type, *Asterias*; three planes.

INSTRUCTIONAL PROGRAM: Occasional courses given in the summer. Research fellowships.

SIZE OF STAFF: One hundred and thirty-four at professional level; 166 technicians (including shop, crew and secretaries).

IMPORTANT SPECIES AVAILABLE FOR LABORATORY STUDIES: See *A Catalogue of the Marine Fauna* in *A Biological Survey of the Waters of Woods Hole and Vicinity* by Francis B. Sumner, Raymond C. Obsorn and Leon J. Cole, *Bulletin, Bureau of Fisheries* 31:547-794 (1911).

MAJOR CURRENT BIOLOGICAL RESEARCH PROJECTS AND SCIENTIFIC LEADERS:

Beach studies (John M. Zeigler)
Chemistry and biology of sea water in relation to productivity and ocean currents (Bostwick H. Ketchum)
Geology and geophysics of marine areas (Kenneth O. Emery, John W. Graham, J. Brackett Hersey and John M. Zeigler)
Development of oceanographic instruments (William S. Richardson and Karl E. Schleicher)
Underwater photography (David M. Owen)
Biogeochemistry (Vaughn T. Bowen)
Radioelement studies (Vaughn T. Bowen)
Environment of fish (Dean F. Bumpus)
Primary productivity of the sea (John H. Ryther)
Measurement of light in the sea (George L. Clarke)
Productivity of the benthos of coastal and deep waters (Howard L. Sanders)
Vertical movement of zooplankton (Edward R. Baylor)
Environmental cetology (William E. Schevill)
Biology of the larger pelagic fishes (William C. Schroeder)
Environmental influences on reproductive cycles of benthonic marine invertebrates (Harry J. Turner, Jr.)
Feeding, metabolism and growth of zooplankton (George L. Clarke)
Composition of ocean deep scattering layers (Richard H. Backus)

Environmental physiology of marine plankton algae (John H. Ryther)
Nitrogen cycle in the sea (Bostwick H. Ketchum and Ralph F. Vaccaro)
Energy requirements of benthic marine communities (John W. Kanwisher)
Environmental factors in zooplankton distribution (Mary Sears)
Great South Bay survey (John H. Ryther)

Other Laboratories for Which Details Were Not Available:

Arctic Research Laboratory

U.S. Navy facility operated by University of Alaska, Barrow, Alaska, USA.

Director: Max C. Brewer.

URUGUAY

Servicio Oceanografico y de Pesca, Departamento Cientifico y Tecnico

OCEANOGRAPHY AND FISHERY SERVICE, DEPARTMENT OF SCIENCE AND TECHNOLOGY

POSTAL ADDRESS:
Headquarters: Julio Herrera y Obes No. 1467, Montevideo, Uruguay.
Laboratorio Central: Juan Lindolfo Cuestas No. 1409.
Laboratorio (en formacion): Punta del Este.
Estacion de Piscicultura (Fish-culture Station): Laguna del Sauce.
EXECUTIVE OFFICER: Professor Raul Vaz Ferreira, Director del Departamento.
SPONSORING AGENCY: Ministerio de Industrias y Trabajo (Ministry of Industry and Labor).
YEAR FOUNDED: 1960.
SCOPE OF ACTIVITIES: Research on general marine biology; plankton studies, ecology of crustaceans, fishery technology, and biology of sea lions.
SEASON OF OPERATION: All year.
PHYSICAL ENVIRONMENT ACCESSIBLE: Atlantic Ocean.
PROVISIONS FOR VISITING SCIENTISTS: Planned for the Punta del Este laboratory.
MAJOR RESEARCH FACILITIES: One vessel.
SIZE OF STAFF: Four at professional level; 4 technicians.
MAJOR CURRENT RESEARCH PROJECTS AND SCIENTIFIC LEADERS:
Quantitative and qualitative studies of plankton (Hugo Ferrando)
Fishery technology and fish-culture (Andres Meaves and Germinal Gil Watson)
Limnology and oceanography (Mario Siri)

Universidad de Montevideo, Instituto de Investigaciones Pesqueras

UNIVERSITY OF MONTEVIDEO, FISHERIES RESEARCH INSTITUTE

POSTAL ADDRESS: Facultad de Veterinaria, Alberto Lasplaces 1550 (ex-Larranaga) Montevideo, Uruguay.
EXECUTIVE OFFICER: Dr. Victor H. Bertullo, Professor de Tecnologia de Pesca.
YEAR FOUNDED: 1954.
SCOPE OF ACTIVITIES: Fisheries biology, general marine biology, fishery technology and fish-culture, marine bacteriology, fish systematics; instruction.
SEASON OF OPERATION: All year.
PHYSICAL ENVIRONMENT ACCESSIBLE: Atlantic Ocean.
PROVISIONS FOR VISITING SCIENTISTS: Space for visitors; no fees charged; living quarters available nearby.
MAJOR RESEARCH AND TEACHING FACILITIES: Equipment for experimental research; fishing boats of the Servicio Oceanografico y de Pesca and the hydrographical ship, *Captain Miranda,* of the Navy are used.
INSTRUCTIONAL PROGRAM: Fish technology, marine bacteriology, systematics of fishes, mollusks and crustaceans, fish-culturing, aquarium culture and general marine biology.
SIZE OF STAFF: Three at professional level; 2 technicians.
PUBLICATIONS ISSUED: *Revista del Instituto de Investigaciones Pesqueras*

VENEZUELA

Venezuela Ministerio de Agricultura y Cria, Division de Pesca y Caza, Laboratorio de Biologia Pesquera

VENEZUELA MINISTRY OF AGRICULTURE AND LIVESTOCK, DIVISION OF FISH AND GAME, FISHERY BIOLOGY LABORATORY

LABORATORIO DE BIOLOGIA PESQUERA, CUMANA

POSTAL ADDRESS: Caiguire-Cumana Estado Sucre, Venezuela.
EXECUTIVE OFFICER: Lic. Sc. German Gonzales, Jefe.
YEAR FOUNDED: 1956.
SCOPE OF ACTIVITIES: Restricted research on commercial fisheries.
SEASON OF OPERATION: All year.
PHYSICAL ENVIRONMENT ACCESSIBLE: Gulf of Cariaco; open ocean, sandy and silty beaches, rocky and gravelly shores, estuarine conditions, rivers and streams, mangroves and anaerobic trench (Cariaco).
PROVISIONS FOR VISITING SCIENTISTS: Research and living space for 2 visitors; no fees charged for research space.
MAJOR RESEARCH FACILITIES: Small library; research and identified reference collections of fishes and commercial invertebrates (shrimps and crabs); small boats and outboard motors; 65 ft LOA vessel, *Golfo de Cariaco.*
SIZE OF STAFF: Two at professional level; 3 technicians.
IMPORTANT SPECIES AVAILABLE FOR LABORATORY STUDIES:
- Angiospermae: *Talassia testudinum, Rhizophora mangle*
- Crustacea: *Callinectes bocourti, Cardisoma guanhumi*
- Pisces: *Clupanodon pseudohispanicus*

MAJOR CURRENT RESEARCH PROJECTS AND SCIENTIFIC LEADERS:
- Sardine (*Clupanodon pseudohispanicus*) biology (German Gonzales and John Simpson)
- Raboamarillo (*Cetengraulis edentulus*) biology (German Gonzalez and John Simpson)
- General hydrography of the Gulf of Cariaco (German Gonzalez and John Simpson)

Estacion de Investigaciones Marinas de Margarita

MARGARITA MARINE RESEARCH STATION

ESTACION DE INVESTIGACIONES MARINAS DE MARGARITA, NR. PORLAMAR

POSTAL ADDRESS: Punta de Piedras, Estado Nueva Esparta, Venezuela.
LOCATION: Near Porlamar.
EXECUTIVE OFFICER: Fernando Cervigon, Jefe de Laboratorios.
SPONSORING AGENCY: Fundacion La Salle de Ciencias Naturales (La Salle Foundation of Natural Sciences).
YEAR FOUNDED: 1960.
SCOPE OF ACTIVITIES: Unrestricted research on general marine biology, plankton, bottom ecology, general oceanography and fisheries biology; undergraduate instruction.
SEASON OF OPERATION: All year.
PHYSICAL ENVIRONMENT ACCESSIBLE: Caribbean Sea; sandy and silty beaches, rocky and gravelly shores, estuarine conditions, coral reefs and mangrove swamps.
PROVISIONS FOR VISITING SCIENTISTS: Research and living space for 8 visitors; fees charged for research space.
MAJOR RESEARCH AND TEACHING FACILITIES: Moderately complete library; running sea and fresh-water, small and large aquarium tanks; research collections of fishes (about 2,500 specimens), crustaceans (about 1,000 specimens), mollusks, zooplankton, etc.; identified reference collections of fishes, crustaceans and mollusks; machine and wood shop, skilled shop workman available; vessels, 72 ft LOA, *Biomar I.*
INSTRUCTIONAL PROGRAM: The program is in planning stages.
SIZE OF STAFF: Three at professional level; 8 technicians.
MAJOR CURRENT RESEARCH PROJECTS AND SCIENTIFIC LEADERS:
- Phytoplankton and primary productivity (Ramon Margalef)
- Ichthyology (Fernando Cervigon)
- Hydrography and chemistry (Antonio Ballester)
- Zooplankton (Copepoda and Siphonophora) (Fernando Cervigon)
- Fishing techniques (Alberto Mendez A. and J. M. Burgana)
- Physical oceanography (Jiro Fukuoka)
- Shrimp biology (A. Vildoso)
- Systematics of algae (Hno. Gines)

Universidad de Oriente, Instituto Oceanografico

UNIVERSITY OF ORIENTE, OCEANOGRAPHIC INSTITUTE

POSTAL ADDRESS: Av. Gran Mariscal-Qta. Mary, Cumana, Venezuela.
EXECUTIVE OFFICER: Dr. Pedro Roa Morales, Director.
SPONSORING AGENCY: Ministerio de Educacion (Ministry of Education).
YEAR FOUNDED: 1959.
SCOPE OF ACTIVITIES: Unrestricted research on general oceanography.

UNIVERSIDAD DE ORIENTE, INSTITUTO OCEANOGRAFICO, CUMANA

SEASON OF OPERATION: All year.
PHYSICAL ENVIRONMENT ACCESSIBLE: Gulf of Cariaco and the Caribbean Sea.
PROVISIONS FOR VISITING SCIENTISTS: Space for 3 visitors; no fees charged.
MAJOR RESEARCH FACILITIES: Small library; running sea and fresh-water, large outdoor ponds and tanks; machine and wood shop, skilled shop workman available; small boats and outboard motors; one 40 m LOA vessel, *Guaiqueri.*
SIZE OF STAFF: Fifteen at professional level; 10 technicians.
MAJOR CURRENT RESEARCH PROJECTS AND SCIENTIFIC LEADERS:
Ichthyology (Francisco Mago Leccia)
Sediments (Pedro Roa Morales)
Ecology (Gilberto Rodriguez)
Zooplankton (Evelyn Zoppi)
Phytoplankton (Lieselotte Hammer)
Zooplankton (J. E. Henri Legare)

WEST INDIES FEDERATION

Bellairs Research Institute

POSTAL ADDRESS: St. James, Barbados, West Indies Federation.
LOCATION: Near Bridgetown.
EXECUTIVE OFFICER: Dr. John B. Lewis, Director.
SPONSORING AGENCY: McGill University, Montreal, Canada.
YEAR FOUNDED: 1954.
SCOPE OF ACTIVITIES: Unrestricted research on general marine biology and fisheries.
SEASON OF OPERATION: All year.
PHYSICAL ENVIRONMENT ACCESSIBLE: South Atlantic Ocean; sandy beaches, rocky shores, coral reefs, streams and ponds.
PROVISIONS FOR VISITING SCIENTISTS: Research and living space for 6-8 visitors; fees charged for research space.
MAJOR RESEARCH FACILITIES: Small library; small aquarium tanks, outdoor tubs and indoor deep water tables; machine and wood shop; small boats and outboard motors, one 30 ft LOA power vessel.
SIZE OF STAFF: Four-five at professional level; 1 technician.
IMPORTANT SPECIES AVAILABLE FOR LABORATORY STUDIES: Typical West Indian tropical marine fauna and flora.
MAJOR CURRENT RESEARCH PROJECTS AND SCIENTIFIC LEADERS:
Biology of flying fish (J. B. Lewis)
Ecology of coral reefs and coral communities (J. B. Lewis)

BELLAIRS RESEARCH INSTITUTE, BARBADOS

University of the West Indies Marine Laboratory at Port Royal

POSTAL ADDRESS: c/o Zoology Department, University of the West Indies, Mona, St. Andrew, Jamaica, West Indies Federation.
LOCATION: Port Royal.
EXECUTIVE OFFICER: Dr. David M. Steven, Director.
YEAR FOUNDED: 1956.
SCOPE OF ACTIVITIES: Unrestricted research and instruction in general marine biology.
SEASON OF OPERATION: All year.
PHYSICAL ENVIRONMENT ACCESSIBLE: Caribbean Sea, Kingston Harbor; estuarine conditions, coral reefs, mangrove swamps, lagoons and salinas.
PROVISIONS FOR VISITING SCIENTISTS: Space for 2 visitors; fees charged; living quarters nearby.
MAJOR RESEARCH AND TEACHING FACILITIES: Moderately complete library available at the University Col-

COLLECTIONS: Research collections of fresh-water fishes from West Indies, Mexico, Central and South America as well as other parts of the world; identified reference collection of local fishes.
SIZE OF STAFF: Two full time at professional level and 1 part-time.
MAJOR CURRENT RESEARCH PROJECTS AND SCIENTIFIC LEADERS:
Revision of Pomacentridae (Loren P. Woods)
Revision of berycoids (Loren P. Woods)
Miscellaneous studies on West Indian fauna (Loren P. Woods)
Revision of Gonostomatidae (Marion Grey)
Study of the genus *Anoplogaster* (Marion Grey)

Division of Lower Invertebrates

EXECUTIVE OFFICER: Dr. G. Alan Solem, Curator.
SCOPE OF ACTIVITIES: Unrestricted research on invertebrates, especially mollusks.
PROVISIONS FOR VISITING SCIENTISTS: Space for 2 visitors; no fees charged; living quarters available nearby.

CHICAGO NATURAL HISTORY MUSEUM, USA

COLLECTIONS: Research collections of about 1,100,000 mollusks, representing 55 per cent of non-marine species and 20 per cent of marine species; about 10,000 other non-terrestrial arthropods; identified reference collection of local mollusks.
SIZE OF STAFF: One at professional level; 1 technician.
MAJOR CURRENT RESEARCH PROJECTS AND SCIENTIFIC LEADERS:
Non-marine mollusks of Panama (A. Solem)
Endodontid land snails of the Pacific Ocean (A. Solem)

Institut Royal des Sciences Naturelles de Belgique

THE BELGIUM ROYAL INSTITUTE FOR NATURAL SCIENCES

POSTAL ADDRESS: rue Vautier, 31, Bruxelles 4, Belgique (Brussels 4, Belgium).
EXECUTIVE OFFICER: Dr. A. Capart, Directeur.
SPONSORING AGENCY: Ministere de Education Nationale.
YEAR FOUNDED: 1846.
SCOPE OF ACTIVITIES: Public education and research in the natural sciences; studies of marine ecology as well as fresh-water and brackish-water ecology in different regions, Mediterranean, Antarctic and south Atlantic.
PROVISIONS FOR VISITING SCIENTISTS: Space for 10 visitors; no fees charged; living quarters available nearby.
MAJOR RESEARCH FACILITIES: Very extensive library; running fresh-water, small aquarium tanks; important research and identified reference collections of most fresh-water and marine organisms of Belgium and the Congo; machine and wood shop.
SIZE OF STAFF: Thirty-four at professional level; 99 technicians.
PUBLICATIONS ISSUED: *Bulletin* and *Memoires* (regularly published journals)

SECTIONS DEVOTED TO AQUATIC BIOLOGY:

Service D'Hydrobiologie

EXECUTIVE OFFICER: A. Capart, Director.

Laboratoire D'Oceanographie

EXECUTIVE OFFICER: M. Steyaert, Assistant.
SCOPE OF ACTIVITIES: Physics, chemistry and plankton.

Laboratoire Eaux Douces et Saumatres (Fresh- and Brackish-Water Laboratory)

EXECUTIVE OFFICER: L. van Meel Sc.D., Assistant.
SCOPE OF ACTIVITIES: Physics, chemistry and plankton.

Service des Vertebres, Laboratoire des Poissons (Vertebrate Section, Ichthyology Laboratory)

INSTITUT ROYAL DES SCIENCES NATURALLES DE BELGIQUE

EXECUTIVE OFFICER: Dr. J. P. Gosse, Assistant.
SCOPE OF ACTIVITIES: Systematics.

Section des Invertebres

EXECUTIVE OFFICER: Dr. E. Leloup, Director.

Section des Mollusques (Mollusk Section)

EXECUTIVE OFFICER: Prof. Dr. W. Adam, Laboratory Director.

Institut fuer Spezielle Zoologie und Zoologisches Museum, der Humboldt-Universitaet zu Berlin

INSTITUTE OF SYSTEMATIC ZOOLOGY AND ZOOLOGICAL MUSEUM, HUMBOLDT UNIVERSITY OF BERLIN

POSTAL ADDRESS: Invalidenstrasse 43, Berlin N. 4, Deutsche Demokratische Republik (East Germany).
EXECUTIVE OFFICER: Professor Dr. Fritz Peus, Direktor.
YEAR FOUNDED: 1810.
SCOPE OF ACTIVITIES: Systematic zoology.
PROVISIONS FOR VISITING SCIENTISTS: Space for several visitors.
MAJOR RESEARCH FACILITIES: Very extensive library; small aquarium tanks; extensive research and identified reference collections of fauna and flora.
SIZE OF STAFF: Twenty-one at professional level; about 50 technicians.
PUBLICATIONS ISSUED:
Mitteilungen aus dem Zoologischen Museum in Berlin (regularly published journal)
Deutsche Entomologische Zeitschrift, Neue Folge (regularly published journal)
DEPARTMENTS OF MUSEUM DESCRIBED: (Activities include aquatic biology)
1. Abteilung Crustacea (Department of Crustacea)
2. Ichthyologische Abteilung (Department of Ichthyology)
3. Malakologische Abteilung (Department of Malacology)

MUSEUM FUER NATURKUNDE, DER HUMBOLT-UNIVERSITAET ZU BERLIN

Abteilung Crustacea

EXECUTIVE OFFICER: Dr. Hans-Eckhard Gruner, Kustos.
SCOPE OF ACTIVITIES: Unrestricted research on taxonomy and ecology of crustaceans.
PROVISIONS FOR VISITING SCIENTISTS: Space for 4 visitors; no fees charged; living quarters available nearby.
MAJOR RESEARCH FACILITIES: Small aquarium tanks; research collections of Crustacea from all over the world; identified reference collection of most of the Crustacea of central Europe.
SIZE OF STAFF: One at professional level; 1 part-time technician.
MAJOR RESEARCH PROJECTS AND SCIENTIFIC LEADERS:
Card index of decapod Crustacea (H. E. Gruner)
Hyperiid Amphipoda (H. E. Gruner)

Ichthyologische Abteilung

EXECUTIVE OFFICER: Professor Dr. Kurt Deckert, Leiter.
SCOPE OF ACTIVITIES: Extensive studies in taxonomy and comparative anatomy of fishes.
PROVISIONS FOR VISITING SCIENTISTS: Space for several visitors.
MAJOR RESEARCH FACILITIES: Extensive research collections of fishes; optical and microscopical technique equipment.

Malakologische Abteilung

EXECUTIVE OFFICER: Dr. Rudolf Kilias, Kustos und Abteilungsleiter.
SCOPE OF ACTIVITIES: Unrestricted research on the systematics and biology of marine mollusks.
PROVISIONS FOR VISITING SCIENTISTS: Space for visitors; no fees charged; living quarters available nearby.
MAJOR RESEARCH FACILITIES: Research and identified reference collections of marine, fresh-water and terrestrial mollusks from all over the world.
MAJOR CURRENT RESEARCH PROJECTS AND SCIENTIFIC LEADERS:
Comparative anatomy of Lamellibranchia (Rudolf Kilias)
Physiology of marine Prosobranchia (Rudolf Kilias)
Monographic studies on the families of Tonnacea (Rudolf Kilias)

Koebenhavns Universitets Zoologiske Museum

COPENHAGEN UNIVERSITY ZOOLOGICAL MUSEUM

POSTAL ADDRESS: Krystalgade 27, Koebenhavn K, Denmark (Denmark).
EXECUTIVE OFFICER: Dr. R. Spaerck, President of the

Board and Professor of Zoology, Koebenhavns Universitet. Dr. Volsaee, Director.
YEAR FOUNDED: 1770.
SCOPE OF ACTIVITIES: Systematics, distribution and ecology of marine animals, mainly specimens collected by the expeditions equipped by the Museum (Galathea I, 1845-47; Ingolf, 1895-96; Th. Mortensen's expeditions, 1914-30; Atlantide, 1945-46; Galathea II, 1950-52); lectures on marine research and oceanology.
PROVISIONS FOR VISITING SCIENTISTS: Space for visitors.
COLLECTIONS: Extensive collections and type specimens of marine fauna, including whales and Arctic animals, Danish and South American fossils.
SIZE OF STAFF: Five directors of departments, 20 curators and assistant curators, 1 librarian and 24 technicians.

Madras Government Museum

POSTAL ADDRESS: Egmore, Madras, India.
EXECUTIVE OFFICER: Dr. S. T. Satyamurti, Superintendent.

MADRAS STATE MUSEUM

YEAR FOUNDED: 1851.
SCOPE OF ACTIVITIES OF THE NATURAL HISTORY SECTION: Restricted research on systematics of marine and fresh-water fauna and ferns; instruction.
PHYSICAL ENVIRONMENT ACCESSIBLE: Madras Harbor, Ennore, Gulf of Manaar, Krusadai Island, Pulicat Lake; open ocean, sandy and silty beaches, rocky and gravelly shores, estuarine conditions, brackish, shallow bays, coral reef, eutrophic and oligotrophic lakes, rivers and streams.
PROVISIONS FOR VISITING SCIENTISTS: None.
MAJOR RESEARCH AND TEACHING FACILITIES: Very extensive library; large outdoor ponds and tanks; research and identified reference collections of local flora and fauna.
INSTRUCTIONAL PROGRAM: Museum technique course; lectures to college biology students based on museum materials.
SIZE OF STAFF: Ten at professional level; 13 technicians.
PUBLICATIONS ISSUED: *Madras Museum Bulletin* (occasionally published journal)

Museo Argentino de Ciencias Naturales "Bernardino Rivadavia"

ARGENTINA MUSEUM OF NATURAL SCIENCES

POSTAL ADDRESS: Avenida Angel Gallardo 470, Casilla de Correo 10, Sucursal 5, Buenos Aires, Argentina.
EXECUTIVE OFFICER: Dr. Max Biraben, Director.
SPONSORING AGENCY: Secretaria de Educacion (Secretary of Education).
YEAR FOUNDED: 1823.
MAJOR RESEARCH FACILITIES: Very extensive library; research and identified reference collections of fauna and flora.
RESEARCH STATIONS: See Estacion Hidrobiologica de Puerto Quequen, page 5.

Museo Civico di Storia Naturale "Giacomo Doria"

"G. DORIA" MUNICIPAL MUSEUM OF NATURAL HISTORY

POSTAL ADDRESS: Via Brigata Liguria, 9, Genova, Italia (Genoa, Italy).
EXECUTIVE OFFICER: Professore Enrico Tortonese, Direttore.
SPONSORING AGENCY: Municipality of Genoa.
YEAR FOUNDED: 1867.
SCOPE OF ACTIVITIES IN AQUATIC BIOLOGY: Unrestricted research in ichthyology, marine invertebrates and marine benthos; instruction.
PHYSICAL ENVIRONMENT ACCESSIBLE: Gulf of Genoa; rocky and gravelly shores.

MUSEO CIVICO DI STORIA NATURALE "GIACOMO DORIA," GENOA

PROVISIONS FOR VISITING SCIENTISTS: Space for 4 visitors; living quarters available nearby.
MAJOR RESEARCH FACILITIES: Very extensive library; small aquarium tanks; research and identified reference collections of fishes and invertebrates from all over the world; herbarium of algae.
INSTRUCTIONAL PROGRAM: General marine biology.
SIZE OF STAFF: Three at professional level; 3 technicians.
MAJOR CURRENT RESEARCH PROJECTS AND SCIENTIFIC LEADERS:
Fishes of the Gulf of Genoa (E. Tortonese)
Benthos of the Gulf of Genoa (L. Rossi)
PUBLICATIONS ISSUED: *Annals* (regularly published journal)

Museo de Historia Natural "Javier Prado"

"JAVIER PRADO" NATURAL HISTORY MUSEUM

POSTAL ADDRESS: Avenida Arenales 1256, Casilla 1109, Lima, Peru.
EXECUTIVE OFFICER: Dr. Ramon Ferreya H., Director.
SPONSORING AGENCY: Universidad Nacional Mayor de San Marcos.
YEAR FOUNDED: 1918.
PROVISIONS FOR VISITING SCIENTISTS: None.
MAJOR RESEARCH FACILITIES: Small library.
SIZE OF STAFF: Ten at professional level; 6 technicians.
PUBLICATIONS ISSUED:
Publicaciones del Museo de Historia Natural "Javier Prado" (occasionally published journal)
Memorias del Museo de Historia Natural "Javier Prado" (occasionally published journal)
SECTIONS OF MUSEUM DESCRIBED: (Activities include aquatic biology)
1. Seccion de Ictiologia (Ichthyological Section)
2. Seccion de Criptogamas (Cryptogamy Section)

Seccion de Ictiologia

EXECUTIVE OFFICER: Dr. Hans-Wilhelm Koepcke, Jefe.
SCOPE OF ACTIVITIES: Unrestricted research on systematics, ecology and zoogeography of fishes.
COLLECTIONS: Research collections of fishes and birds; identified reference collections of local fishes, birds, mollusks and crustaceans.
SIZE OF STAFF: One at professional level.
MAJOR CURRENT RESEARCH PROJECTS AND SCIENTIFIC LEADERS:
Studies on fishes of Peru (Hans-Wilhelm Koepcke)
Studies on the birds of Peru (in part) (Hans-Wilhelm Koepcke)

Seccion de Criptogamas

EXECUTIVE OFFICER: Dr. Oscar Tovar, Jefe.
COLLECTIONS: Partially identified collection of algae (part of Herbaria San Marcos).

MUSEO DE HISTORIA NATURAL "JAVIER PRADO," PERU

Museo Nacional de Historia Natural, Seccion Hidrobiologia

NATIONAL MUSEUM OF NATURAL HISTORY, HYDROBIOLOGICAL SECTION

POSTAL ADDRESS: Casilla 787, Santiago, Chile.
EXECUTIVE OFFICERS: Humberto Fuenzalida V., Director del Museo. Nibaldo Bahamonde N., Jefe del Seccion Hidrobiologia.
YEAR FOUNDED: Museum—1830. Seccion—1949.
SCOPE OF ACTIVITIES: Unrestricted research on biology and the taxonomy of aquatic fauna.
PROVISIONS FOR VISITING SCIENTISTS: Space for 3 visitors; no fees charged.
MAJOR RESEARCH FACILITIES: Moderately complete library; small aquarium tanks; good research collections of mollusks.
SIZE OF STAFF: Two at professional level; 1 technician.
IMPORTANT SPECIES AVAILABLE FOR LABORATORY STUDIES:
Crustacea: *Aegla laevis laevis, Parastacus pugnax*
Pisces: *Cheirodon pisciculus, Pygidium maculatus*
MAJOR CURRENT RESEARCH PROJECTS AND SCIENTIFIC LEADERS:
Systematics of Chilean decapods (Nibaldo Bahamonde)
Life history of *Cervimunida johni* (Nibaldo Bahamonde)
Systematics of Chilean fishes (Fernando De Buen)
PUBLICATIONS ISSUED: *Boletin del Museo Nacional* (regularly published journal)

Museum National d'Histoire Naturelle

NATIONAL MUSEUM OF NATURAL HISTORY

POSTAL ADDRESS: 57, rue Cuvier, Paris Ve, France.
EXECUTIVE OFFICER: Professeur Roger Heim, Directeur.
SPONSORING AGENCY: Ministere de l'Education nationale.
YEAR FOUNDED: 1635.

SCOPE OF ACTIVITIES: Exhibition, research and education.

MAJOR RESEARCH AND TEACHING FACILITIES: Very extensive library (other facilities indicated under appropriate divisions).

LABORATORIES OF MUSEUM DESCRIBED: (Activities include aquatic biology)

1. Laboratoire de Cryptogamy
2. Laboratoire de Biologie marine et de Malacologie
3. Laboratoire Maritime
4. Laboratoire des Peches Outre-Mer
5. Laboratoire de Physiologie
6. Laboratoire de Zoologie (Reptiles et Poissons) (Zoological Laboratory—Reptiles and Fish)
7. Laboratoire de Zoologie (Vers et Crustaces) (Zoological Laboratory—Annelida and Crustacea)

Laboratoire de Cryptogamy

POSTAL ADDRESS: 12, rue de Buffon, Paris Ve, France.

EXECUTIVE OFFICER: Professeur Roger Heim, Directeur.

YEAR FOUNDED: 1904.

SCOPE OF AQUATIC ACTIVITIES: Unrestricted research in algology; instruction.

PROVISIONS FOR VISITING SCIENTISTS: Research space for 10 visitors.

MAJOR RESEARCH FACILITIES: Large herbarium of fresh-water algae including living unialgal cultures.

INSTRUCTIONAL PROGRAM: Algology.

SIZE OF STAFF: Eight at professional level; 1 technician.

MAJOR CURRENT RESEARCH PROJECTS:

Marine algae, particularly of France, Portugal and Africa

Fresh-water algae, particularly of France, South America and Africa

PUBLICATIONS ISSUED: *Revue Algologique*

Laboratorie de Biologie Marine et de Malacologie

POSTAL ADDRESS: 55 rue de Buffon, Paris Ve, France.

EXECUTIVE OFFICER: Professeur E. Fischer-Piette.

YEAR FOUNDED: 1793.

SCOPE OF ACTIVITIES: Anatomy, histology, systematics, biology and ecology of mollusks, coelenterates, echinoderms, sponges and tunicates.

PROVISIONS FOR VISITING SCIENTISTS: Space for visitors.

INSTRUCTIONAL PROGRAM: Ecology of mollusks.

SIZE OF STAFF: Four at professional level; 3 technicians.

MAJOR CURRENT RESEARCH PROJECTS AND SCIENTIFIC LEADERS:

Biology and systematics of oysters and pearl oysters (G. Ranson)

Anatomy, histology and systematics of alcyonarians (M. Tixier-Durivault)

Systematics of echinoderms (G. Cherbonnier)

Ecology of littoral mollusks of France (J. Gaillard)

Interstitial population studies of sand beaches (B. Salvat)

Ecology of mollusks of European coasts (E. Fischer)

Laboratoire Maritime

POSTAL ADDRESS: 17 avenue George-V, Dinard (Cotes du Nord), France.

EXECUTIVE OFFICER: Robert Lami, Directeur adjoint.

YEAR FOUNDED: 1882.

SCOPE OF ACTIVITIES: Unrestricted research in littoral ecology and algology.

SEASON OF OPERATION: All year.

PHYSICAL ENVIRONMENT ACCESSIBLE: Gulf of St. Malo; sandy, muddy and rocky shores, variable conditions of salinity, tidal range of 13 m.

PROVISIONS FOR VISITING SCIENTISTS: Research and living space for 10-12 visitors; no fees charged for research space.

MAJOR RESEARCH AND TEACHING FACILITIES: Very extensive library; running sea and fresh-water, small aquarium tanks; identified reference collections of local marine fauna, algae, lichens, etc.; machine, wood and electrical shops; vessels, 6 m LOA, *Sepiole*, and 12 m LOA, *Lamarck.*

INSTRUCTIONAL PROGRAM: Algology; field studies in marine biology.

SIZE OF STAFF: Four at professional level.

MAJOR CURRENT RESEARCH PROJECTS AND SCIENTIFIC LEADERS:

Botanical ecology of the Rance (R. Corillion)

Chemistry of the gases of stagnant shore water (Pa. Montagne)

Chemistry of algae (Pa. Quillet)

PUBLICATIONS: *Bulletin du Laboratoire Maritime de Dinard* (occasionally published journal)

Laboratoire des Peches Outre-Mer

POSTAL ADDRESS: 57, rue Cuvier, Paris Ve, France.

EXECUTIVE OFFICER: Professeur Th. Monod, Directeur.

YEAR FOUNDED: 1906.

SCOPE OF ACTIVITIES: Unrestricted research on general marine biology; officially restricted research on tropical fisheries, whaling, tropical biological oceanography, tropical hydrobiology and fresh-water fishing.

PROVISIONS FOR VISITING SCIENTISTS: Space for 2 visitors.

MAJOR RESEARCH FACILITIES: Small library.

SIZE OF STAFF: Four at professional level; 3 technicians.

MAJOR CURRENT RESEARCH PROJECTS AND SCIENTIFIC LEADERS:

Oceanography (Th. Monod)

Tropical fishes, oceanography and whale biology (P. Budker and Ch. Roux)

Ichthyology of the Atlantic (Ch. Roux)

Ecology of coastal invertebrates (Y. Plessis)

Laboratoire de Physiologie

POSTAL ADDRESS: 7, rue Cuvier, Paris Ve, France.
EXECUTIVE OFFICER: Professeur M. Fontaine, Directeur.
YEAR FOUNDED: Early 1800's.
SCOPE OF ACTIVITIES: Unrestricted research on aquatic fauna with special emphasis on migratory fish.
PROVISIONS FOR VISITING SCIENTISTS: Space for 2 visitors.
MAJOR RESEARCH AND TEACHING FACILITES: Radiobiological laboratory; sea and fresh-water aquaria.
INSTRUCTIONAL PROGRAM: Biological oceanography.
SIZE OF STAFF: Eight at professional level; 3 technicians.
MAJOR CURRENT RESEARCH PROJECTS:
Migrations of salmon and eels

Laboratoire de Zoologie (Reptile et Poissons)

(ZOOLOGICAL LABORATORY—REPTILES AND FISH)

POSTAL ADDRESS: 25 rue Cuvier, Paris Ve, France.
EXECUTIVE OFFICER: Dr. Jean Guibe, Professor and Administrator.
YEAR FOUNDED: 1794.
SCOPE OF ACTIVITIES: Unrestricted research on the anatomy, systematics and biology of fishes; undergraduate instruction.
PROVISIONS FOR VISITING SCIENTISTS: Research space for visitors.
MAJOR RESEARCH AND TEACHING FACILITIES: Small aquarium tanks; important collection of fish, batrachians and reptiles from all over the world.
INSTRUCTIONAL PROGRAM: General ichthyology and herpetology offered through the University of Paris.
SIZE OF STAFF: Five at professional level; 2 technicians.

Laboratoire de Zoologie (Vers et Crustaces)

(ZOOLOGICAL LABORATORY—ANNELIDA AND CRUSTACEA)

POSTAL ADDRESS: 61, rue de Buffon, Paris Ve, France.
EXECUTIVE OFFICER: Professor Max Vachon.
YEAR FOUNDED: 1917.
SCOPE OF ACTIVITIES: Unrestricted research on the biology and systematics of arthropods with the exception of insects.
PROVISIONS FOR VISITING SCIENTISTS: Space for 2 visitors.
MAJOR RESEARCH AND TEACHING FACILITIES: Small aquarium tanks; national collection of Bryozoa, Crustacea and Brachiopoda.
INSTRUCTIONAL PROGRAM: Biology and systematics.
SIZE OF STAFF: Seven at professional level; 3 technicians.
MAJOR CURRENT RESEARCH PROJECTS AND SCIENTIFIC LEADERS:
Marine biology, Amphipoda and Pycnogonida (Louis Fage)
Marine biology, decapod Crustacea (J. Forest)
Decapoda (Brachyura) (Mme. Guinot-Dumortier)
PUBLICATIONS ISSUED: *Crustaceana.*

National Museum of Canada, Natural History Branch, Zoology Section

POSTAL ADDRESS: Ottawa, Ontario, Canada.
EXECUTIVE OFFICERS: Dr. L. S. Russell, Director of Branch. Dr. A. W. F. Banfield, Chief Zoologist.
SPONSORING AGENCY: Canadian Department of Northern Affairs and National Resources.
YEAR FOUNDED: 1910.
SCOPE OF ZOOLOGY SECTION ACTIVITIES: Unrestricted research on systematic zoology.
PROVISIONS FOR VISITING SCIENTISTS: Space for 1-2 visitors; no fees charged; living quarters available nearby.
MAJOR RESEARCH FACILITIES: Moderately complete library; research collections of marine and fresh-water fishes of Canada, mollusks of Canada, and, to a smaller extent, of the world; identified reference collection of Canadian mollusks.
SIZE OF STAFF: Three at professional level in aquatic zoology.
MAJOR CURRENT RESEARCH PROJECTS AND SCIENTIFIC LEADERS:
Marine fishes of Arctic Canada (D. E. McAllister and J. G. Hunter)
Fresh-water crustaceans of Canada (Edward L. Bousfield)
Littoral marine invertebrates of the Atlantic Coast of Canada (Edward L. Bousfield)
Littoral marine amphipods of the Pacific Coast of Canada and adjacent waters (Edward L. Bousfield and Eric L. Mills)
Fresh-water mollusks of the St. Lawrence and Hudson Bay drainage areas (Arthur H. Clarke, Jr.)
Abyssal marine mollusks of the world (Arthur H. Clarke, Jr.)
Fresh-water mollusks of southern Ontario (Rev. H. B. Herrington)
Land and fresh-water mollusks of western British Columbia (Robert J. Drake)
PUBLICATIONS ISSUED: *National Museum Bulletins* (occasionally published)

Philippines National Museum

POSTAL ADDRESS: Manila, Filipinas (Philippines).
EXECUTIVE OFFICERS: Galo B. Ocampo, Director. Godofredo L. Alcasid, Chief, Division of Zoology.
SPONSORING AGENCY: Department of Education.
YEAR FOUNDED: 1901.
SCOPE OF ACTIVITIES OF THE DIVISION OF ZOOLOGY:

Research on taxonomy, ecology, systematic ichthyology, herpetology, carcinology and conchology.

PROVISIONS FOR VISITING SCIENTISTS: Space for visitors.

MAJOR RESEARCH FACILITIES: A new museum building is under construction. There are zoological collections of mammals, birds, fishes, reptiles, amphibians, insects, shells and corals.

SIZE OF ZOOLOGICAL STAFF: Five at professional level.

MAJOR CURRENT ZOOLOGICAL RESEARCH PROJECTS AND SCIENTIFIC LEADERS:

Mammals and corals (Godofredo L. Alcasid)
Carcinology (Agustin F. Umali)
Conchology (Fernando G. Dayrit)
Ichthyology (Pedro Gonzales)
Entomology (Romualdo Alagar)

Royal Ontario Museum, University of Toronto

POSTAL ADDRESS: 100 Queen's Park, Toronto 5, Canada.

YEAR FOUNDED: 1914.

MAJOR RESEARCH FACILITIES: Moderately complete library (other facilities indicated under appropriate divisions).

SIZE OF STAFF: Fifty at professional level; 50 technicians.

DIVISIONS OF MUSEUM DESCRIBED: (Activities include aquatic biology)

1. Department of Ichthyology and Herpetology
2. Department of Entomology and Invertebrate Zoology

Department of Ichthyology and Herpetology

EXECUTIVE OFFICER: Dr. W. B. Scott, Curator.

SCOPE OF ACTIVITIES: Systematic and distributional studies of fishes, principally New World.

PROVISIONS FOR VISITING SCIENTISTS: Space for 2 visitors; no fees charged; living quarters available nearby.

COLLECTION: Research collection of fishes, principally Canadian—ordinal representation for teaching ichthyology; most comprehensive identified reference collection of Canadian fresh-water fishes in existence.

SIZE OF STAFF: Two at professional level; 1 technician.

MAJOR CURRENT RESEARCH PROJECTS AND SCIENTIFIC LEADERS:

Systematic study of haplomous fishes (E. J. Crossman)
Systematic study of coregonid fishes (W. B. Scott)
Zoogeographic studies of Canadian fishes (E. J. Crossman and W. B. Scott)

Department of Entomology and Invertebrate Zoology

EXECUTIVE OFFICER: Dr. G. B. Wiggins, Associate Curator.

SCOPE OF ACTIVITIES: Systematics and ecology of invertebrates, with particular reference to insects inhabiting fresh-waters.

THE ROYAL ONTARIO MUSEUM, CANADA

PROVISIONS FOR VISITING SCIENTISTS: Space for 2-3 visitors; no fees charged; living quarters available nearby.

MAJOR RESEARCH FACILITIES: Facilities for rearing aquatic insects in running tap water; specialized research and identified reference collections of Odonata and Trichoptera; general collections of variable size in other groups.

SIZE OF STAFF: One at professional level.

MAJOR CURRENT RESEARCH PROJECTS AND SCIENTIFIC LEADERS:

Systematics and ecology of Trichoptera (G. B. Wiggins)
Systematics and ecology of Odonata (E. M. Walker, Honourary Curator)

Smithsonian Institution, United States National Museum

POSTAL ADDRESS: Washington 25, D. C., USA.

EXECUTIVE OFFICERS: Mr. Frank M. Taylor, Director. Dr. I. E. Wallen, Assistant Director of the Museum of Oceanography.

YEAR FOUNDED: 1846.

SCOPE OF ACTIVITIES: Public education and research in anthropology, botany, geology, and zoology.

MAJOR RESEARCH AND TEACHING FACILITIES: Very extensive library (other facilities indicated under appropriate divisions).

PUBLICATIONS ISSUED: *Bulletin and Proceedings of the U.S. National Museum* (regularly published)

DIVISIONS OF MUSEUM DESCRIBED: (Activities include aquatic biology)

1. Division of Fishes
2. Division of Marine Invertebrates
3. Division of Mollusks

Division of Fishes

EXECUTIVE OFFICER: Dr. Leonard P. Schultz, Curator of Fishes.

PROVISIONS FOR VISITING SCIENTISTS: Research space for two visitors.

COLLECTIONS: Research collections of 1,800,000 fish specimens, 5,000 holotypes, 5,000 paratypes, 15,000 fish species represented; identified world reference collections including local fish fauna.

SIZE OF STAFF: Five at professional level; 2 technicians.

MAJOR CURRENT RESEARCH PROJECTS AND SCIENTIFIC LEADERS:

Revision of Conger eels (R. H. Kanazawa)
Revision of Sternoptychidae (L. P. Schultz)
Revision of Echeneidae (E. A. Lachner)
Revision of Apogonidae (E. A. Lachner)
Revision of Mullidae (E. A. Lachner)
Revision of Noturus (W. R. Taylor)
Fishes of the Marshall and Marianas Islands (L. P. Schultz and E. A. Lachner)
Shark attacks on man and analysis of factors involved (L. P. Schultz)
Osteological relationships of fishes (W. R. Taylor)

Division of Marine Invertebrates

EXECUTIVE OFFICER: Dr. Fenner A. Chace, Jr., Curator.

PROVISIONS FOR VISITING SCIENTISTS: Research space for two visitors.

COLLECTIONS: Research and identified reference collections of more than half a million specimens of invertebrates.

SIZE OF STAFF: Four at professional level; 3 technicians.

MAJOR CURRENT RESEARCH PROJECTS AND SCIENTIFIC LEADERS:

Systematics of hyperiid amphipods (Thomas E. Bowman)
Systematics of cymothoid isopods (Thomas E. Bowman)
Systematics of calanoid copepods (Thomas E. Bowman)
Systematics of decapod crustaceans (Fenner A. Chace, Jr.)
Systematics of sea anemones (Charles E. Cutress)
Systematics of micrabaciidae (Donald F. Squires)
Systematics of scleractenia (Donald F. Squires)

Division of Mollusks

EXECUTIVE OFFICER: Dr. Harald A. Rehder, Curator.

PROVISIONS FOR VISITING SCIENTISTS: Research space for two visitors; no fees charged.

COLLECTION: 9,740,000 specimens of mollusks for research, including much type material (largest study collection in the world); identified reference collection of local mollusks available.

SIZE OF STAFF: Three at professional level; 2 technicians.

MAJOR CURRENT RESEARCH PROJECTS AND SCIENTIFIC LEADERS:

Systematics of marine mollusks of Indo-Pacific area (Harald A. Rehder)
Marine mollusks of Caribbean region (Harald A. Rehder)
Mollusks of family Hydrobiidae of America (Joseph P. E. Morrison)
Revision of Ellobiidae of America (Joseph P. E. Morrison)
American brackish water clams of the family Mactridae (Joseph P. E. Morrison)

South African Museum, Marine Biology Department

POSTAL ADDRESS: P. O. Box 61, Cape Town, Republic of South Africa.

EXECUTIVE OFFICER: Dr. F. H. Talbot, Assistant Director.

SCOPE OF ACTIVITIES: Unrestricted research on fish taxonomy and ecology, mollusk systematics, copepod systematics and ecology.

PROVISIONS FOR VISITING SCIENTISTS: Space for 2 visitors; no fees charged; living quarters available nearby.

MAJOR RESEARCH FACILITIES: Very extensive library; large research and identified reference collection of South African land and marine animals.

SIZE OF STAFF: Four at professional level; 1 technician.

MAJOR CURRENT RESEARCH PROJECTS AND SCIENTIFIC LEADERS:

South African molluscan systematics (K. H. Barnard)
Tuna survey (F. H. Talbot)
Systematics of deep sea fishes (F. H. Talbot)
Copepod systematics and ecology (J. R. Grindley)

PUBLICATIONS ISSUED: *Annals of the South African Museum* (regularly published journal)

South Australian Museum

POSTAL ADDRESS: North Terrace, Adelaide, South Australia.

EXECUTIVE OFFICER: W. Peter Crowcroft, Director.

SPONSORING AGENCY: South Australian government.

YEAR FOUNDED: 1856.

SCOPE OF ACTIVITIES: Unrestricted research on taxonomy and general marine biology.

PROVISIONS FOR VISITING SCIENTISTS: Space for 1-2 visitors; no fees charged; living quarters available nearby.

MAJOR RESEARCH FACILITIES: Very extensive library; research and identified reference collections of fauna and flora.

SIZE OF STAFF: Nine at professional level, including 3 who are working on marine biology; 7 technicians.

PUBLICATIONS ISSUED: *Records of the South Australian Museum* (regularly published journal)

Stanford University, Division of Systematic Biology

POSTAL ADDRESS: Stanford University, Stanford, California, USA.

LOCATION: Near San Francisco.

EXECUTIVE OFFICER: Dr. Richard W. Holm, Director.

YEAR FOUNDED: 1891.

SCOPE OF ACTIVITIES: Unrestricted research; graduate and undergraduate instruction.

SEASON OF OPERATION: All year.

PHYSICAL ENVIRONMENT ACCESSIBLE: Pacific Ocean, San Francisco Bay, Searsville Lake, Felt Lake, Lagunita Lake (temporary), San Francisquito Creek (temporary); sandy and silty beaches, rock and gravelly shores brackish, shallow bays, oligotrophic lakes, temporary lakes and stream waters in winter and spring only.

PROVISIONS FOR VISITING SCIENTISTS: Research space for 1 or 2 visitors; fees charged; living quarters nearby.

MAJOR RESEARCH AND TEACHING FACILITIES: Very extensive library; large outdoor pond, small aquarium tanks; research collection of higher plants, mollusks, echinoderms, fishes, amphibians, reptiles; identified reference collections of plants, algae, mollusks, echinoderms, fishes, amphibians, reptiles, birds, mammals.

INSTRUCTIONAL PROGRAM: Department of Biology of Stanford University offers cellular physiology, amphibian morphogenesis, population dynamics, systematic botany, systematic malacology, systematic ichthyology, fish ecology and population dynamics, limnology, fish morphology and other courses in biology, zoology, and botany.

SIZE OF STAFF: Ten at professional level; varying number of technicians.

MAJOR CURRENT RESEARCH PROJECTS AND SCIENTIFIC LEADERS:

- Fish systematics and morphology; herpetology (G. S. Myers and A. E. Leviton)
- Fish ecology, metabolism and population growth (D. E. Wohlschlog)
- Biosystematics of plants (Ira L. Wiggins, R. W. Holm and P. H. Raven)
- Amphibian morphogenesis and population studies (V. C. Twitty)
- Mollusk systematics (Myra Keen)
- Cellular physiology (A. C. Giese)
- Population dynamics and numerical taxonomy (P. R. Ehrlich)

PUBLICATIONS ISSUED:

- *Stanford Ichthyological Bulletin* (occasionally published)
- *Occasional Papers of the Division of Systematic Biology* (occasionally published)
- *Microentomology* (occasionally published)

University of Michigan, Museum of Zoology

POSTAL ADDRESS: Ann Arbor, Michigan, USA.

EXECUTIVE OFFICER: Dr. Theodore H. Hubbell.

YEAR FOUNDED: 1903.

SCOPE OF ACTIVITIES: Emphasis on North American fauna.

MAJOR RESEARCH FACILITIES: Very extensive library (other facilities indicated under appropriate subdivisions).

DIVISIONS OF MUSEUM DESCRIBED:

1. Division of Fishes
2. Division of Mollusks

Division of Fishes

EXECUTIVE OFFICER: Reeve M. Bailey, Curator.

YEAR FOUNDED: 1920.

SCOPE OF ACTIVITIES: Unrestricted research on general ichthyology; graduate instruction.

PROVISIONS FOR VISITING SCIENTISTS: Space for 2 visitors; no fees charged; living quarters available nearby.

MAJOR RESEARCH FACILITIES: Small aquarium tanks; extensive research collections of fishes, about 70% of which are from American fresh-waters; extensive identified reference collections of Michigan fish fauna.

INSTRUCTIONAL PROGRAM: Ichthyology: investigations and seminars.

SIZE OF STAFF: Two at professional level; 3 technicians.

IMPORTANT SPECIES AVAILABLE FOR LABORATORY STUDIES:

- Cyclostomata: *Petromyzon marinus, Lampetra lamottei*
- Osteichthyes: *Ictalurus nebulosus, Lepomis macrochirus, Micropterus salmoides, Cyprinus carpio, Semotilus atromaculatus, Pimephales notatus*

MAJOR CURRENT RESEARCH PROJECTS AND SCIENTIFIC LEADERS:

- Phylogeny of percoid fishes (Reeve M. Bailey)
- Biosystematics of viviparous fishes (Robert R. Miller)

Division of Mollusks

EXECUTIVE OFFICER: Henry van der Schalie, Curator and Professor of Zoology.

YEAR FOUNDED: 1907.

SCOPE OF ACTIVITIES: Unrestricted research on ecology, distribution, life history and basic studies of mollusks.

PROVISIONS FOR VISITING SCIENTISTS: Space for 1-2 visitors; no fees charged; living quarters available nearby.

MAJOR RESEARCH AND TEACHING FACILITIES: Small aquarium tanks, special aquarium and vivarium facilities; outstanding research collections of land and fresh-water mollusks—some 200,000 lots of land, fresh-water and marine mollusks are catalogued; well represented identified reference collections of local fauna and most groups in North America; machine and wood shop, skilled shop workman available; small boats and outboard motors.

INSTRUCTIONAL PROGRAM: All the basic courses in University of Michigan graduate program; a special course given in malacology.

SIZE OF STAFF: Eight at professional level; 4 technicians.

IMPORTANT SPECIES AVAILABLE FOR LABORATORY STUDIES:

Mollusk; fresh-water Mussel: *Actinonaias ellipsiformis*

Mollusks; amphibious operculate: *Pomatiopsis lapidaria, P. cincinnatiensis*

Mollusk; fresh-water operculate: *Goniobasis livescens*

Mollusks; fresh-water pulmonate: *Aplexa hypnorum, Australorbis glabratus*

MAJOR CURRENT RESEARCH PROJECTS AND SCIENTIFIC LEADERS:

Studies of vector snails of schistosomiasis (Henry van der Schalie, Lowell Getz)

Snails involved in "swimmer's itch" (John Burch, Harold J. Walter)

Sphaeriids of North America (H. B. Herrington, William Heard)

Pleurocerids: ecology, life history and distribution (Bonifacio Dazo)

Zoologisches Institut und Museum der Universitaet Kiel

ZOOLOGICAL INSTITUTE AND MUSEUM OF KIEL UNIVERSITY

POSTAL ADDRESS: Hegewischstrasse 3, Kiel, Bundesrepublik Deutschland (West Germany).

EXECUTIVE OFFICER: Professor Dr. A. Remane, Direktor.

YEAR FOUNDED: 1868.

SCOPE OF ACTIVITIES: Unrestricted research on general marine and terrestrial biology and ecology, interstitial fauna; morphology, embryology and systematics of primates, vertebrates and invertebrates; general morphology and phylogeny; graduate instruction.

SEASON OF OPERATION: All year.

PHYSICAL ENVIRONMENT ACCESSIBLE: Ostsee (Baltic Sea), Nordsee (North Sea), Nordostsee-Kanal (Kiel Channel); sandy and silty beaches, brackish, shallow bays.

PROVISIONS FOR VISITING SCIENTISTS: Space for about 3 visitors; no fees charged; living quarters available nearby.

MAJOR RESEARCH AND TEACHING FACILITIES: Small library; running sea and fresh-water, small aquarium tanks; machine and wood shop, skilled shop workman available; 24.5 m LOA vessel, *Herman Wattenberg* (belonging to the University).

INSTRUCTIONAL PROGRAM: See Universitaet Kiel, Institut fuer Meereskunde, page 60.

SIZE OF STAFF: Twelve at professional level; 5 technicians.

MAJOR CURRENT RESEARCH PROJECTS AND SCIENTIFIC LEADERS:

Morphology, embryology, systematics and ecology of marine invertebrates, especially interstitial fauna (A. Remane, R. Siewing, H. Korn, and staff)

Temperature adaptation of fresh-water fauna, etiology (Prof. Precht and Dr. Faukowsky)

Ecology of beach and salt marshes (Prof. Tischler, Dr. Remmert, Dr. Noodt, P. Olun and Dr. Heydemann)

PUBLICATIONS ISSUED:

Kieler Meeresforschungen (regularly published journal)

Faunistische Mitteilungen aus Norddeutschland (regularly published journal)

ACKNOWLEDGMENTS OF PHOTOGRAPHS

1. Allan Hancock Foundation for Scientific Research (*S. C. photo*)
2. Benner Spring Fish Research Station (*Pennsylvania Fish Commission photograph*)
3. Fishery Research Station, Delafield, Wisconsin (*Wisconsin Conservation Department photograph*)
4. Kellogg Gull Lake Biological Station, Michigan (*Kalamazoo Gazette photograph*)
5. Marine Biological Laboratory, Woods Hole (*photograph by Edwin Gray, Falmouth*)
6. New York Aquarium (*New York Zoological Society photograph*)
7. Patamological Institute (*Courier-Journal photograph*)
8. Ridge Lake Laboratory (*Illinois Natural History Survey photograph*)
9. Saskatchewan Research Council building (*Saskatchewan Photo Services*)
10. Underwater observation tank, Sagehen Creek Project (*AIBS Bulletin*)
11. University of Miami Marine Laboratory (*Miami Sesquarium photograph*)
12. U. S. Navy Mine Defense Laboratory (*U. S. Navy photograph*)

INDEX

Laboratoire de Sete (France), 72